Preface

Dear Parents,

The daily practice in this book will help consolidate what your child has learned in Math and English. There are two sections: one on Math and the other, English. Each section comprises 90 practice units, and each practice is a two-page spread that provides integrated activities/exercises to build up your child's skills.

Depending on the time allocated, you may either have your child work through a two-page practice in Math one day and a two-page practice in English on another day. Or you may let them complete a Math practice unit and an English one on the same day. The essence, however, is to ensure that your child gets regular but not too much practice. Over-drilling could kill their interest in learning.

Two assessments are provided after the two daily practice sections: one on Math and the other, English. They serve more like overall reviews to let your child know how much they have mastered working through DailySmart. The assessments also enable you to know your child's weak areas so that you know where additional guidance is needed.

There is an answer key at the end of DailySmart. You may check the answers with your child and explain or clarify any items when necessary.

With DailySmart, your child will be able to make steady progress in their learning and develop the confidence and skills needed to perform well at school and feel good about themselves.

Your Partner in Education,
Popular Book Co. (Canada) Ltd.

Printed in China

Contents

Daily Smart

Mathematics

Contents

DATE: ____________

Numbers to 100 000 (1)

Write the numbers in numerals and in words.

①

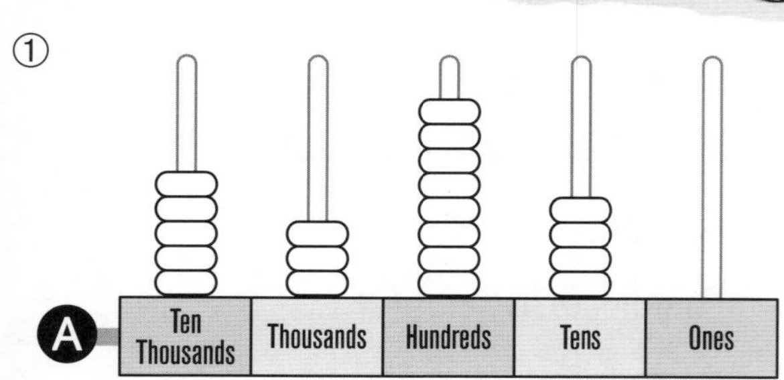

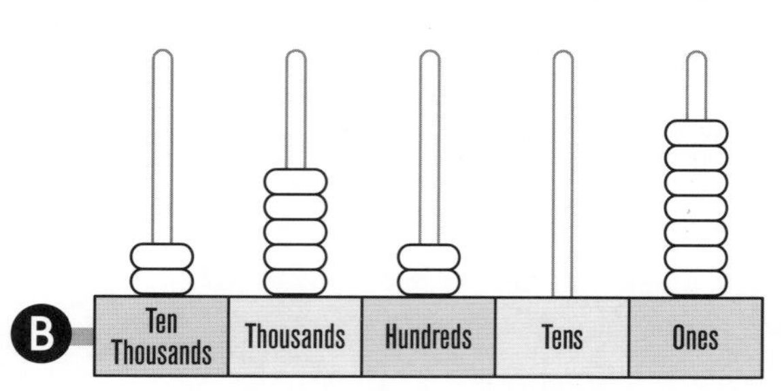

Ⓐ In numerals: 53,840

In words: 50,000+3000+800+ 40=53,840

Ⓑ In numerals: 25,207

In words: 20,000+5,000+200+ 7

Place Value Chart:

Thousands					
Hundred	Ten	One	Hundreds	Tens	Ones
	3	5	6	1	4

In numerals: 35 614

When you write a 5-digit number, remember to leave a space between the hundreds and the thousands digits.

In words:

Thirty-five thousand six hundred fourteen

Write the numbers in numerals.

② 2 ten thousands 4 hundreds 20,400

③ 3 ten thousands 1 ten 30,010

④ 1 ten thousand 6 thousands 7 hundreds 2 tens 16,720

⑤ 4 ten thousands 3 thousands 2 hundreds 5 ones 43,205

⑥ 8 ten thousands 2 thousands 1 ten 6 ones 82,016

⑦ 9 ten thousands 5 hundreds 6 tens 2 ones 90,562

Write the numbers in expanded form.

⑧ 25 473 = 20 000 + 5000 + 400 + 70 + 3

⑨ 17 689 = 10 000 + 7000+600+80+9

⑩ 68 237 = 60000+8000+200+30+7

⑪ 59 164 = 50000+9000+100+60+4

Write the meaning of each coloured digit.

⑫ **2**5 174 20 000

⑬ 6**8** 273 8000

⑭ 34 **7**16 700

⑮ **5**7 690 50 000

⑯ 35 29**3** 3

⑰ 62 9**8**1 80

⑱ **4**1 069 40 000

⑲ 88 **5**74 500

Fill in the missing numbers.

⑳

43 000	50 000	51000	58 000	59 000	66 000	67000
44 000	49 000	52000	57000	60 000	65 000	68 000
45 000	48 000	53 000	56000	61 000	64000	69 000
46000	47000	54 000	55 000	62 000	63000	

㉑

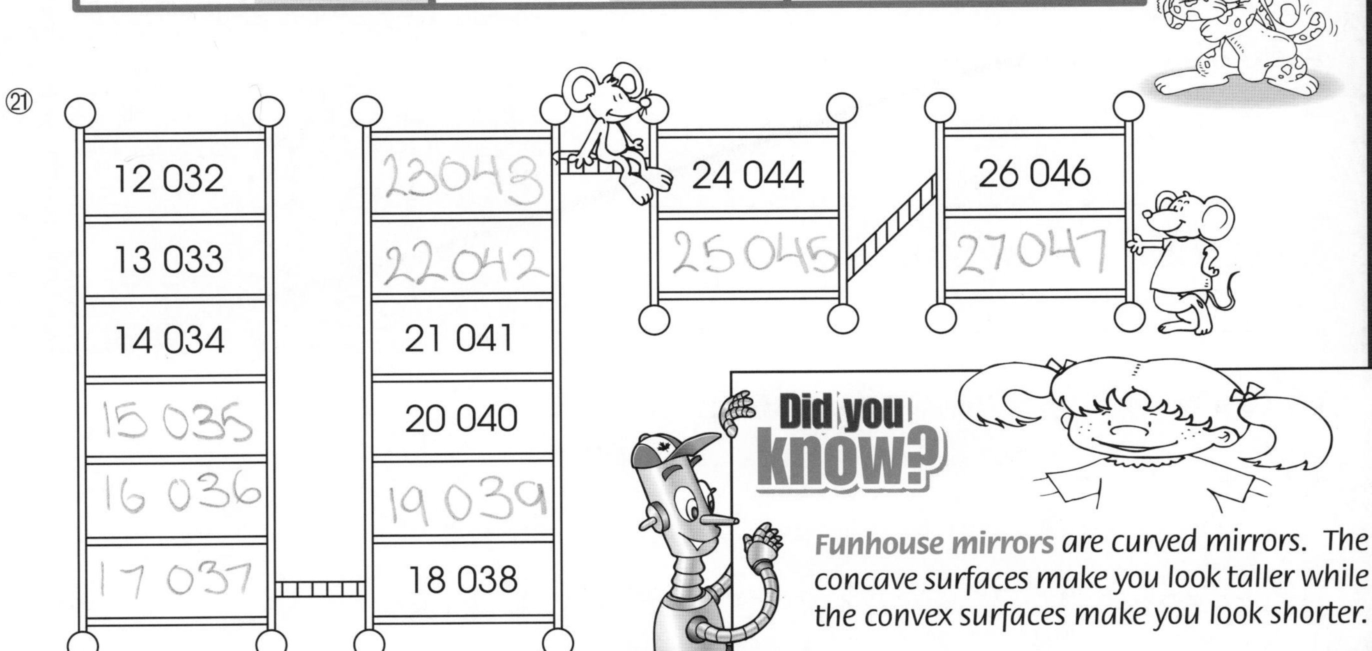

DATE: ____________

Day 2

Numbers to 100 000 (2)

Circle the greater number in each pair.

① 35 631 (circled)
34 170

② 65 479 (circled)
56 397

③ 20 773
20 816 (circled)

④ 58 006
60 000 (circled)

⑤ 84 972
89 427 (circled)

⑥ 71 654 (circled)
71 653

Comparing 5-digit numbers:

Compare the digits in the ten thousands place. If they are the same, compare the digits in the thousands place and so on. The number with the greater digit is greater.

e.g. **14 539** and **16 498**

- Compare the ten thousands digits.

14 539
16 498
↑
same

- Compare the thousands digits.

14 539
16 498
↑
6 > 4

16 498 > 14 539

Put the numbers in order from least to greatest.

⑦ 94 657 65 479 76 549

65479; 76,549; 94,657

⑧ 32 068 31 004 32 011

31004, 32011, 32068

Write a number that lies between the given numbers.

⑨ 25 167 < 26000 < 30 000

⑩ 80 179 < 83000 < 85 000

⑪ 43 654 < 43700 < 44 000

⑫ 74 086 < 75000 < 75 111

Answer the questions.

⑬ What number is right before 74 000? 73999

⑭ What number is right after 24 999? 25000

⑮ How many numbers are there between 39 027 and 39 030? three

⑯ What number is 4 thousand less than 48 096? 44 096

⑰ What number is 3 hundred greater than 76 533? 76 833

Use the given digits in each group to form six 5-digit numbers.

⑱

20450, 54002, 40205, 45200, 52004, 52040

⑲

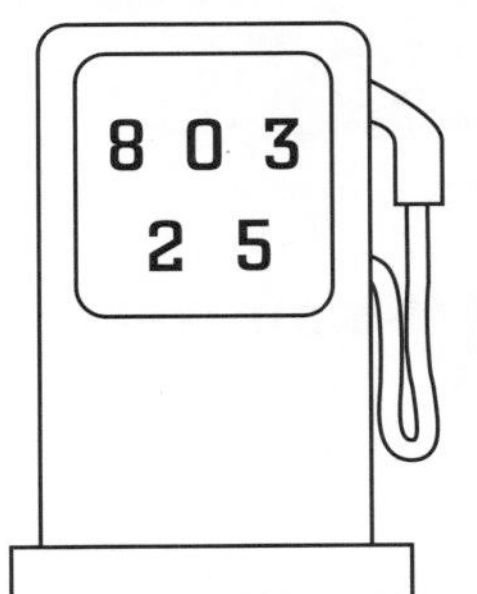

80325, 52308, 80352, 52380, 80532, 52830

Round to the nearest thousand:

1st Look at the digit in the hundreds place.

2nd If it is 5 or greater, round the number up. Otherwise, round the number down.

e.g. 25 **7**43 ($7 > 5$) 34 **1**89 ($1 < 5$)

25 743 —round up→ 26 000

34 189 —round down→ 34 000

Round each number to the nearest thousand.

⑳ 18 539 19 000

㉑ 27 108 27000

㉒ 34 190 34 000

㉓ 87 653 88 000

㉔ 38 654 39,000

㉕ 29 867 30 000

㉖ 94 940 95,000

㉗ 85 588 86,000

Did you know?

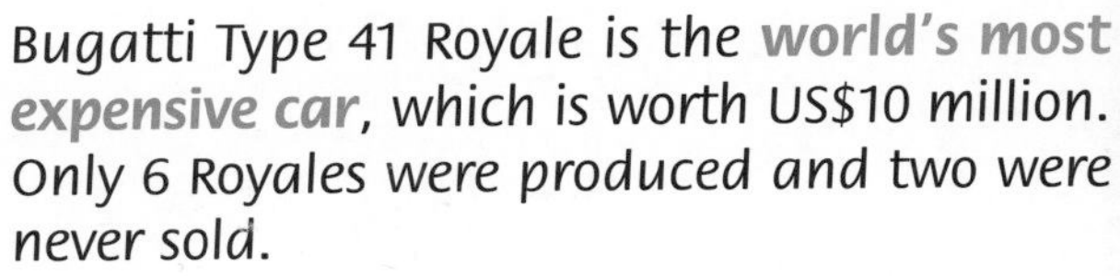

Bugatti Type 41 Royale is the **world's most expensive car**, which is worth US$10 million. Only 6 Royales were produced and two were never sold.

Round each number to the nearest ten thousand.

㉘ 68 270 70 000

㉙ 34 659 30 000

㉚ 88 866 90 000

DATE: ______________________

Counting by 11's and 12's

Look at their eyes: 11, 22, 33. They have 33 eyes in all.

Look at their fingers: 12, 24, 36. The have 36 fingers in all.

Circle the insects. Find the answers.

① Circle by 11′s.

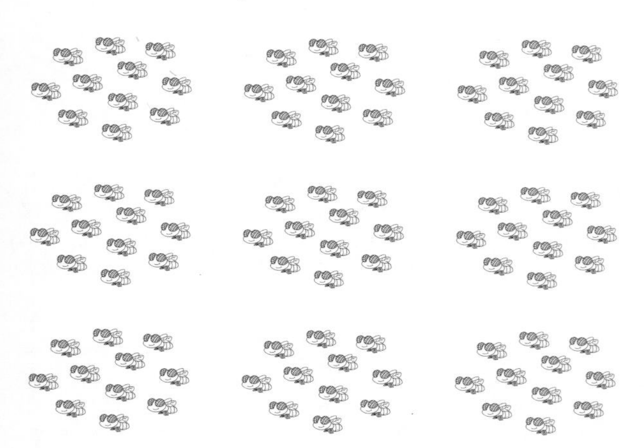

11 x 1 = 11

11 x 2 = 22

11 x 3 = 33

11 x 4 = 44

11 x 5 = 55

11 x 6 = 66

11 x 7 = 77

11 x 8 = 88

11 x 9 = 99

② Circle by 12′s.

12 x 1 = 12

12 x 2 = 24

12 x 3 = 36

12 x 4 = 48

12 x 5 = 60

12 x 6 = 72

12 x 7 = 84

12 x 8 = 96

12 x 9 = 108

Complete the diagrams to show the countings.

③ Count by 11's.

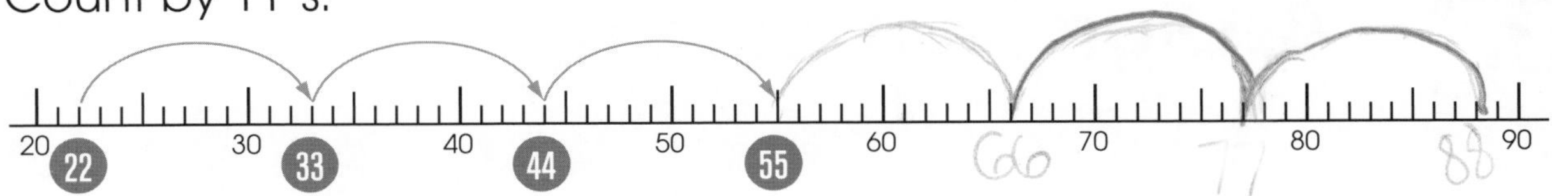

④ Count by 12's.

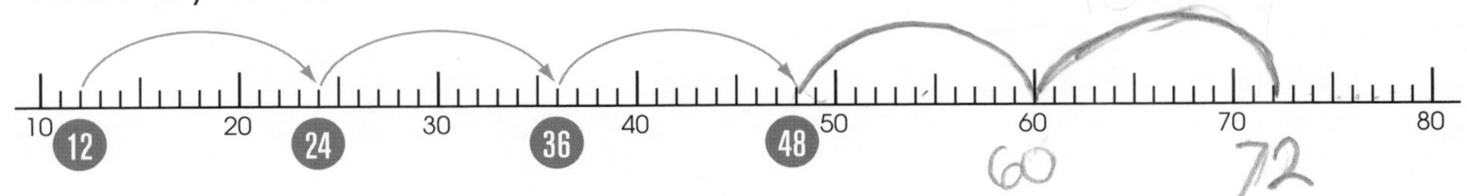

⑤ Count by 11's.

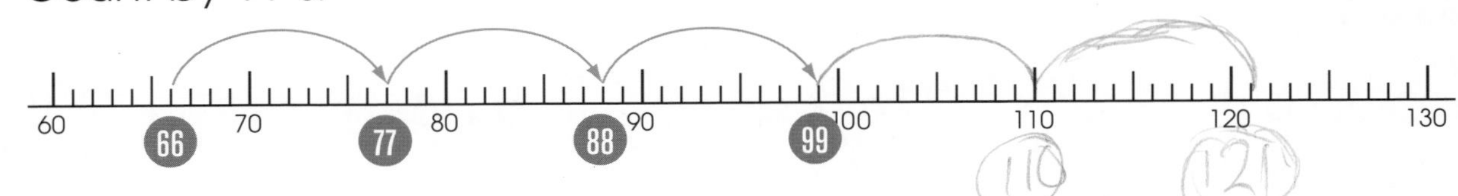

⑥ Count by 12's.

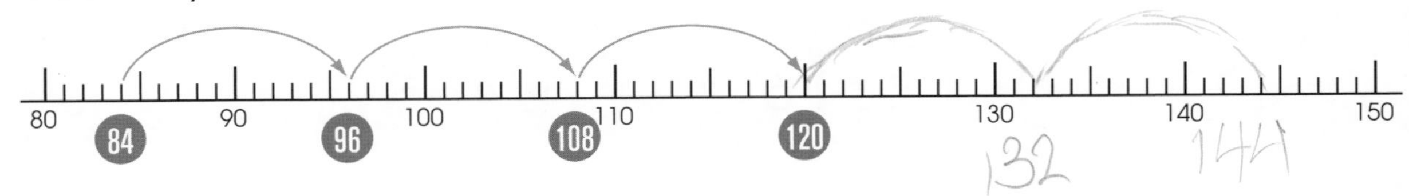

Draw lines to join the dots to complete the pictures.

⑦ Count by 11's. Start with 11.

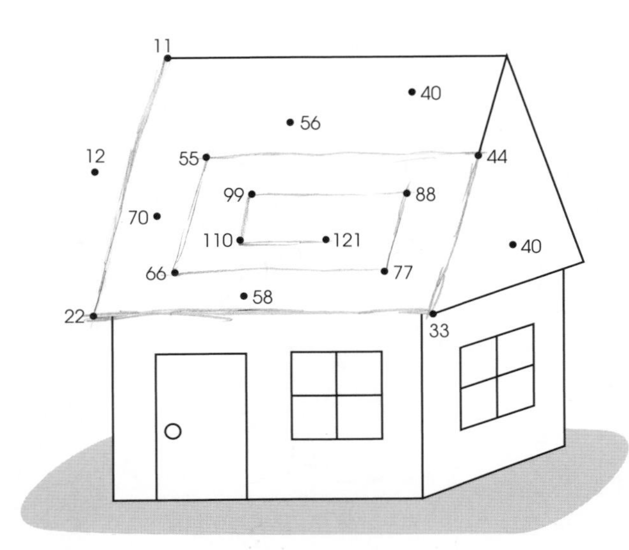

⑧ Count by 12's. Start with 12.

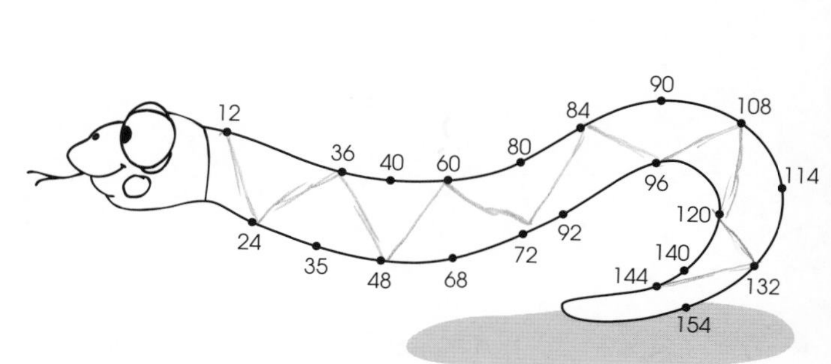

DATE: ____________________

Addition & Subtraction of 4-Digit Numbers (1)

Add or subtract.

① 3254 + 1683 = 4937

② 2564 + 1827 = 4391

③ 5283 − 1075 = 4208

④ 6818 − 4683 = 2135

⑤ 4905 + 3291 = 8196

⑥ 3951 − 2816 = 1135

⑦ 2733 + 4659 = 7392

⑧ 7026 − 5314 = 12340

⑨ 2649 + 1014 = 3663

⑩ 5682 − 1842 = 3840

⑪ 6205 − 3300 = 2905

⑫ 947 + 5921 = 6868

Fill in the missing numbers.

⑬ 2 5 [4] 7 − 1 6 4 [2] = [1] 0 5

⑭ 8 6 3 [5] − 2 [5] [9] 4 = [6] 0 4 1

⑮ 1 [6] 6 [4] + 2 3 [0] 5 = [3] 9 0 9

⑯ 3 [0] [6] 9 + [1] 6 5 [2] = 4 7 2 1

⑰ 1 [0] 0 [8] − 9 [4] 5 = 6 3

⑱ 2 [4] [4] 1 + [5] 4 7 [7] = 7 9 1 8

Look at the pictures. Solve the problems.

a. If Mrs. Smith buys 2 bags of flour, how many grams of flour does Mrs. Smith buy in all?

2450 + 2450 = 4900 4900 g

b. If Uncle Joe has a bag of flour and he uses 1090 g of the flour to make a cake, how much flour is left?

2450 - 1090 = 1360 1360 g

a. Liza mixes a carton of apple juice with a carton of orange juice. How much juice does she get?

988 + 1480 = 2468 2468 mL

b. After filling up a bowl with apple juice, Joe finds that he has 379 mL of apple juice left. What is the capacity of the bowl?

1480 - 379 = 1101 1101 mL

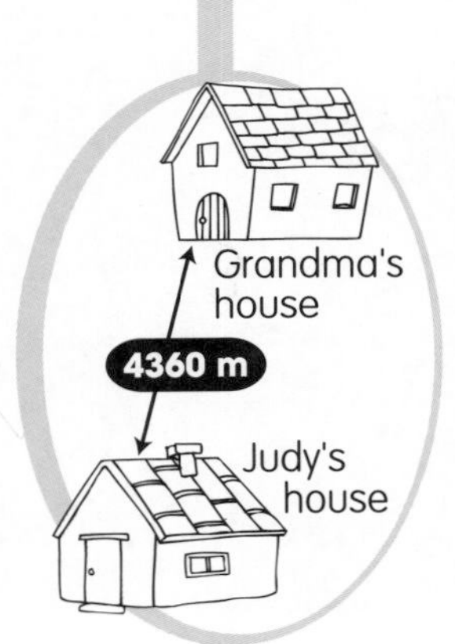

a. Judy visits her grandma. If she has already travelled 2665 m, how much farther does she need to go?

4360 - 2665 = 1695 1695 m

b. If Judy goes from her house to Grandma's house and then returns, how many metres does Judy travel in all?

4360 + 4360 = 8720 8720 m

㉒

a. If Aunt Sue earns $353 less than Uncle Sam, how much does Aunt Sue earn in a month?

2800 - 353 = 2447 $ 2447

b. If Uncle Sam saves $280 monthly, how much does he spend every month?

2800 - 280 = 2520 $ 2520

DATE: ______________

Day 5

Addition & Subtraction of 4-Digit Numbers (2)

You can subtract one of the numbers in the question from the answer to check the sum. If the difference is the same as the other number in the addition problem, the sum you got is correct.

e.g. Is 3564 + 1763 = 5327 correct?

Check

$$\begin{array}{r} 5327 \\ -\ 1763 \\ \hline 3564 \end{array}$$ ← same as the other number

5327 is the sum of 3564 and 1763.

Do the addition. Then use subtraction to check the answers.

① $\begin{array}{r} 3524 \\ +\ 1837 \\ \hline 5361 \end{array}$ Check $\begin{array}{r} 5361 \\ -\ 3524 \\ \hline 1837 \end{array}$

② $\begin{array}{r} 2817 \\ +\ 3988 \\ \hline 6805 \end{array}$ Check $\begin{array}{r} 6805 \\ -\ 3988 \\ \hline 2817 \end{array}$

③ 2086 + 1793 = 3879 Check 3879 - 2086 = 1793

④ 3224 + 986 = 4210 Check 4210 - 3224 = 986

⑤ 1294 + 3869 = 5163 Check 5163 - 3869 = 1294

⑥ 4816 + 827 = 5643 Check 5643 - 827 = 4816

⑦ 1948 + 2563 = 4511 Check 4511 - 1948 = 2563

⑧ 4066 + 2579 = 6645 Check 6645 - 4066 = 2579

Think: Add 6 to this number to make it 4000.

3994 + 1827
= 3994 + **6 + 1821**
= **3994 + 6** + 1821
= 4000 + 1821
= 5821

Think: Make this number have the same ones digit as the number to be subtracted.

7400 – 1802
= **7402 – 2** – 1802
= **7402 – 1802** – 2
= 5600 – 2
= 5598

Find the answers in a faster way.

Think: Add 3 to 2197 to make it 2200.

Think: Make this number into 2094.

⑨ 2197 + 825
= 3022

⑩ 3261 – 1166
= 2094

⑪ 5299 + 3101 = 8400

⑫ 6712 – 1022 = 5680

⑬ 3953 – 1258 = 2695

⑭ 2992 + 539 = 3531

⑮ 2936 + 1006 = 3942

⑯ 5245 – 3249 = 1996

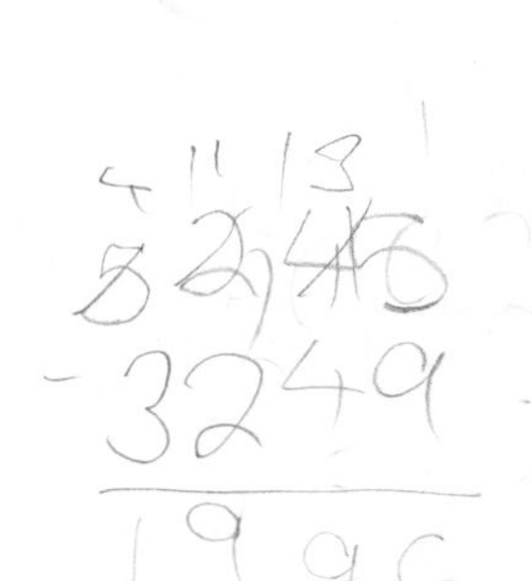

Solve the problems.

For question ⑱, make sure all the measurements are in the same unit first.

1 m = 100 cm

⑰ 

If a carton holds 826 mL less than a bottle, what is the capacity of the carton?

1624

⑱ 

Uncle Sam has a roll of string. If Uncle Sam uses 9 m 16 cm to make a net, how much string is left?

3948

⑲ 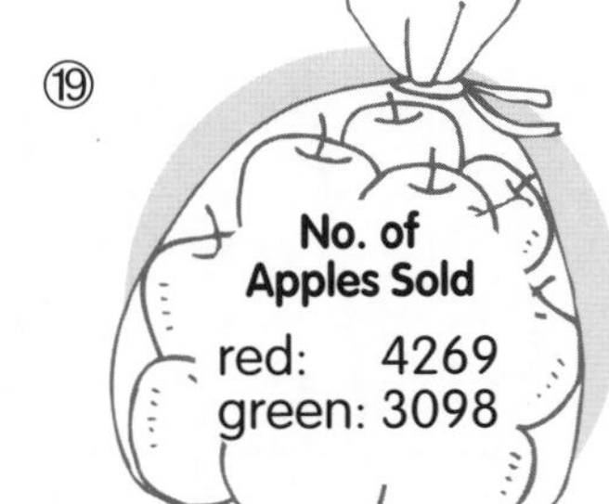

How many apples did Mr. Taylor sell in all last week?

7367

Did you know?

*Both snatch (213 kg) and clean & jerk (263 kg) **weightlifting** world records were set by an Iranian in 2000.*

DATE: ____________________

Multiplication of 2-Digit Numbers

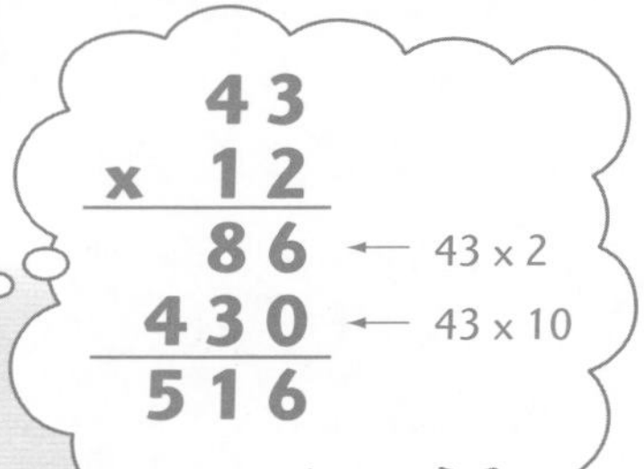

Each fish weighs 43 g.

They weigh 516 g in all.

Do the multiplication.

① 18 x 46 =

② 47 x 25 =

③ 23 x 17 =

④ 54 x 32 =

Multiplying by a 2-digit number:

1st Multiply by the ones.

2nd Multiply* by the tens.

3rd Add.

e.g. 39 x 27 = ____

* Remember to put a '0' in the ones column.

1st	2nd	3rd
39	39	39
x 27	x 27	x 27
273	273	273
	780	780
		1053

39 x 27 = 1053

⑤ 15 x 23 = ________ ⑥ 29 x 36 = ________ ⑦ 64 x 19 = ________

⑧ 44 x 51 = ________ ⑨ 27 x 35 = ________ ⑩ 18 x 18 = ________

Round each number to the nearest ten to do the estimation.

⑪ 49 x 28 Estimate _____ x _____ = ________

⑫ 26 x 72 Estimate ________________

⑬ 41 x 57 Estimate ________________

⑭ 35 x 23 Estimate ________________

A quick way to multiply 2-digit numbers with zeros in the ones places:

e.g.

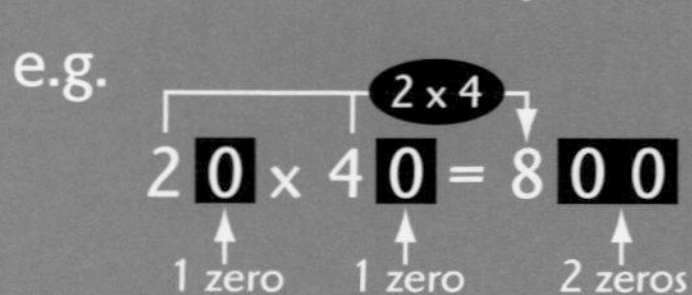

Solve the problems. Show your work in the spaces provided.

⑮ Each box contains 36 cans of tuna. How many cans of tuna are there in 25 boxes? 900 cans

⑯ Cindy Cat eats 12 fish a day. How many fish does Cindy Cat eat in 2 weeks? 168 fish

⑰ Each bag has 46 treats for cats. How many treats are there in 38 bags? 1748 treats

⑱ There are 97 fish in a school of fish. How many fish are there in 12 schools? 1164 fish

⑲ A fish swims 16 m in 1 minute. How far does the fish swim in 33 minutes? 528 m

⑳ A cat walks 18 m in 1 minute. How far does the cat walk in three quarters of an hour? 810 m

36×25: 180, 720, 900

12×14: 48, 120, 168

46×38: 368, 1380, 1748

97×12: 194, 970, 1164

16×33: 48, 480, 528

18×45: 90, 720, 810

DATE: ____________________

Distributive Property of Multiplication

6 x (50 + 2)
= 6 x 50 + 6 x 2
= 300 + 12
= 312

I have one box only, but I have more coloured pencils than you.

400

I have 6 boxes of coloured pencils.

Fill in the blanks. Then find the answers.

① 8 x 63 = 8 x (60 + __3__)
= 8 x __60__ + 8 x __3__
= ______ + ______
= ______

② 7 x 98 = 7 x (100 – ______)
= 7 x ______ – 7 x ______
= ______ – ______
= ______

③ 81 x 4 = (______ + ______) x 4
= ______ x 4 + ______ x 4
= ______ + ______
= ______

You can make use of the distributive property of multiplication to help you find the answers in a faster way.

e.g. **9 x 86** ← Think: 86 = 80 + 6
= 9 x (80 + 6) ← Multiply each number in the brackets by 9.
= 9 x 80 + 9 x 6
= 720 + 54
= 774

8 x 39 ← Think: 39 = 40 – 1
= 8 x (40 – 1) ← Multiply each number in the brackets by 8.
= 8 x 40 – 8 x 1
= 320 – 8
= 312

④ 9 x 77 = 9 x (______ – ______)
= 9 x ______ – 9 x ______
= ______ – ______
= ______

⑤ 89 x 6 = (______ – ______) x 6
= ______ x 6 – ______ x 6
= ______ – ______
= ______

Do the multiplication in a faster way. Show your work.

⑥ 9 x 48

=

⑦ 92 x 7

=

⑧ 67 x 5

=

⑨ 53 x 8

=

⑩ 76 x 2

=

⑪ 3 x 99

=

Find the answers in two different ways. Then tell which way is more efficient. Put a checkmark in the circles.

⑫ Ⓐ 99 x 12 =

Ⓑ 12 x 99
= 12 x ( )

⑬ Ⓐ 71 x 21 =

Ⓑ 21 x 71
= 21 x ( )

⑭ Ⓐ 58 x 16 =

Ⓑ 58 x 16
= ( ) x 16

⑮ Ⓐ 98 x 32 =

Ⓑ 98 x 32
= ( ) x 32

DATE: ____________________

Dividing 4-Digit Numbers (1)

Do the division.

8 ⟌5243 ← 5 < 8; consider 1 more digit

```
   655R3
8 ⟌5243   ← There are 6 8's in 52.
   48
    44
    40
     43
     40
      3
```

5243 ÷ 8 = <u>655R3</u>

① 2 ⟌3275

② 9 ⟌6094

③ 5 ⟌7293

④ 7 ⟌5421

⑤ 6 ⟌4664

⑥ 3006 ÷ 3 = ____________

⑦ 4289 ÷ 9 = ____________

⑧ 9723 ÷ 5 = ____________

⑨ 6944 ÷ 8 = ____________

⑩ 3288 ÷ 4 = ____________

⑪ 4091 ÷ 2 = ____________

⑫ 8273 ÷ 7 = ____________

⑬ 7523 ÷ 6 = ____________

Check the answers. Put a checkmark in the circle if the answer is correct; otherwise, put a cross and write the correct answer on the line.

Use multiplication and addition to check answers.

e.g. Is 3076 ÷ 5 = 615R1 correct?

Check 615 x 5 = 3075
3075 + 1 = 3076 ← same as the dividend

3076 ÷ 5 = 615R1 is correct.

⑭ 2866 ÷ 8 = 358R2 ◯ ; ______
Check

⑮ 4274 ÷ 4 = 1068R6 ◯ ; ______
Check

⑯ 3816 ÷ 7 = 545R1 ◯ ; ______
Check

⑰ 8659 ÷ 2 = 4329R1 ◯ ; ______
Check

⑱ 5027 ÷ 3 = 1676R1 ◯ ; ______
Check

⑲ 3908 ÷ 6 = 650R3 ◯ ; ______
Check

Complete the tables. Then solve the problems.

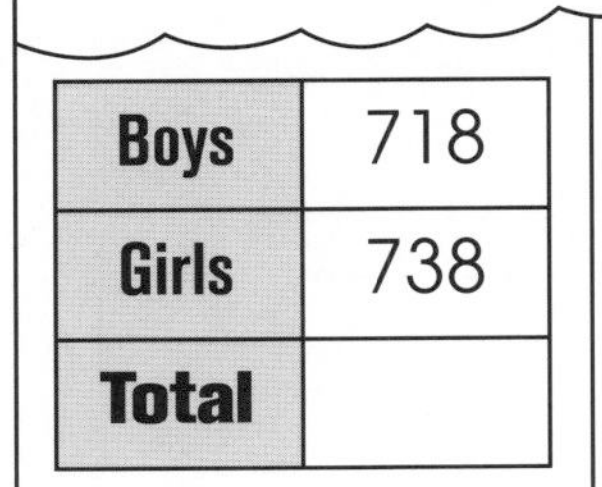

⑳

Boys	718
Girls	738
Total	

a. If Calvin Clown puts every 7 children into a group, how many groups of children are there in all?

______ = ______ ______ groups

b. A pizza has 8 slices. If Cindy Clown wants to give each child a slice of pizza, how many pizzas does she need to buy?

______ = ______ ______ pizzas

㉑

Bag A	Bag B	Total
3115 g		7875 g

If a bead weighs 5 g, how many beads are there in Bag B?

______ = ______

______ beads

*The **most valuable model car** is a 1937 Bentalls store delivery truck. It was sold for £12 650 in London in 1994.*

DATE: ____________________

Dividing 4-Digit Numbers (2)

Each of us has collected 68 eggs on average.

There are 18 children in your class.

4-digit number ÷ 2-digit number:

If the first 2 digits of the 4-digit number is smaller than the divisor, the quotient must be a 2-digit number.

e.g. 36) **24**49 ← 24 < 36; consider 1 more digit

```
       68R1
36 ) 2449     ← There are 6 36's in 244.
     216↓
      289
      288
        1
```

2449 ÷ 36 = <u>68R1</u>

Do the division.

① 42) 2573

② 28) 3444

③ 24) 3840

④ 60) 4574

⑤ 4263 ÷ 84 = ________

⑥ 8400 ÷ 75 = ________

⑦ 7682 ÷ 46 = ________

⑧ 6177 ÷ 80 = ________

⑨ 4929 ÷ 53 = ________

⑩ 6930 ÷ 67 = ________

Fill in the missing numbers.

⑪
```
        6 8 R□□
53 ) 3 □ 4 □
     3 1 8
       4 6 □
       □ □ □
         4 3
```

⑫
```
         7 □ R□□
□8 ) □ 6 2 □
     □ 3 6
       □ □ 0
       2 4 0
         2 0
```

Round to the nearest hundred:

1st Look at the digit in the tens place.

2nd If it is 5 or greater, round the number up. Otherwise, round it down.

e.g. 4 2 **9** 3

↑ $9 > 5$ round up

4293 ⟶ 4300

Round each dividend to the nearest hundred and each divisor to the nearest ten to estimate the answer. Then find the exact answer.

⑬ $7169 \div 93 =$ ____________

Estimate ______________________________

⑭ $6894 \div 48 =$ ____________

Estimate ______________________________

⑮ $5016 \div 37 =$ ____________

Estimate ______________________________

Look at the pictures. Solve the problems.

⑯

If Uncle Sam puts 3429 candies into bags, how many bags of candies will he get? How many candies are left?

________________________ = ___________

He will get ______ bags of candies; ______ candies are left.

⑰ If a shop got $4446 selling the shoes, how many pairs of shoes were sold in all?

$38

________________________ = ___________

______ pairs of shoes were sold in all.

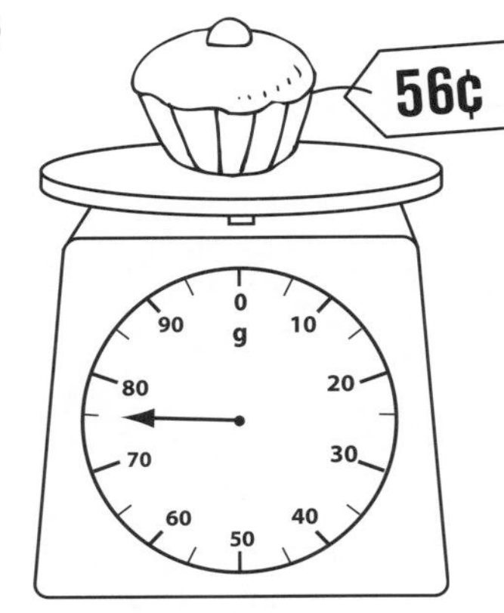

a. If Judy has $10, how many muffins can she buy? How much is left?

________________________ = ___________

She can buy ______ muffins with ______ ¢ left.

b. A box of muffins weighs 3 kg. How many muffins are there in a box?

________________________ = ___________

There are ______ muffins in a box.

DATE: ____________________

Day 10

Solving Problems Involving Division

Solve the problems.

① Uncle Louis earned $3565 in May. If Uncle Louis earned the same amount every day, how much did he earn per day?

____________________ = ________ $________

② A keychain costs $4. If Aunt Sue pays $1024 to the cashier, how many keychains does she buy in all?

____________________ = ________ ________ keychains

③ Andy has a roll of string that is 2 km long. If he cuts the string into 8-m strips, how many strips will he get?

____________________ = ________ ________ strips

④ A tank can hold 6 L of water. If a cup has a capacity of 75 mL, how many cups of water are needed to fill up a tank?

____________________ = ________

________ cups

1 km = 1000 m
1 L = 1000 mL

The numbers in a number sentence must be in the same unit.

Solve the problems. Round the answers to whole numbers if necessary.

⑤ How many pairs of shoes at most can be bought with $1000? How much money is left?

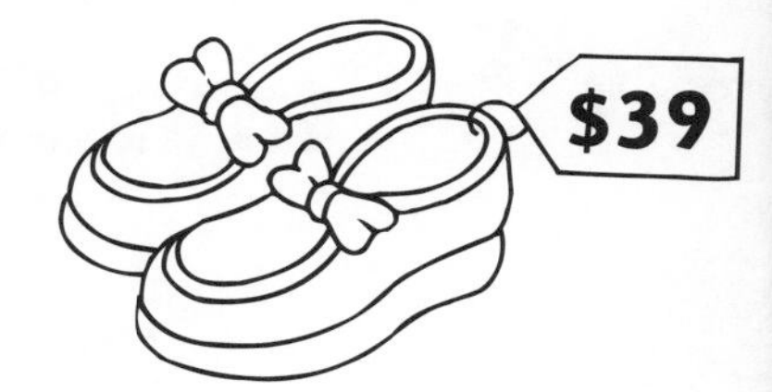

______________ = ________

________ pairs of shoes; $ ________ left

⑥ Raymond is building cubes with sticks. If he has 1288 sticks, how many cubes can be built at most? How many sticks are left?

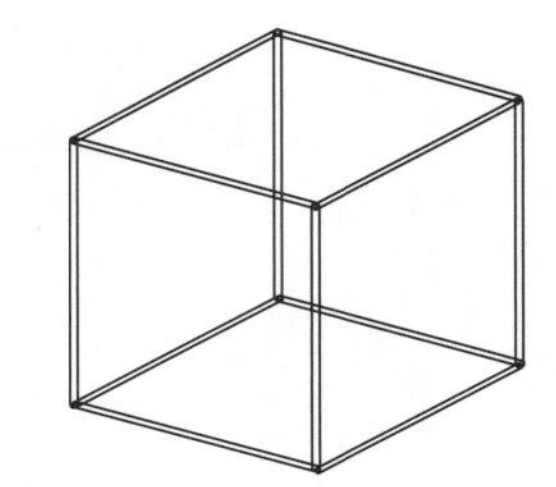

______________ = ________

________ cubes; ________ sticks left

⑦ Mrs. Scott will use 5000 light bulbs to decorate her house. How many boxes of light bulbs does she need to buy?

______________ = ________

________ boxes of light bulbs

⑧ Mr. Taylor wants to give each child a chocolate. If there are 1008 children, how many boxes of chocolates does Mr. Taylor need to buy?

______________ = ________

________ boxes of chocolates

⑨ There are 4 groups of 12 children in the art room. If they share a pile of drawing paper equally, how many pieces of drawing paper will each child get? How many pieces are left?

______________ = ________

For question ⑨, find out how many children there are in all first.

________ pieces of drawing paper each;

________ pieces left

DATE: ______________

Multiplication and Division

Fill in the blanks with the help of the given number sentences.

① 29 x 83 = 2407
2407 ÷ 29 = ______

② 64 x 16 = 1024
______ ÷ 64 = 16

③ 3608 ÷ 82 = 44
44 x 82 = ______

④ 1218 ÷ 7 = 174
174 x ______ = 1218

⑤ 2350 ÷ 25 = 94
94 x ______ = 2350

⑥ 56 x 71 = 3976
______ ÷ 71 = 56

A Fact Family

76 x 59 = 4484
59 x 76 = 4484

4484 ÷ 59 = 76
4484 ÷ 76 = 59

Choose three numbers from each group to form a multiplication and a division sentence.

⑦ 46, 25, 48, 1200

______ x ______ = ______
______ ÷ ______ = ______

⑧ 1776, 74, 24, 1876

______ x ______ = ______
______ ÷ ______ = ______

⑨ 2780, 82, 35, 2870

______ x ______ = ______
______ ÷ ______ = ______

⑩ 155, 9, 145, 1395

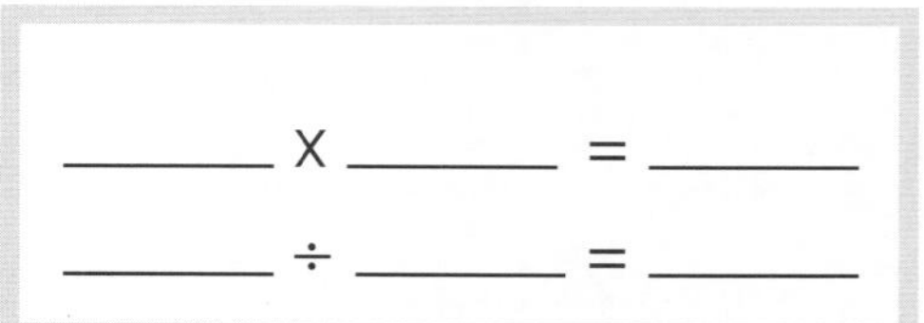

______ x ______ = ______
______ ÷ ______ = ______

Solve the problems by using the given number sentences.

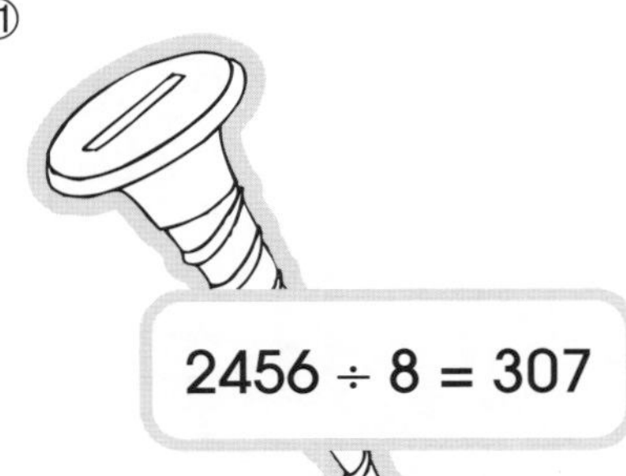

a. Mrs. Taylor has 2456 stickers. If 307 children share her stickers equally, how many stickers will each child get?

_______ stickers

b. Each box contains 307 screws. How many screws are there in 8 boxes?

_______ screws

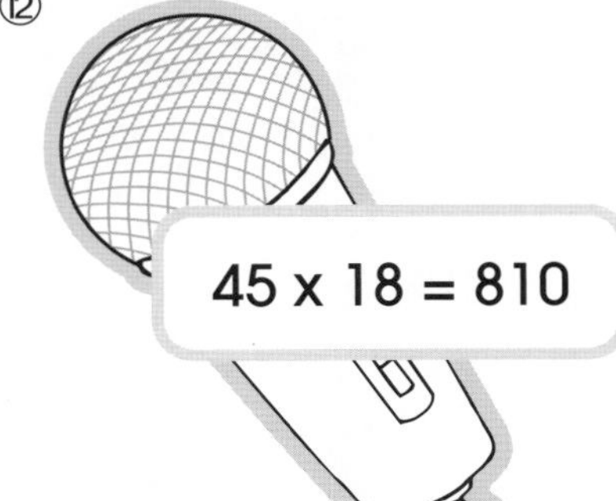

a. There are 18 judges in a singing contest. If Judy gets 810 points, how many points does each judge give her on average?

_______ points

b. There are 18 tattoos on a sheet. If Uncle Ted buys 40 sheets in Store A and 5 sheets in Store B, how many tattoos will he buy in all?

_______ tattoos

Time yourself to see whether you can find the answers within 5 minutes.

 2686 ÷ 4 = _________

⑭ 34 x 67 = _________

⑮ 1782 ÷ 7 = _________

⑯ 26 x 26 = _________

⑰ 2983 ÷ 22 = _________

⑱ 35 x 72 = _________

⑲ 62 x 19 = _________

⑳ 3068 ÷ 11 = _________

㉑ 2527 ÷ 34 = _________

㉒ 28 x 59 = _________

㉓ 1818 ÷ 8 = _________

㉔ 33 x 15 = _________

㉕ 16 x 78 = _________

㉖ 27 x 94 = _________

㉗ 2007 ÷ 12 = _________

㉘ 3399 ÷ 41 = _________

㉙ 5245 ÷ 18 = _________

㉚ 46 x 46 = _________

㉛ 71 x 23 = _________

㉜ 2019 ÷ 5 = _________

Starting Time:

Finishing Time:

DATE: ____________________

Day 12

Word Problems

Look at the pictures. Solve the problems.

① How many grams do 15 boxes of candies weigh?

______________ = ________ ________ grams

② Uncle Jimmy got $1038 selling hamburgers. How many hamburgers did Uncle Jimmy sell in all?

______________ = ________ ________ hamburgers

③ There are 2034 heart stickers in all. How many sheets of stickers are there?

______________ = ________ ________ sheets

④ How many pizzas are there in 45 boxes?

______________ = ________ ________ pizzas

⑤ How many minutes does it take to make 18 jack-o-lanterns?

______________ = ________ ________ minutes

Solve the problems and put a cross on the extra information. Show your work.

⑥ A birthday cake costs $36 and weighs 2320 g. If Tina cuts her birthday cake equally into 16 slices, how heavy is each slice?

Each slice weighs ______ g.

⑦ There are 75 men and 69 women dining in a restaurant. If the restaurant owner wants to give every woman customer a dozen roses, how many roses does the owner need to buy?

____

⑧ Aunt Sophie has baked 1008 cookies and 576 muffins. If Aunt Sophie packs every 8 cookies into a box, how many boxes does she need?

____

⑨ Mrs. Smith buys a bottle of orange juice and a bottle of apple juice. How many cups are needed to hold all the apple juice?

____

____

Did you know?

In 1995, Canada hosted the **International Mathematical Olympiad**. Canada was ranked 19th out of 73 competitors.

DATE: ____________

Day 13

Two-step Problems (1)

Use the clues to solve the problems.

① Each stackable chair costs $15 and a table costs $79. If Aunt Anita buys 26 chairs and 1 table, how much does she need to pay?

Cost of chairs: ________________ = ______

Cost in total: ________________ = ______

She needs to pay $______ .

X +

② Nathan has 3 boxes with 225 cubes in each. If Nathan gives 308 cubes to his friends, how many cubes will he have left?

No. of cubes Nathan has: ________________ = ______

No. of cubes left: ________________ = ______

He will have ______ cubes left.

③ Bruce and his 4 friends share a box of 1120 baseball cards equally. If Bruce has 39 baseball cards at first, how many baseball cards will he have after the share?

For question ③, Bruce and his 4 friends are 5 children in all.

No. of cards each child gets:

________________ = ______

No. of cards Bruce has in all: ________________ = ______

He will have ______ cards.

Look at the pictures. Then use the clues to solve the problems.

④

Mrs. Goldberg brings 3 children to the clown show. How much do their tickets cost?

Cost of children's tickets: ________________ = ______

Total: ________________ = ______

Their tickets cost $ ______ .

⑤

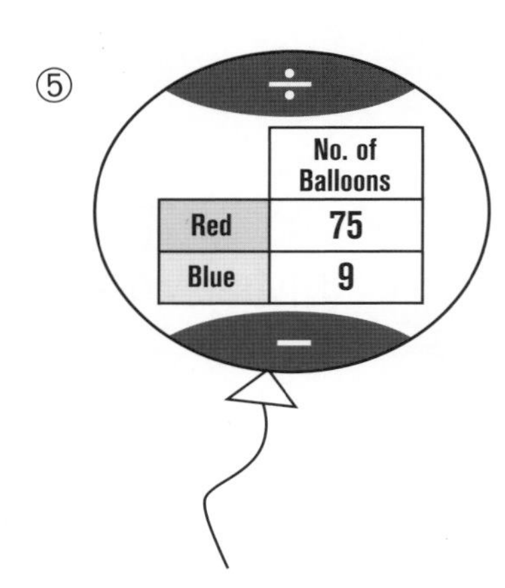

	No. of Balloons
Red	75
Blue	9

The number of red balloons is three times the number of green balloons. How many more green balloons than blue balloons are there?

Number of green balloons: ________________ = ______

Difference: ________________ = ______

There are ______ more green balloons than blue balloons.

⑥

286 visitors to the zoo are children. If an adult ticket costs $9, how much is gained selling the adult tickets?

Number of adult tickets: ________________ = ______

Cost in total: ________________ = ______

$________ is gained selling the adult tickets.

⑦

Ted got half as many points as Andy. If the points that Louis got was 3 times Ted's, how many points did Louis get?

Ted's score: ________________ = ______

Louis's score: ________________ = ______

Louis got ________ points.

DATE: ____________

Two-step Problems (2)

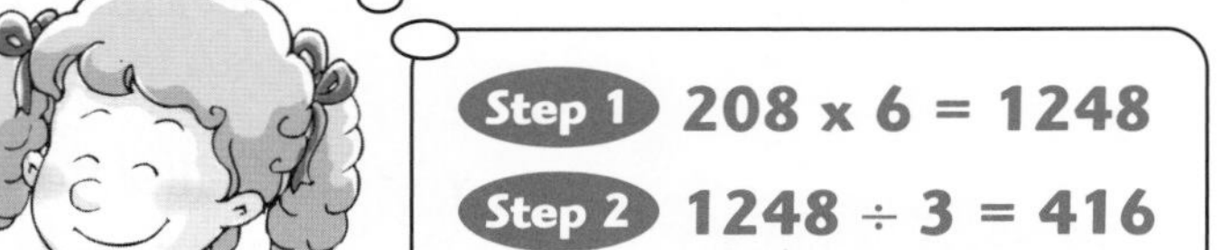

Decide what operation to use first. Then solve the problems.

① Mrs. Winter has 3 bags of sugar weighing 485 g each. If Mrs. Winter uses 326 g to make a dessert, how much sugar will be left?

Step 1 485 ◯ 3 = ______

Step 2 ______ ◯ 326 = ______

______ g of sugar will be left.

② A pile of 38 identical storybooks is 1216 mm high. What is the height of a pile of 16 such storybooks?

Step 1 1216 ◯ 38 = ______

Step 2 ______ ◯ 16 = ______

The height is ______ mm.

③ Erica has twice as many red paper clips as the blue ones. If she has 118 blue paper clips, how many paper clips does she have in all?

Step 1 118 ◯ ______ = ______

Step 2 ______ ◯ 118 = ______

She has ______ paper clips in all.

④ Sue has two bags of candies that weigh 827 g and 458 g. If she puts the candies equally into 5 containers, how many grams of candies are there in each container?

Step 1 827 ◯ ______ = ______

Step 2 ______ ◯ 5 = ______

There are ______ g of candies in each container.

Write short descriptions. Then solve the problems.

⑤ Uncle Tim buys 34 dozen eggs. If he breaks 59 eggs by accident, how many eggs will be left?

:

:

_______ eggs will be left.

⑥ A tank is half-filled with water. After pouring 345 mL of water into the tank, it contains 1195 mL of water. What is the capacity of the tank?

:

:

The capacity of the tank is _______ mL.

⑦ Uncle Leon earns $2680 a month. He spends $2480 and saves the rest each month. How long does it take him to save enough money to buy the laptop computer?

$1800

:

:

It takes Uncle Leon _______ months.

⑧ Aunt Linda has baked 456 chocolate cookies and 126 peanut butter cookies. If she wants to put the cookies equally into bags with no cookies left, should the cookies be put into bags of 4, 6, or 9? How many bags are needed?

:

:

For question ⑧, try the divisor 4, 6, or 9 to do division.

_______ bags of _______ cookies each are needed.

DATE: ______________

Day 15

Standard Units for Lengths

Fill in the blanks with the correct units.

km m dm cm mm

Kilometre (**km**) Big Unit
Metre (**m**)
Decimetre (**dm**)
Centimetre (**cm**)
Millimetre (**mm**) Small Unit

Relationships between the units:

1 km = 1000 m
1 m = 10 dm or 100 cm
1 dm = 10 cm
1 cm = 10 mm

① The highway is about 46 _____ long.

② The little worm is about 12 _____ long.

③ A whale shark can grow up to 13 _____ long.

④ The depth of a bookshelf is about 2 _____ .

⑤ The distance between Toronto and Vancouver is about 2900 _____ .

⑥ The height of a cup is about 11 _____ .

Fill in the blanks.

⑦ 4 km = _______ m

⑧ 400 cm = _______ m

⑨ 30 mm = _______ cm

⑩ 50 dm = _______ m

⑪ 5 cm = _______ mm

⑫ 2000 m = _______ km

⑬ 4 dm = _______ m

⑭ 80 mm = _______ cm

Put '>' or '<' in the circles.

⑮ 62 cm ◯ 8 m

⑯ 3 km ◯ 60 m

⑰ 4 cm ◯ 80 mm

⑱ 78 dm ◯ 9 m

⑲ 45 cm ◯ 80 mm

⑳ 9 m ◯ 700 cm

Measure and record the sides of the triangles. Then answer the questions with letters.

㉑

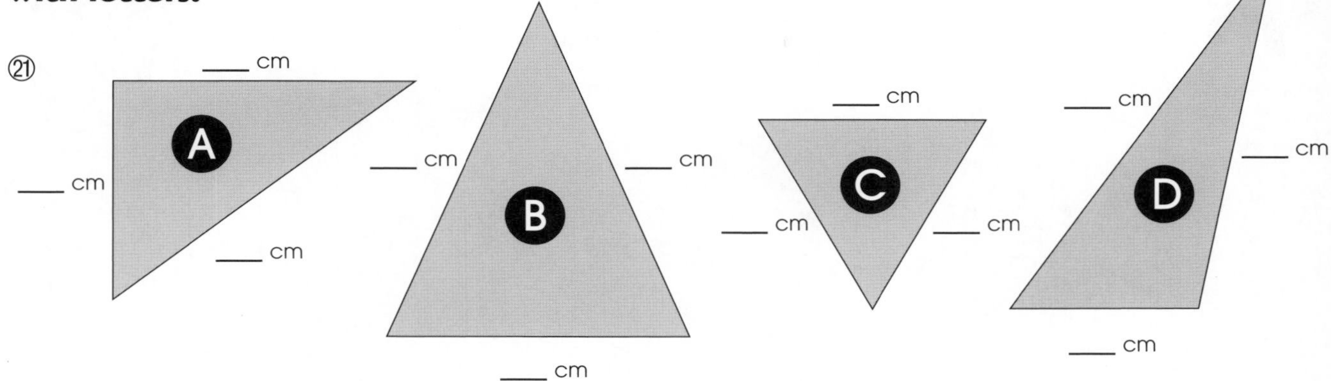

a. Which triangles have a side of 4 cm? ____________

b. Which triangles have at least two sides each measuring 5 cm or longer? ____________

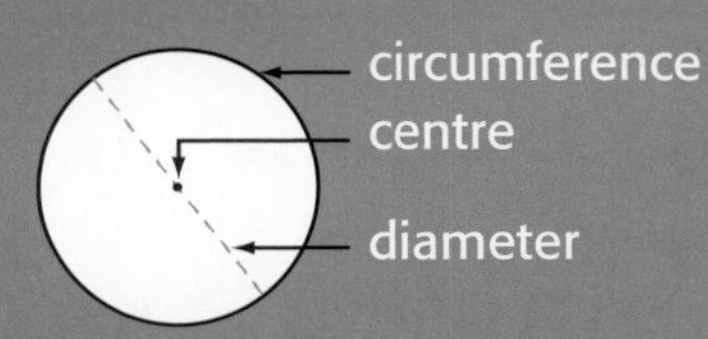

Circumference:
the distance around the outside of a circle

Diameter:
a line segment passing through the centre of a circle

Steps to measure the circumference of a circle:

1st Put a string around the circle.

2nd Measure the length of the string.

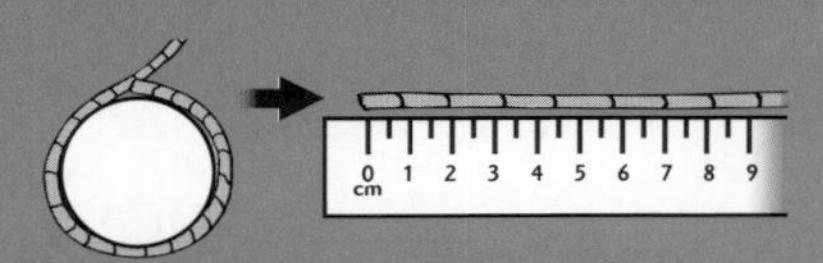

The length of the string = The circumference of the circle

Use a ruler and a piece of string to find the circumference and diameter of each circle in cm to the nearest tenth.

㉒

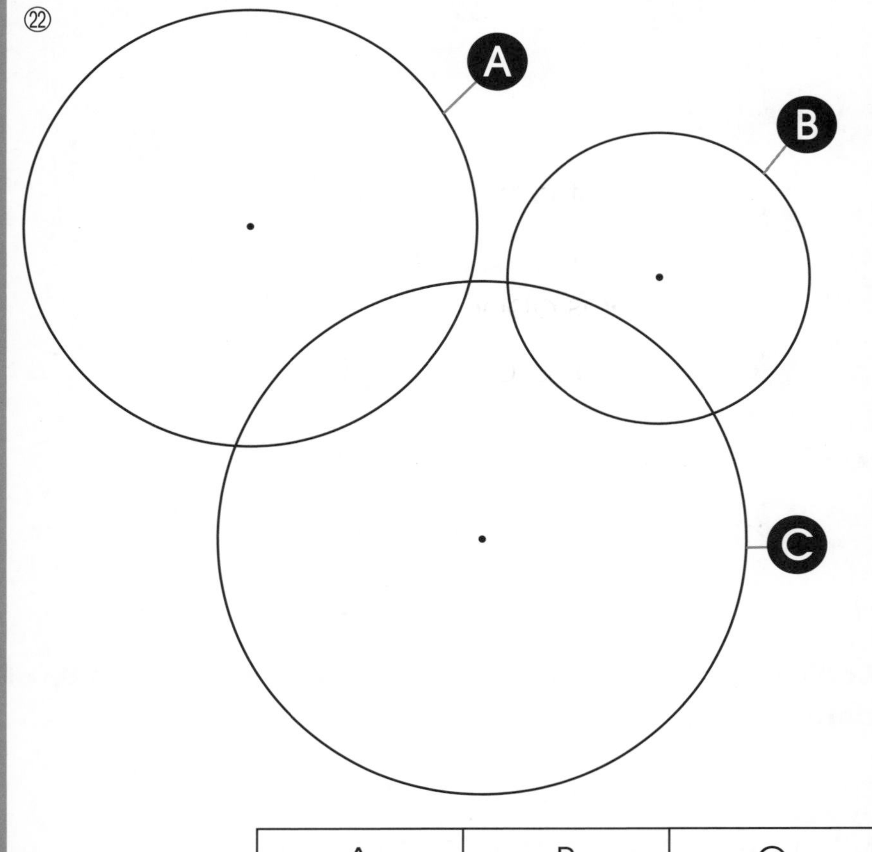

	A	B	C
Circumference			
Diameter			

DATE: ____________________

Day 16 Time (1)

Can you tell me how to write the date again?

First, write the year 2008. Then, write the month 10. Finally, write the day 08.

Look at the calendars. Write the dates in 2 ways.

In **SI** (International System) notation, June 24, 1998 is written as 1998 06 24.

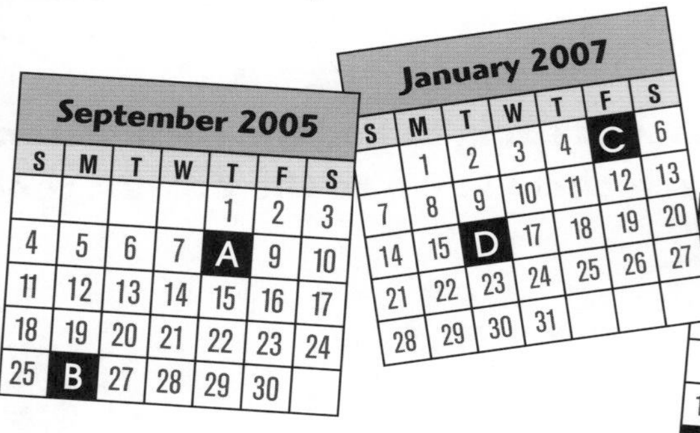

September 2005

S	M	T	W	T	F	S
				1	2	3
4	5	6	7	A	9	10
11	12	13	14	15	16	17
18	19	20	21	22	23	24
25	B	27	28	29	30	

January 2007

S	M	T	W	T	F	S
	1	2	3	4	C	6
7	8	9	10	11	12	13
14	15	D	17	18	19	20
21	22	23	24	25	26	27
28	29	30	31			

April 2008

S	M	T	W	T	F	S
		1	2	3	4	5
6	7	8	9	10	11	12
13	14	15	16	E	18	19
F	21	22	23	24	25	26
27	28	29	30			

May (*The year right after 2009*)

S	M	T	W	T	F	S
						1
2	3	4	5	6	7	G
9	10	11	12	13	14	15
16	17	18	19	20	21	22
23	24	25	26	27	28	29
30	31					

① A : Sept ______, 2005
2005 ______ 08

B : ______________
____

C : ______________
____

D : ______________
____

E : ______________
____

F : ______________
____

G : ______________
____

Look at the calendars above. Then find the number of days between the following dates.

② From 2005 09 13 to 2005 09 25 ______ days

③ From 2008 04 21 to 2008 05 04 ______ days

④ From May 10, 2010 to June 3, 2010 ______ days

⑤ From Dec 30, 2006 to Jan 9, 2007 ______ days

Hour Minute Second
11 : 22 : 40

Look at the clocks. Tell the times.

⑥

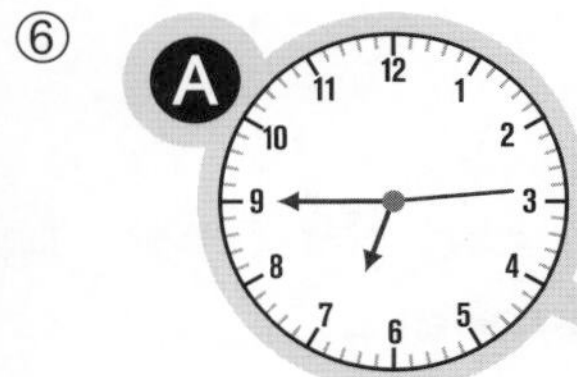

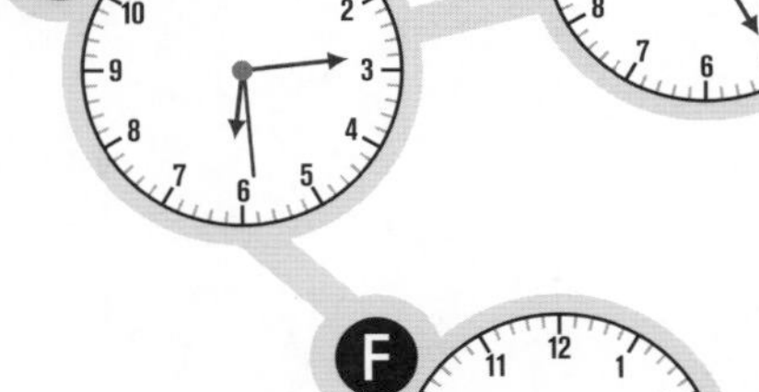

Ⓐ ____________

Ⓑ ____________

Ⓒ ____________

Ⓓ ____________

Ⓔ ____________

Ⓕ ____________

Ⓖ ____________

Ⓗ ____________

Steps to draw clock hands to show times:

1st Draw the minute hand.

2nd Draw the hour hand.

e.g. 09:36

1st

36 min

2nd

The hour hand is pointing at about the middle of 9 and 10.

Draw the clock hands to show the given times.

⑦

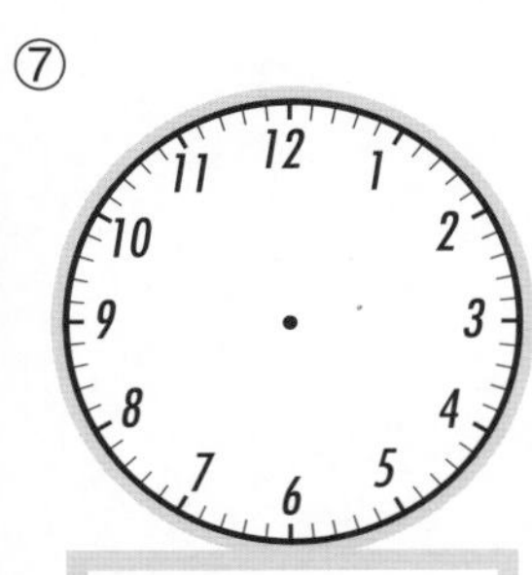

4:36

⑧

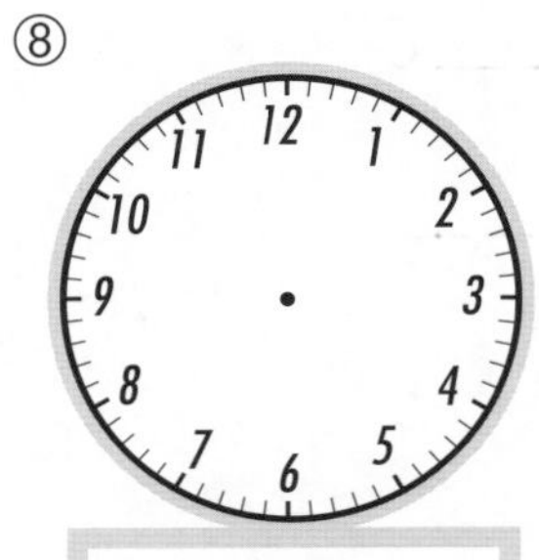

5:49

⑨

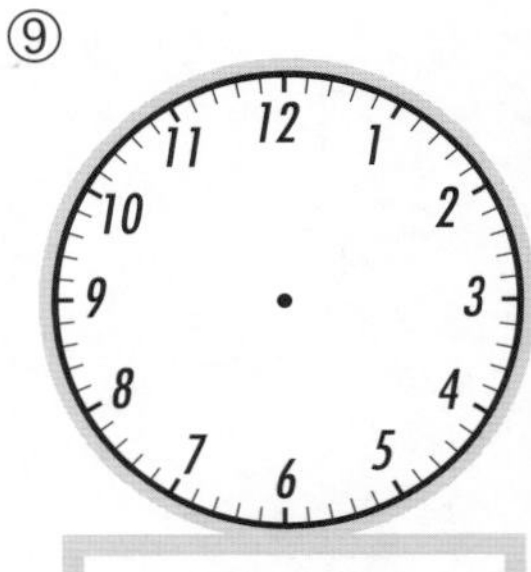

9:18

⑩

12:53

⑪

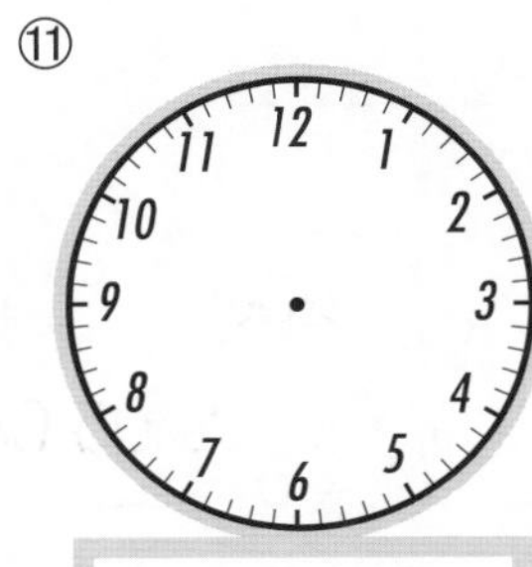

7:04

⑫

3:42

DATE: ____________

REVIEW

Use the digits in each group to form the greatest, the least, and a number that lies between the greatest and the least 5-digit numbers.

① 3, 6, 9, 7, 5 ____________ ____________ ____________

② 0, 6, 8, 1, 9 ____________ ____________ ____________

③ 5, 3, 2, 4, 6 ____________ ____________ ____________

Find the answers.

④ $\begin{array}{r} 5283 \\ +\ 1739 \\ \hline \end{array}$

⑤ $\begin{array}{r} 2754 \\ -\ 1086 \\ \hline \end{array}$

⑥ $\begin{array}{r} 3675 \\ -\ 2198 \\ \hline \end{array}$

⑦ $\begin{array}{r} 1753 \\ +\ 989 \\ \hline \end{array}$

⑧ $\begin{array}{r} 39 \\ \times\ 46 \\ \hline \end{array}$

⑨ $\begin{array}{r} 54 \\ \times\ 73 \\ \hline \end{array}$

⑩ $9\overline{)3674}$

⑪ $4\overline{)6807}$

⑫ 2766 + 1789 = ____________

⑬ 3583 – 1894 = ____________

⑭ 3011 – 749 = ____________

⑮ 867 + 2893 = ____________

⑯ 48 x 48 = ____________

⑰ 8069 ÷ 19 = ____________

⑱ 17 x 56 = ____________

⑲ 3114 ÷ 7 = ____________

⑳
11 x 5 = ________ 11 x 6 = ________
11 x 7 = ________ 11 x 9 = ________

㉑
12 x 3 = ________ 12 x 4 = ________
12 x 7 = ________ 12 x 8 = ________

Solve the problems.

㉒ There are 76 boys and 68 girls building sandcastles at the beach. If Uncle Joe wants to give each child 8 candies, how many candies does Uncle Joe need?

No. of children: ________________ = ________

No. of candies: ________________ = ________

Uncle Joe needs ________ candies.

㉓ Aunt Stephanie got $1275 selling shell necklaces yesterday. How many shell necklaces did she sell in all?

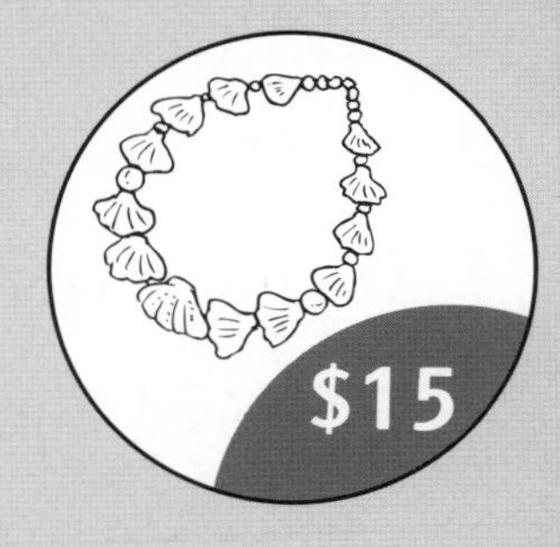

No. of shell necklaces: ________________ = ________

She sold ________ shell necklaces in all.

㉔ Emma buys 1250 g of salted peanuts and 982 g of unsalted peanuts. If she shares her peanuts equally with her sister, how many grams of peanuts does each girl get?

Amount of peanuts in all: ________________ = ________

Amount of peanuts each girl gets: ________________ = ________

Each girl gets ________ grams of peanuts.

Tell the times or draw the clock hands to show the times.

㉕ 

____

㉖ 

____

㉗ 

____

㉘ 

㉙ 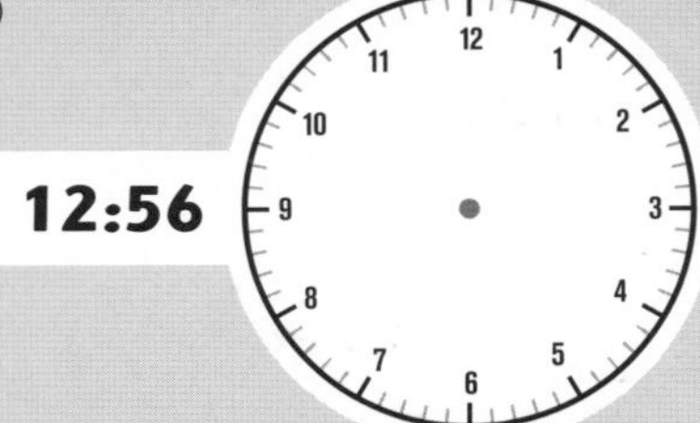

㉚ 

DATE:

You Deserve A

The cat will only let the mice go if they can solve the problems on the cards. Solve the problems to help free the mice.

① Do multiplication in a faster way. Show your work.

a. 99 x 8 = (100 – 1) x 8 = 792

b. 104 x 9 = (100 + 4) x 9 = 936

c. 6 x 58 = 6 x (60 – 2) = 348

② The gift with quotient 126 belongs to Cathy Cat. Which gift is it? Check ✔ the letter.

③ Mario Mouse has 12 bags of cat treats containing 85 pieces each. If Mario gives Cathy Cat 15 pieces of treat every day, how many days will Mario's treats last?

Step 1 12 x 85 = 60 + 960 = 1020

1020 treats in total

Step 2 1020 ÷ 15 = 68

Mario's treats will last for 68 days.

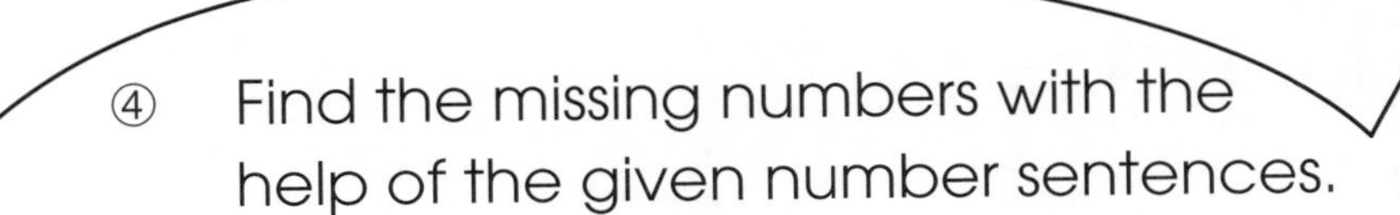

④ Find the missing numbers with the help of the given number sentences.

a. 16 x 89 = 1424

1424 ÷ 16 = 89

b. 92 x 17 = 1564

1564 ÷ 92 = 17

c. 3388 ÷ 44 = 77

44 x 77 = 3388

d. 1575 ÷ 63 = 25

25 x 63 = 1575

⑤ Round each number to the nearest

a. thousand.

94 163 94 000

37 952 38 000

88 759 89 000

60 137 60 000

52 064 52 000

b. ten thousand.

92 048 92 000

19 074 19 000

32 945 33 000

76 186 76 000

58 943 59 000

⑥ Look at the calendar and the clock. Tell the dates in 2 ways and tell the time.

May						2006
S	M	T	W	T	F	S
	1	2	3	4	5	6
7	8	9	10	11	12	13
14	15	16	17	18	19	20
21	22	23	24	25	26	27
28	29	30	31			

wednesday, May 3rd 2006

05/03/06

Friday, May 12th, 2006

05/12/06

08 : 27 : 52

DATE: ____________

Day 19

Time (2)

Find the time intervals. Show your work.

① **A** 9:15:47 a.m. ➔ 9:18:19 a.m.
Time interval: 2m32s

B 7:31:46 a.m. ➔ 8:32:15 a.m.
Time interval: 1:00:46

C 11:27:31 a.m. ➔ 12:09:34 p.m.
Time interval: ____________

D 2:26:26 p.m. ➔ 3:36:05 p.m.
Time interval: ____________

Use subtraction to find time intervals.

Time Interval	=	Final Time	–	Initial Time

e.g. From 8:47:36 a.m. to 9:02:19 a.m.

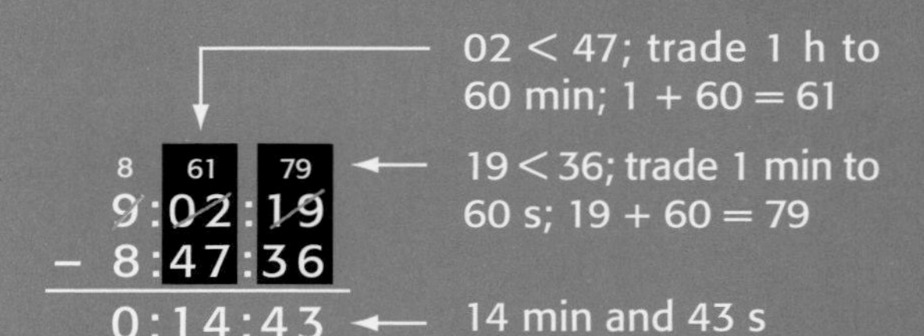

The time interval is 14 min and 43 s.

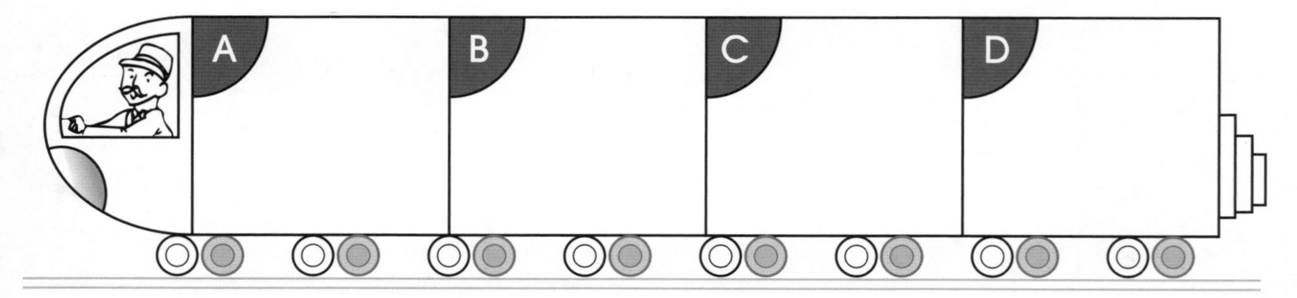

Find the time intervals.

② 8:15:42 a.m. ➔ 9:04:13 a.m. ____________

③ 12:30:46 p.m. ➔ 12:41:11 p.m. ____________

④ 5:18:03 p.m. ➔ 8:16:25 p.m. ____________

⑤ 6:04:28 a.m. ➔ 7:15:06 a.m. ____________

12:00 (noon) → 3:25 p.m.

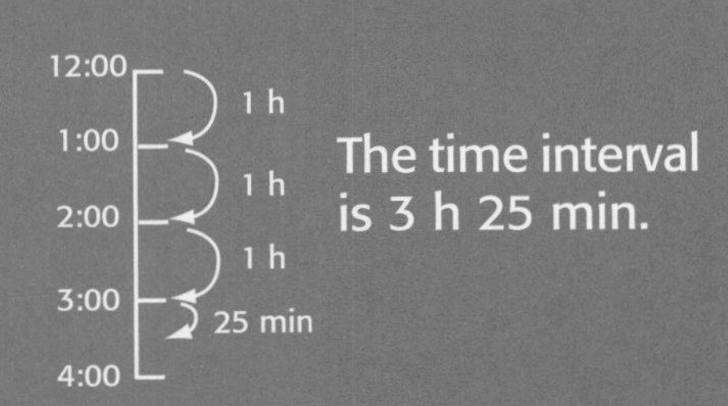

The time interval is 3 h 25 min.

e.g. From 8:04 a.m. to 2:25 p.m.
morning → afternoon

Split the time into 2 parts and find the time intervals separately.

Part 1 8:04 a.m. → 12:00 (noon)

$$\begin{array}{r} \overset{11}{\cancel{12}}:\overset{60}{\cancel{00}} \\ -\ 8:04 \\ \hline 3:56 \end{array}$$ ← 3 h 56 min

Part 2 12:00 (noon) → 2:25 p.m.

2 h 25 min

Time interval:

3 h 56 min + 2 h 25 min

= 5 h 81 min

= 6 h 21 min

Find the time intervals mentally.

⑥ 12:00 (noon) → 4:16 p.m. ____________

⑦ 12:00 (midnight) → 8:17 a.m. ____________

⑧ 12:00 (noon) → 2:42 p.m. ____________

⑨ 12:00 (midnight) → 1:08 a.m. ____________

Find how long the children took to finish their scrapbooks. Then answer the questions.

⑩

From 9:16 a.m. to 12:18 p.m.

Lisa took ____________ .

⑪

From 10:36 a.m. to 1:43 p.m.

Sam took ____________ .

⑫

From 11:28 a.m. to 3:41 p.m.

Sue took ____________ .

⑬
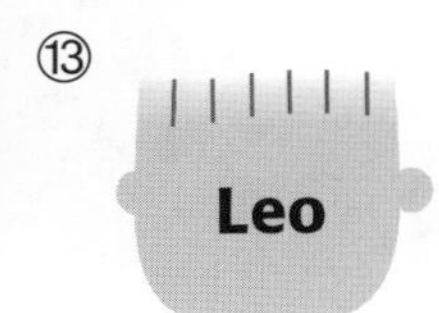

From 8:27 a.m. to 12:05 p.m.

Leo took ____________ .

⑭ Who took the shortest time to finish his or her own scrapbook? ________

⑮ Who took the longest time to finish his or her own scrapbook? ________

Find the times.

⑯ 9:43 a.m. —36 min→ ________

⑰ 10:25 a.m. —1 h 3 min→ ________

⑱ 4:27 p.m. —1 h 35 min→ ________

⑲ 2:52 p.m. —2 h 15 min→ ________

⑳ 3:34 p.m. —49 min→ ________

㉑ 10:54 p.m. —23 min→ ________

㉒ 6:08 a.m. —1 h 44 min→ ________

㉓ 8:38 a.m. —1 h 40 min→ ________

DATE: ____________

Day 20 Speed

Find the speeds.

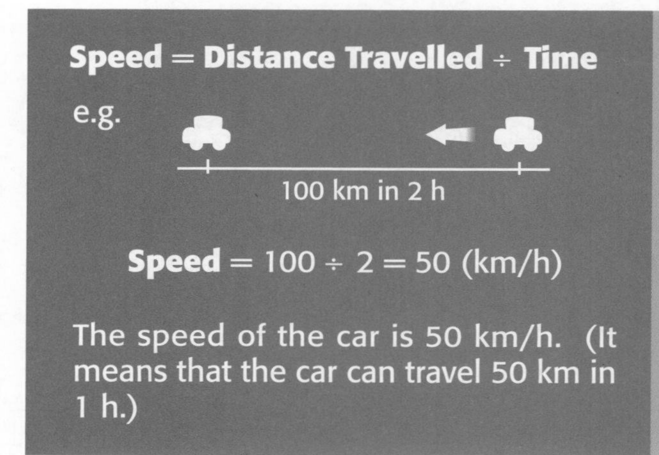

①

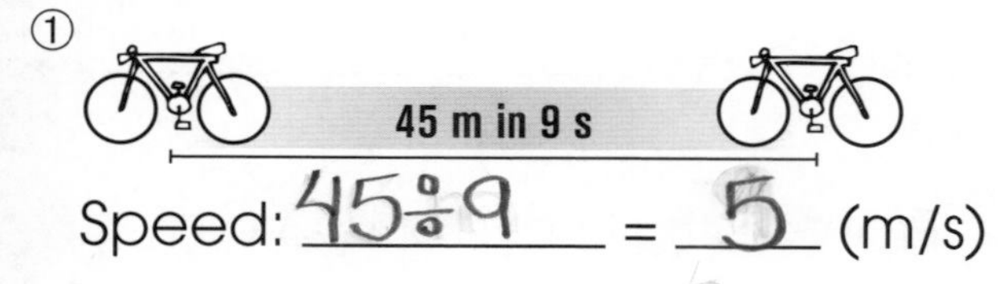

Speed: 45 ÷ 9 = 5 (m/s)

②

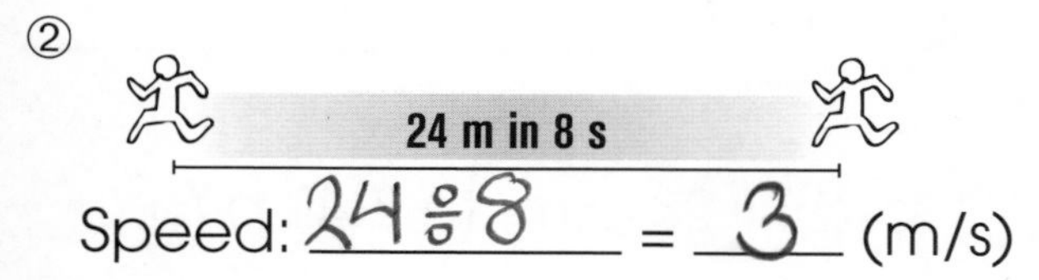

Speed: 24 ÷ 8 = 3 (m/s)

③

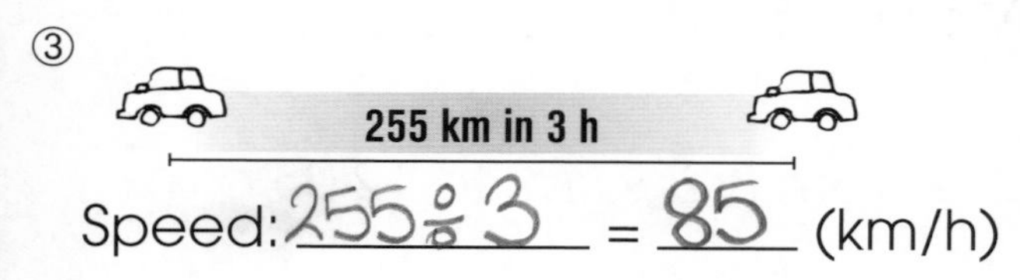

Speed: 255 ÷ 3 = 85 (km/h)

④

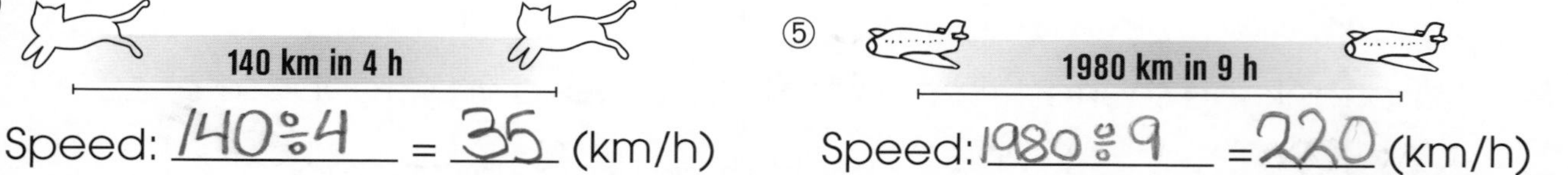

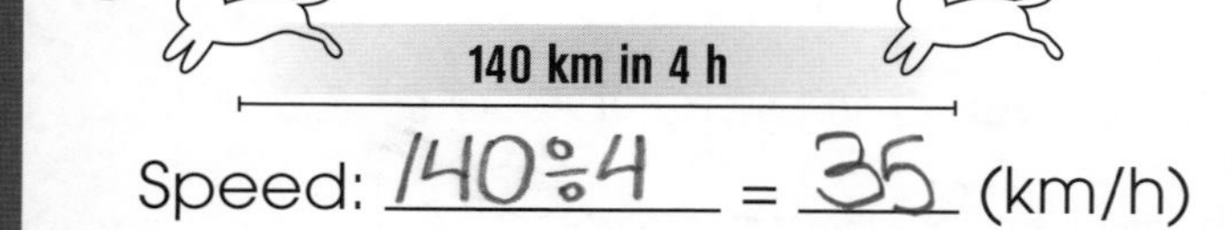

Speed: 140 ÷ 4 = 35 (km/h)

⑤ Speed: 1980 ÷ 9 = 220 (km/h)

Help the children find their speeds.

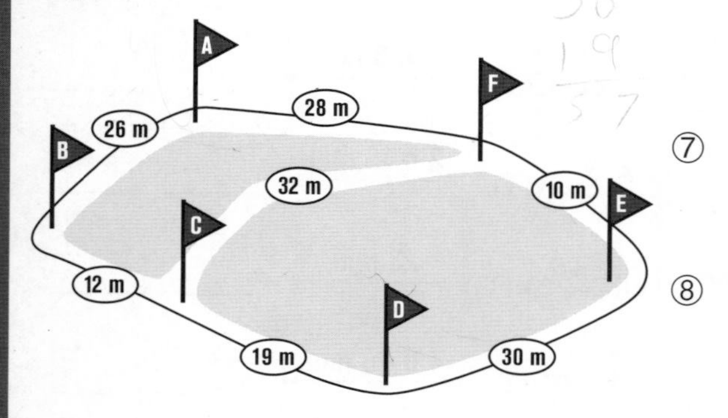

⑥ It takes Judy 19 s to cycle from A to D passing through B and C. Her speed is 3 m/s.

⑦ It takes Tony 30 s to hop from A to C passing through F. His speed is 2 m/s.

⑧ It takes Cathy 20 s to cycle back and forth between F and D using the shortest route. Her speed is 4 m/s.

Mr. Smith is driving to different places. Help him solve the problems.

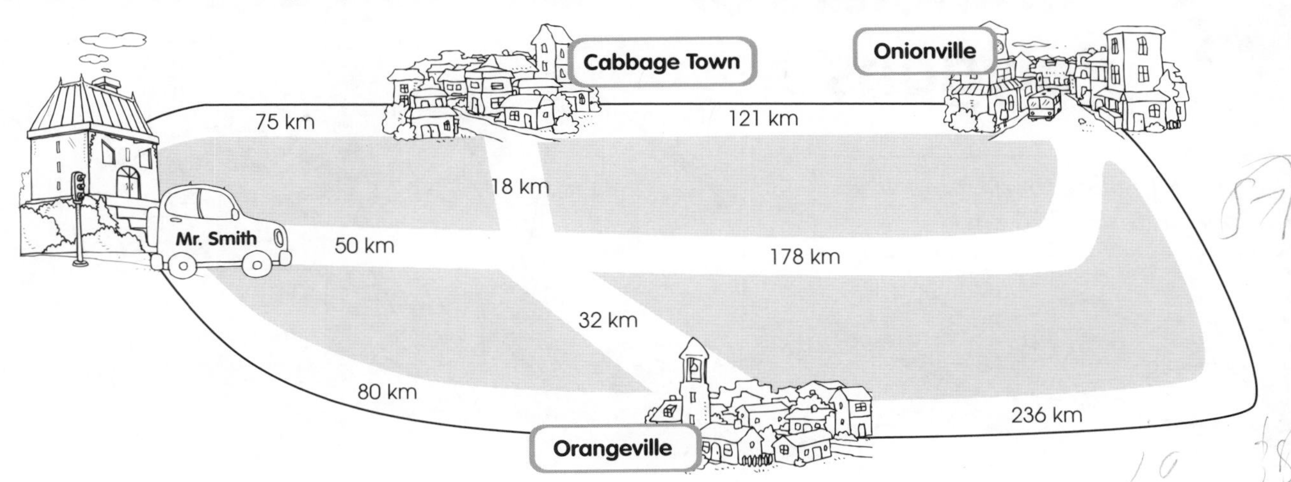

⑨ The shortest route that Mr. Smith drives to

a. Cabbage Town is 68 km. (50 + 18)

b. Orangeville is 80 km. (80 + 0)

c. Onionville is 189 km. (50 + 18 + 121)

⑩ If it takes Mr. Smith 2 h to drive from his house to Cabbage Town, what is his average speed?

68 ÷ 2 = 34

His average speed is 34 km/h.

⑪ If it takes Mr. Smith 3 h to drive from his house to Onionville, what is his average speed?

189 ÷ 3 = 63

His average speed is 63 KM/H.

⑫ If it takes Mr. Smith 10 h to drive back and forth 5 times between his house and Orangeville, what is his average speed?

(5 × 2) × 80 = 800 ÷ 10 = 80

His average speed is 80 km/h

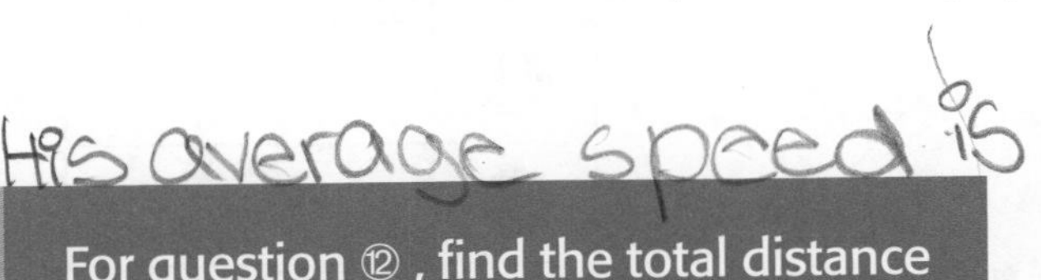

For question ⑫, find the total distance travelled first.

Mr. Smith's house → 80 km → Orangeville
Orangeville → 80 km → Mr. Smith's house

Did you know?

Tim Montgomery of USA is officially the ***world's fastest man***, clocking an incredible 100 m time of 9.78 seconds in 2002.

DATE:

Day 21

Perimeters of Polygons

Measure and record the sides in mm for each polygon. Then find its perimeter.

Polygon:
a closed figure formed by three or more line segments

e.g.

Polygon | Not Polygon

①

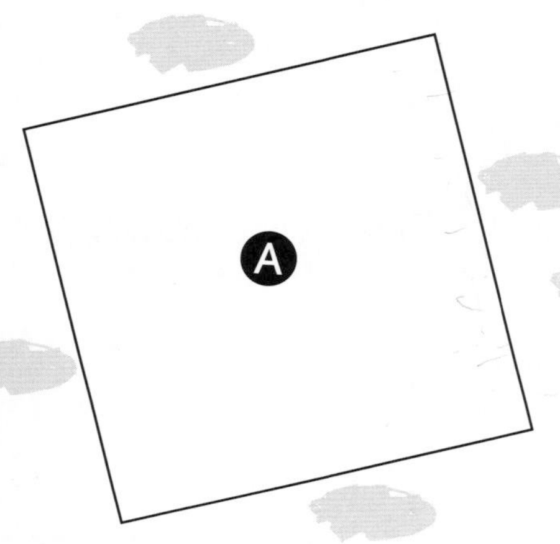

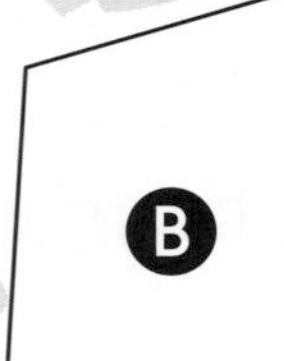

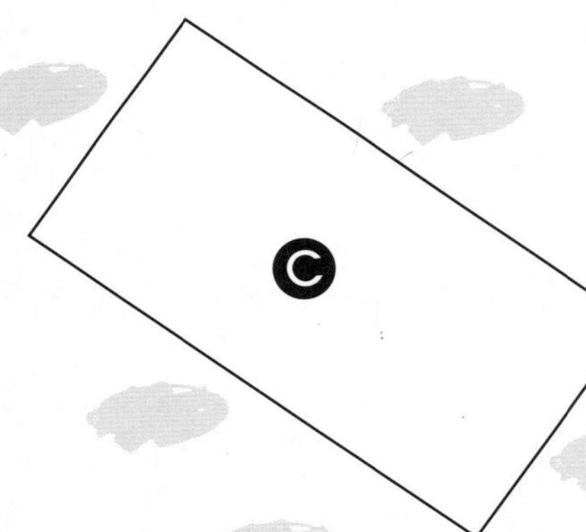

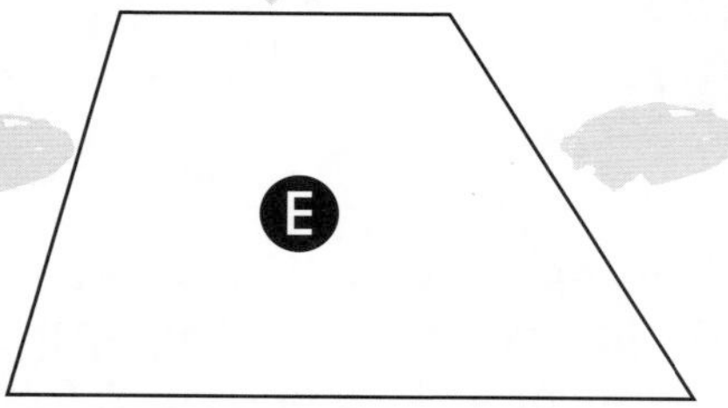

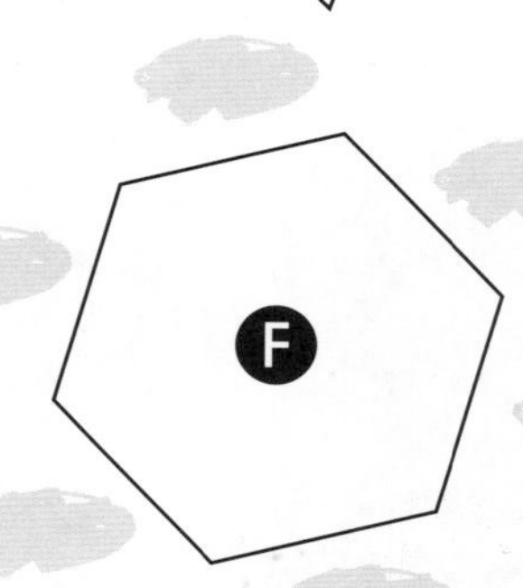

	Perimeter
A	22cm.
B	10cm
C	14cm
D	17cm
E	14cm
F	

Draw a shape in the circle to match each problem. Then solve the problems.

② A square has a length of 2 km. What is its perimeter?

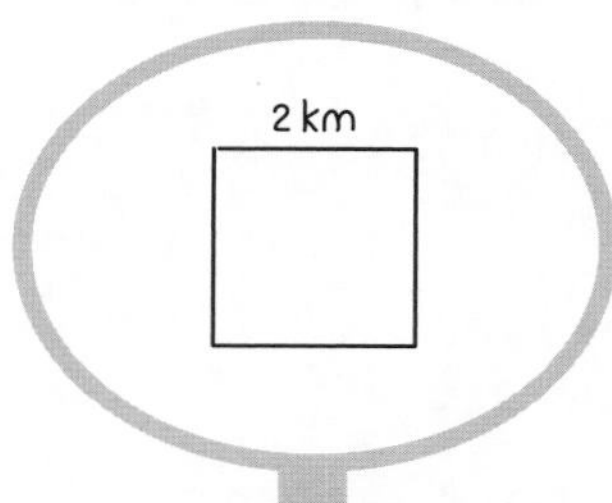

8 km

③ A regular hexagon has a length of 48 m. What is its perimeter?

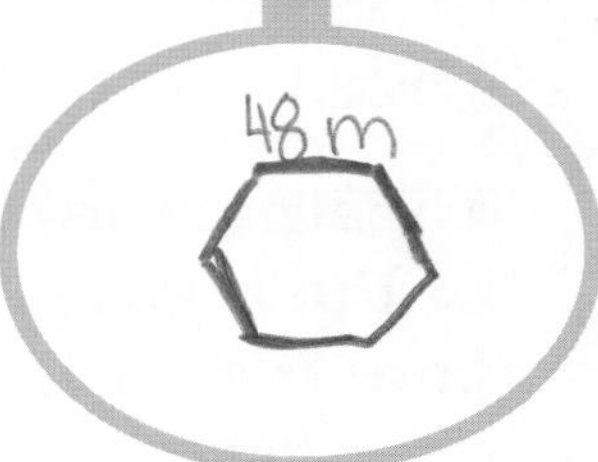

282 m

④ A regular octagon has a length of 125 cm. What is its perimeter?

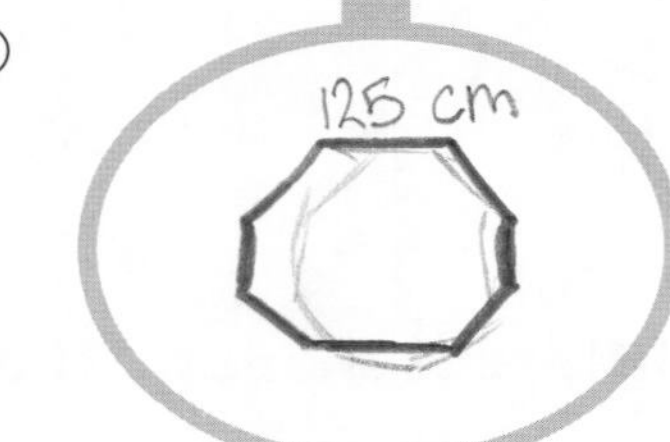

1000 cm

Solve the problems. Show your work.

⑤ If Jason cuts the rectangle along the dotted lines, what is the perimeter of the triangle?

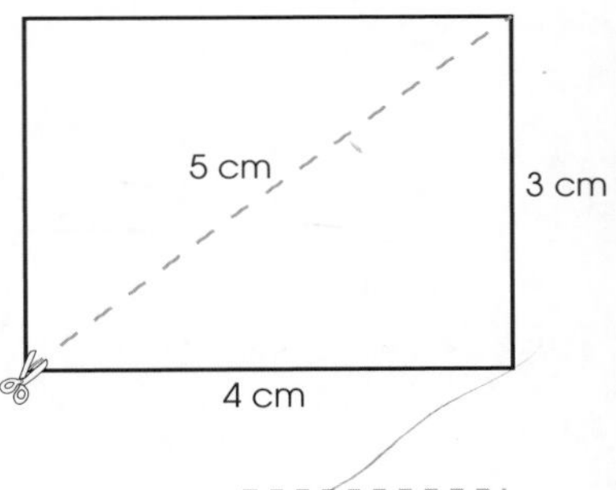

The perimeter of the triangle is 12 cm.

⑥ If Henry cuts the triangle along its line of symmetry, what is the perimeter of one of the small triangles?

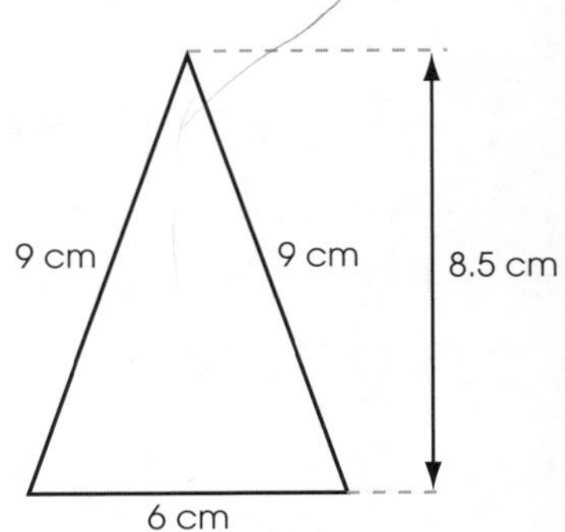

20.5 cm or 205 mm

⑦ If Josephine cuts out the greatest square from the rectangle, what is the perimeter of the square?

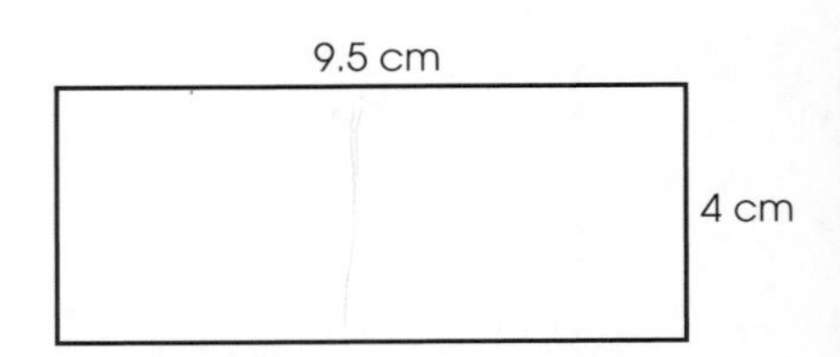

17.5 cm or 175 mm

DATE: ______________________

Day 22

Perimeters of Irregular Polygons

Draw lines on the figures to show how they are formed by different shapes. Then find their perimeters.

① It is formed by 5 identical squares.

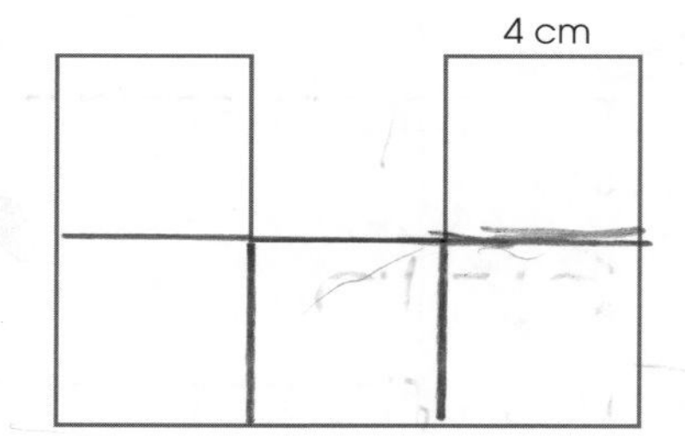

The perimeter is 44 cm

② It is formed by 1 square and 1 regular hexagon.

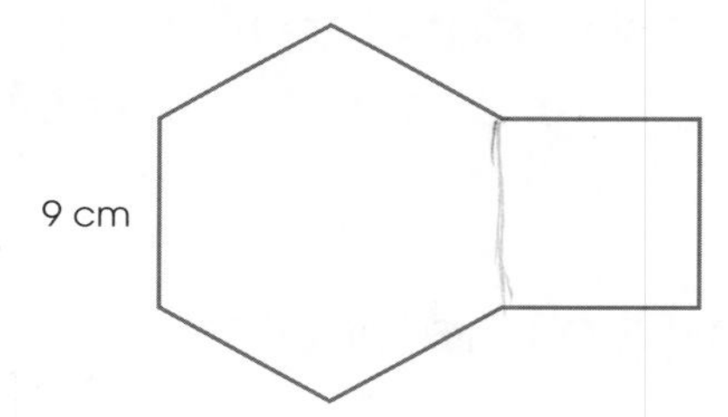

The perimeter is 72 cm .

③ It is formed by 1 rectangle and 1 parallelogram.

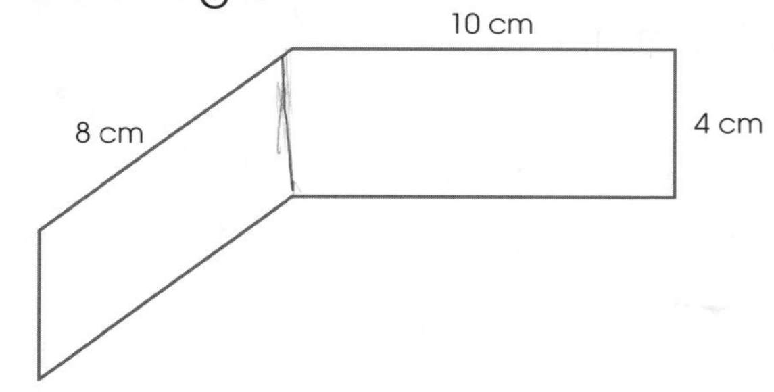

The perimeter is 48 cm .

④ It is formed by 2 identical parallelograms and 1 square.

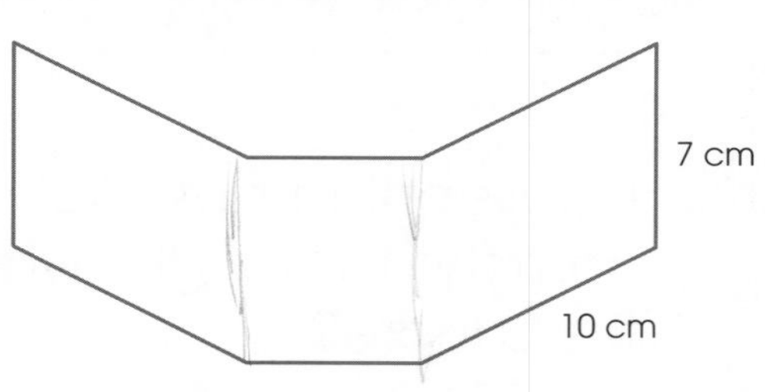

The perimeter is 42 cm .

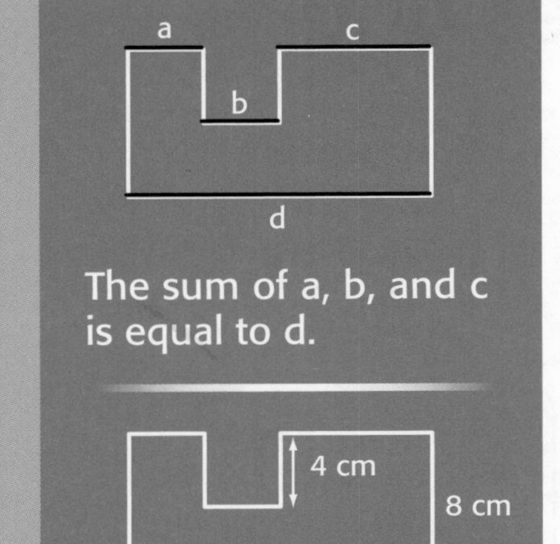

The sum of a, b, and c is equal to d.

Perimeter:
8 + 8 + 4 + 4 + 15 + 15
= 54 (cm)

Find the perimeters of the irregular polygons. You can draw lines on the shapes if necessary.

⑤

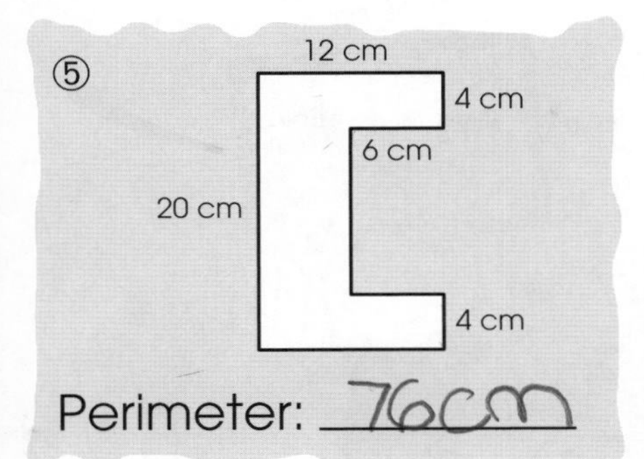

Perimeter: 76cm

⑥

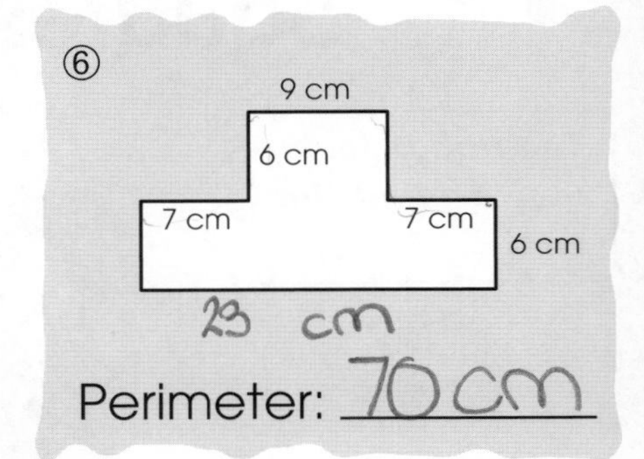

Perimeter: 70 cm

⑦

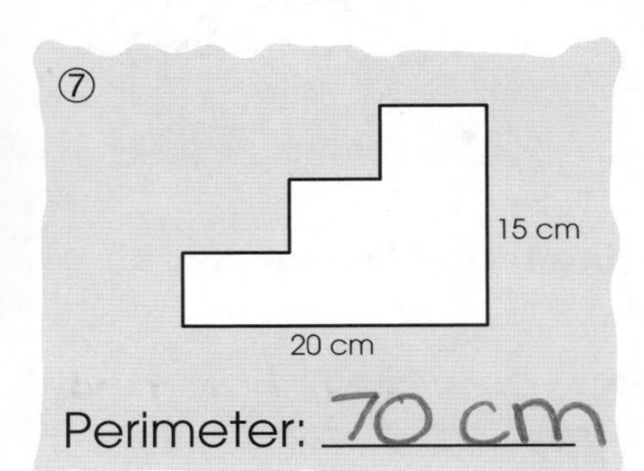

Perimeter: 70 cm

⑧

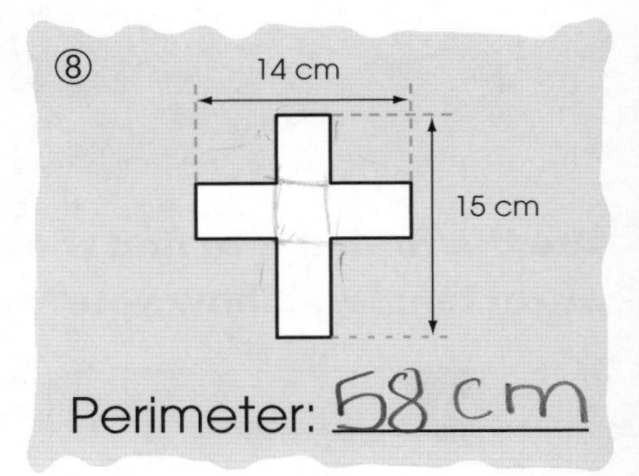

Perimeter: 58 cm

Solve the problems. Show your work.

⑨

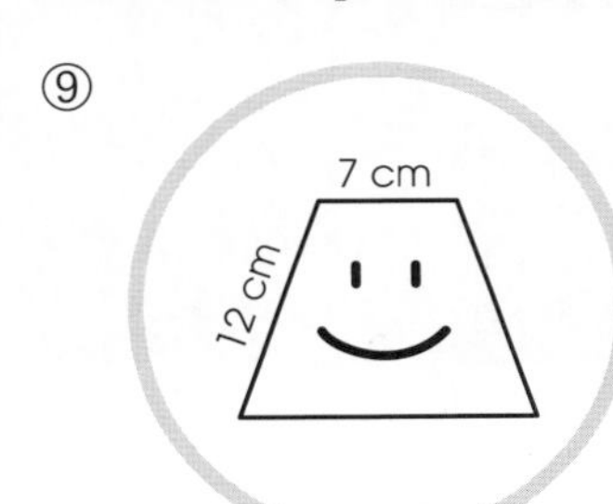

If the perimeter of the symmetrical trapezoid is 46 cm, what is the length of its base?

(12x2)+7=31 46-31=15

The length of its base is 15 cm.

⑩

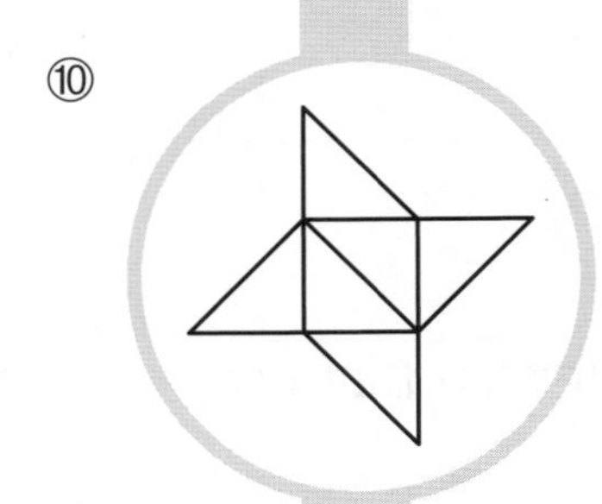

The flower is formed by 6 identical triangles each with sides 5 cm, 5 cm, and 7 cm. What is the perimeter of the flower?

(5+7) x4=48

The perimeter of the floweris 48 cm

⑪

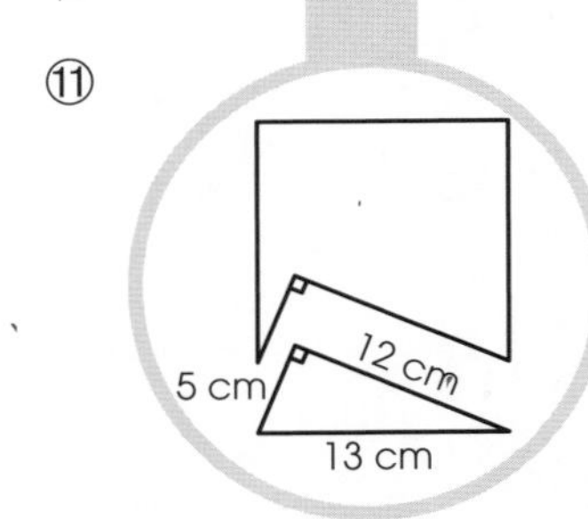

Wayne has cut out a triangle from the square. What is the perimeter of the irregular shape?

(13x3)+5+12=56 cm

The perimeter of the irregular shape is 56 cm

DATE: ____________________

Day 23

Perimeters of Rectangles and Squares

36 cm

19 cm

Dear Mom,

Happy Mother's Day!

with ♥,
Alex & Ann

The ribbon looks nice around the card.

Perimeter:

$$2 \times 36 + 2 \times 19$$
$$= 72 + 38$$
$$= 110 \text{ (cm)}$$

Since the perimeter of this card is 110 cm, we used 110 cm of ribbon.

Formulas for finding perimeters:

side length

Perimeter of a **square**:
4 x side length

length

width

Perimeter of a **rectangle**:
2 x length + 2 x width

Use the formulas to find the perimeters of the squares or rectangles. Show your work.

①

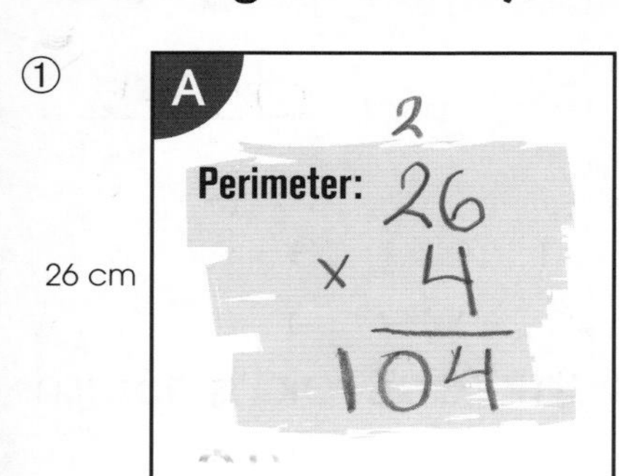

A

26 cm

Perimeter:

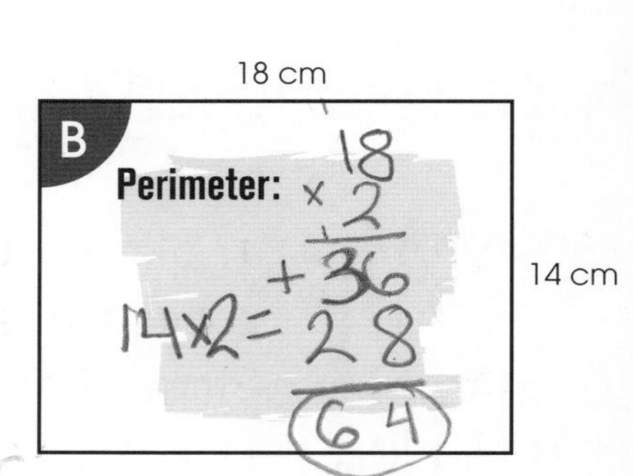

B

18 cm

14 cm

Perimeter:

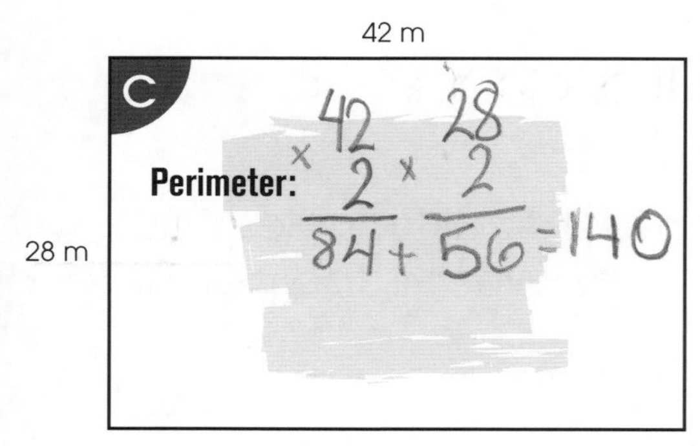

C

42 m

28 m

Perimeter:

D

64 cm

30 cm

Perimeter:

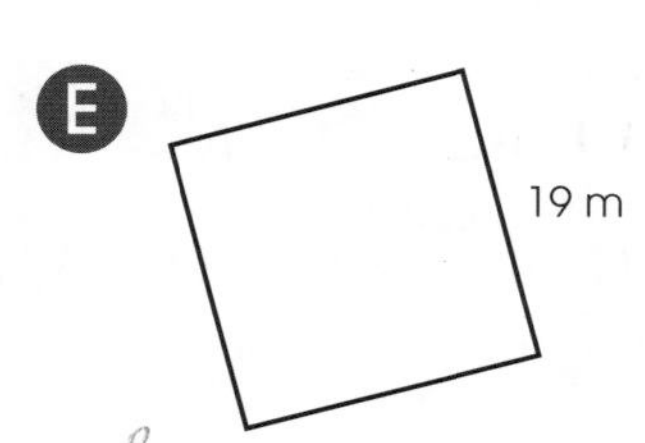

E

19 m

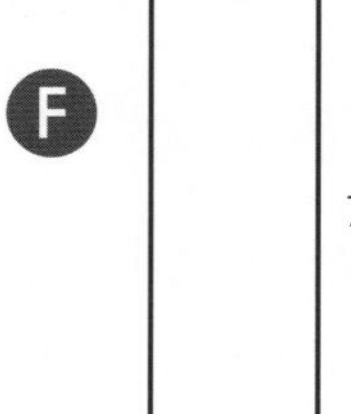

F

25 mm

72 mm

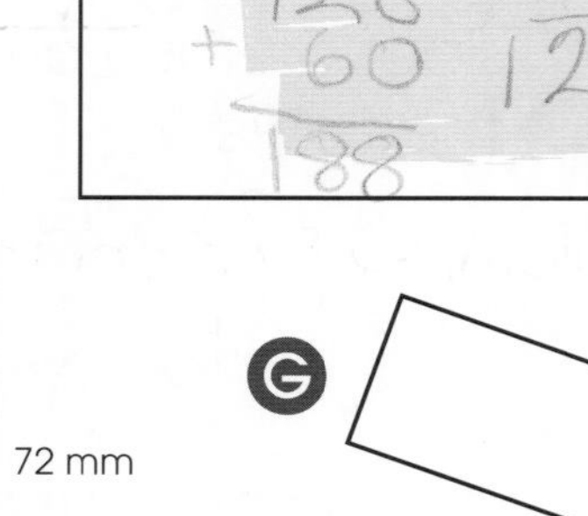

G

45 m

12 m

Perimeter:

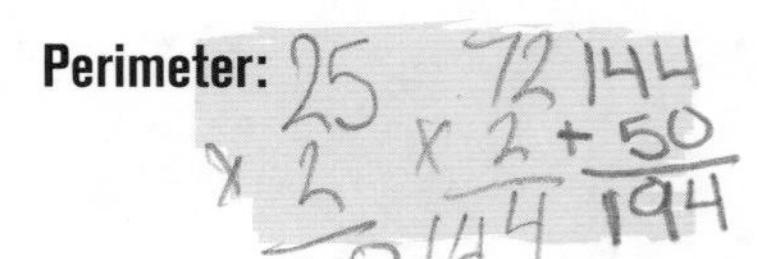

Perimeter:

Perimeter:

Complete the tables.

②

Square	Side Length	Perimeter
A	5 cm	
B	14 m	
C	4 km	
D		28 cm
E		72 m
F		136 cm

③

Rectangle	Length	Width	Perimeter
A	9 cm	4 cm	
B	18 m	15 m	
C	29 m	16 m	
D	14 cm		78 cm
E	5 m		28 m
F	48 mm		16 cm

Solve the problems.

④ Uncle Morgan has a piece of 45 cm by 35 cm cardboard. What is the perimeter of the cardboard?

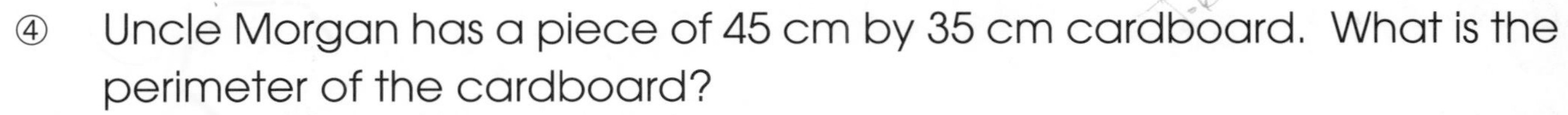

 =  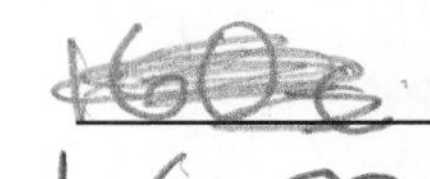

⑤

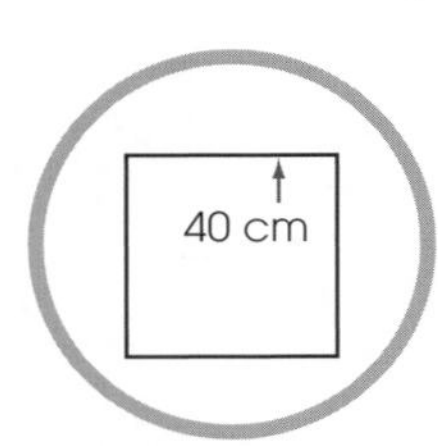

Tim bends a wire to form the square in the circle. If he cuts away 8 cm from the wire and bends a new square with the remaining wire, what is the side length of the new square?

= 

⑥ The perimeter of a rectangle is 84 cm. If its width is 16 cm, what is its length?

 = 

⑦

If Jason wants to frame the picture with a border of 1 cm, how long is the frame?

=

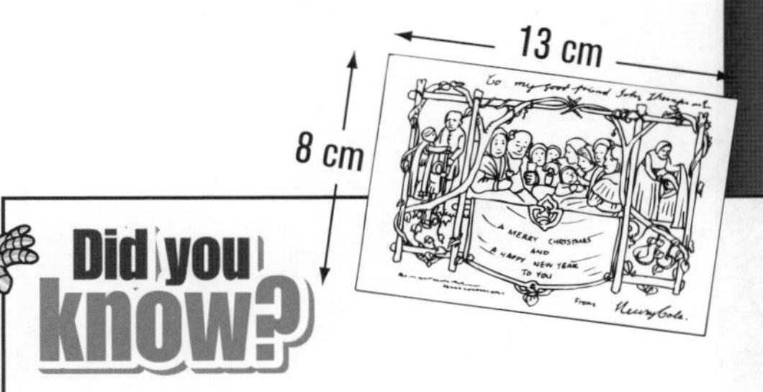

Did you know?

The **most valuable Christmas card** in the world was sold at auction in UK for £20 000 in 2001. It has a perimeter of 42 cm.

DATE: ____________

Day 24

Areas of Polygons

Draw lines to complete the grid to find the areas of the shapes. Then answer the questions.

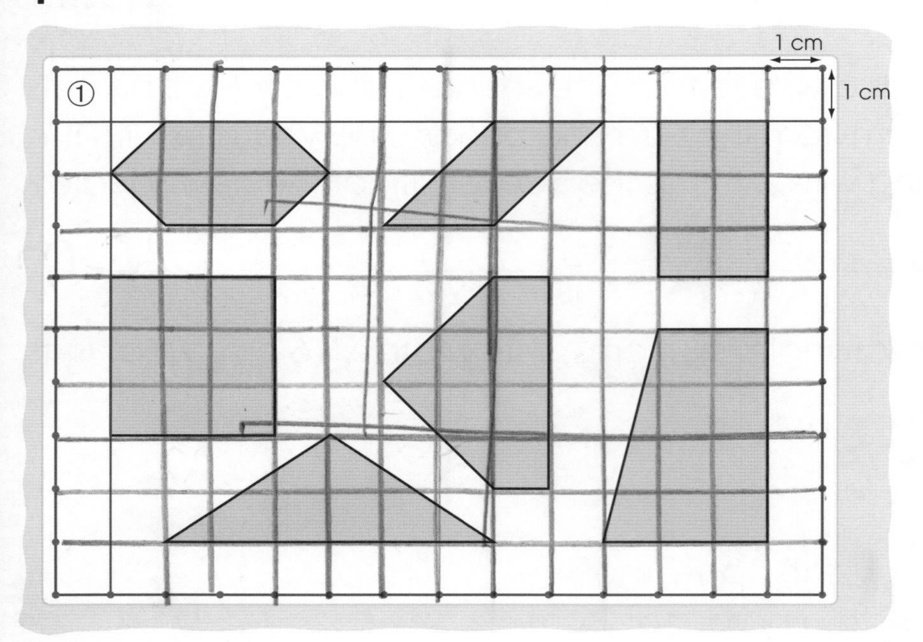

Square: 9 cm²

Triangle: 5 cm²

Parallelogram: 4 cm²

Rectangle: 6 cm²

Trapezoid: 10 cm²

Pentagon: 8 cm²

Hexagon: 6 cm²

② Which shape has the greatest area? trapezoid

③ Which shape has the smallest area? paralelogram

④ Which shapes have the same area? rectangle, hexagon

⑤ If 4 of the above rectangles are needed to cover a bookmark, what is the area of the bookmark? 24 cm²

Find the areas of the polygons.

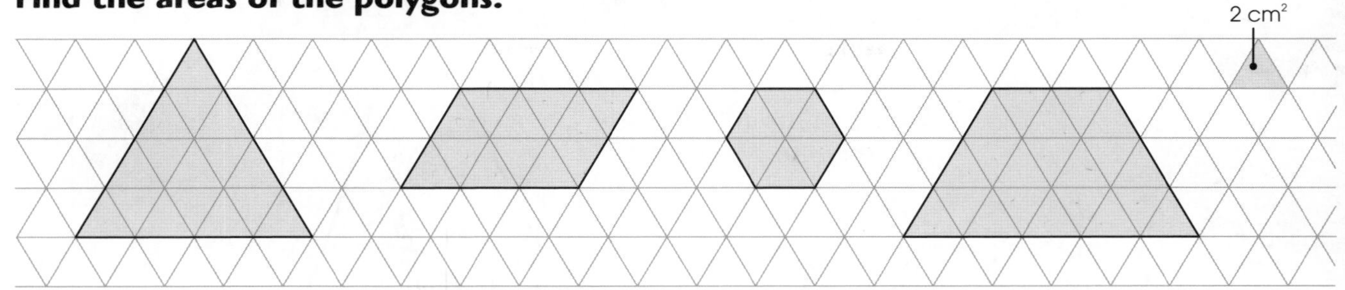

⑥ Triangle: 32 cm² Parallelogram: 24 cm²

Hexagon: 12 cm² Trapezoid: 42 cm²

Draw the polygons.

⑦ Draw 1 rectangle, 1 hexagon, and 1 triangle each having an area of 12 cm^2.

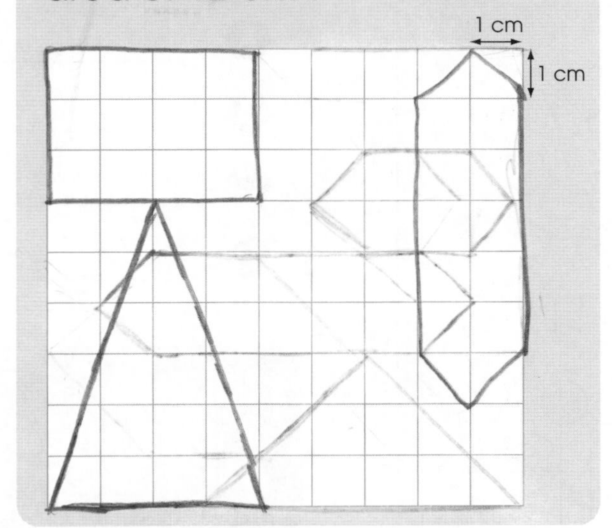

⑧ Draw 1 square, 1 parallelogram, and 1 trapezoid each having an area of 9 cm^2.

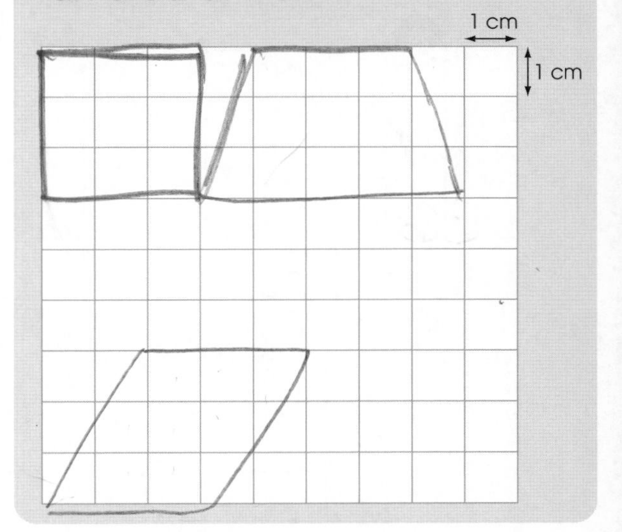

⑨ Draw 1 pentagon and 1 rectangle each having an area of 10 cm^2.

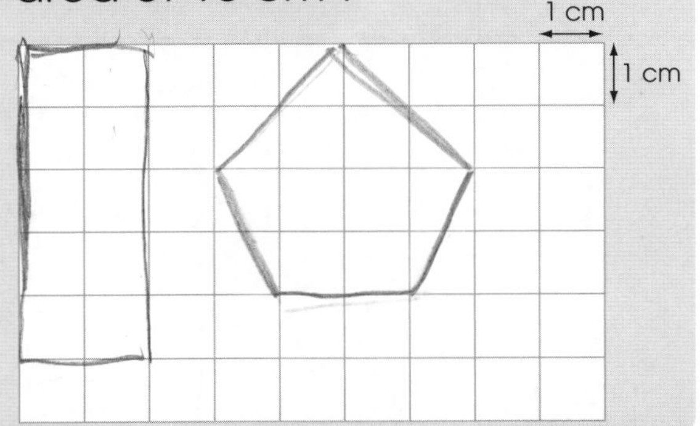

In 2004, a Japanese scientist invented an ***invisible cape****. A background image is projected onto the cape to make the wearer appear transparent.*

DATE: ______________

Day 25

Areas of Irregular Polygons

Find the area of each sticker and answer the questions.

①

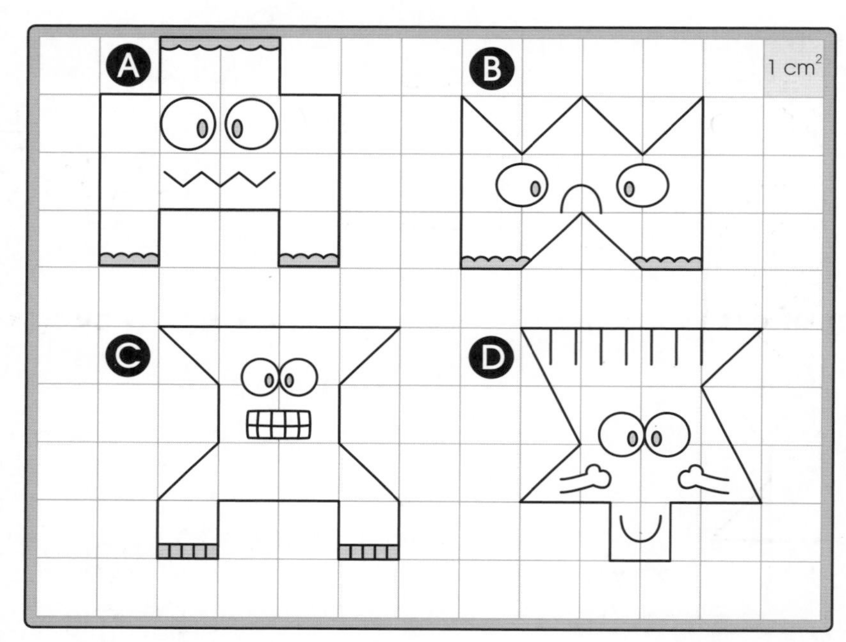

A : 12 cm²

B : 9 cm²

C : 10 cm²

D : 10 cm²

Tessellation:
A tiling pattern in which shapes are fitted together with no gaps or overlaps.

② A has the greatest area and B has the least.

③ Which sticker can form a tile pattern? Use that sticker to create a tessellation.

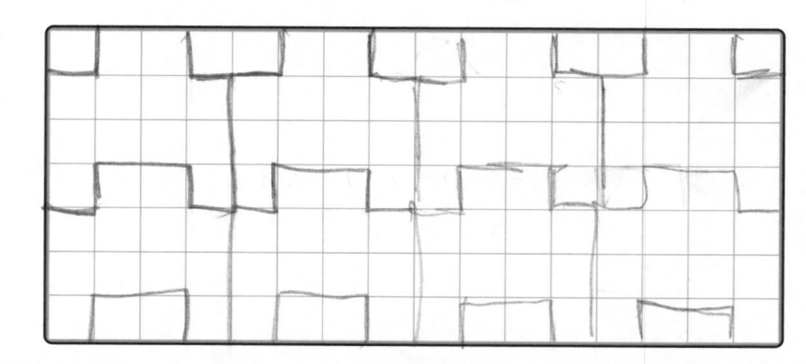

Find the area of each irregular polygon. Draw a line on it to show how it is formed by two regular polygons. Then name the regular polygons and find their areas.

④

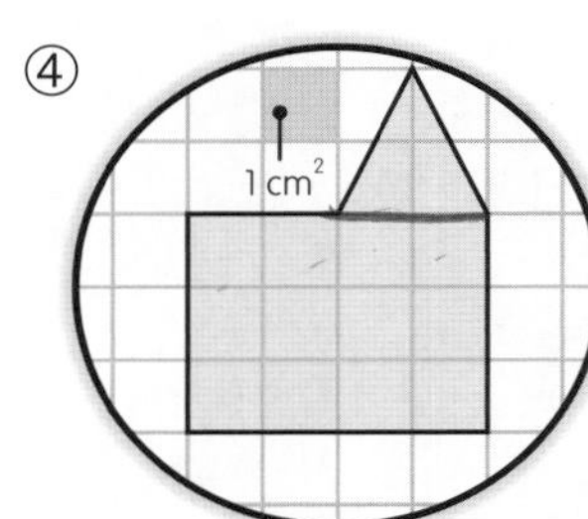

Area of the irregular polygon: ________

Two regular polygons: ________ (an area of ________)

________ (an area of ________)

⑤

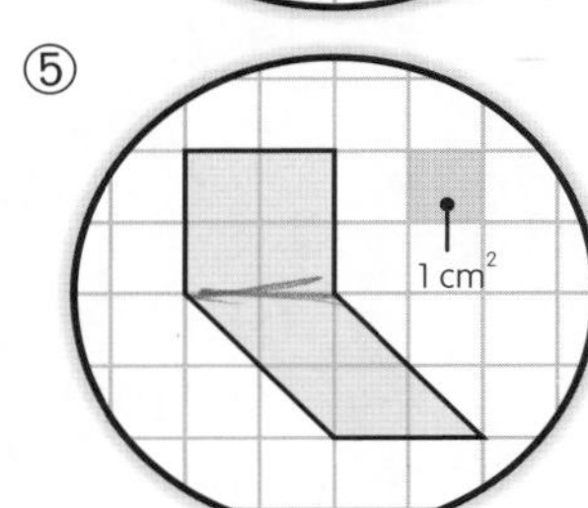

Area of the irregular polygon: ________

Two regular polygons: ________ (an area of ________)

________ (an area of ________)

⑥

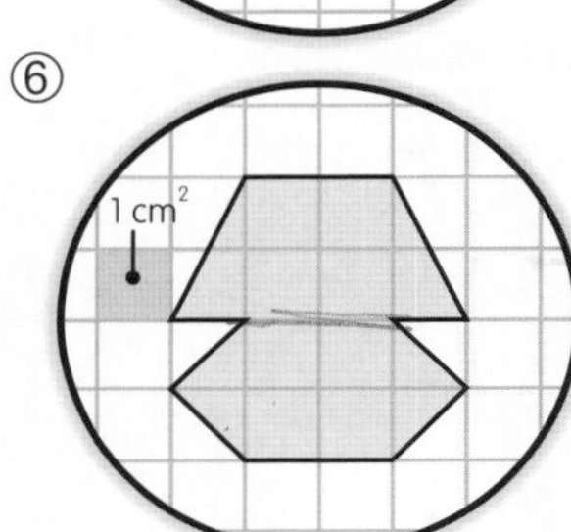

Area of the irregular polygon: ________

Two regular polygons: ________ (an area of ________)

________ (an area of ________)

Find the area and perimeter of each irregular polygon. Then answer the questions.

⑦

1 cm

1 cm

1 cm²

Area	________	________	________	________
Perimeter	________	________	________	________

⑧ Does the shape with the greatest area have the greatest perimeter? ________

⑨ Do the shapes having the same perimeter have the same area? ________

DATE: ____________

Day 26

Areas of Rectangles and Squares

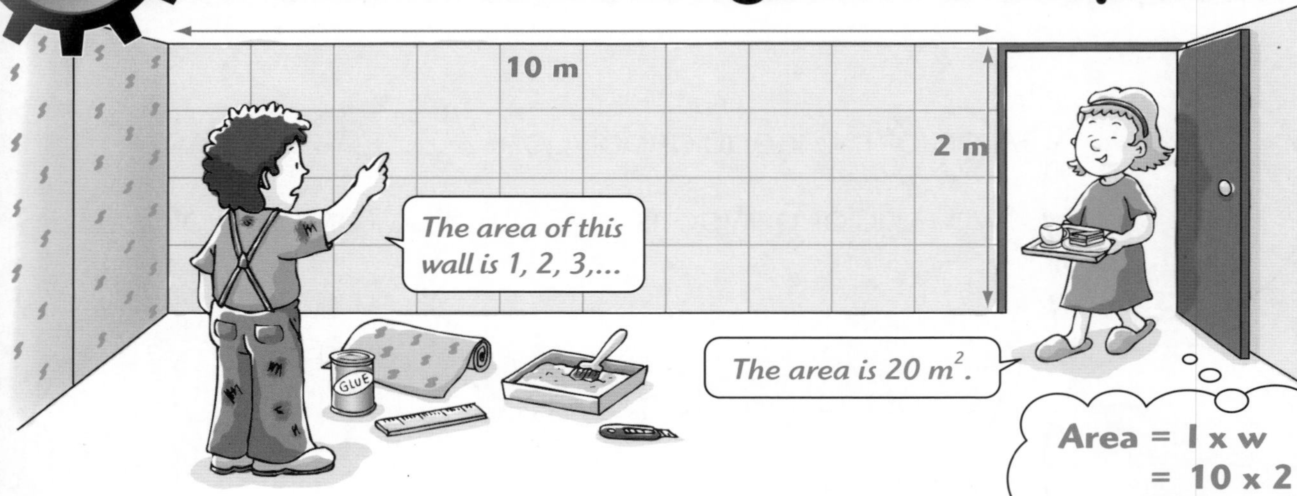

Use the formulas to find the areas of the rectangles or squares. Show your work.

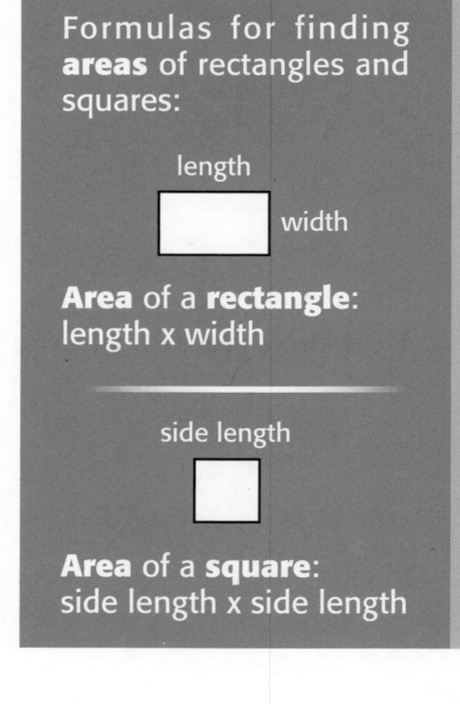

①

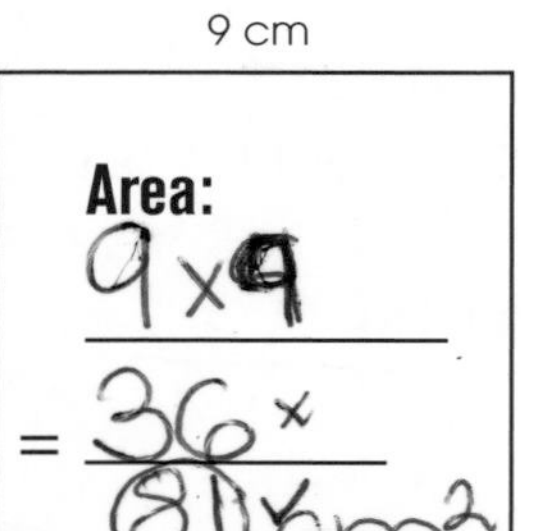

②

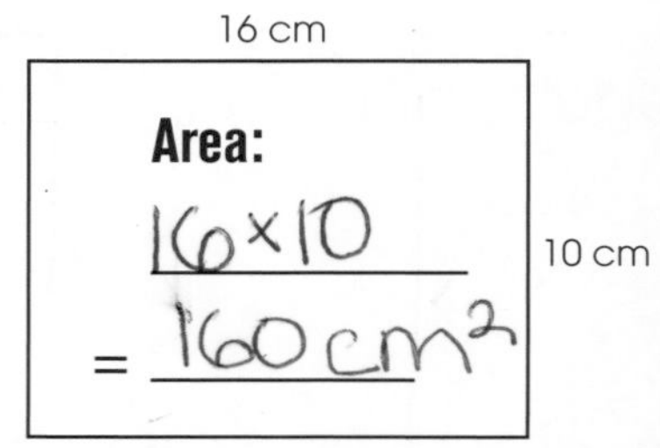

③

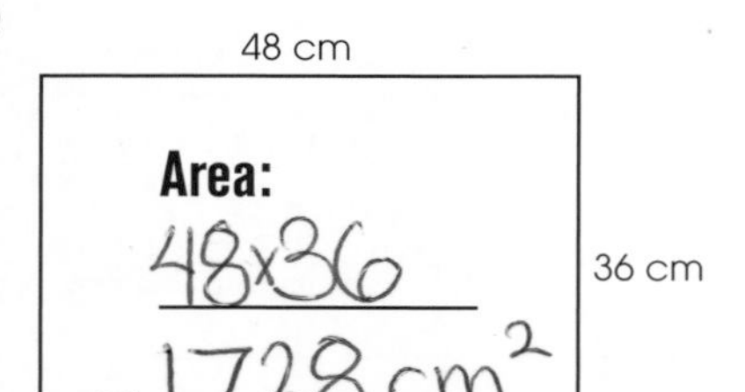

④

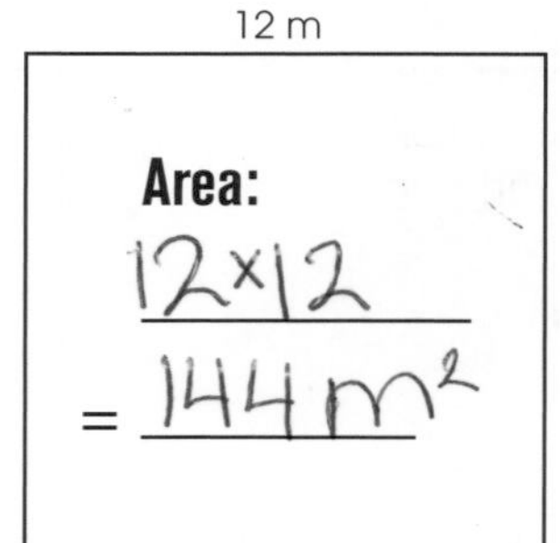

⑤

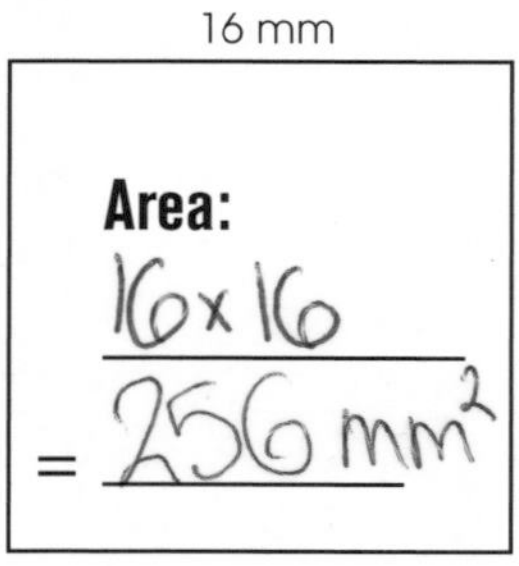

⑥

4 m

Area:

4x2

= 8m²

2 m

⑦

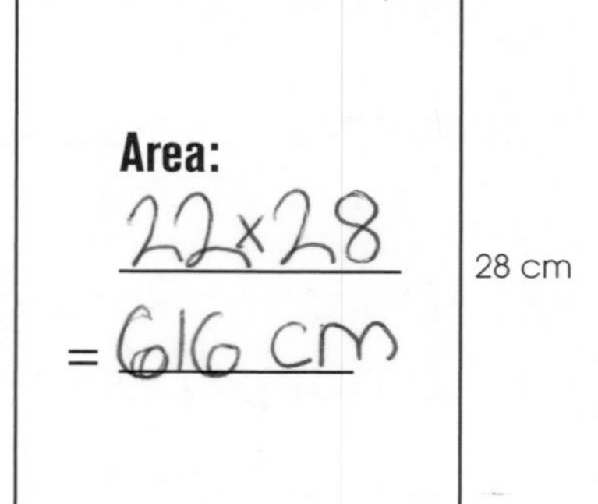

Use subtraction to find the shaded area.

e.g.

Area: $3 \times 3 = 9$ (cm^2)

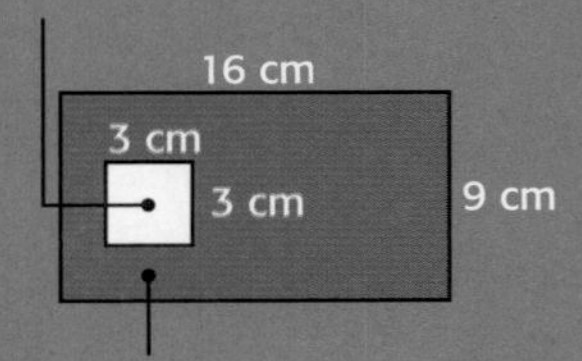

Area: 16×9
$= 144$ (cm^2)

Area of the shaded part:
$144 - 9 = 135$ (cm^2)

Find the area of the shaded part for each figure.

A
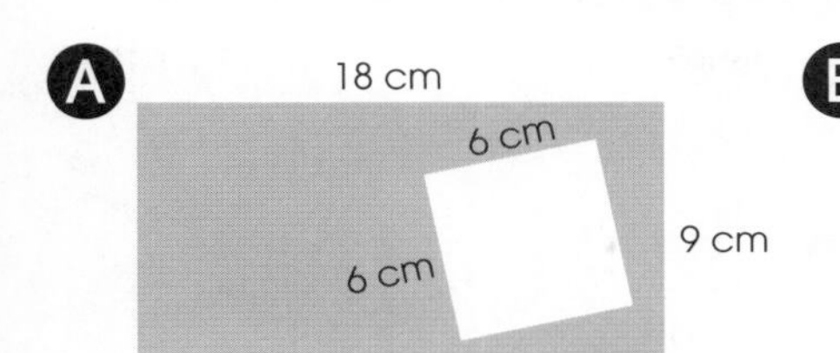

B
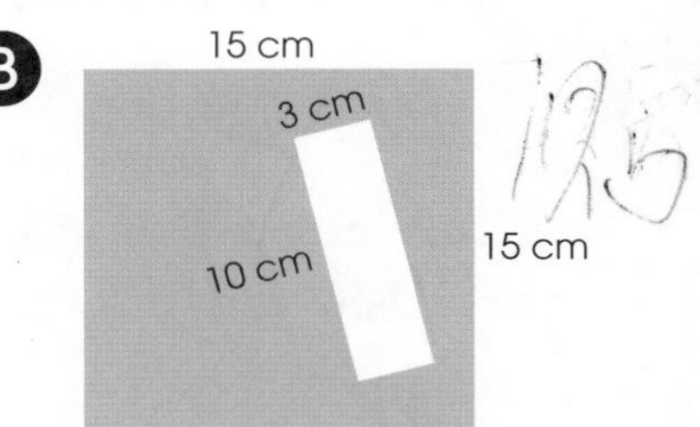

C
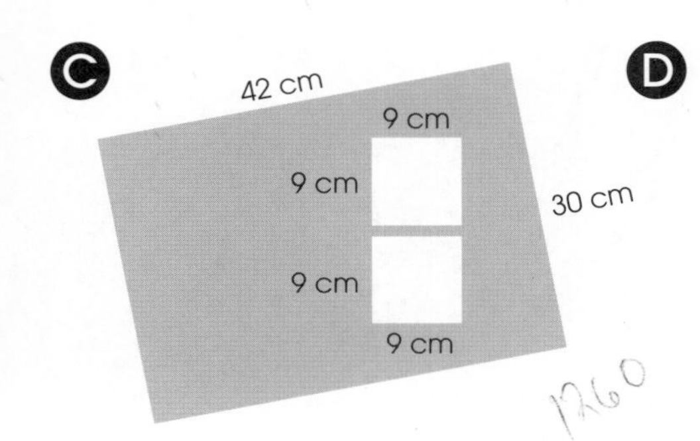

D
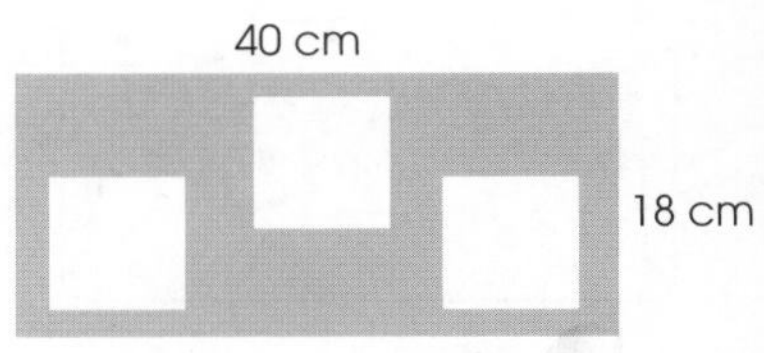

* Each square has a side length of 9 cm.

E
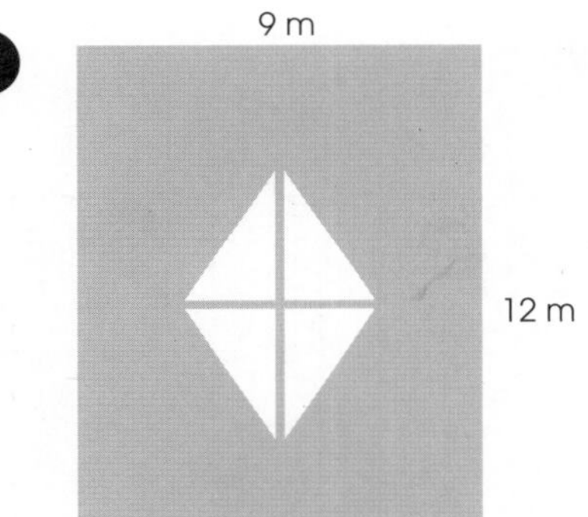

* Each triangle has an area of 3 m^2.

F

* Each triangle has an area of 2 cm^2.

⑧ A : 126 cm^2

B : 195 cm^2

C : 1098 cm^2

D : 476 cm^2

E : 9068 cm^2

F : 32 cm^2

Solve the problems.

⑨ The dimensions of the picture are 25 cm by 18 cm. The picture is mounted on a frame with a 2 cm-wide border.

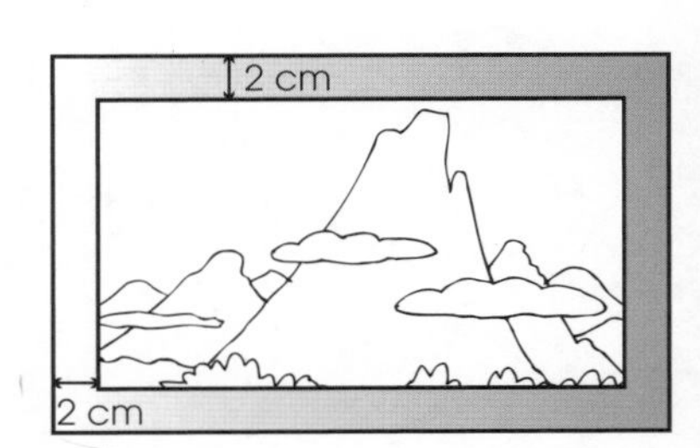

a. What are the dimensions of the framed picture?

27 cm by 20 cm

b. What is the area of the framed picture?

594 cm^2

Did you know?

*In 1778, King Louis XVI of France issued a decree that required the length of a **wallpaper roll** be 10.36 m.*

DATE: ____________________

Volume (1)

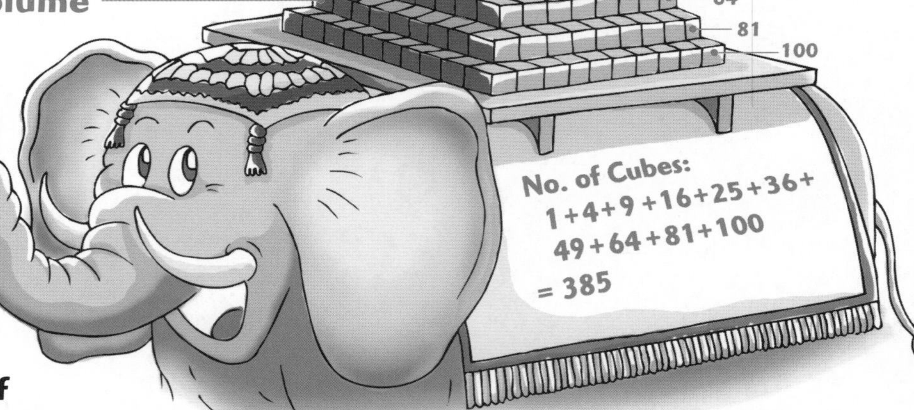

Count the number of centimetre cubes used. Determine the volume of each model. Write the answer on the line. Then answer the questions.

The **volume** of a centimetre cube is 1 cubic centimetre.

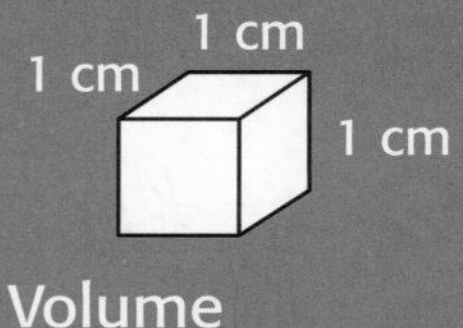

Volume
= 1 cubic centimetre
= 1 cm^3

①

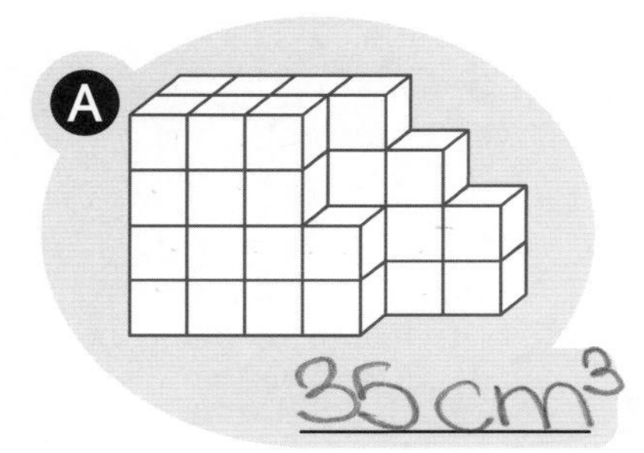

35 cm^3

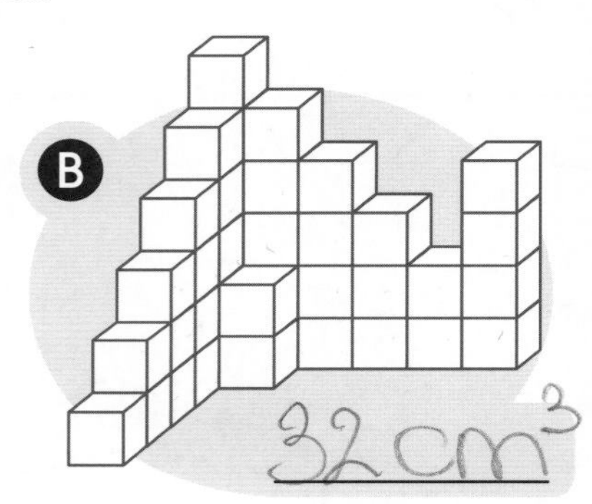

32 cm^3

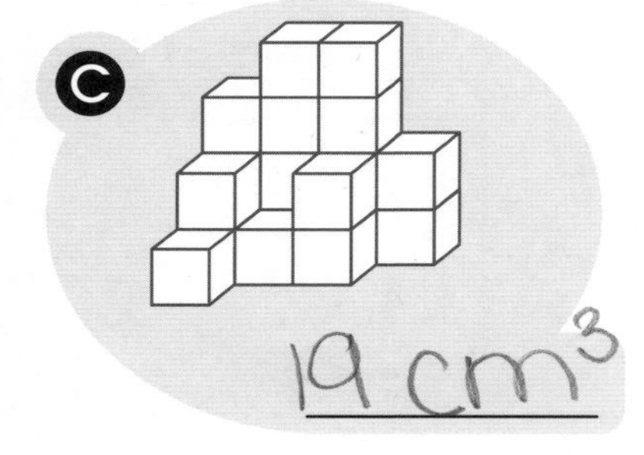

19 cm^3

26 cm^3

16 cm^3

② Which model has the greatest volume? A

③ Which two models have the same total volume as that of Ⓐ? C&E

④ 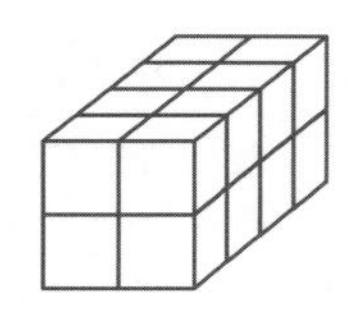

If Jason takes some cubes from Ⓐ to build the model on the left, how many cubes will be left in Ⓐ? 27 cubes

Find the volume of each model. Then check the one with the greatest volume.

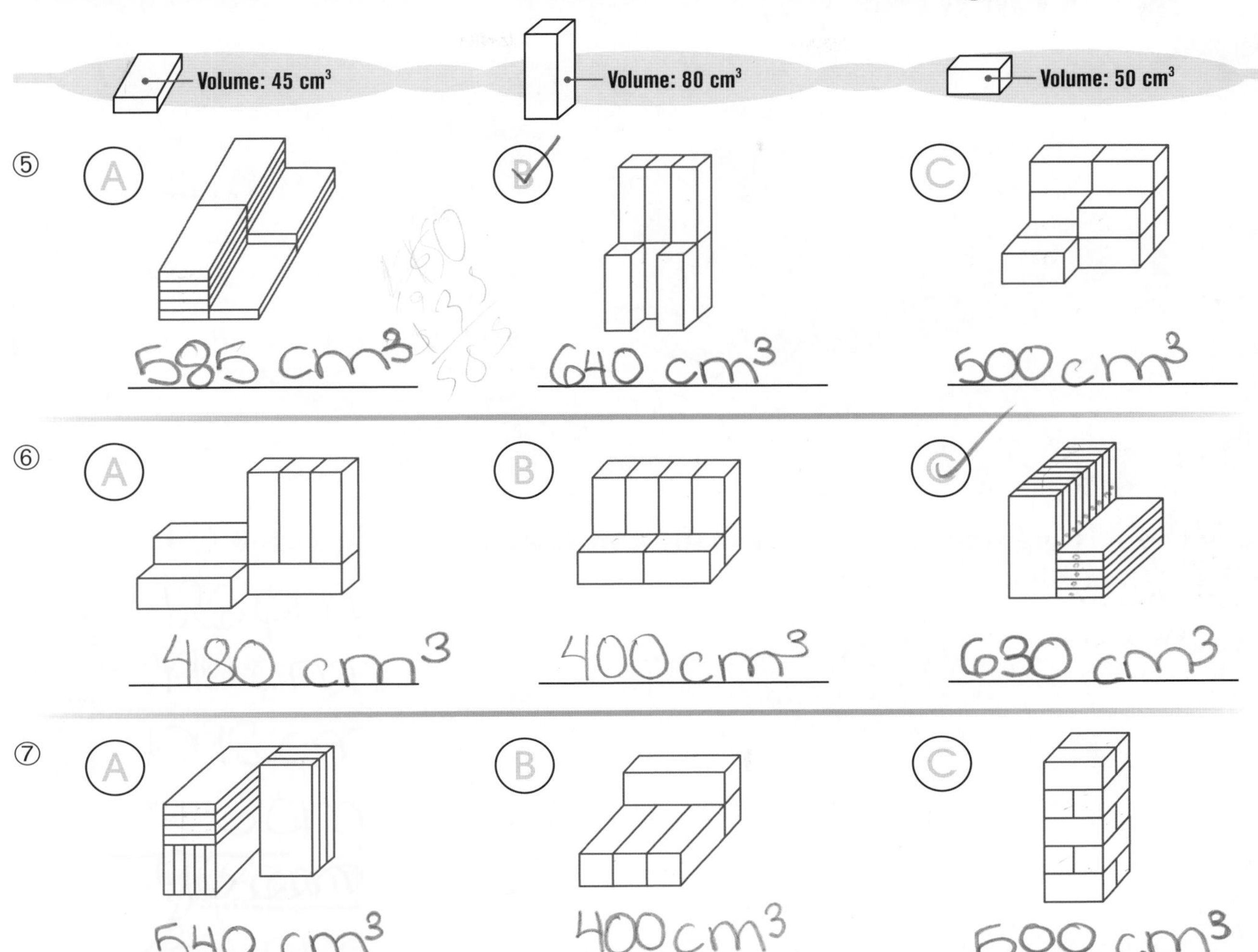

Look at the volume of each model. Then find the volume of each kind of block.

⑧

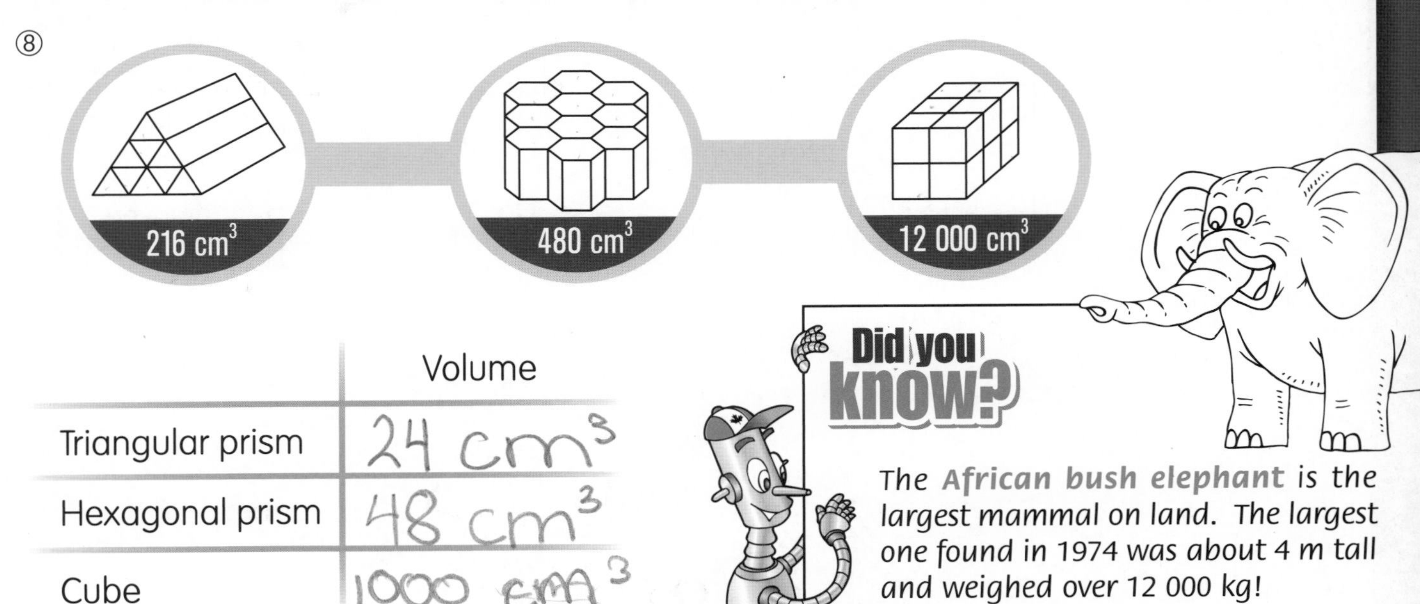

	Volume
Triangular prism	24 cm³
Hexagonal prism	48 cm³
Cube	1000 cm³

Did you know?

The **African bush elephant** is the largest mammal on land. The largest one found in 1974 was about 4 m tall and weighed over 12 000 kg!

DATE:

Day 28

Volume (2)

Draw the missing lines to see how many centimetre cubes are used to build each model. Then fill in the blanks.

①

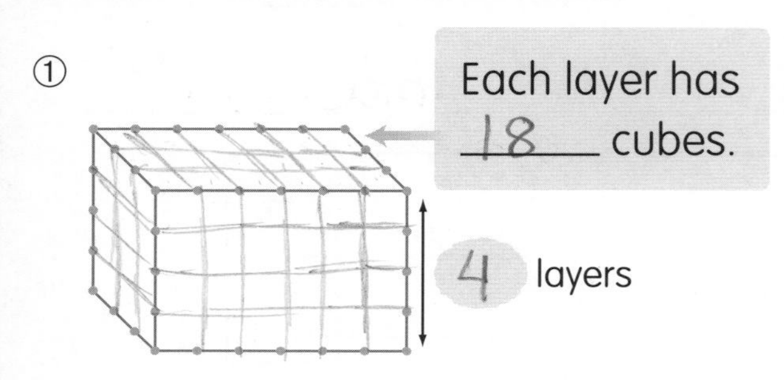

Each layer has 18 cubes.

4 layers

Volume: 72 cm^3

②

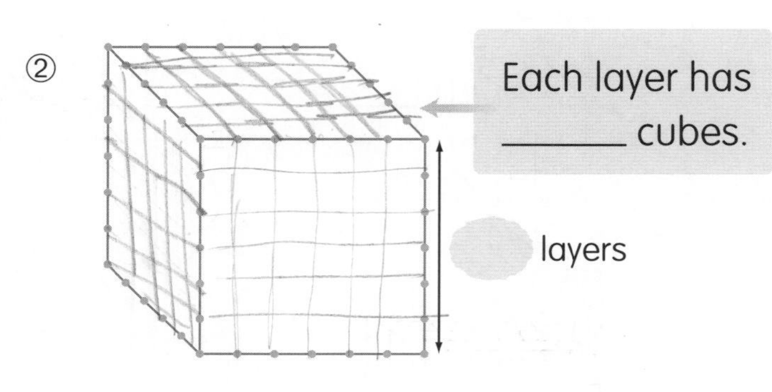

Each layer has ______ cubes.

layers

Volume: ______ cm^3

③

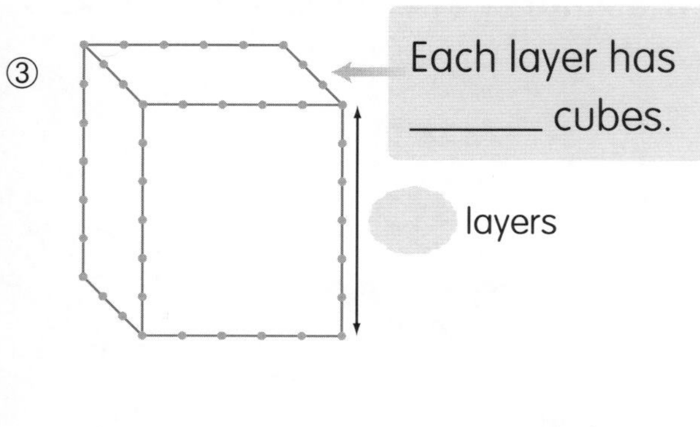

Each layer has ______ cubes.

layers

Volume: ______ cm^3

④

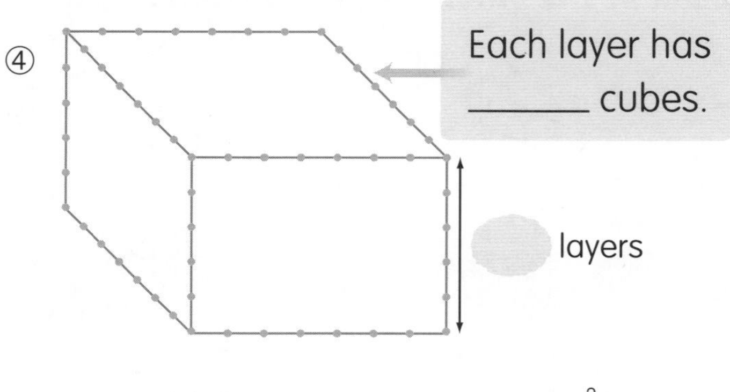

Each layer has ______ cubes.

layers

Volume: ______ cm^3

⑤

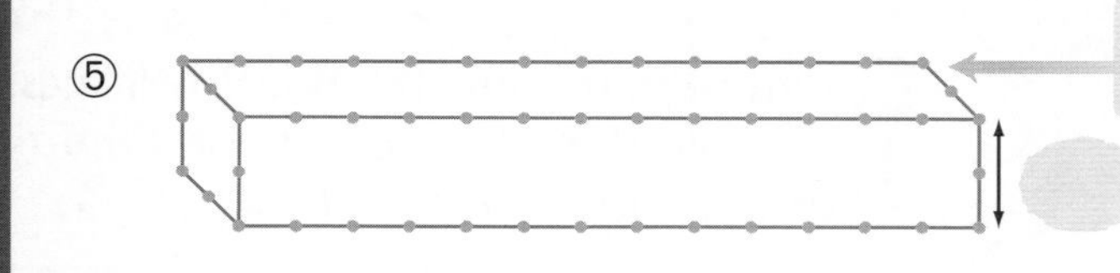

Each layer has ______ cubes.

layers

Volume: ______ cm^3

Volume of a **rectangular prism**:

No. of cubes in each layer x No. of layers

e.g.

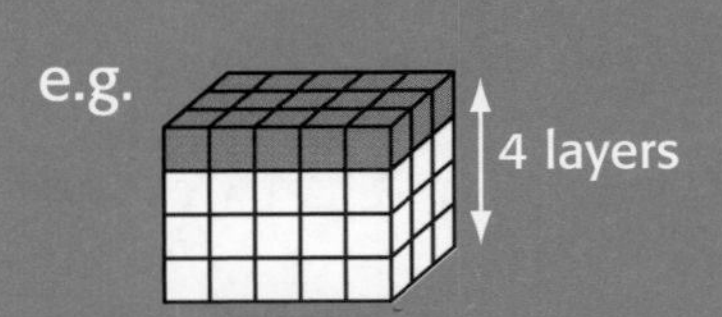

There are 15 cubes in each layer.
Volume:
15 x 4 = 60 (cm^3)

Find the volume of each rectangular prism built with centimetre cubes. Show your work.

⑥

	No. of Cubes in Each Layer	No. of Layers	Volume
A	45	6	45 x 6 = 270 (cm^3)
B	30	13	30 x 13 = 390 (cm^3)
C	98	7	98 x 7 = 686 (cm^3)
D	35	10	35 x 10 = 350 (cm^3)
E	108	4	108 x 4 = 432 (cm^3)

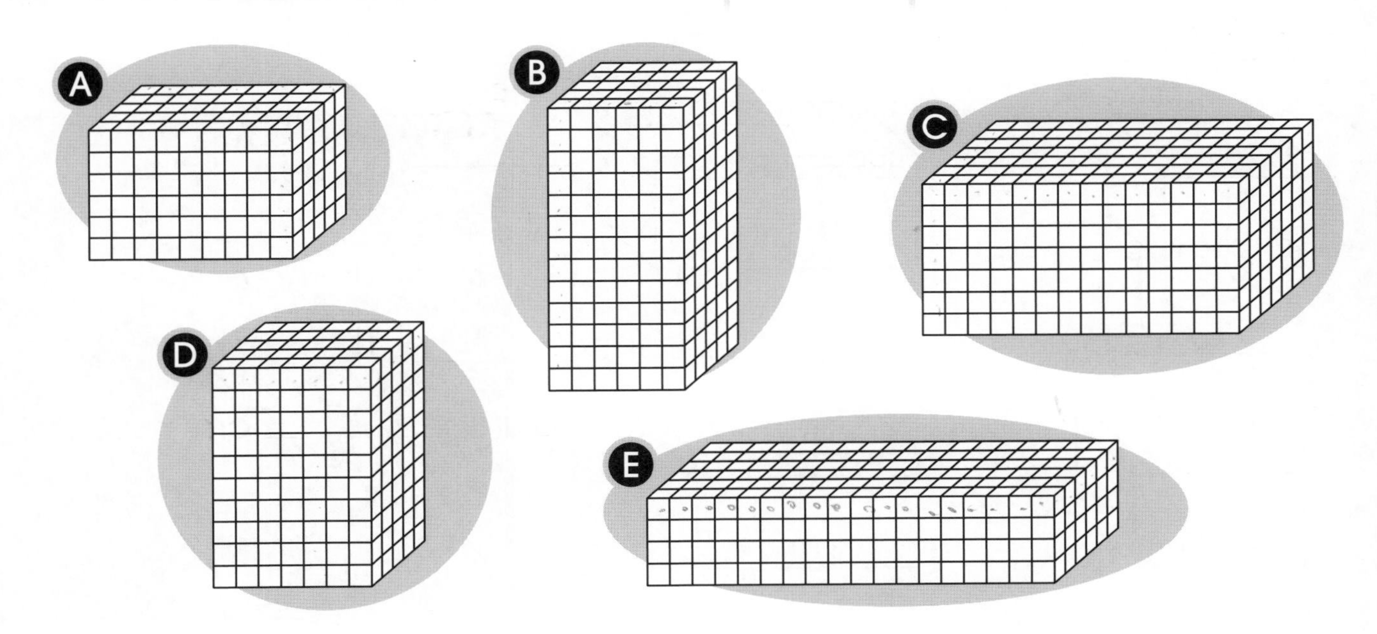

Solve the problems.

⑦

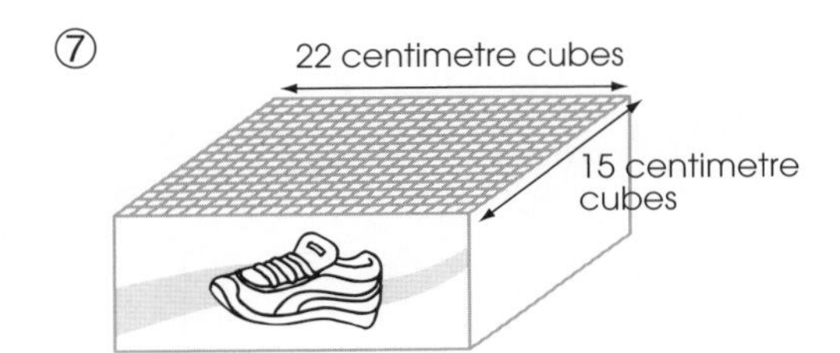

If there are 9 layers of centimetre cubes in the shoe box, what is the volume of the box?

The volume is 2970 cm^3

⑧ If Uncle Jack uses all the cubes in the shoe box to build a rectangular prism with 30 centimetre cubes in each layer, how many layers will there be?

There will be 99 layers.

DATE: ____________________

Day 29

Relating Volume and Capacity (1)

Find the capacity or volume of each fish tank.

①

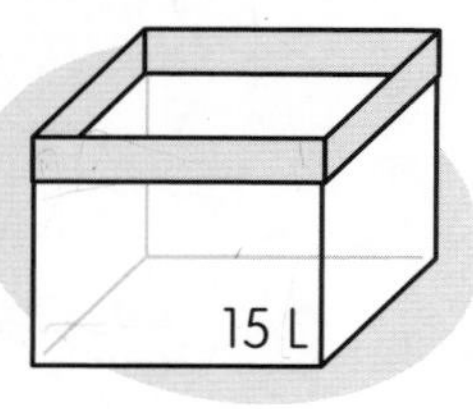

________ cm^3

②

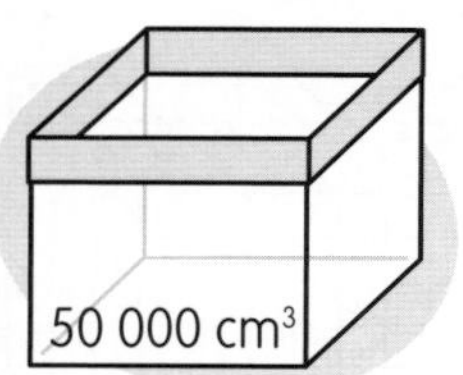

________ L

③

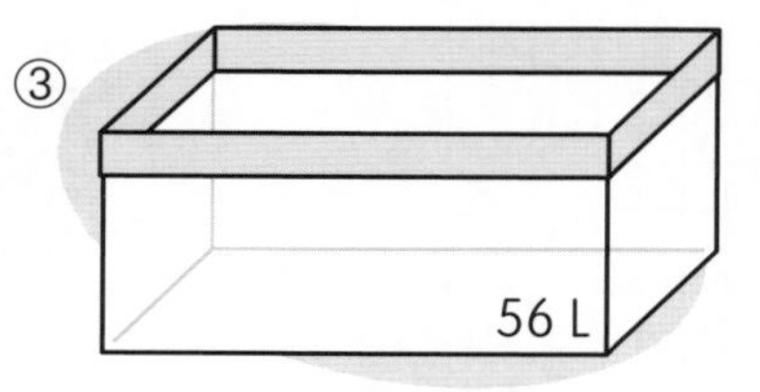

________ cm^3

④

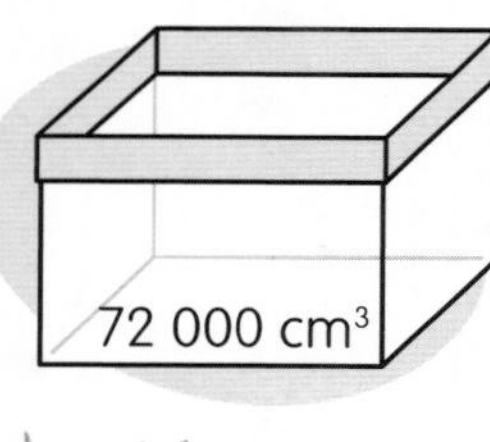

________ L

⑤

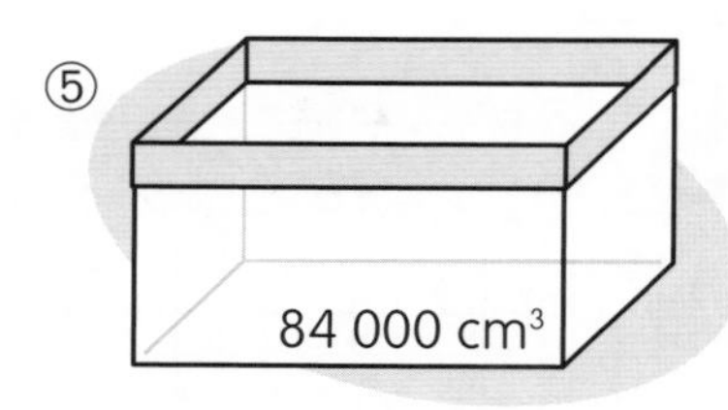

________ L

The **capacity** (the greatest amount of liquid a container can hold) of a container can be measured by its volume.

A **centimetre cube**

1 cm^3 = 1 mL

1000 cm^3 = 1000 mL = 1 L

Check the container with the greater volume in each pair.

⑥

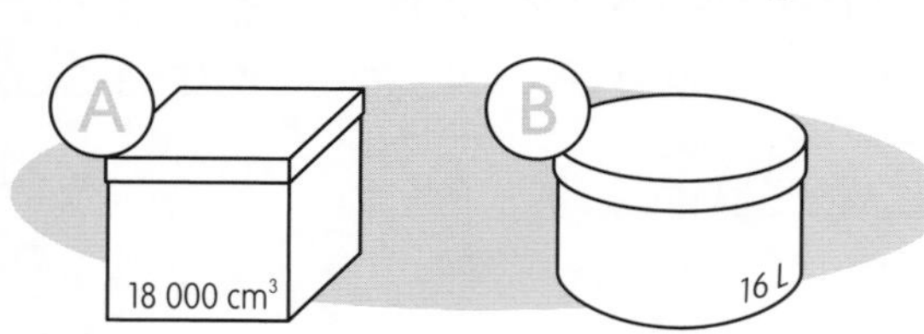

⑦

⑧

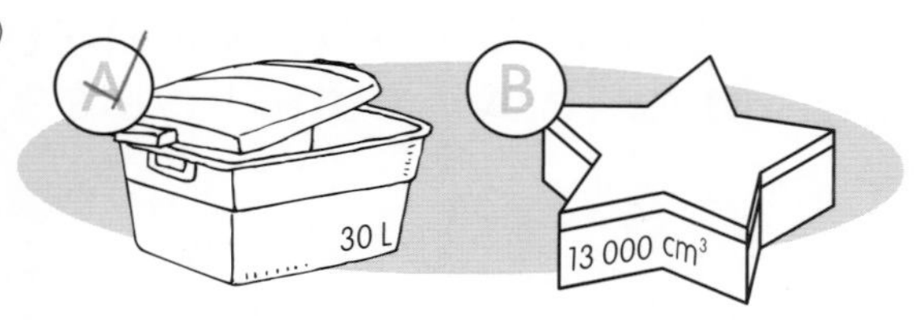

⑨

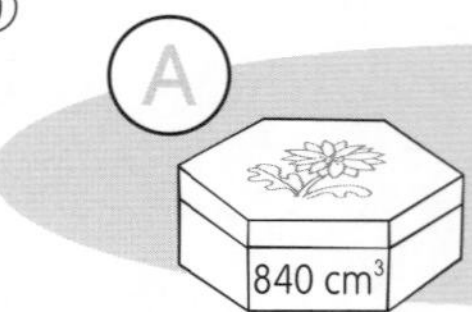

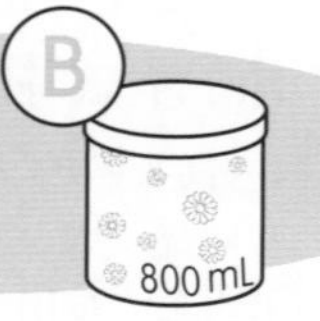

Find the volumes of the models. Then match them with the containers that have the same volumes.

⑩

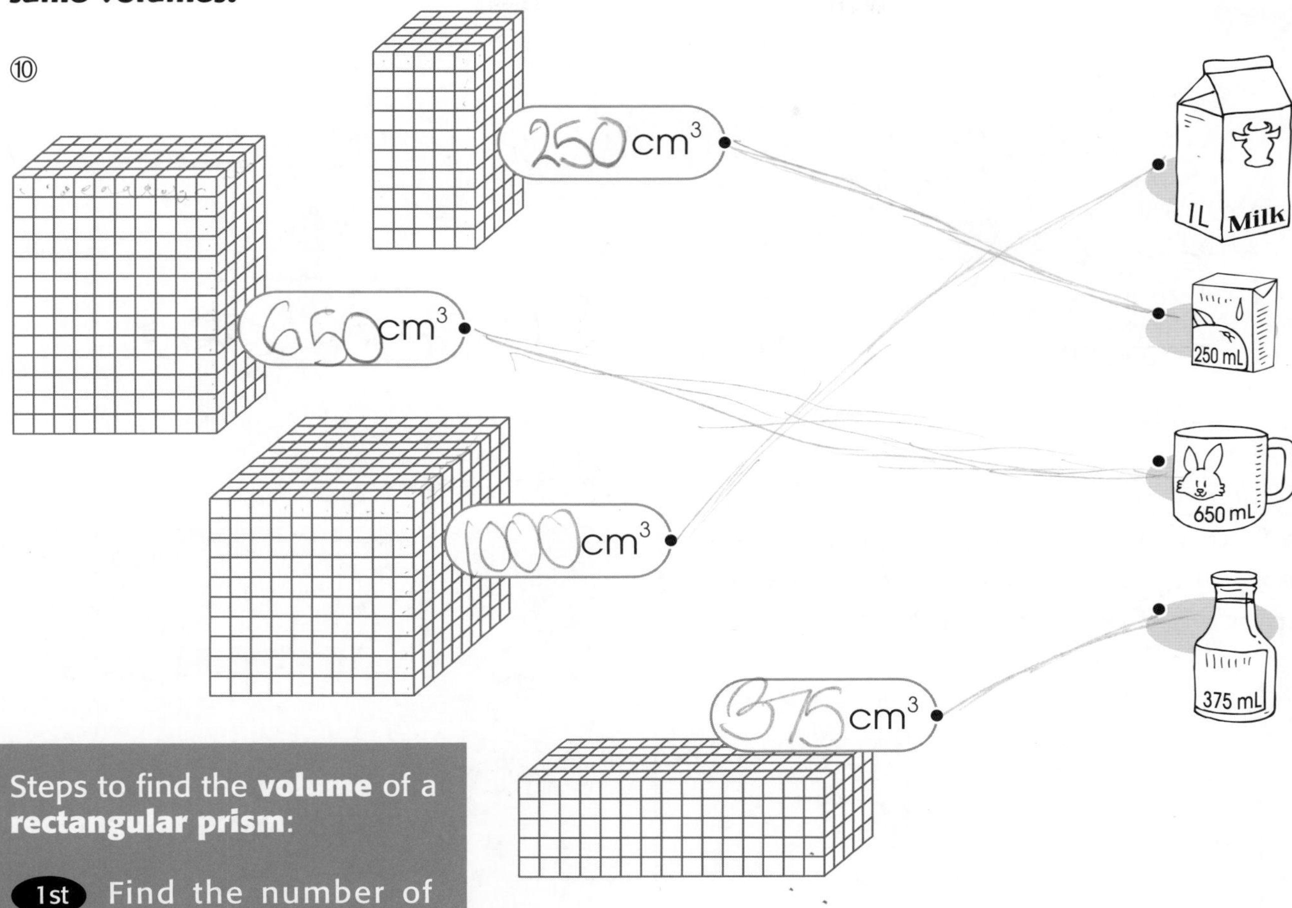

Steps to find the **volume** of a **rectangular prism**:

1st Find the number of cubes in each layer.

2nd Find the number of layers in the model.

3rd Use multiplication to find the volume.

Look at the bottles. Solve the problems.

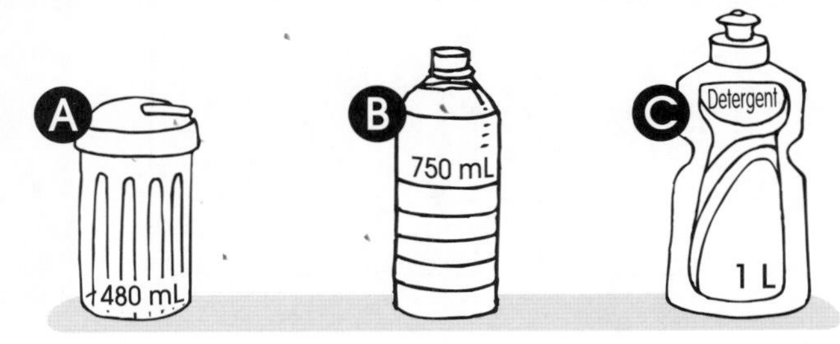

⑪ If 4 Ⓒ are needed to fill up a container, what is the volume of the container? 4L

⑫ If the volume of a box is 40 cm^3, how many boxes are needed to hold all the water in Ⓐ? 12 boxes

⑬ A bowl has a volume of 900 mL. If Jason pours all the water in Ⓑ into the bowl, how many more water can the bowl hold? 250 ml

DATE: ______________

Relating Volume and Capacity (2)

Find the volume of each irregular object by measuring the amount of liquid being displaced. Complete the table.

①

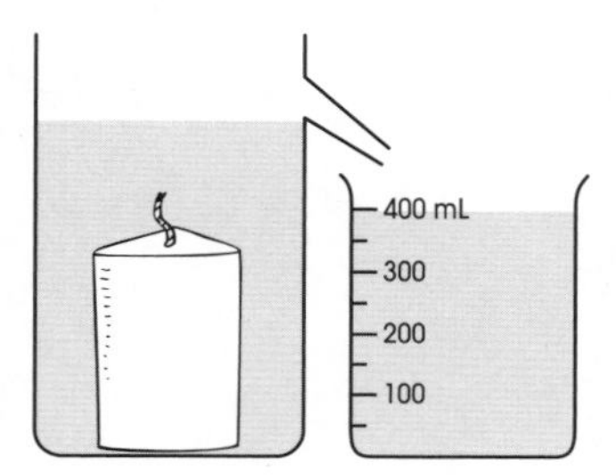

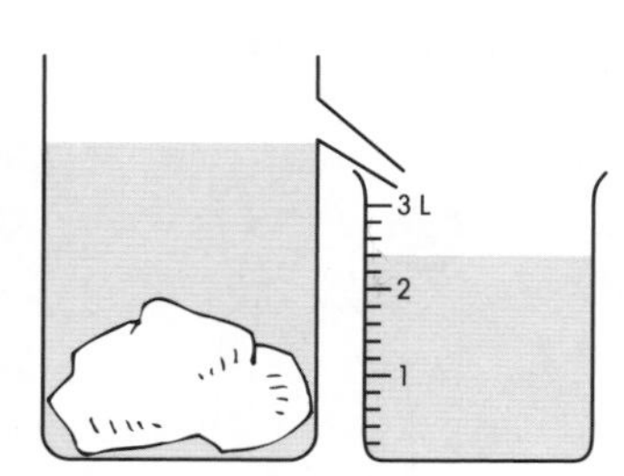

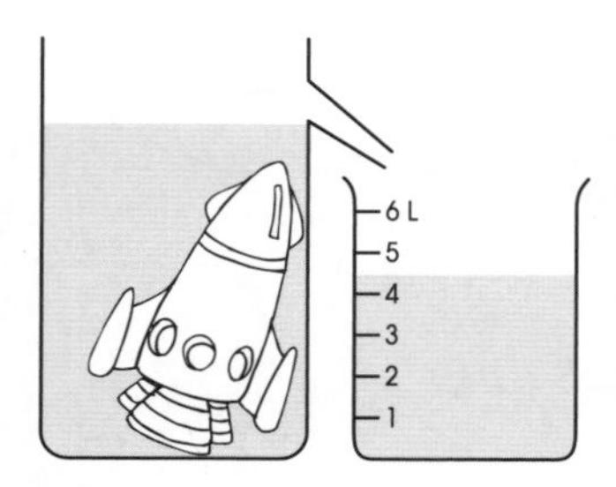

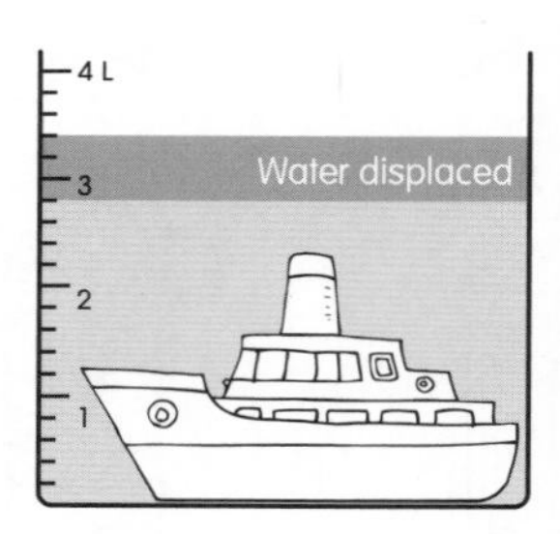

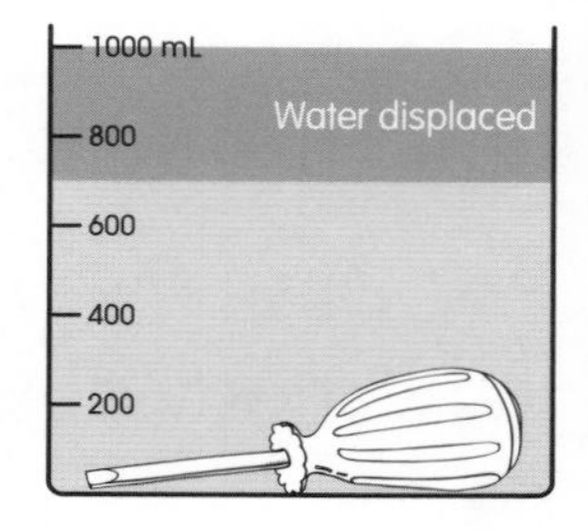

Steps to find the volume of an irregular object with a measuring cup:

1st Pour some water into a measuring cup.

2nd Put the object into the measuring cup and make sure it is completely immersed in the water.

3rd Record the amount of water displaced.

4th Amount of water displaced = Volume of the object

e.g.

Water displaced: 500 mL

Amount of water displaced
= Volume of the robot
= 500 cm^3

Object	Candle	Car	Rock	Ship	Rocket	Screwdriver
Volume	0.4 L	0.5 L	2.04 L	0.06 L	4.5 L	0.3 L

Find the volume of each item. Then draw a line on the measuring cup to show the amount of water displaced by the item.

②

Volume: 720 cm^3

a. Each die has a volume of 120 cm^3.

b.

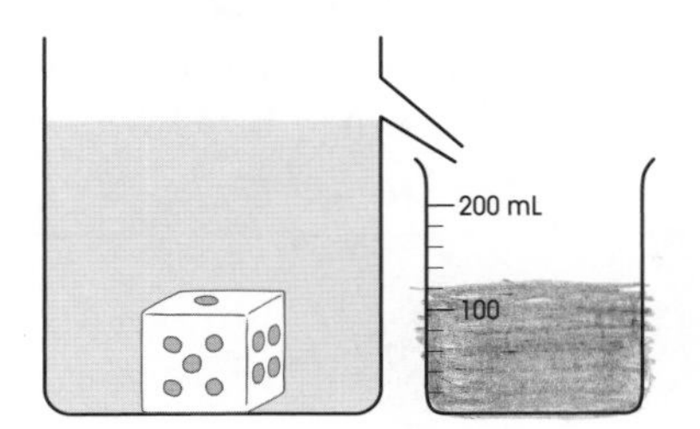

③

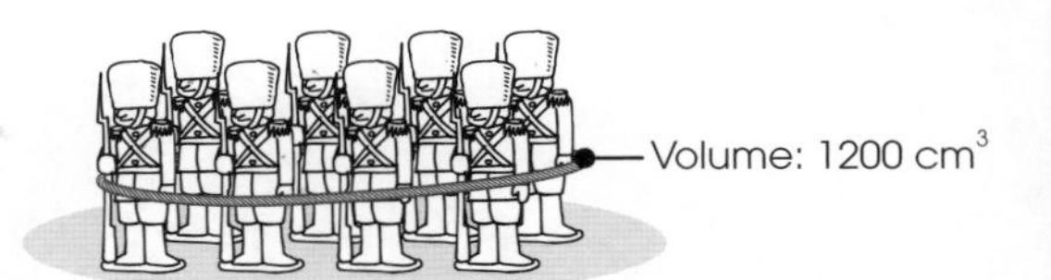

a. Each soldier has a volume of 150 cm^3.

b.

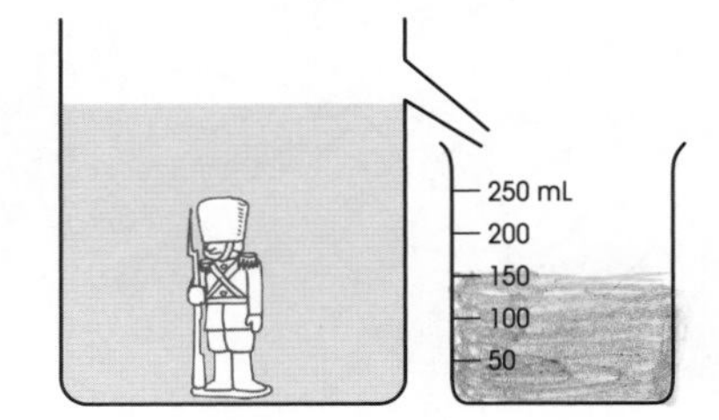

Look at each pair of pictures. Find the volume of each solid.

④

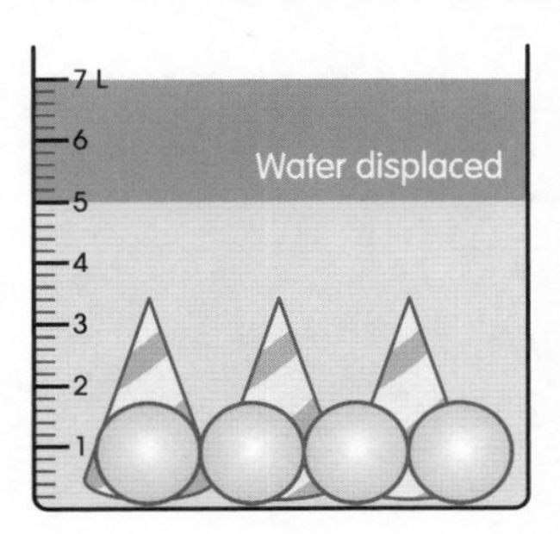

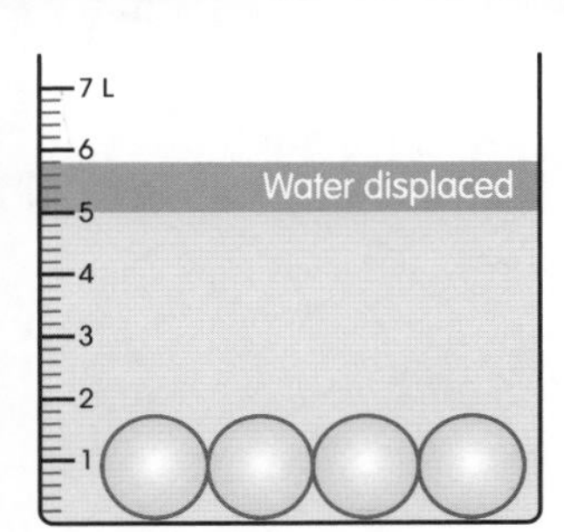

	Volume
Cone	1.02 L
Sphere	0.08 L

⑤

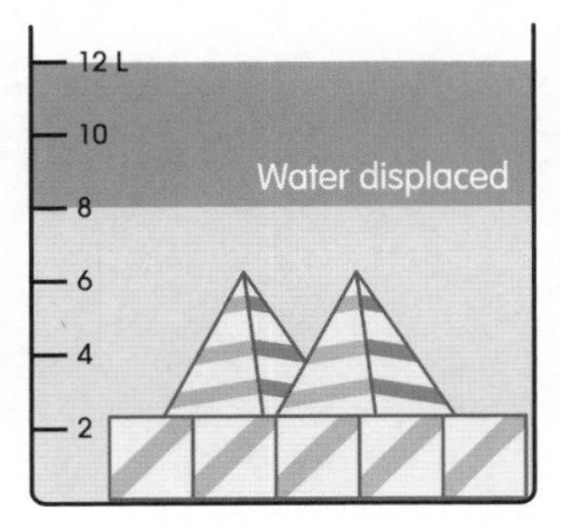

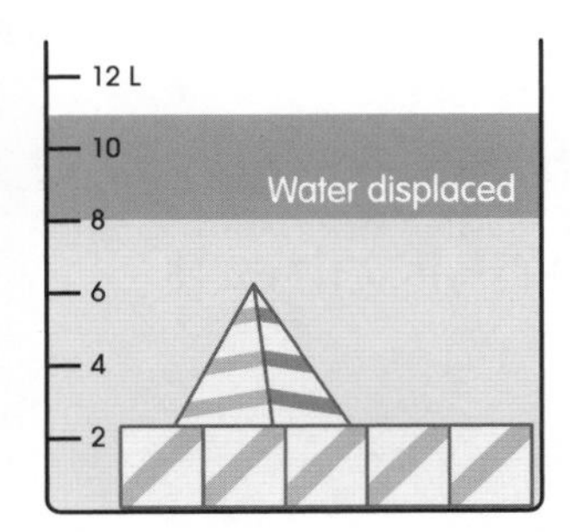

	Volume
Pyramid	0.5 L
Cube	1.6 L

⑥

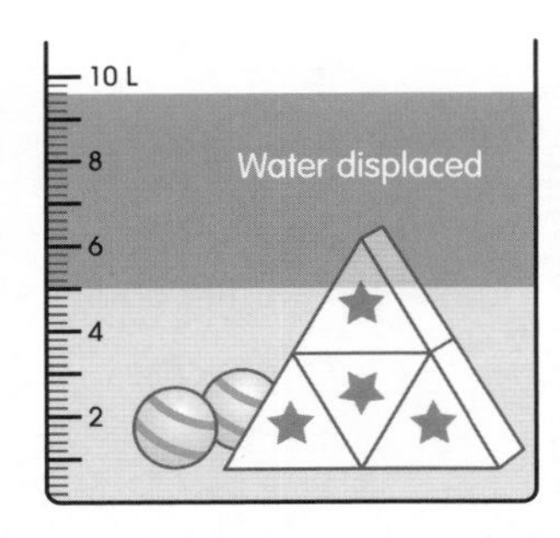

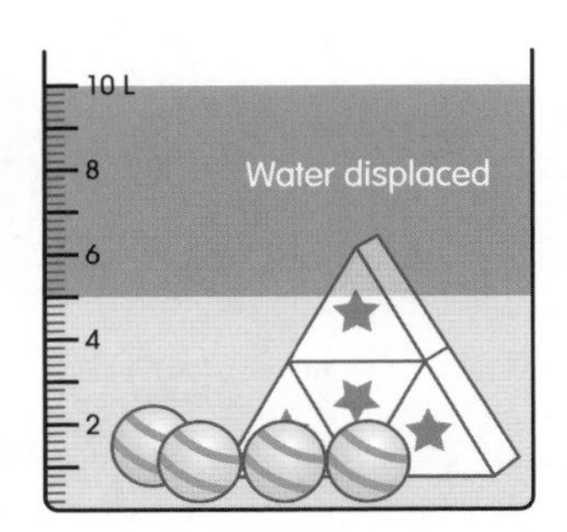

	Volume
Prism	1050 cm
Sphere	200 cm

DATE: ____________________

Day 31

Mass (1)

Fill in the blanks with the correct units.

t kg g mg

① Uncle Sam weighs about 82 ________ .

② A nickel weighs about 5 ________ .

③ A strand of hair weighs about 50 ________ .

④ A horse weighs about 1 ________ .

⑤ A blue whale weighs about 150 ________ .

⑥ A box of laundry detergent is about 3 ________ .

tonne (**t**)
kilogram (**kg**)
gram (**g**)
milligram (**mg**)

Big Unit → Small Unit

Relationships between the units:

1 t = 1000 kg

1 kg = 1000 g

1 g = 1000 mg

Fill in the blanks.

⑦ 3 t = ________ kg

⑧ 6000 mg = ________ g

⑨ 32 kg = ________ t

⑩ 2500 kg = ________ t

⑪ 9 mg = ________ g

⑫ 886 mg = ________ g

⑬ 4 g = ________ mg

⑭ 460 g = ________ kg

⑮ 2.5 g = ________ mg

⑯ 1.04 t = ________ kg

Write the measurements in 2 different ways.

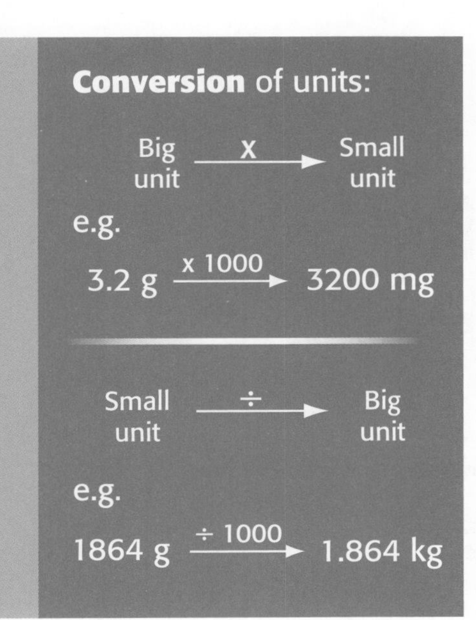

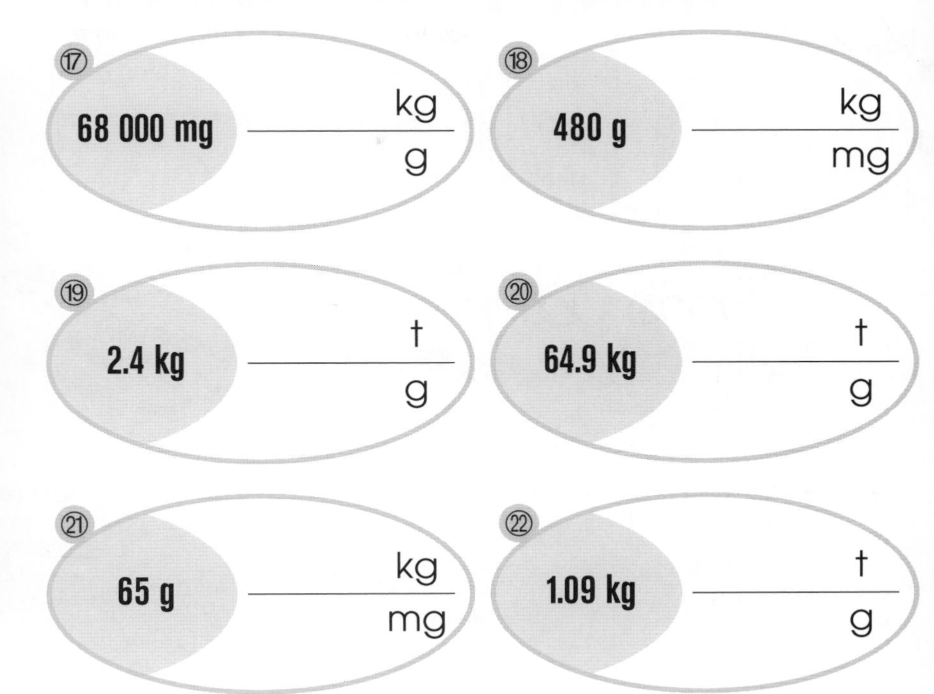

Put the things in order from heaviest to lightest.

㉓

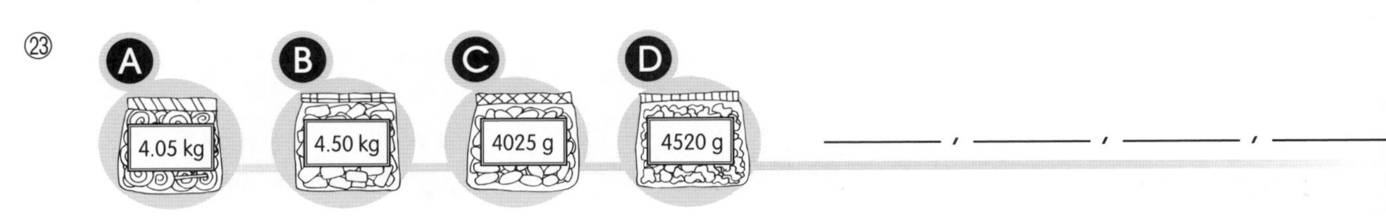

______ , ______ , ______ , ______

㉔

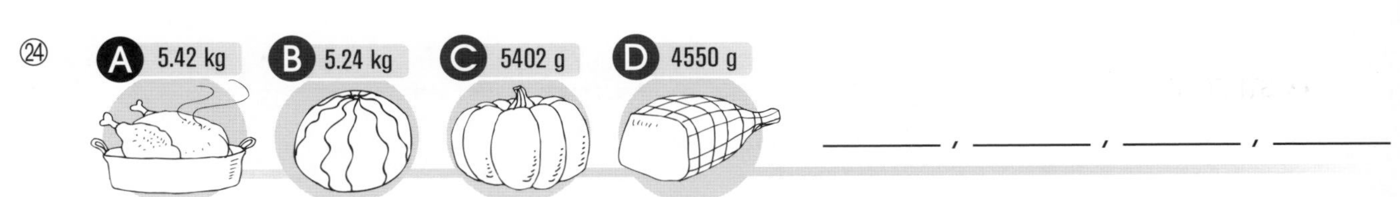

______ , ______ , ______ , ______

㉕

______ , ______ , ______ , ______ , ______

Did you know?

Argentinosaurus, discovered in Argentina, is probably the heaviest dinosaur ever known. It weighed about 22 t, which was as heavy as 5 African bush elephants.

DATE: ______________

Day 32

Mass (2)

Record the weights of the items. Then answer the questions.

①

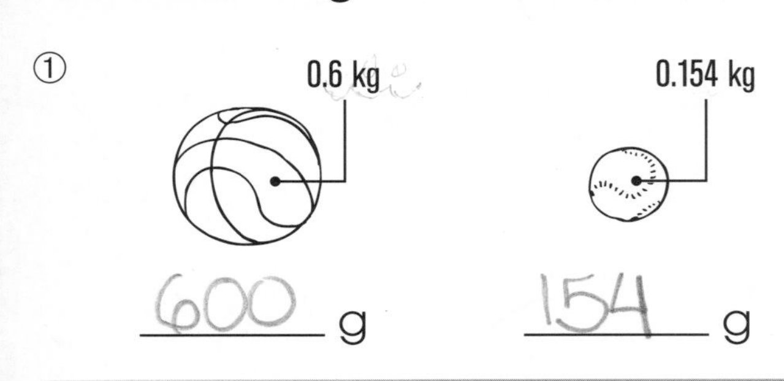

600 g   154 g

About how many baseballs would have the same mass as a basketball?

4 times

②

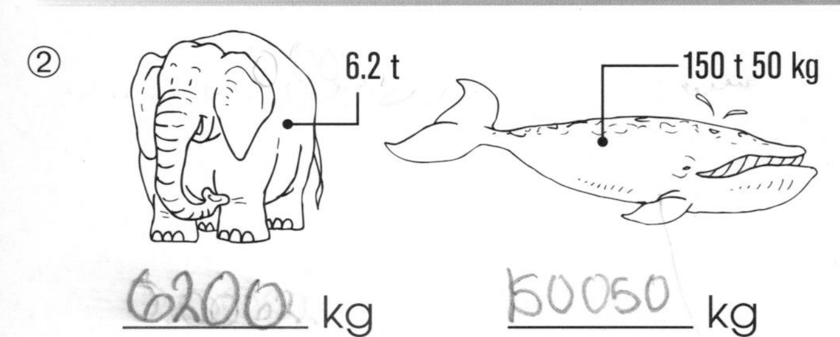

6200 kg   150050 kg

About how many elephants would have the same mass as a whale?

____

③

________ g   ________ g

The weight of the lollipop is about ________ times the weight of one leaf.

④

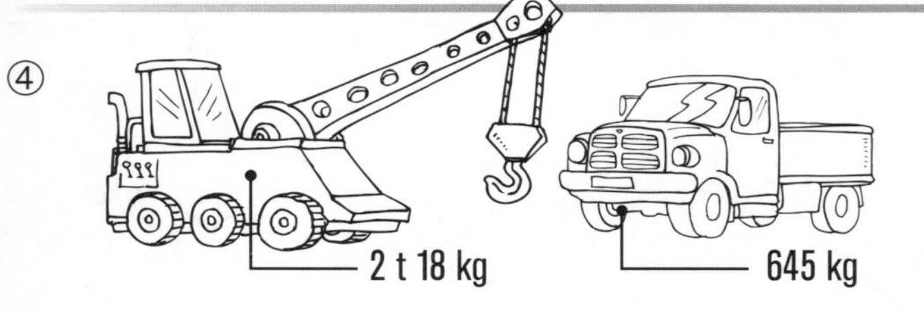

________ t   ________ t

The weight of the construction vehicle is about ________ times the weight of the truck.

Find the weight of each group of items. Then solve the problems.

⑤

		Quantity to be transported	Total weight
A	20 kg	60 logs	1200 kg or 1.2 t
B	85 g	100 000 cans	8500000 kg or 8.5 t
C	CHOCOLATES 1.5 kg	2000 boxes	3000 kg or 3 t

⑥ Uncle Tim will deliver the chocolates to the destination by crossing one of the bridges. Which bridge should he use?

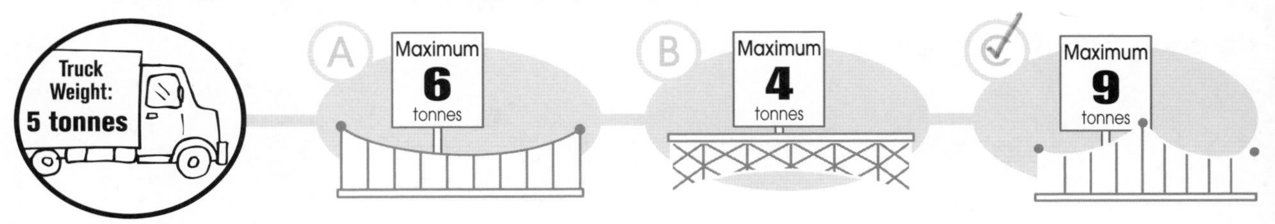

⑦ Mr. Smith is using the bridge to deliver one of the above items to its destination. Which item does he deliver?

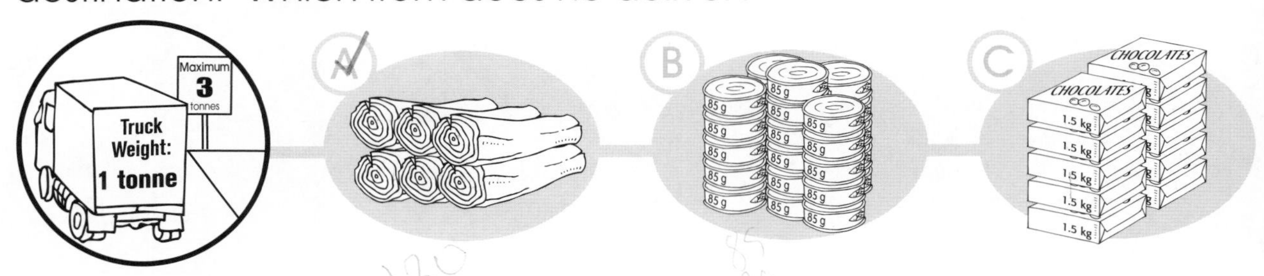

⑧ Which truck should Mr. White use to deliver the canned fish via the bridge in the circle?

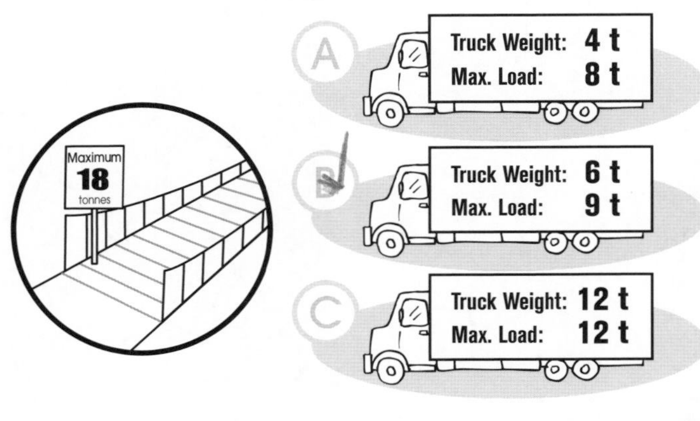

Did you know?

The gorilla is the largest of the primates. It weighs about 150 kg, which is as heavy as 1000 ***pygmy marmosets*** *– the smallest primates.*

DATE: ____________

Improper Fractions and Mixed Numbers

Write an improper fraction and a mixed number for the shaded part of each group of pictures.

① 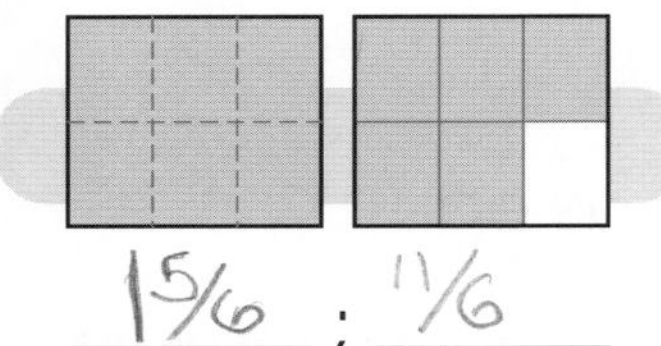

$1\frac{5}{6}$; $\frac{11}{6}$

② 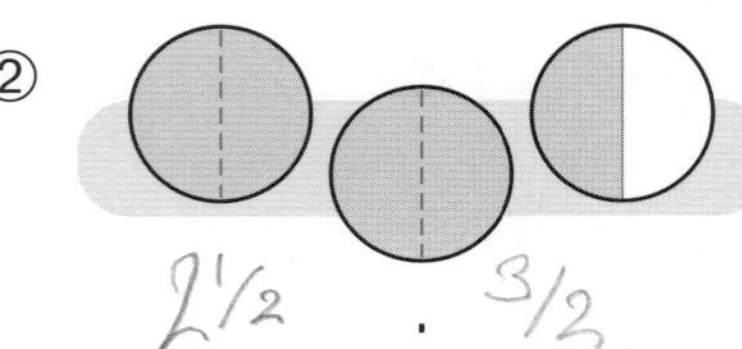

$2\frac{1}{2}$; $\frac{3}{2}$

③ 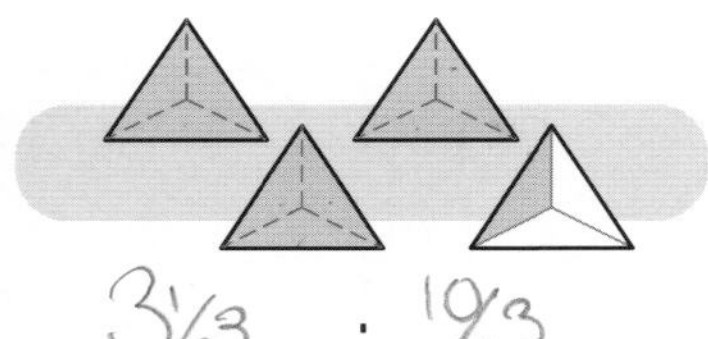

$3\frac{1}{3}$; $\frac{10}{3}$

④ 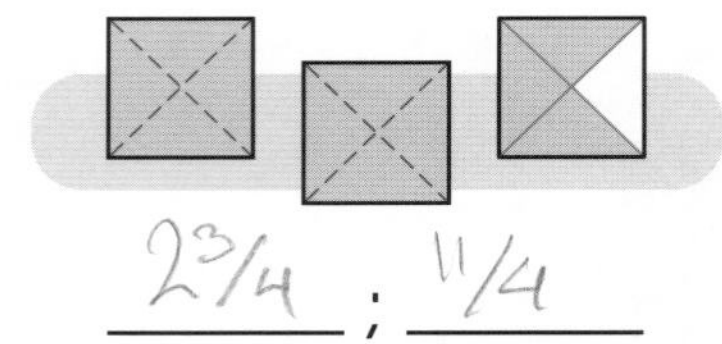

$2\frac{3}{4}$; $\frac{11}{4}$

Write each improper fraction as a mixed number. Show your work.

⑤ $\frac{10}{3}$ = $3\frac{1}{3}$ (work: 10 ÷ 3 = 3, 9, remainder 1)

⑥ $\frac{12}{7}$ = $1\frac{5}{7}$ (work: 12 ÷ 7 = 1, 7, remainder 5)

⑦ $\frac{17}{5}$ = $3\frac{1}{5}$ (work: 17 ÷ 5 = 3, 15, remainder 2)

⑧ $\frac{25}{9}$ = $2\frac{7}{9}$ (work: 25 ÷ 9 = 2, 18, remainder 7)

Improper fraction:

The numerator is greater than or equal to the denominator,

e.g. $\frac{4}{4}$, $\frac{7}{6}$

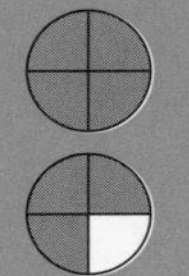

$\frac{7}{4}$ are shaded.

Mixed number:

There is a whole number and a proper fraction,

e.g. $1\frac{1}{3}$, $2\frac{5}{6}$

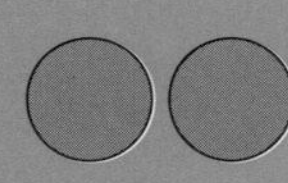

$2\frac{1}{5}$ are shaded.

Converting an improper fraction to a mixed number:

$\frac{16}{3}$

$= 5\frac{1}{3}$

16 ÷ 3: 3 goes into 16 five times (5 is the whole number); 16 − 15 = 1 (1 is the numerator); 3 is the denominator.

whole number — 5
denominator — 3
numerator — 1

> Converting a mixed number to an improper fraction:
>
> $2\frac{1}{5} = \frac{2 \times 5 + 1}{5}$
>
> $= \frac{10 + 1}{5}$
>
> $= \frac{11}{5}$

Write each mixed number as an improper fraction. Show your work.

⑨ $4\frac{2}{3} = \frac{4 \times \underline{\quad} + 2}{3}$

⑩ $2\frac{4}{5} =$

⑪ $1\frac{3}{7} =$

⑫ $3\frac{5}{6} =$

⑬ $2\frac{3}{4} =$

Solve the problems.

⑭

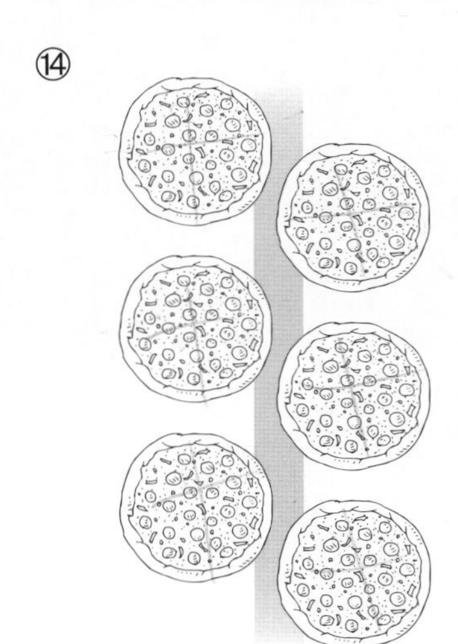

Uncle Louis has 6 pizzas.

a. If Uncle Louis divides his pizzas equally among 5 children, each gets ________ (improper fraction) or ________ (mixed number) pizzas.

b. If Uncle Louis divides his pizzas equally among 4 children, each gets ________ (improper fraction) or ________ (mixed number) pizzas.

⑮

Elaine has 5 bags of chips.

a. If Elaine shares her chips equally with her sister, each gets ________ (improper fraction) or ________ (mixed number) bags of chips.

b. If Elaine shares her chips equally with 2 friends, each gets ________ (improper fraction) or ________ (mixed number) bags of chips.

DATE: ______

Day 34

Equivalent Fractions

Write a fraction to tell the shaded parts of the first figure. Then colour the second figure to match the first one and write an equivalent fraction to describe the parts coloured.

Equivalent fractions:
Fractions that represent the same part of a whole or group.

e.g.

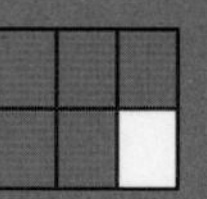

$\frac{5}{6}$ $\frac{10}{12}$

$\frac{5}{6}$ and $\frac{10}{12}$ are equivalent fractions.

①

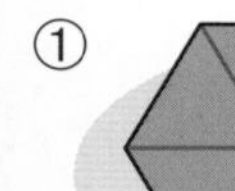

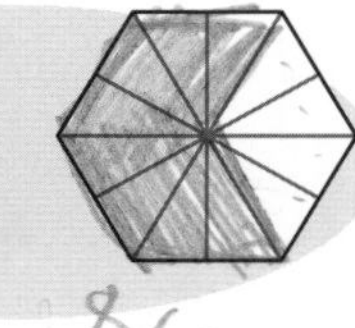

4/6 8/12

②

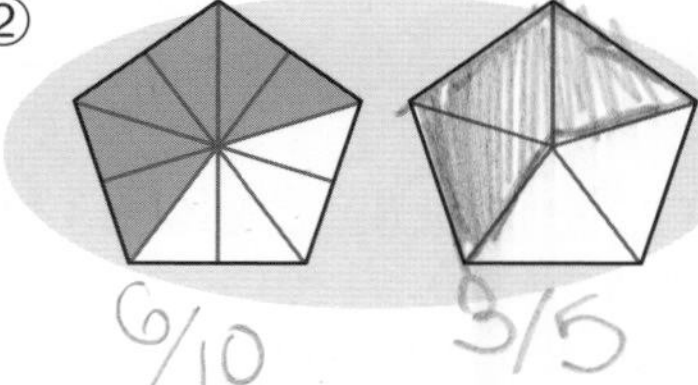

6/10 3/5

③

3/8 6/16

④

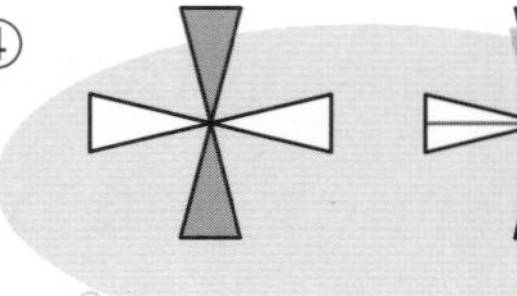

2/4 4/8

⑤

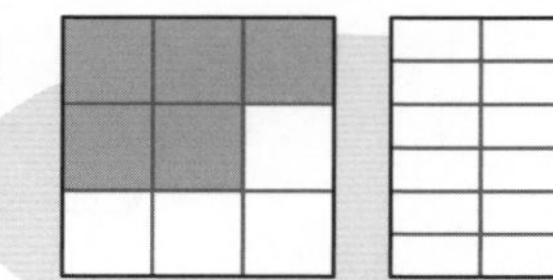

______ ______

Complete the equivalent fractions by filling in the missing numerators or denominators.

⑥ $\frac{2}{5} = \frac{4}{10}$ ⑦ $\frac{3}{4} = \frac{9}{12}$ ⑧ $\frac{3}{15} = \frac{1}{5}$

⑨ $\frac{6}{9} = \frac{2}{3}$ ⑩ $\frac{8}{16} = \frac{4}{8}$ ⑪ $\frac{20}{25} = \frac{4}{5}$

⑫ $\frac{4}{20} = \frac{2}{10}$ ⑬ $\frac{4}{12} = \frac{1}{3}$ ⑭ $\frac{5}{6} = \frac{15}{18}$

Multiply or **divide** both the numerator and denominator by the same number to get an equivalent fraction.

e.g.

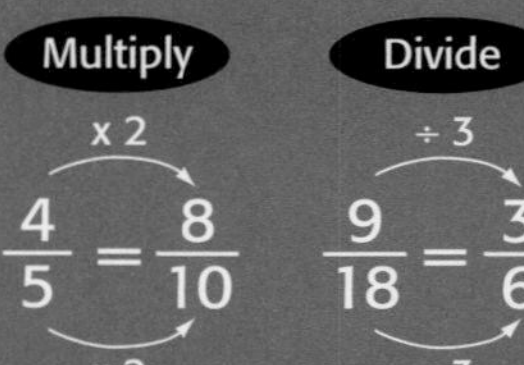

Write two equivalent fractions for each fraction.

⑮ $\frac{4}{9}$ $\frac{8}{18}$ $\frac{12}{27}$

⑯ $\frac{40}{50}$ $\frac{20}{25}$ $\frac{4}{5}$

⑰ $\frac{36}{54}$ $\frac{18}{27}$ $\frac{72}{108}$

⑱ $\frac{12}{16}$ $\frac{6}{8}$ $\frac{3}{4}$

$\frac{2}{5}$ is in simplest form since the numerator and the denominator have no more common factors except 1.

Use division to reduce a fraction to its lowest terms:

e.g. $\frac{4}{10} = \frac{2}{5}$ (÷ 2, ÷ 2)

Write each fraction in its simplest form.

⑲ $\frac{8}{10}$ $\frac{4}{5}$

⑳ $\frac{4}{9}$ $\frac{4}{9}$

㉑ $\frac{10}{15}$ $\frac{2}{3}$

㉒ $\frac{7}{18}$ $\frac{7}{18}$

㉓ $\frac{14}{20}$ $\frac{7}{10}$

㉔ $\frac{4}{6}$ $\frac{2}{3}$

㉕ $\frac{9}{21}$ $\frac{9}{21}$

㉖ $\frac{12}{16}$ $\frac{3}{4}$

㉗ $\frac{19}{22}$ $\frac{19}{22}$

Cross out the ones that are not equivalent to the others.

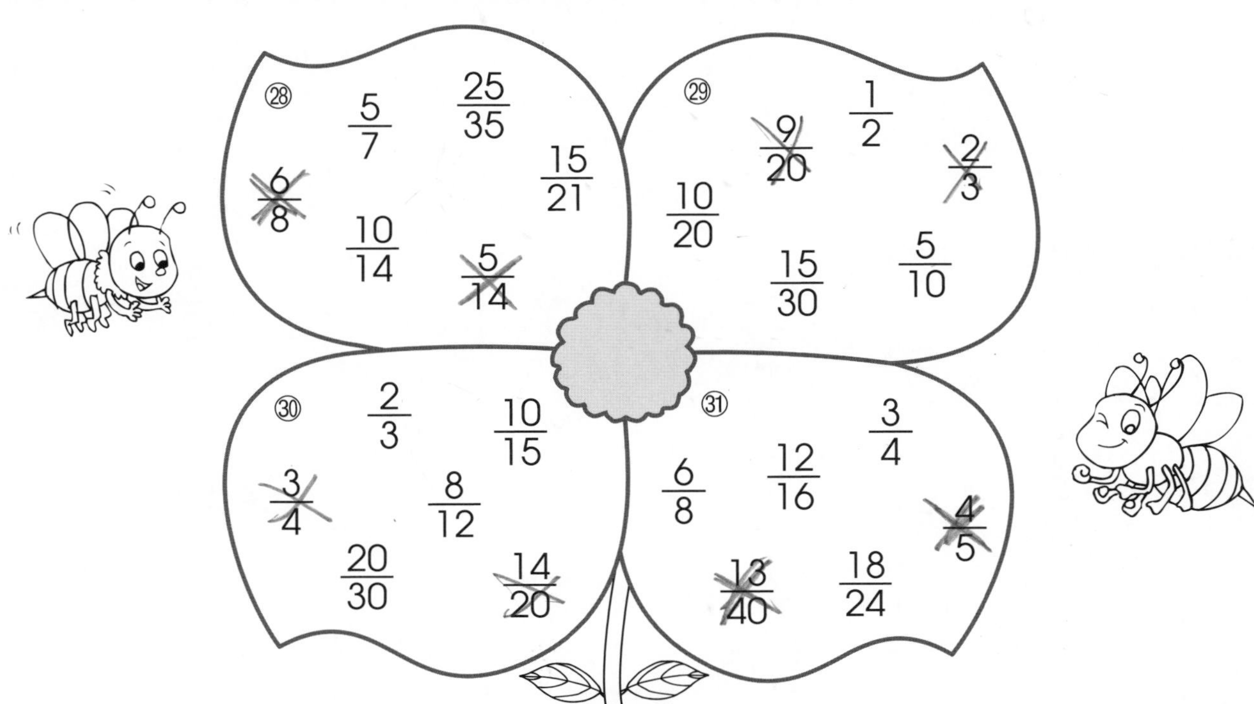

DATE: ____________________

REVIEW

180 180
8 64
244

Find the perimeters and areas of the polygons.

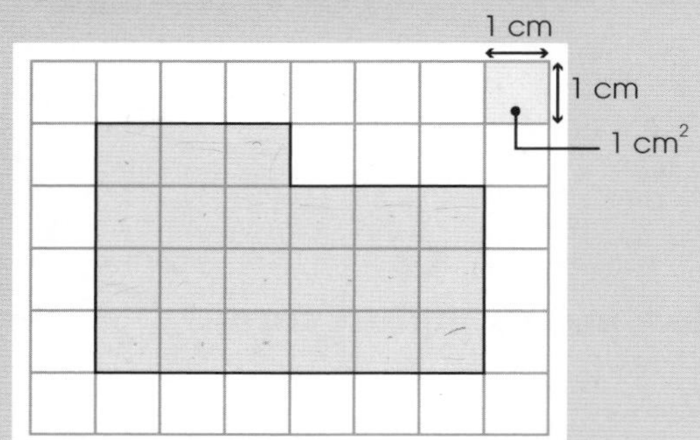

Perimeter: 20 cm

Area: 21 cm²

②

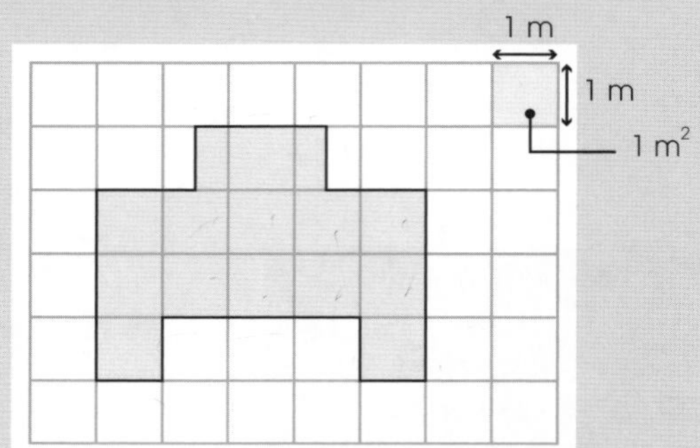

Perimeter: 18 cm

Area: 14 cm²

Find the side length, perimeter, or area of each rectangle or square. Show your work.

③ 18 mm, Square

Perimeter: 72 mm

Area: 244 mm

④ 4 cm, 10 cm

Perimeter: 28 cm

Area: 40 cm

⑤ 9 m, Perimeter: 28 m

Width: 5 m

Area: 45 m

⑥ Perimeter: 20 cm

Side length: 5 cm

Area: 25 cm

Find the time intervals or time.

⑦ From 5:27:16 p.m. to 5:51:42 p.m.

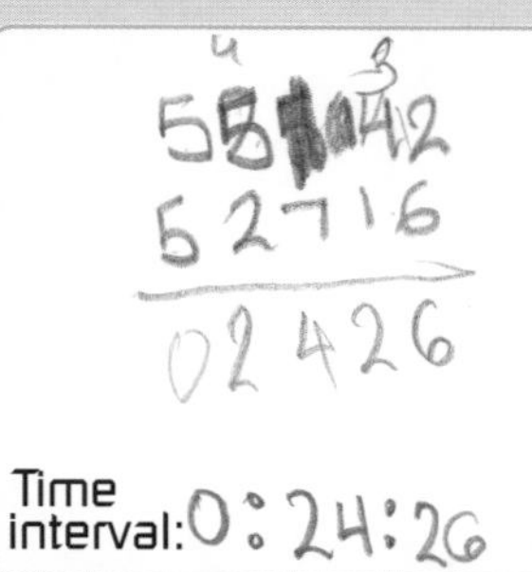

⑧ From 2:19:54 a.m. to 3:27:32 a.m.

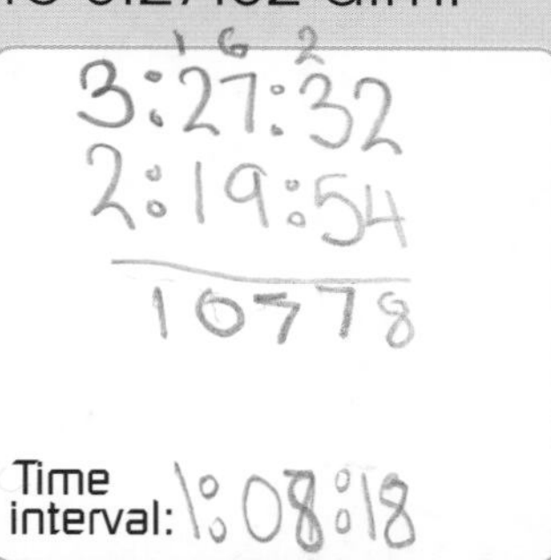

⑨ 46 min after 9:34 a.m.

9:34
+ 46
80 - 60 = 20
(60 + 20)

Time: 10:20

Find the volumes of the items. Then match each item with the group of centimetre cubes that has the same volume. Write the letters in the circles.

⑩

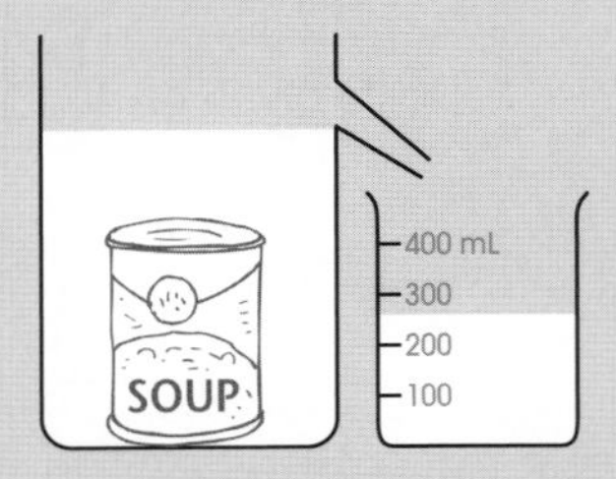

250 ml ; (C)

⑪

500 mL
Water displaced
400
300
200
100

50 ml ; (A)

⑫

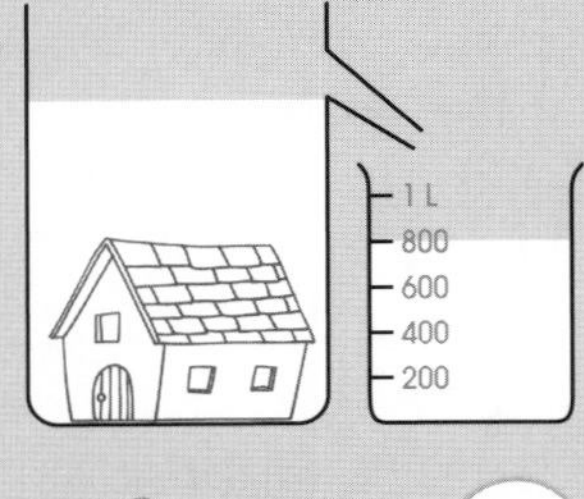

800 ml ; (D)

⑬

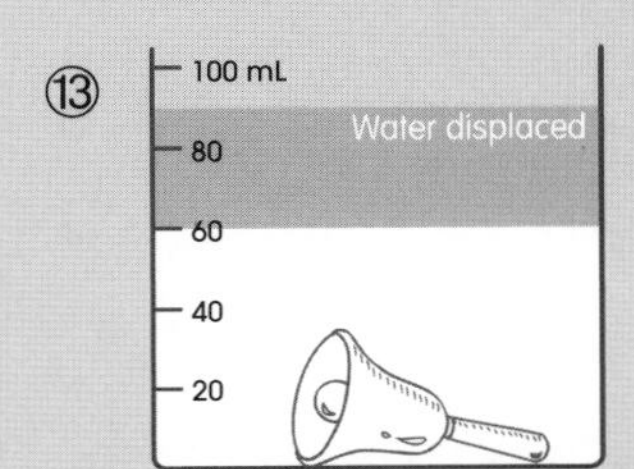

30 ml ; (B)

A 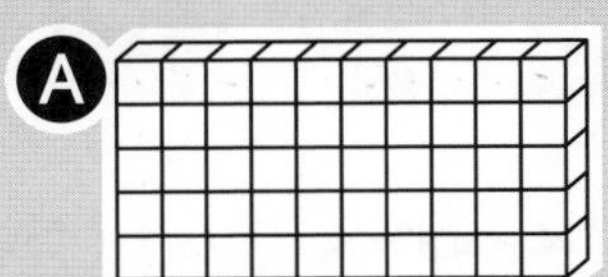

B 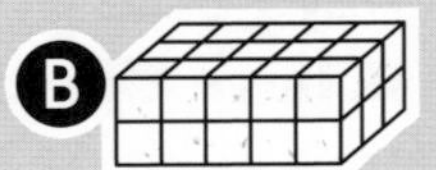

C 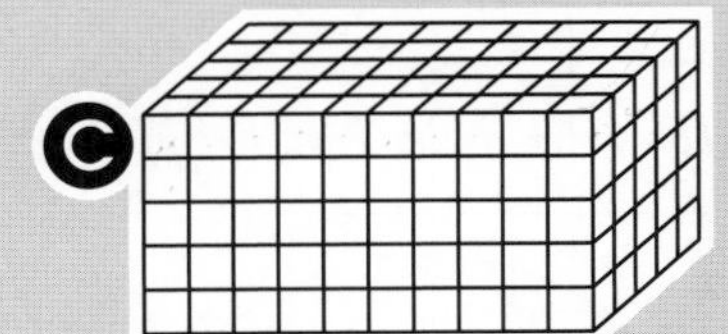

D 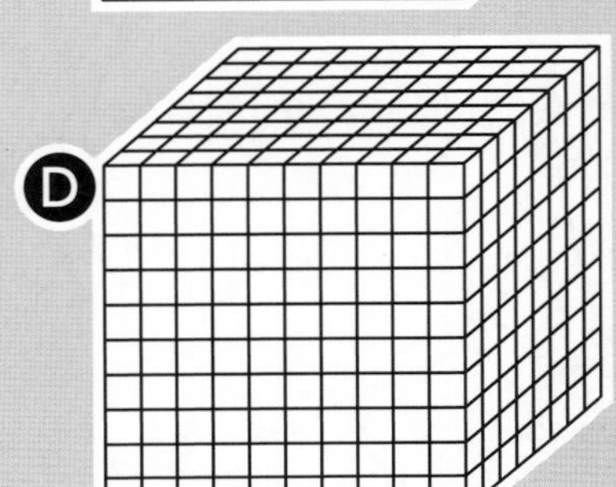

Write two equivalent fractions for each fraction.

⑭ $\frac{4}{12}$ $\frac{2}{6}$ $\frac{1}{3}$

⑮ $\frac{2}{10}$ $\frac{1}{5}$ $\frac{4}{20}$

Write each mixed number as an improper fraction or each improper fraction as a mixed number.

⑯  $3\frac{1}{5}$ $\frac{16}{5}$

⑰ 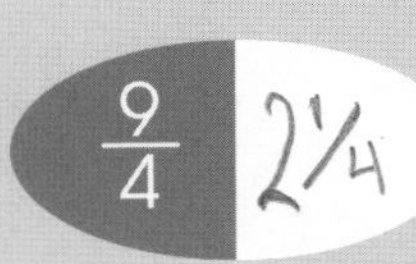 $\frac{9}{4}$ $2\frac{1}{4}$

⑱ 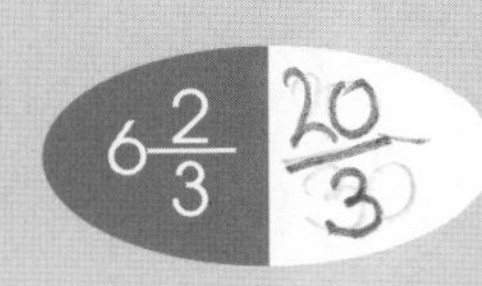 $6\frac{2}{3}$ $\frac{20}{3}$

⑲  $\frac{15}{7}$ $2\frac{1}{7}$

Find the speeds. Show your work.

⑳ 96 km in 3 h

Speed: 32 km/h

96÷3=32

㉑ 78 km in 2 h

Speed: 39 km/h

78÷2=39

㉒ 368 km in 4 h

Speed: 92 km/h

368÷4=92

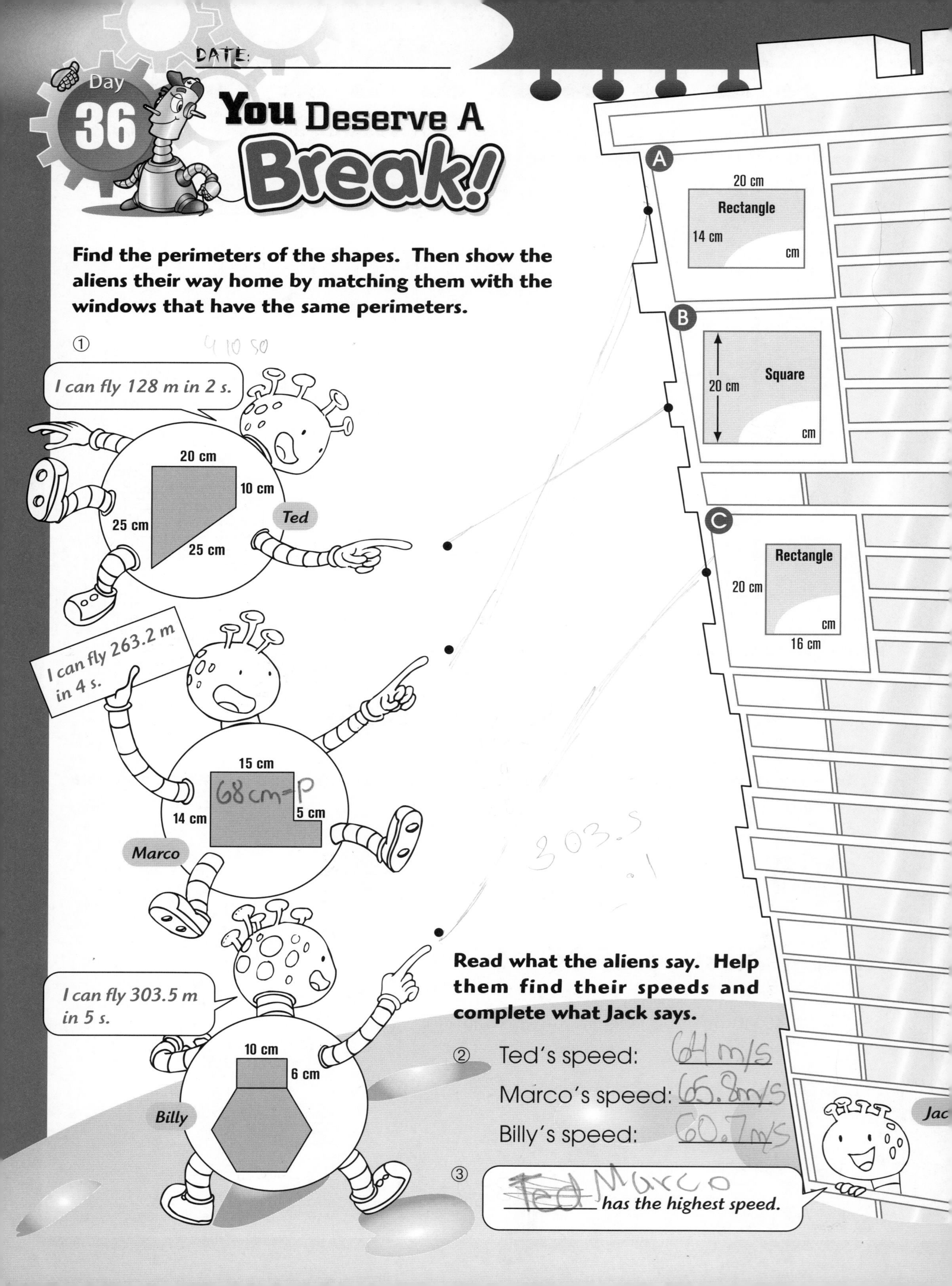
DATE:
Day 36
You Deserve A Break!
Find the perimeters of the shapes. Then show the aliens their way home by matching them with the windows that have the same perimeters.
①
I can fly 128 m in 2 s.
20 cm
10 cm
25 cm
25 cm
Ted
I can fly 263.2 m in 4 s.
15 cm
14 cm
5 cm
Marco
I can fly 303.5 m in 5 s.
10 cm
6 cm
Billy
A
20 cm
Rectangle
14 cm
cm
B
Square
20 cm
cm
C
Rectangle
20 cm
cm
16 cm
Read what the aliens say. Help them find their speeds and complete what Jack says.
② Ted's speed:
Marco's speed:
Billy's speed:
③ has the highest speed.
Jac

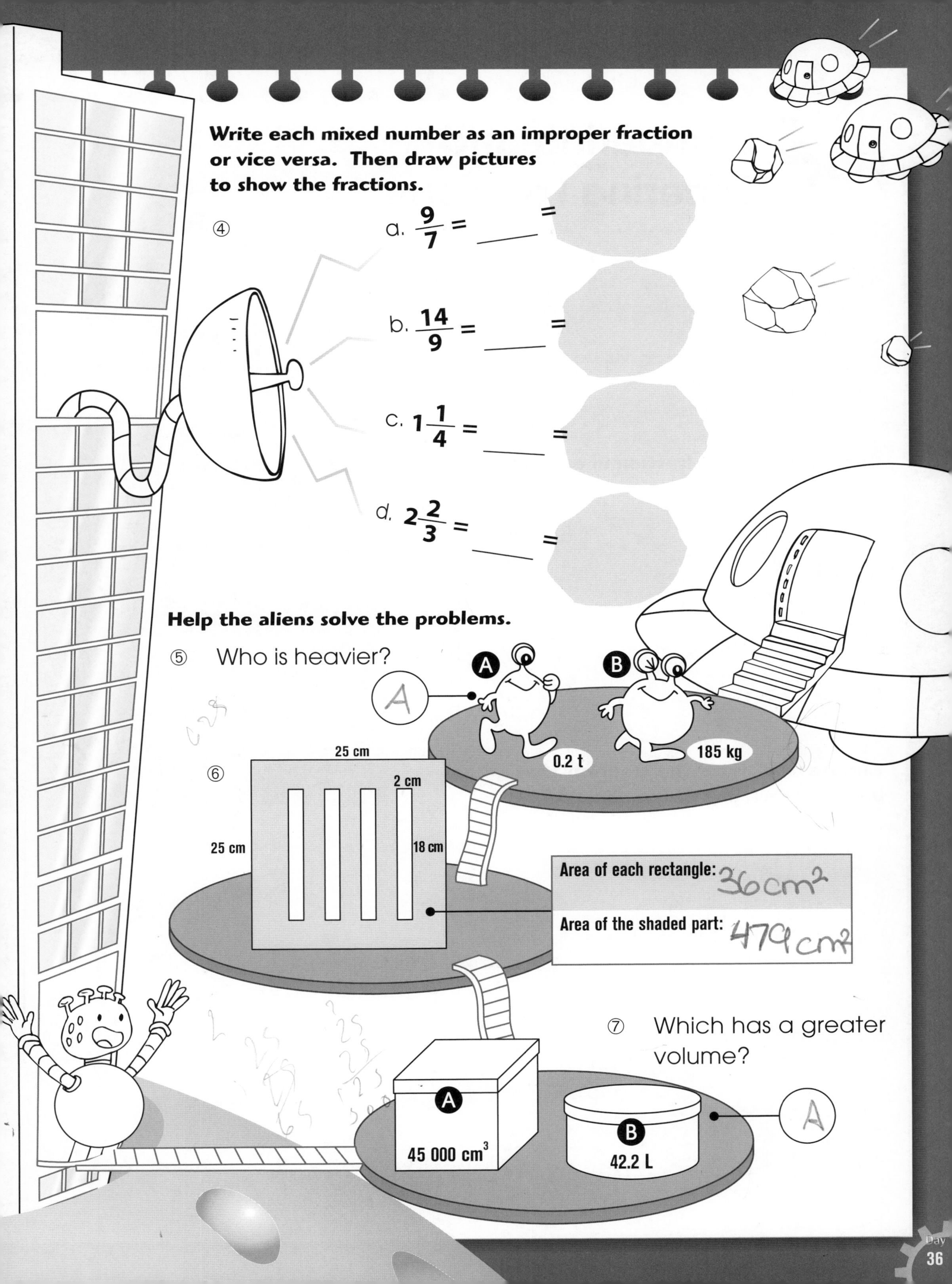

Write each mixed number as an improper fraction or vice versa. Then draw pictures to show the fractions.

④

a. $\frac{9}{7}$ = ______ =

b. $\frac{14}{9}$ = ______ =

c. $1\frac{1}{4}$ = ______ =

d. $2\frac{2}{3}$ = ______ =

Help the aliens solve the problems.

⑤ Who is heavier?

⑥

Area of each rectangle:

Area of the shaded part:

⑦ Which has a greater volume?

DATE: ____________________

Comparing and Ordering Fractions

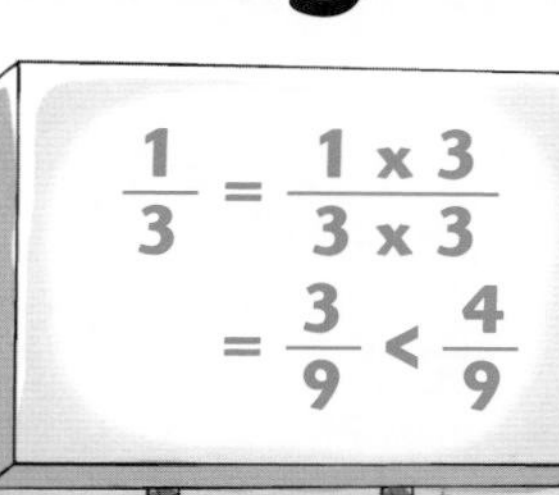

Comparing fractions:

- When the denominators are the same, the greater the numerator, the greater the fraction.

  e.g. $\frac{3}{10} > \frac{1}{10}$ ← 3 > 1 (numerators); ← same (denominators)

- When the numerators are the same, the smaller the denominator, the greater the fraction.

  e.g. $\frac{4}{5} > \frac{4}{9}$ ← same (numerators); ← 5 < 9 (denominators)

Circle the greatest fraction in each group.

① $\frac{4}{9}$ $\frac{5}{9}$ $\frac{1}{9}$

② $\frac{7}{8}$ $\frac{5}{8}$ $\frac{2}{8}$

③ $\frac{3}{7}$ $\frac{3}{2}$ $\frac{3}{9}$

④ $\frac{1}{10}$ $\frac{1}{7}$ $\frac{1}{3}$

⑤ $\frac{4}{6}$ $\frac{1}{6}$ $\frac{3}{6}$

⑥ $\frac{2}{12}$ $\frac{2}{9}$ $\frac{2}{10}$

⑦ $\frac{9}{7}$ $\frac{5}{7}$ $\frac{12}{7}$

⑧ $\frac{22}{5}$ $\frac{1}{5}$ $\frac{18}{5}$

Choose and write the fraction that comes between each pair of fractions.

⑨

⑩

⑪

⑫

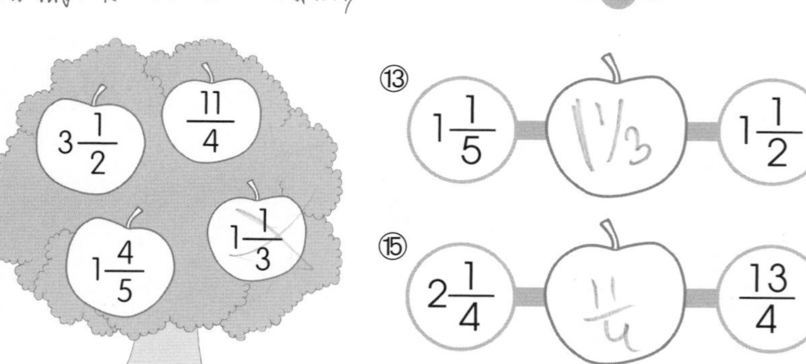

⑬ $1\frac{1}{5}$ ____ $1\frac{1}{2}$

⑮ $2\frac{1}{4}$ ____ $\frac{13}{4}$

⑭

⑯

Comparing fractions with different denominators:

- **1st** Find a common denominator.
- **2nd** Write equivalent fractions.
- **3rd** Compare the numerators.

e.g. Compare $\frac{3}{4}$ and $\frac{5}{8}$.

8 is the common denominator.

$$\frac{3}{4} \overset{\times 2}{=} \frac{6}{8} > \frac{5}{8}$$

$$\frac{3}{4} > \frac{5}{8}$$

Compare the fractions. Put '>' or '<' in the circles.

⑰ $\frac{4}{5}$ ◯ $\frac{11}{15}$

⑱ $\frac{5}{9}$ ◯ $\frac{17}{18}$

⑲ $\frac{13}{20}$ ◯ $\frac{3}{10}$

⑳ $\frac{5}{8}$ ◯ $\frac{19}{24}$

㉑ $\frac{1}{2}$ ◯ $\frac{9}{14}$

㉒ $\frac{8}{15}$ ◯ $\frac{2}{3}$

㉓ $\frac{5}{6}$ ◯ $\frac{1}{3}$

㉔ $\frac{11}{12}$ ◯ $\frac{3}{4}$

㉕ $\frac{1}{8}$ ◯ $\frac{7}{24}$

㉖ $\frac{9}{10}$ ◯ $\frac{29}{30}$

Put the fractions in order from least to greatest.

㉗ $\frac{5}{12}$ $\frac{1}{2}$ $\frac{2}{3}$

____

㉘ $\frac{5}{9}$ $\frac{2}{3}$ $\frac{7}{18}$

____

㉙ $\frac{6}{7}$ $\frac{11}{14}$ $\frac{9}{7}$

____

㉚ $\frac{4}{5}$ $\frac{11}{20}$ $\frac{7}{10}$

____

Read what the children say. Write the missing information.

㉛

I have 2 bags of candies weighing $\frac{3}{5}$ kg and $\frac{9}{10}$ kg. The smaller bag is lighter.

㉜

The juice boxes contains $\frac{5}{6}$ L and $\frac{2}{3}$ L of juice respectively.

DATE: ______________

Day 38

More about Fractions

Draw and colour the pictures to show the amounts of food that the giants have for lunch.

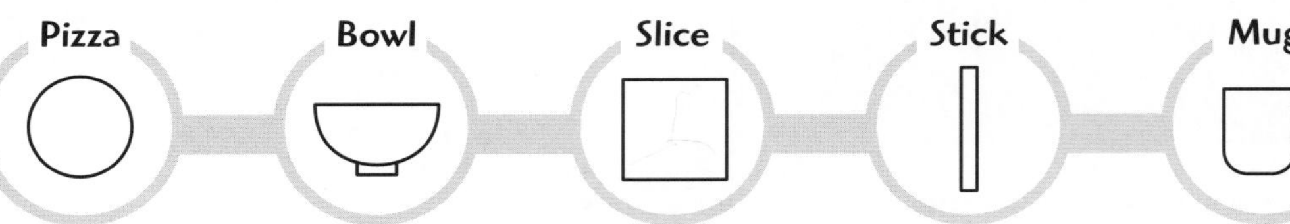

① **Gary Giant's Lunch**

$1\frac{3}{8}$ pizzas

$1\frac{1}{2}$ bowls of noodles

$2\frac{1}{3}$ slices of bread

$1\frac{3}{4}$ slices of ham

$\frac{7}{4}$ cheese sticks

$\frac{8}{5}$ mugs of milk

② **Kevin Giant's Lunch**

$\frac{9}{5}$ pizzas

$2\frac{1}{2}$ bowls of cereal

$1\frac{3}{4}$ slices of bread

$\frac{5}{4}$ slices of ham

$\frac{4}{3}$ carrot sticks

$1\frac{1}{3}$ mugs of juice

③ **Victor Giant's Lunch**

$1\frac{5}{6}$ pizzas

$\frac{3}{2}$ bowls of pasta

$1\frac{1}{5}$ slices of bread

$\frac{9}{5}$ slices of chicken breast

$2\frac{1}{5}$ cheese sticks

$\frac{9}{4}$ mugs of milk

Look at the clocks. Tell the durations in 2 different ways. Write fractions in simplest form.

④
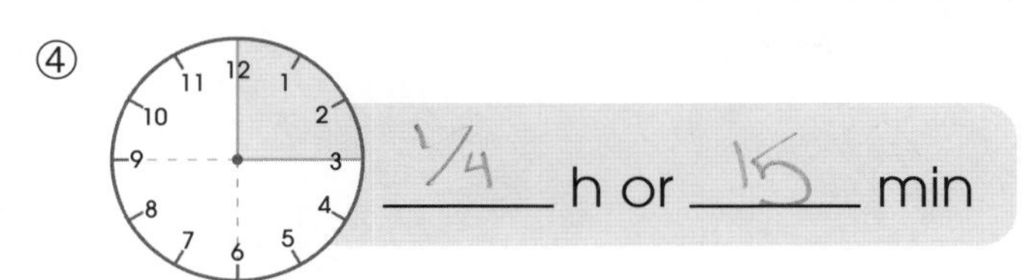

⑤
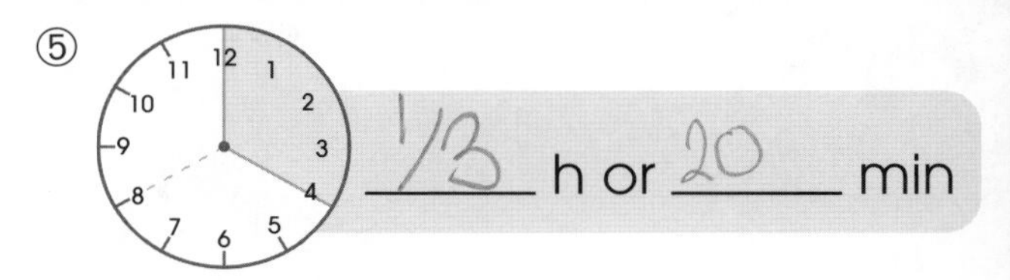

⑥
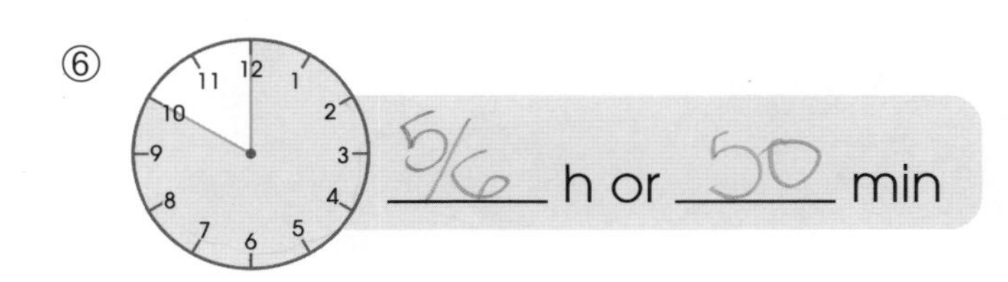

⑦
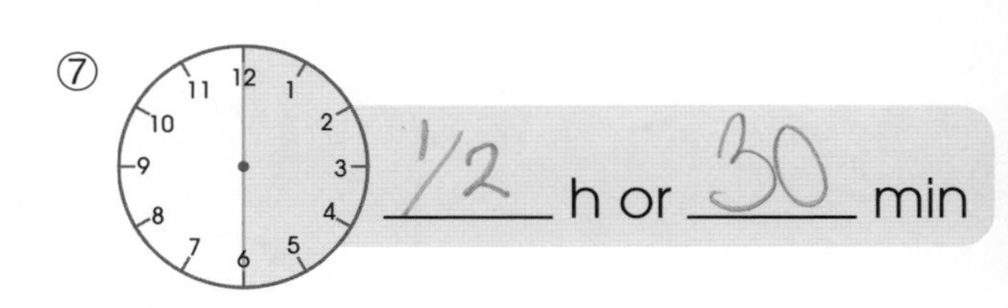

Find the length of each string in metres. Write fractions in simplest form.

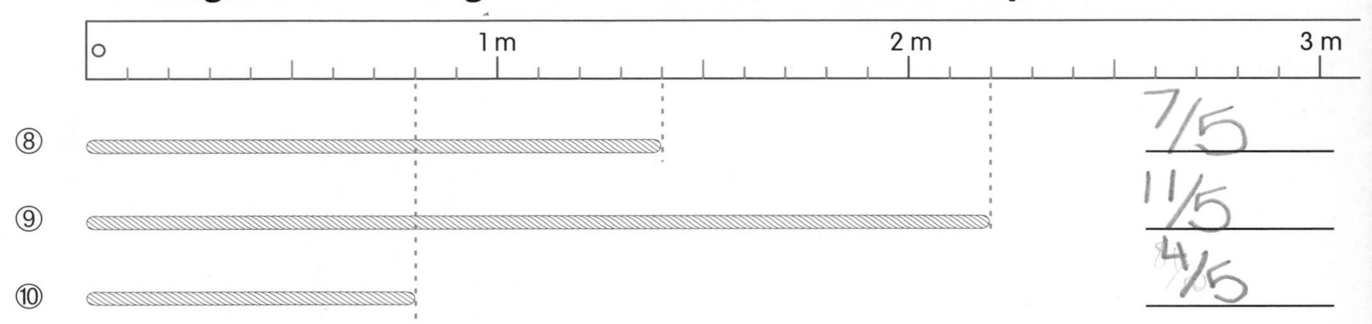

Write the measurements in fraction:

e.g. 1 m 40 cm $= 1\frac{40}{100}$ m
(1 m = 100 cm)
$= 1\frac{2}{5}$ m

e.g. 1 kg 50 g $= 1\frac{50}{1000}$ kg
(1 kg = 1000 g)
$= 1\frac{1}{20}$ kg

Find the weight of each item in kilograms. Write fractions in simplest form.

⑪
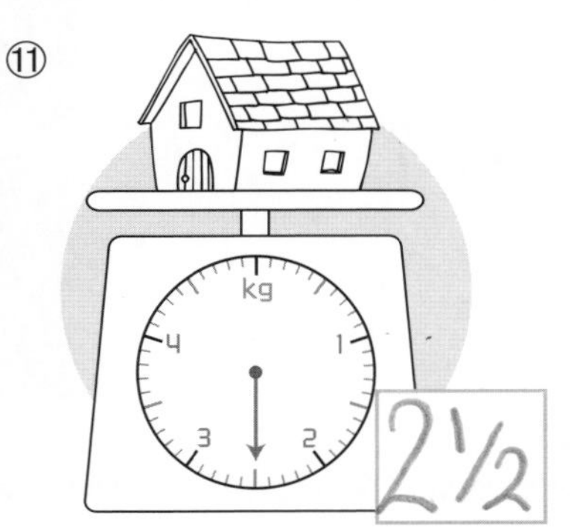

⑫
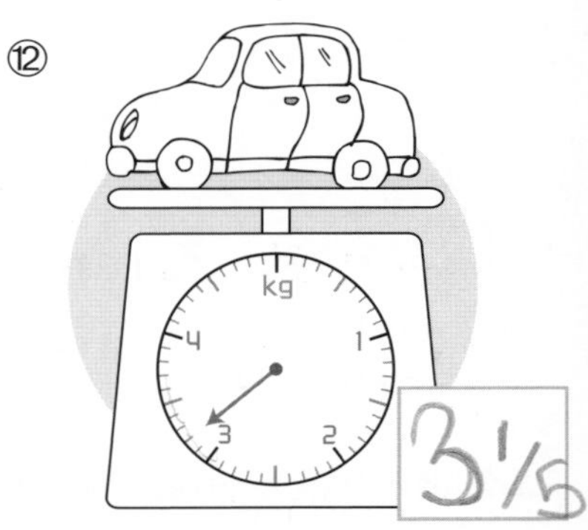

⑬

⑭
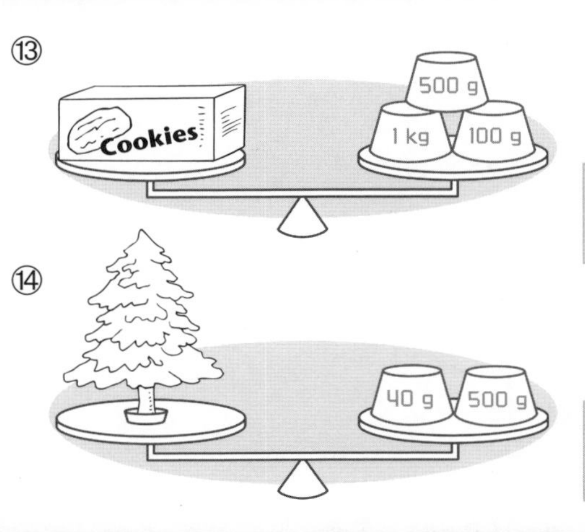

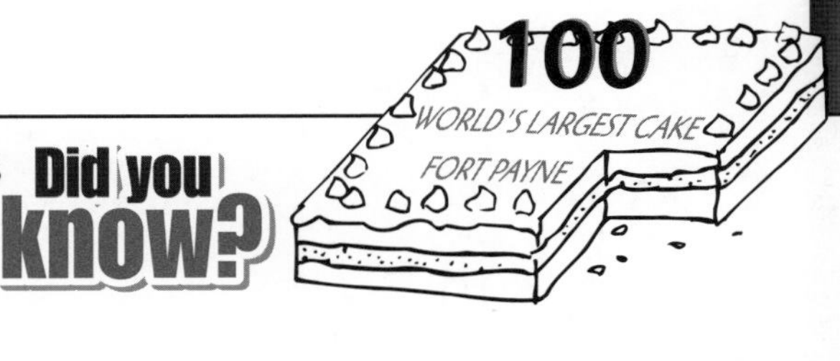

The world's **largest cake** was baked in USA in 1989. It weighed about 58 t, with the icing accounted for $\frac{1}{8}$ of its weight.

DATE: ____________

Day 39

Addition of Fractions (1)

He eats $\frac{5}{8}$ of a pizza at a time!

$$\frac{3}{8} + \frac{2}{8} = \frac{5}{8}$$

Colour the diagrams to show the answers. Then complete the addition sentences.

①

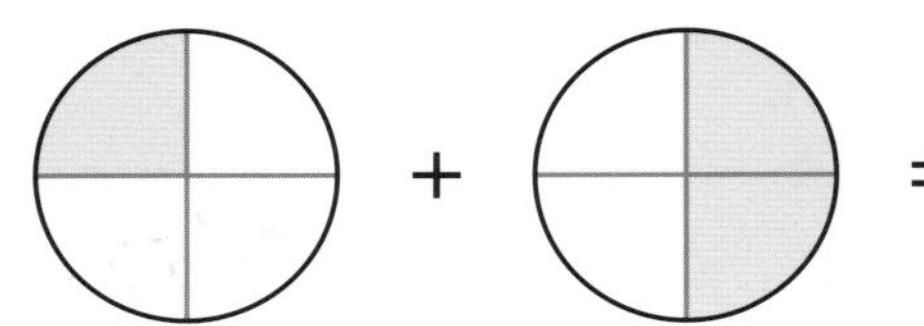

$\frac{1}{4} + \frac{2}{4} = \frac{3}{4}$

②

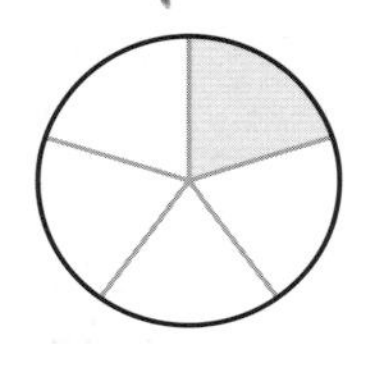

$\frac{1}{5} + \frac{3}{5} = \frac{4}{5}$

Adding fractions with the same denominator:

1st Add the numerators only and leave the denominator the same.

2nd Write the answer in simplest form.

e.g. $\frac{1}{10} + \frac{7}{10}$

$= \frac{1+7}{10}$ ← Add the numerators. ← Keep the denominator the same.

$= \frac{8}{10}$

$= \frac{4}{5}$ ← Write in simplest form.

Add the fractions. Show your work. Write the answers in simplest form.

③ $\frac{2}{9} + \frac{4}{9} = \frac{2}{3}$

④ $\frac{1}{4} + \frac{1}{4} = \frac{1}{2}$

⑤ $\frac{3}{10} + \frac{1}{10} = \frac{2}{5}$

⑥ $\frac{2}{7} + \frac{3}{7} = \frac{5}{7}$

⑦ $\frac{1}{6} + \frac{2}{6} = \frac{1}{2}$

⑧ $\frac{3}{8} + \frac{4}{8} = \frac{7}{4}$

Add the fractions. Write the answers in simplest form.

⑨ $\frac{1}{5} + \frac{3}{5} =$ ______

⑩ $\frac{5}{10} + \frac{4}{10} =$ ______

⑪ $\frac{2}{8} + \frac{4}{8} =$ ______

⑫ $\frac{5}{9} + \frac{1}{9} =$ ______

⑬ $\frac{5}{12} + \frac{5}{12} =$ ______

⑭ $\frac{3}{6} + \frac{1}{6} =$ ______

⑮ $\frac{4}{7} + \frac{1}{7} =$ ______

⑯ $\frac{4}{15} + \frac{8}{15} =$ ______

⑰ $\frac{1}{3} + \frac{1}{3} =$ ______

Solve the problems. Write the answers in simplest form.

⑱

How much juice are there in two boxes in all?

______ = ______

⑲

A box of candies is $\frac{1}{10}$ kg heavier than a bag. How heavy is a box of candies?

______ = ______

⑳

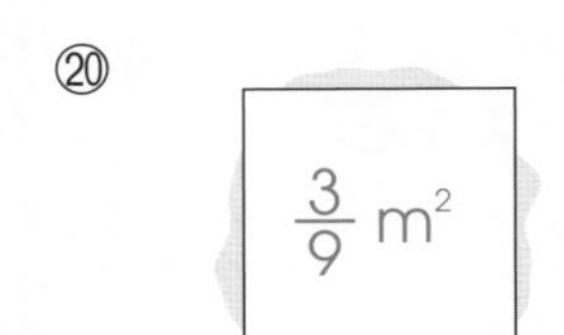

The area of the rectangular cardboard is $\frac{2}{9}$ m² greater than that of the square one. What is the area of the rectangular cardboard?

______ = ______

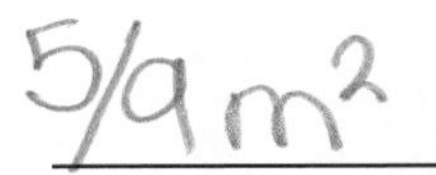

㉑ *A ribbon is $\frac{4}{10}$ m long. I used 2 ribbons to tie a gift box. How much ribbon did I use in all?*

______ = ______

______

㉒ *It took me $\frac{1}{12}$ h to wrap the gift box and $\frac{3}{12}$ h to tie it. How much time did I take to wrap and tie the gift box?*

______ = ______

______

DATE: ____________________

Addition of Fractions (2)

Cheer up! You still have $1\frac{3}{8}$ trays of delicious muffins.

Colour the diagrams to show the answers. Then complete the addition sentences.

If the sum of fractions is an improper fraction, remember to write the final answer as a mixed number.

e.g. 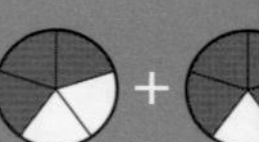 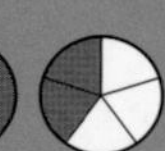 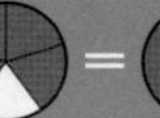

$\frac{3}{5} + \frac{4}{5}$

$= \frac{7}{5}$ ← Add the numerators. ← Leave the denominator the same.

$= 1\frac{2}{5}$ ← Write in simplest form.

① 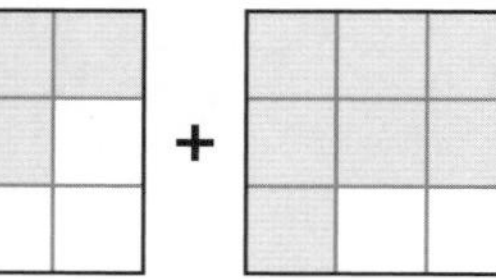 + 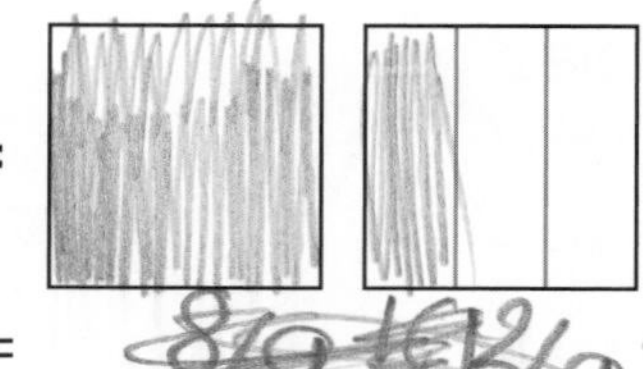

$5/9$ + $7/9$ = ~~8/9 12/9~~ $1\,1/3$

② 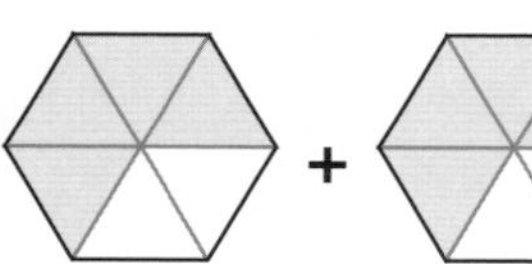 + 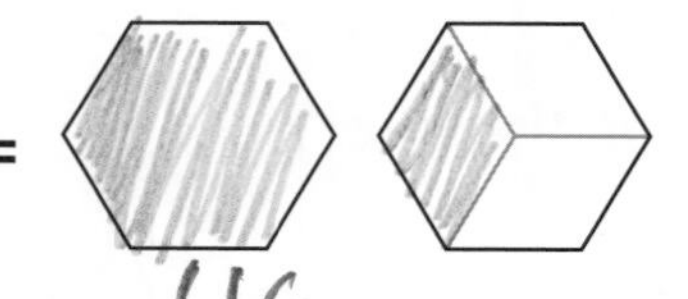

$4/6$ + $4/6$ = $1\,1/3$

Find the totals. Show your work. Write the answers in simplest form.

③ 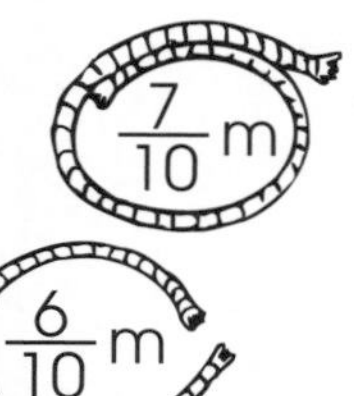

④ 

⑤ 

⑥ 

Do the addition. Write the answers in simplest form.

⑦ $\frac{3}{4}+\frac{1}{4}=$ ______

⑧ $\frac{4}{8}+\frac{5}{8}=$ ______

⑨ $\frac{3}{10}+\frac{9}{10}=$ ______

⑩ $\frac{5}{9}+\frac{7}{9}=$ ______

⑪ $\frac{3}{5}+\frac{4}{5}=$ ______

⑫ $\frac{5}{7}+\frac{4}{7}=$ ______

⑬ $\frac{3}{12}+\frac{8}{12}=$ ______

⑭ $\frac{8}{10}+\frac{5}{10}=$ ______

⑮ $\frac{3}{9}+\frac{8}{9}=$ ______

⑯ $\frac{7}{15}+\frac{11}{15}=$ ______

⑰ $\frac{6}{8}+\frac{7}{8}=$ ______

⑱ $\frac{6}{12}+\frac{9}{12}=$ ______

Read what the children say. Check the items that they bought.

⑲

I bought 2 boxes of cookies. They weighed $1\frac{1}{5}$ kg in all.

⑳

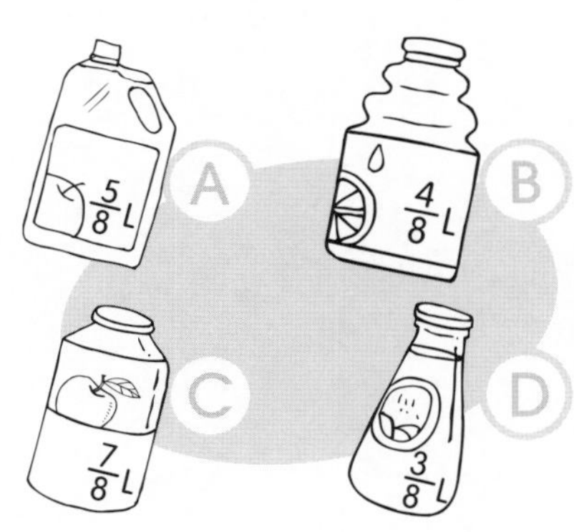

I bought 2 bottles of juice. I have $1\frac{1}{4}$ L of juice in all.

㉑

The total length of two pieces of ropes is $1\frac{1}{2}$ m.

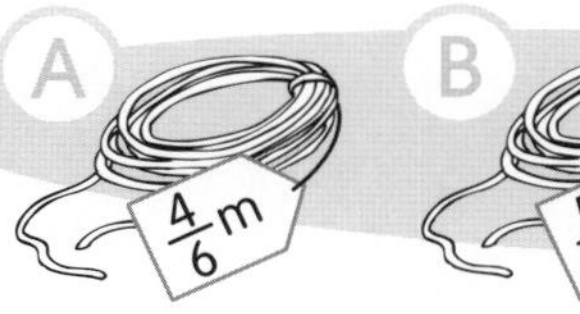

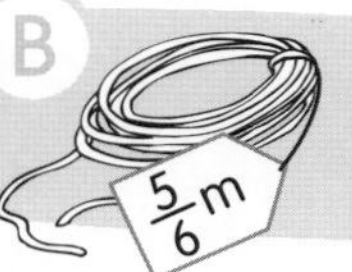

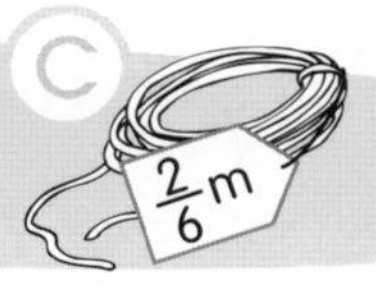

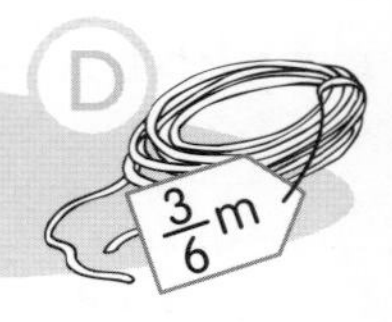

Did you know?

Blueberry muffin is the state muffin of Minnesota, USA. A typical blueberry muffin is about 64 mm in height, with the top $\frac{1}{3}$ as the 'crown'.

DATE: ____________

Day 41

Subtraction of Fractions (1)

Subtracting fractions with same denominator:

1st Subtract the numerators and leave the denominator the same.

2nd Write the answer in simplest form.

e.g.

$$\frac{7}{8} - \frac{1}{8} \leftarrow \text{Subtract the numerators.}$$
$$= \frac{7-1}{8}$$
$$= \frac{6}{8}$$
$$= \frac{3}{4}$$

Look at the pictures. Complete the number sentences. Write the answers in simplest form.

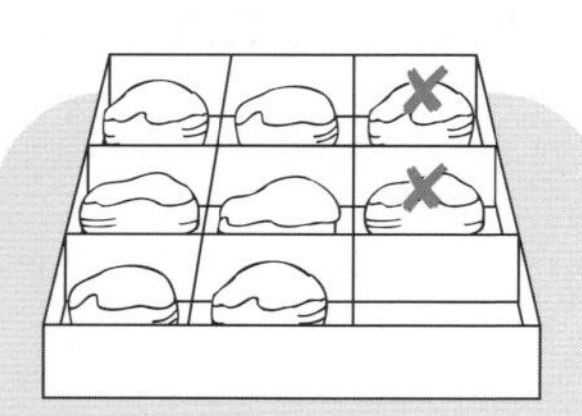

$\frac{8}{9} - \frac{\ }{9} = \frac{\ }{9}$

$= \_\_$

② 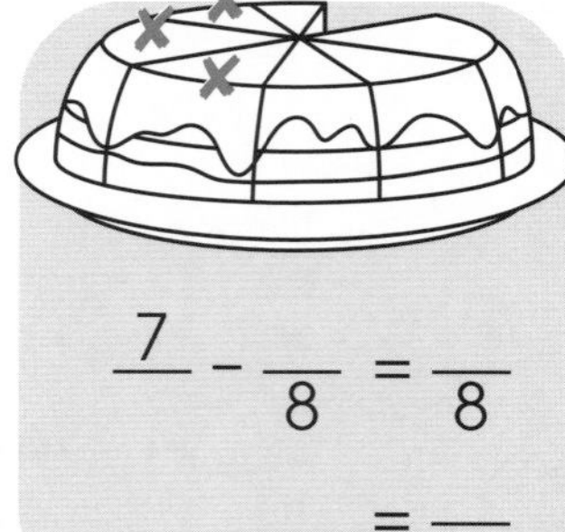

$\frac{7}{\ } - \frac{\ }{8} = \frac{\ }{8}$

$= \_\_$

Do the subtraction. Write the answers in simplest form.

③ $\frac{4}{5} - \frac{1}{5} =$ ______

④ $\frac{3}{4} - \frac{1}{4} =$ ______

⑤ $\frac{5}{6} - \frac{4}{6} =$ ______

⑥ $\frac{5}{8} - \frac{3}{8} =$ ______

⑦ $\frac{5}{7} - \frac{2}{7} =$ ______

⑧ $\frac{7}{9} - \frac{4}{9} =$ ______

⑨ $\frac{7}{12} - \frac{1}{12} =$ ______

⑩ $\frac{6}{10} - \frac{1}{10} =$ ______

⑪ $\frac{2}{3} - \frac{1}{3} =$ ______

⑫ $\frac{8}{11} - \frac{2}{11} =$ ______

⑬ $\frac{7}{8} - \frac{3}{8} =$ ______

⑭ $\frac{8}{10} - \frac{2}{10} =$ ______

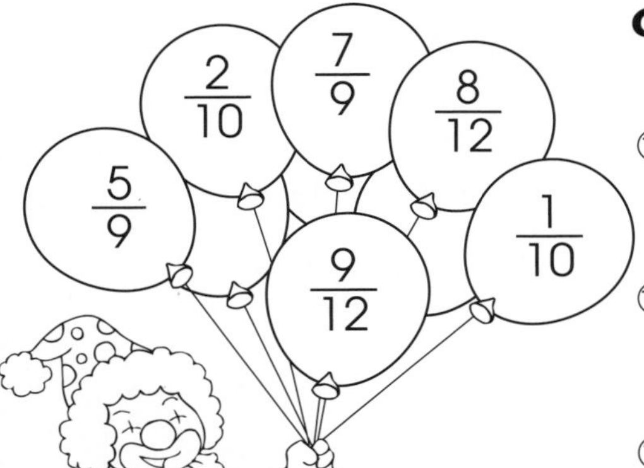

Choose the correct fractions to fill in the blanks.

⑮ $\frac{5}{10} - \_\_\_\_\_ = \frac{2}{5}$

⑯ $\frac{8}{9} - \_\_\_\_\_ = \frac{1}{3}$

⑰ $\_\_\_\_\_ - \frac{1}{9} = \frac{2}{3}$

⑱ $\frac{11}{12} - \_\_\_\_\_ = \frac{1}{4}$

⑲ $\_\_\_\_\_ - \frac{5}{12} = \frac{1}{3}$

⑳ $\frac{7}{10} - \_\_\_\_\_ = \frac{1}{2}$

Solve the problems. Write the answers in simplest form.

㉑ The length of a rectangle is $\frac{9}{10}$ m. If its width is $\frac{1}{10}$ m shorter than its length, what is the width of the rectangle?

____________ = ______ ________

㉒ Judy used $\frac{5}{7}$ kg of peanut butter to make cookies. How much peanut butter was left if Judy had $\frac{6}{7}$ kg of peanut butter at first?

____________ = ______ ________

㉓ It took Katie $\frac{11}{12}$ h to finish an assignment. If Peter took $\frac{1}{12}$ h less than Katie, how long did Peter take to finish the same assignment?

____________ = ______ ________

㉔ How much more water can a pail hold than a mug?

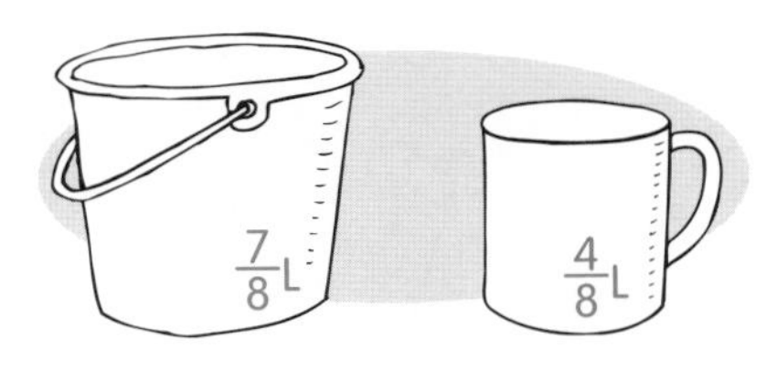

____

= ______

____

Did you know?

The **stinger** is a modified egg-laying organ, so only female bees sting. A honeybee's stinger is about 3 mm long, which is $\frac{1}{4}$ of its body length.

DATE: ______________

Subtraction of Fractions (2)

Mom, I want to have $\frac{1}{3}$ of the pizza and let Eric have the rest.

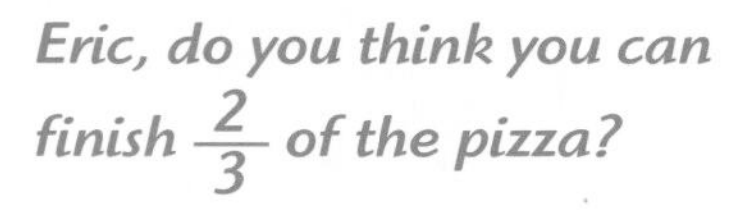

$$1-\frac{1}{3}$$
$$=\frac{3}{3}-\frac{1}{3}$$
$$=\frac{2}{3}$$

Draw lines on the shapes and cross out some parts to match the subtraction sentences. Then find the answers.

① 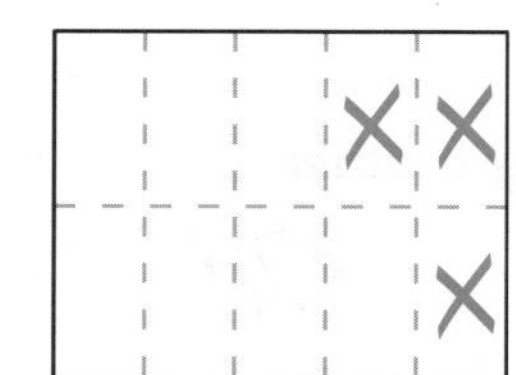

$1-\frac{3}{10}=$ ______ − ______ = ______

② 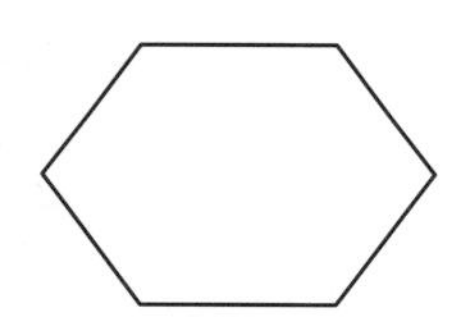

$1-\frac{1}{6}=$ ______ − ______ = ______

③ 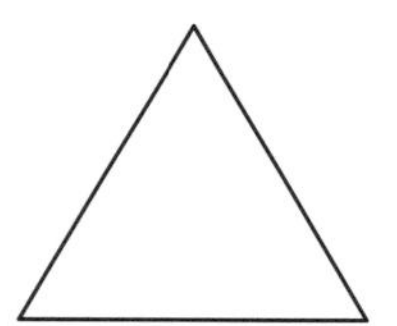

$1-\frac{1}{4}=$ ______ − ______ = ______

1 can be written as a fraction with the same number in the numerator and the denominator.

e.g. $1=\frac{5}{5}$; $1=\frac{9}{9}$

$$1-\frac{4}{10}$$
$$=\frac{10}{10}-\frac{4}{10}$$
$$=\frac{6}{10}$$
$$=\frac{3}{5}$$

fractions with a common denominator

④ 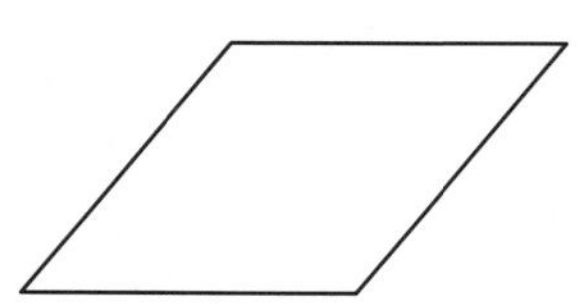

$1-\frac{3}{8}$

=

⑤ 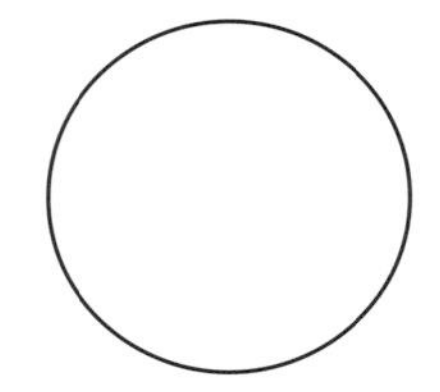

$1-\frac{5}{12}$

=

⑥ 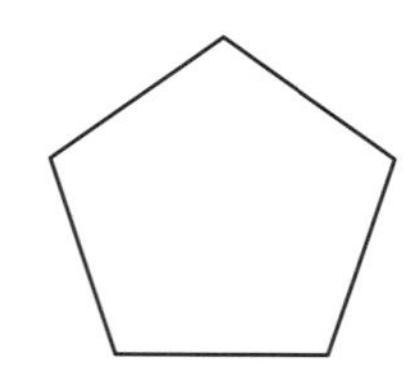

$1-\frac{8}{10}$

=

Look at the pictures. Complete the tables. Write the answers in simplest form.

⑦ Linda has a roll of ribbon. She wants to cut it into 2 pieces.

1 m

Length of 1st piece	$\frac{1}{2}$ m	$\frac{3}{4}$ m	$\frac{2}{8}$ m		
Length of 2nd piece				$\frac{1}{6}$ m	$\frac{3}{10}$ m

⑧ Ted has a bag of candies. He wants to give some to Sue.

1 kg

Amount of candies that Ted gives to Sue	$\frac{4}{5}$ kg	$\frac{2}{6}$ kg	$\frac{4}{8}$ kg		
Amount of candies that Ted has left				$\frac{1}{2}$ kg	$\frac{3}{10}$ kg

Read what Vivian says. Solve the problems. Write the answers in simplest form.

⑨ How much taller is Vivian than her brother, Gary?

________________ = ________

____

⑩ If Vivian was $\frac{8}{9}$ m tall 2 years ago, how much had she grown since then?

________________ = ________

____

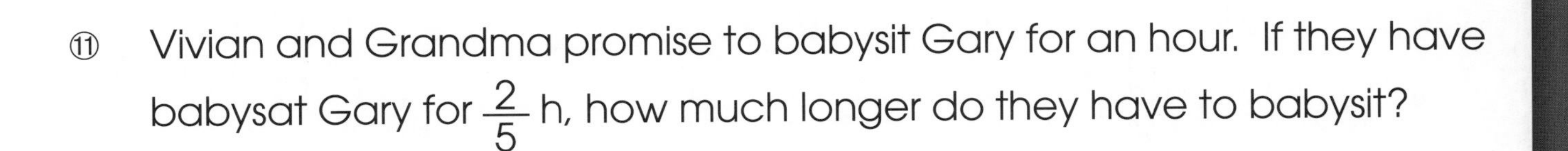

⑪ Vivian and Grandma promise to babysit Gary for an hour. If they have babysat Gary for $\frac{2}{5}$ h, how much longer do they have to babysit?

________________ = ________ ________

⑫ Vivian gives a bottle of milk to Gary. If Gary finishes $\frac{4}{8}$ of it, how much milk is left?

________________ = ________ ________

DATE: ____________________

Day 43 Decimals (1)

In numerals: 1.35
In words: 1 and 35 hundredths

Ones	Tenths	Hundredths
1 .	3	5

Write a decimal for each diagram to show how much is coloured. Then write the decimal in words.

① 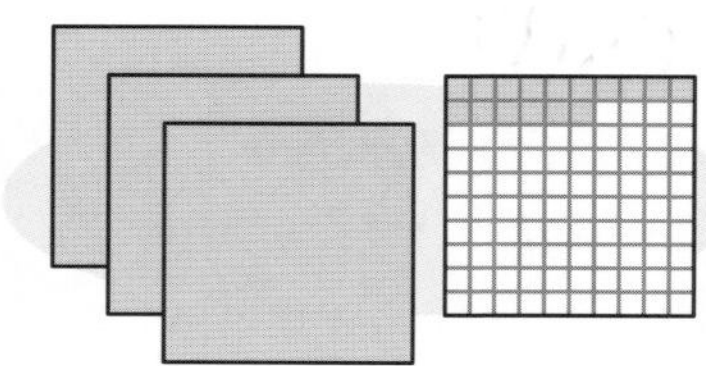

3.16 ; 3 and 16 hundredths

② 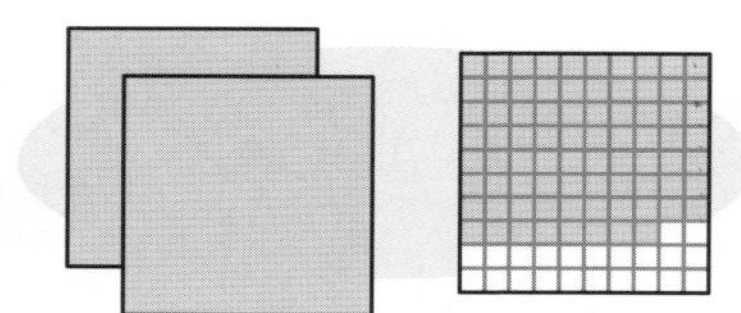

2.78 ; 2 and 78 hundredths

③ 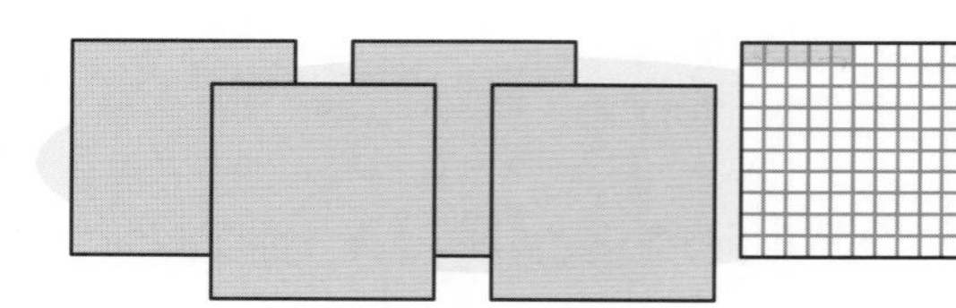

4.05 ; 4 and 5 hundredths

Colour the correct number of squares to match each decimal. Then write the meaning of each digit.

④ **0.58**

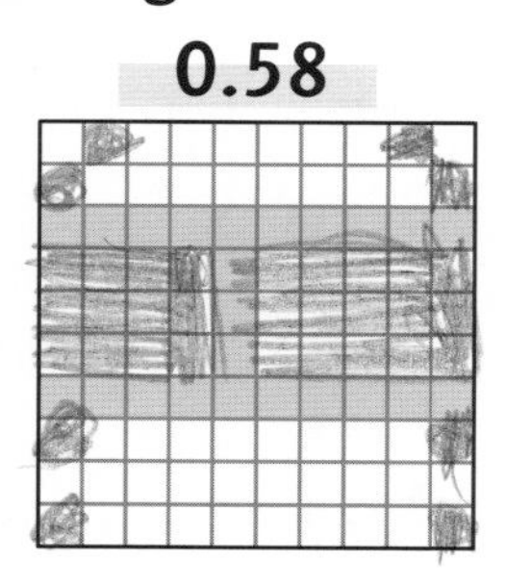

5 means 0.5
8 means 0.08

⑤ **0.42**

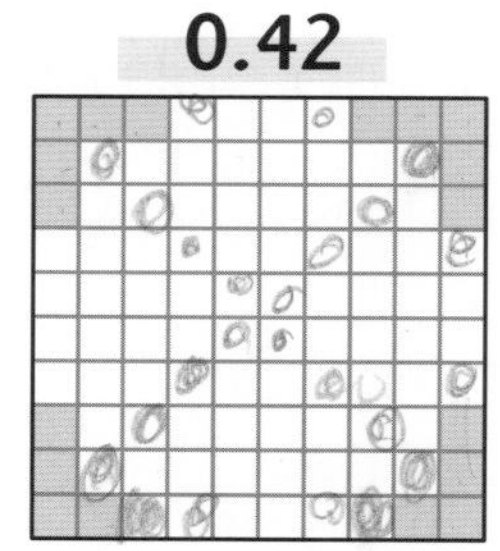

4 means 0.4
2 means 0.02

⑥ **0.19**

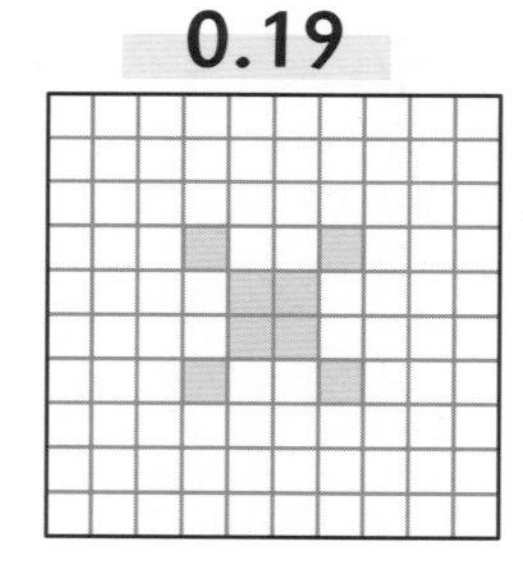

1 means 0.1
9 means 0.09

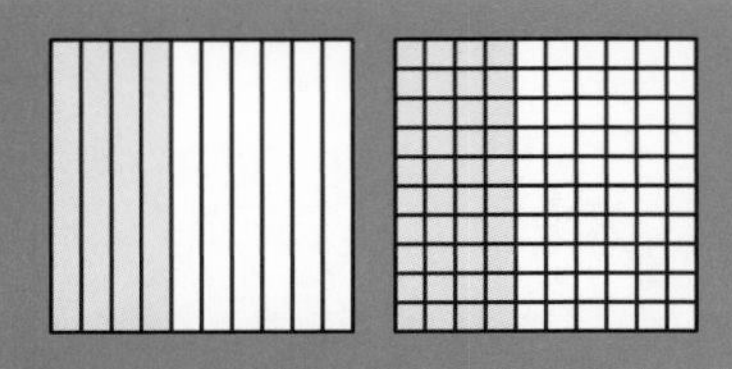

4 tenths = 40 hundredths
0.4 = 0.40

0.4 and 0.40 are equivalent decimals.

Look at each pair of diagrams. Fill in the blanks.

⑦ 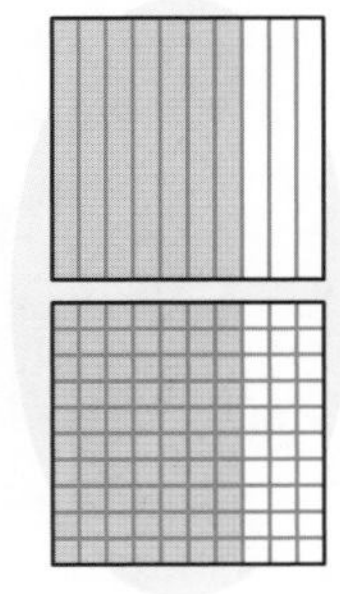

7 tenths = 70 hundredths
0.7 = 0.70
0.7 and 0.70 are equivalent decimals.

⑧ 

6 tenths = 60 hundredths
0.6 = 0.60
0.6 and 0.60 are equivalent decimals.

⑨ 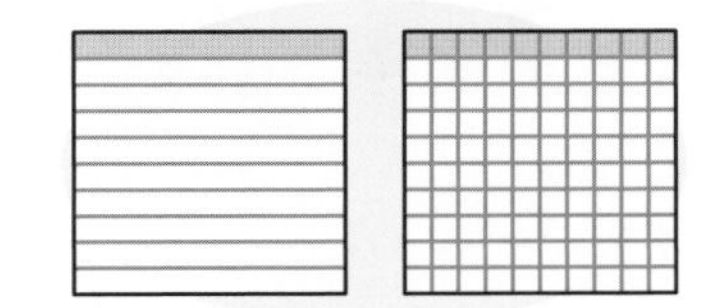

1 tenth = 10 hundredths
0.1 = 0.10
0.1 and 0.10 are equivalent decimals.

Write the decimals.

⑩ 4 in the ones place; 2 in the tenths place; and 3 in the hundredths place 4.23

⑪ 0 in the ones place; 1 in the tenths place; and 9 in the hundredths place 0.19

⑫ one tenth greater than 1.29 1.39

⑬ two tenths less than 4.98 4.78

⑭ one hundredth greater than 3.15 3.16

⑮ two hundredths less than 4.83 4.81

Fill in the missing numbers.

⑯ 3.86 3.88 4.00 4.02 ______ ______

⑰ 9.51 9.47 9.43 9.39 ______ ______

⑱ 0.59 0.89 1.19 1.49 ______ ______

DATE: ____________________

Decimals (2)

Write the measurements in decimals. Place them on the number lines.

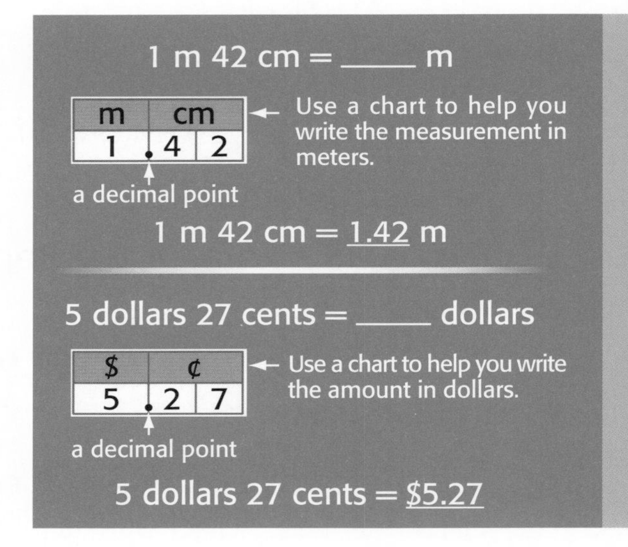

1 m 42 cm = _____ m

m	cm	
1	4	2

Use a chart to help you write the measurement in meters.

a decimal point

1 m 42 cm = 1.42 m

5 dollars 27 cents = _____ dollars

$	¢	
5	2	7

Use a chart to help you write the amount in dollars.

a decimal point

5 dollars 27 cents = $5.27

① 8 m 44 cm = 8.44 m

8 m 24 cm = 8.24 m

8 m 40 cm = 8.4 m

8.2 8.24 8.3 8.4 8.40 8.44 8.5

② 2 dollars 68 cents = $ 2.68

2 dollars 16 cents = $ 2.16

2 dollars 86 cents = $ 2.86

2 dollars 66 cents = $ 2.66

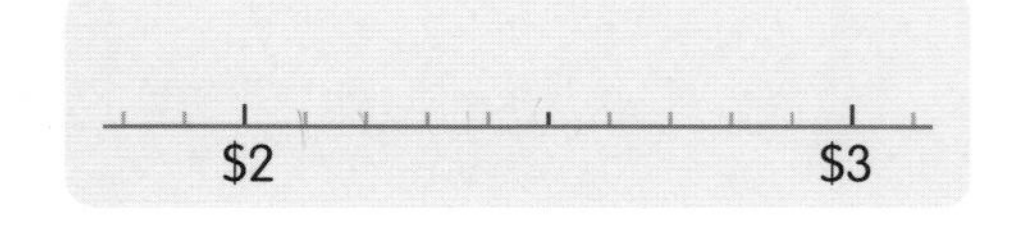

③ 8 dollars 19 cents = $ 8.19

8 dollars 99 cents = $ 8.99

9 dollars 9 cents = $ 9.09

8 dollars 9 cents = $ 8.09

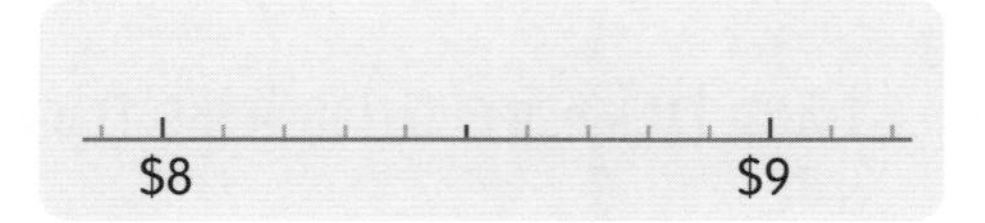

Write a decimal in between.

④ 6.24 < ______ < 6.42

⑤ 3.89 < ______ < 3.98

⑥ 8.89 < ______ < 9.03

⑦ 2.04 < ______ < 3.01

⑧ 7.76 < ______ < 8

⑨ 4.95 < ______ < 5

Rounding a decimal to the nearest whole number:

Look at the digit in the tenths place. If it is 5 or greater, round up; otherwise, round down.

e.g. 4.**6**3

(**6**: greater than 5)

4.63 is rounded up to 5.

Round each decimal to the nearest whole number.

⑩ 3.95 ______ ⑪ 7.14 ______

⑫ 5.28 ______ ⑬ 9.46 ______

⑭ 9.82 ______ ⑮ 7.55 ______

⑯ 6.08 ______ ⑰ 2.17 ______

⑱ 8.32 ______ ⑲ 1.62 ______

Check the correct answers.

If I round a decimal to the nearest whole number, the answer is 4. Which numbers does the decimal lie between?

Ⓐ Between 3.96 and 4.49 Ⓑ Between 3.50 and 3.99

Ⓒ Between 3.50 and 4.49 Ⓓ Between 4.49 and 5.49

I am thinking of a decimal which is less than 8.6. If I round it to the nearest whole number, it is 9. Which numbers does the decimal lie between?

Ⓐ Between 8.61 and 8.99 Ⓑ Between 8.50 and 8.59

Ⓒ Between 8.50 and 9.49 Ⓓ Between 8.01 and 8.59

Rounding a decimal to the nearest tenth:

Look at the digit in the hundredths place. If it is 5 or greater, round up; otherwise, round down.

e.g.

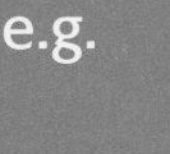

3.7**2**

(**2**: less than 5)

This bag of candies weighs about 3.7 kg.

Round each measurement to the nearest tenth.

㉒

It is about ______ m long.

㉓

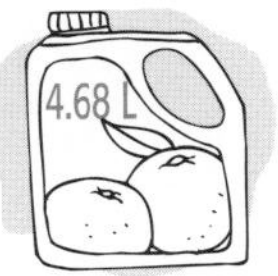

It holds about ______ L of juice.

㉔

It weighs about ______ kg.

DATE: ______________

Relating Fractions and Decimals

Colour the diagrams or write the matching fractions or decimals.

① 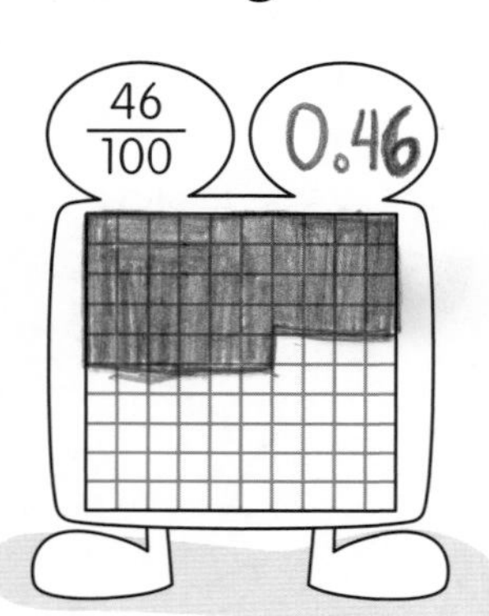

② 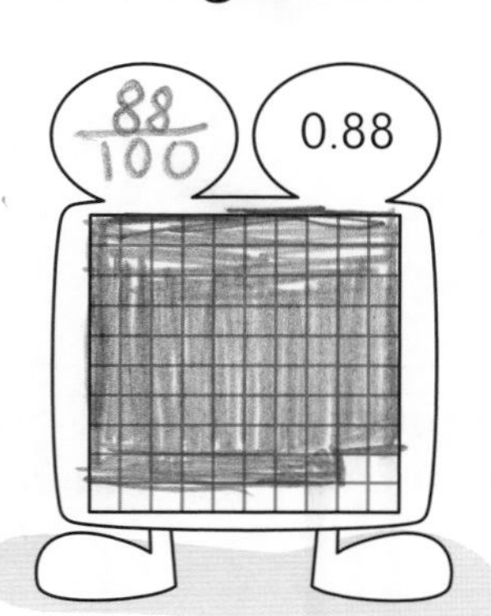

1 hundredth = $\frac{1}{100}$

23 hundredths = $\frac{23}{100}$

= 0.23

③ 

④ 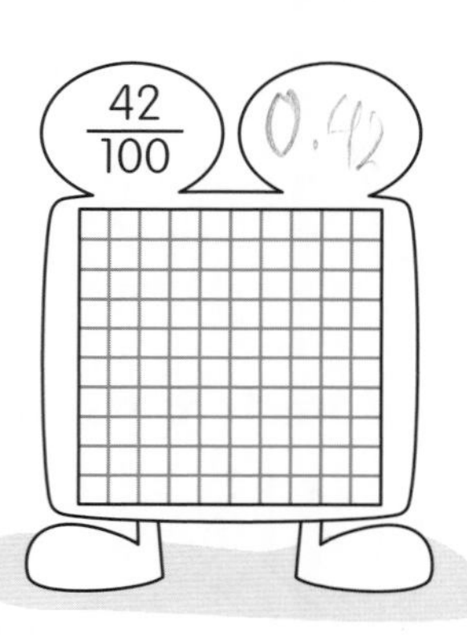

⑤ 

Write the expanded form in 2 ways.

⑥ 0.39

= 0.3 + 0.09

= $\frac{3}{10}$ + ____

⑦ 0.54

= 0.5 + ____

= ____ + ____

⑧ 0.29

= ____ + 0.09

= ____ + ____

Draw lines on the diagrams. Then colour the diagrams and complete the number sentences.

⑨

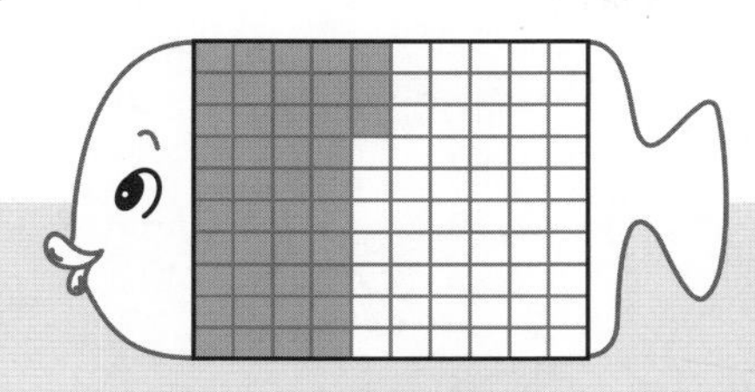

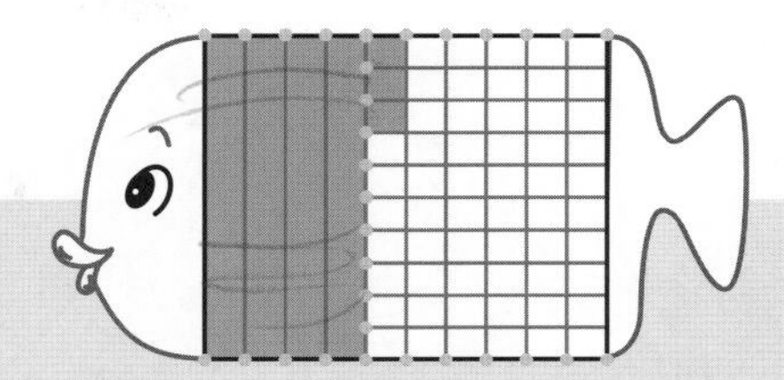

43 hundredths = ____ tenths + ____ hundredths

⑩

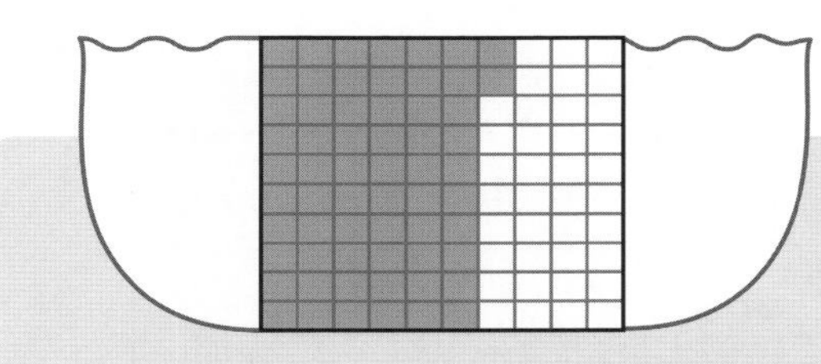

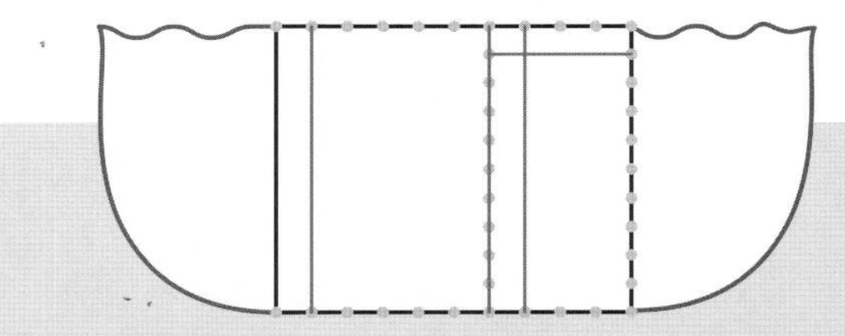

____ hundredths = ____ tenths + ____ hundredths

⑪

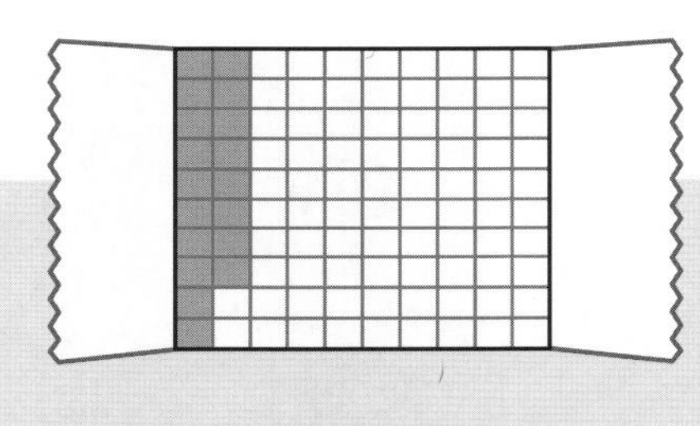

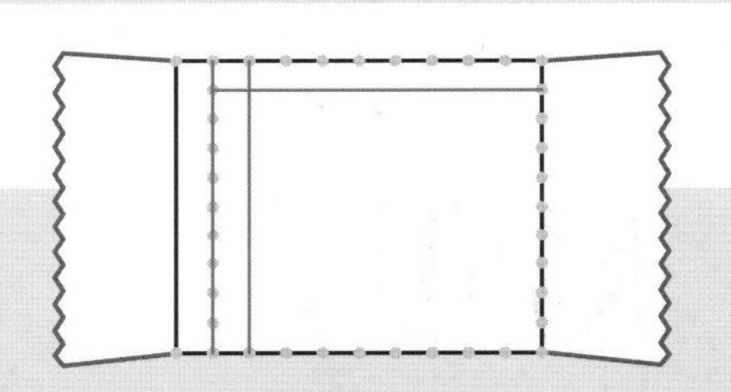

____ hundredths = ____ tenth + ____ hundredths

Answer the questions. Check the letters.

⑫

I want to have a big slice of cake. Which one should I take?

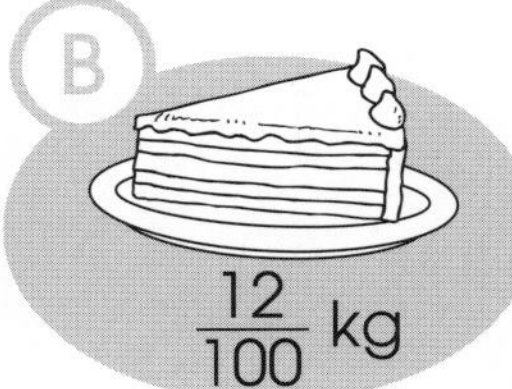

⑬

I need a short stick. Which one should I use?

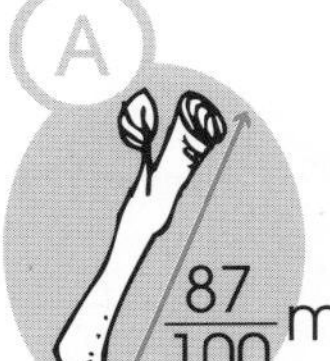

B

0.8 m

Did you know?

ADX Florence in Colorado, USA is the most secure **prison**. It is equipped with 1400 remote-controlled steel doors. Inmates are kept in 3.5 m by 2 m cells at least 23 hours a day.

DATE: ____________________

Day 46

Addition of Decimals

Do the addition. Show your work.

① 32.76 + 74.85

= ________

+

② 95.69 + 13.88

= ________

③ 149.4 + 15.38

= ________

④ 145.97 + 3.6

= ________

Adding decimals:

1st Align the decimal points when doing vertical addition.

2nd Add* decimals the same way we add whole numbers.

3rd Put the decimal point in the answer.

* Add zeros to fill empty spaces

e.g. 3.9 + 6.58 = ____

Align the decimal points.

```
 1
  3.90   ← Write '0' to fill the empty space.
+ 6.58
 10.48   Put the decimal point in the answer.
```

3.9 + 6.58 = 10.48

Find the answers.

⑤ 9.25 + 1.36 = ________

⑥ 18.2 + 1.77 + 88.54 = ________

⑦ 97.47 + 9.8 = ________

⑧ 5.39 + 2.68 + 4.5 = ________

⑨ 3.82 + 12.43 = ________

⑩ 18.9 + 12.56 + 1.7 = ________

⑪ 78.5 + 75.96 = ________

⑫ 3.4 + 90.87 + 15.09 = ________

Each pet has gained 1.28 kg. Look at the old weights of the pets and find their new weights.

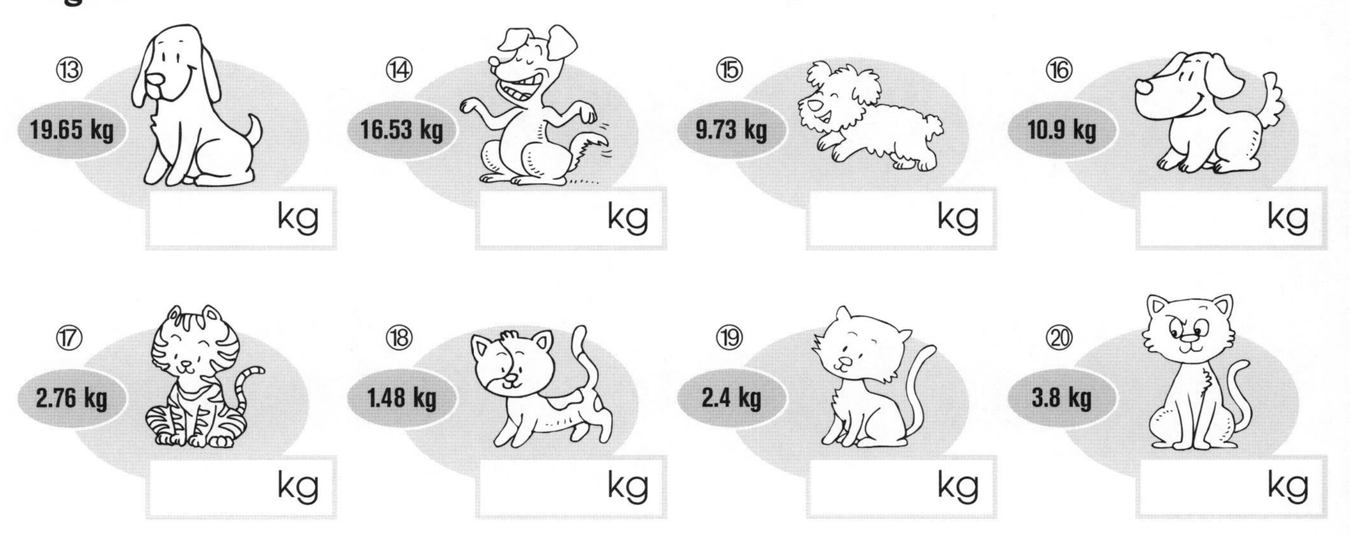

Solve the problems.

㉑ Mrs. Hall buys 2 bags of treats weighing 2.64 kg and 1.59 kg. How much treat has Mrs. Hall bought in all?

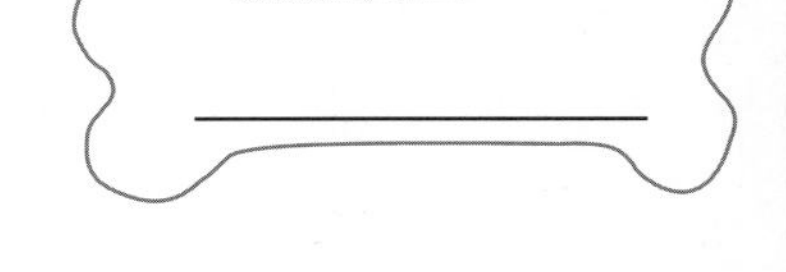

㉒ Each small fish costs $3.29. If a big fish costs 45¢ more than a small one, how much does each big fish cost?

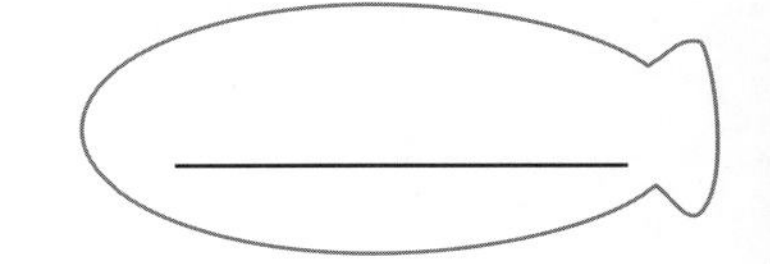

㉓ Cindy Cat drinks 1.34 L of milk every day. If Calvin Cat drinks 0.16 L more than Cindy, how much milk does Calvin drink every day?

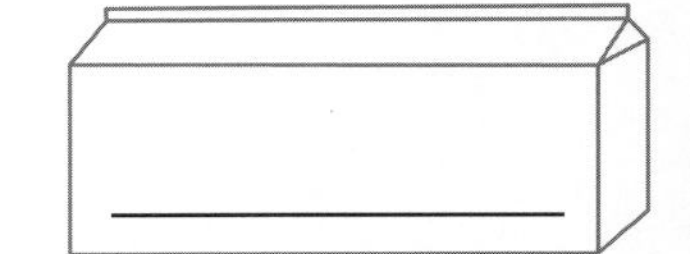

㉔ Danny Dog runs 5.85 km in a given time. If Toby Dog can run 1.09 km farther than Danny, how far can Toby run in the given time?

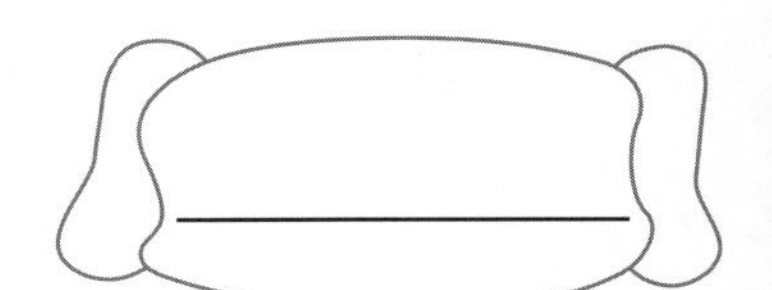

㉕ Katie Cat weighs 2.13 kg and Lily Cat is 0.81 kg heavier than Katie. How heavy is Lily?

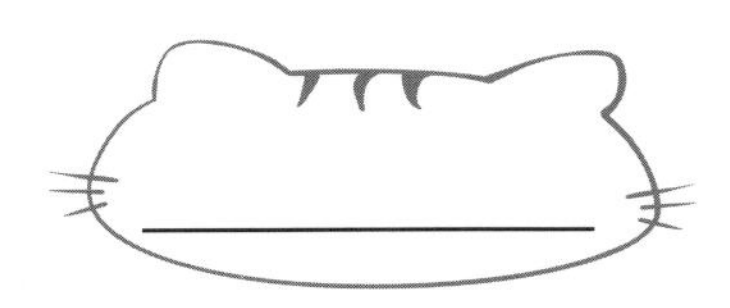

DATE: ______________

Day 47

Subtraction of Decimals (2)

$$\begin{array}{r} 1.19 \\ -\ 0.83 \\ \hline 0.36 \end{array}$$

Do the subtraction.

① $\begin{array}{r} 32.74 \\ -\ \ 4.93 \\ \hline \end{array}$

② $\begin{array}{r} 40.36 \\ -\ 12.54 \\ \hline \end{array}$

③ $\begin{array}{r} 145.03 \\ -\ \ 81.76 \\ \hline \end{array}$

④ $\begin{array}{r} 162.51 \\ -\ \ 92.17 \\ \hline \end{array}$

⑤ 87.2 – 4.86 = ________

⑥ 90.3 – 42.28 = ________

⑦ 71.05 – 11.93 = ________

⑧ 108.8 – 79.94 = ________

⑨ 121.47 – 56.63 = ________

Subtracting decimals:

1st Align the decimal points.

2nd Subtract the same way we subtract whole numbers.

3rd Put the decimal point in the answer.

* Add zeros to fill empty spaces.

e.g. 243.5 – 4.69 = ____

$$\begin{array}{r} 243.50 \\ -\ \ \ 4.69 \\ \hline 238.81 \end{array}$$

Align the decimal points.

Add '0' to fill the empty space.

Put the decimal point in the answer.

243.5 – 4.69 = 238.81

Round each number to the nearest tenth to estimate the answer.

⑩ 82.55 – 18.27 Estimate ________ – ________ = ________

⑪ 104.73 – 40.86 Estimate ________ – ________ = ________

⑫ 96.97 – 72.33 Estimate ________ – ________ = ________

See how much is saved for each item. Find the sale price.

⑬

⑭

⑮

⑯

⑰

⑱

Solve the problems.

⑲ A pair of boots costs $87.55. A pair of running shoes costs $20.99 less than a pair of boots. How much does a pair of running shoes cost?

____________ = ________ ________

⑳

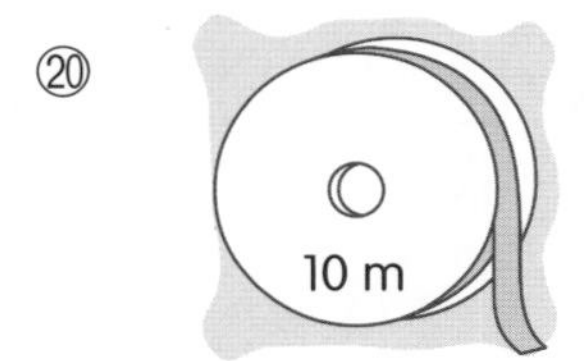

Mrs. Wood cuts a roll of ribbon into 2 pieces. If 1 piece of the ribbon is 3.68 m long, how long is the other piece?

____________ = ________ ________

㉑ Mrs. Hall buys a bag of Halloween treats weighing 1.85 kg. If she gives 1.69 kg of treats to the children, how many kilograms of treats are left?

____________ = ________ ________

㉒

Uncle Bill buys a vacuum cleaner with a $50 bill and two $20 bills. What is his change?

____

= ________

____

Did you know?

The world's largest ***jack o'lantern*** *was carved by an American in 2002 from a pumpkin, that weighed 606.72 kg!*

DATE: ____________________

Day 48

Addition and Subtraction of Decimals

Add or subtract.

① 53.64 + 27.98

② 427.63 + 89.48

③ 65.17 – 46.39

④ 128.94 – 78.06

⑤ 95.87 + 17.65 = ________

⑥ 948.25 + 82.88 = ________

⑦ 100 – 39.84 = ________

⑧ 827.53 – 117.85 = ________

⑨ 210.6 – 94.76 = ________

⑩ 58.9 + 176.47 = ________

⑪ 278.4 – 44.51 = ________

⑫ 76.99 + 82.61 = ________

Round each number to the nearest whole number to estimate the answer. Then find the exact answer.

⑬ 89.67 + 176.53 = ________

Estimate ______ + ______ = ________

⑭ 820.74 – 54.81 = ________

Estimate ______ – ______ = ________

⑮ 352.16 + 82.88 = ________

Estimate

⑯ 106.3 – 76.44 = ________

Estimate

⑰ 82.61 – 33.58 = ________

⑱ 59.64 + 128.3 = ________

Estimate

For problems that involve addition and subtraction, work out the solution from left to right.

e.g. 94.27 + 18.39 – 5.46
= 112.66 – 5.46
= 107.2

Add first; then subtract.

Find the answers.

⑲ 39.74 + 66.97 – 12.63

⑳ 40.25 – 16.71 + 85.68

㉑ 86.48 – 25.77 + 16.49 = ________

㉒ 110.7 – 22.73 + 18.9 = ________

㉓ 42.53 + 42.88 – 50.2 = ________

㉔ 66.5 + 81.94 – 29.56 = ________

㉕ 27.5 + 17.36 – 36.8 = ________

㉖ 102 – 67.5 + 17.61 = ________

Look at the table. Answer the monsters' questions.

Monster	Weight
Tony	85.76 kg
Willy	100.2 kg
Ted	98.1 kg
Leo	103.48 kg

㉗

I gained 4.65 kg; then lost 47.6 kg. How heavy am I now?

____

㉘

I lost 18.27 kg; then gained 63.4 kg. What is my weight now?

____

㉙

I gained 7.66 kg; then gained another 38.25 kg. What is my weight now?

____

㉚

I lost 4.53 kg; then lost another 46.63 kg. How heavy am I now?

____

DATE: ____________________

Day 49

Multiplication of Decimals

A decimal x 10

- Move the decimal point 1 place to the right.

e.g.
32.45 x 10 = **324.5**

A decimal x 100

- Move the decimal point 2 places to the right.

e.g.
29.7 x 100
= **2970.** ← Add zero(s) if necessary.

Find the answers mentally.

① 6.54 x 10 = 65.4
② 1.9 x 10 = 19
③ 5.01 x 100 = 501
④ 3.16 x 10 = 31.6
⑤ 4.7 x 10 = 47
⑥ 8.09 x 100 = 809
⑦ 12.3 x 100 = 1230
⑧ 2.94 x 10 = 29.4
⑨ 6.11 x 10 = 61.1
⑩ 9.7 x 100 = 970

Find the products.

The product has the same number of decimal places as the factor.

e.g.
3.87 ← 2 decimal places
x 4
15.48 ← 2 decimal places

⑪ 4.52 x 3 = 13.56

⑫ 3.8 x 9 = 34.2

⑬ 12.7 x 4 =

⑭ 15.9 x 2 =

⑮ 4.4 x 6 =

⑯ 8.5 x 7 =

⑰ 3.89 x 5 = ________
⑱ 46.75 x 8 = ________
⑲ 12.7 x 9 = ________
⑳ 33.04 x 6 = ________
㉑ 16.8 x 7 = ________
㉒ 19.27 x 4 = ________

Look at the pictures. Complete the tables.

㉓ $5.99 each

No. of Boxes	Total Weight	Total Cost
2		
5		
9		

㉔ $9.42 each

No. of Rolls	Total Length	Total Cost
3		
4		
8		

Solve the problems.

㉕ If Calvin Cat drinks 1.46 L of milk every day, how much milk does he drink in a week? ________

㉖ Ted and his 4 friends each have 46.29 g of chocolates. How much chocolate do the children have in all? ________

㉗ Each container holds 19.65 g of sunflower seeds. How many grams of sunflower seeds are there in 6 containers? ________

㉘ Each ticket costs $12.65. How much does Mr. Hall need to pay if he buys 3 tickets? ________

㉙ A slice of pizza weighs 35.92 g. How heavy do 8 slices weigh?

____

㉚ What is the thickness of a pile of 7 books?

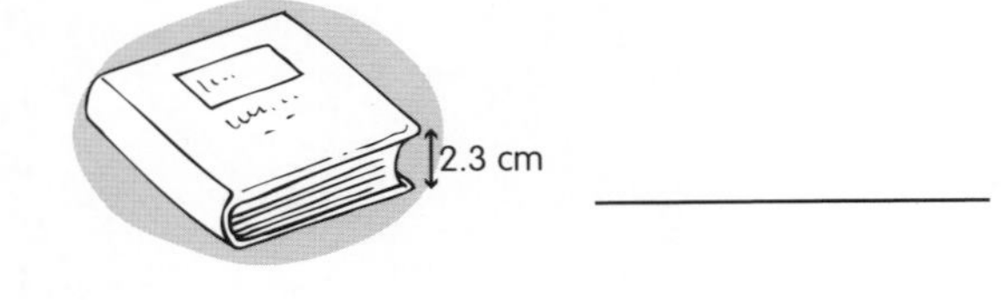

____

Did you know?

The world's ***largest bag of cookies*** *was unveiled in London, Ontario. It contained over 100 000 chocolate chip cookies and weighed about 1.54 tonnes.*

DATE: ______________

Day 50

Division of Decimals

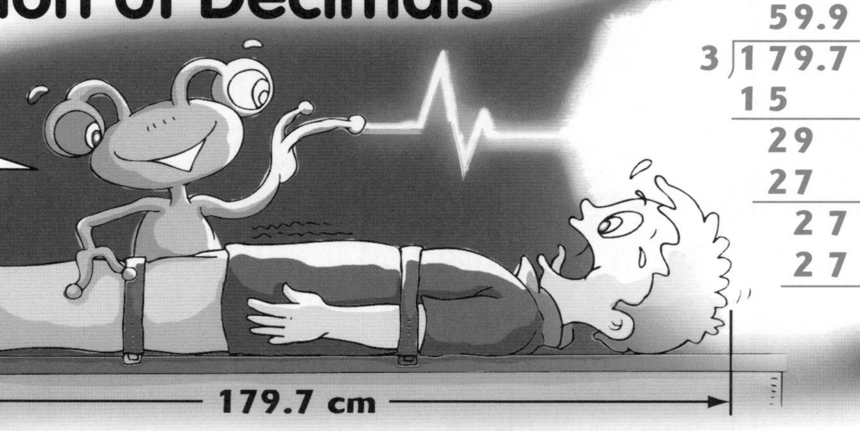

Find the answers mentally.

① 9.6 ÷ 10 = ______

② 18.5 ÷ 100 = ______

③ 9.4 ÷ 10 = ______

④ 2.45 ÷ 100 = ______

⑤ 24.1 ÷ 10 = ______

⑥ 127 ÷ 100 = ______

⑦ 6.8 ÷ 100 = ______

⑧ 25 ÷ 100 = ______

⑨ 0.63 ÷ 10 = ______

⑩ 0.3 ÷ 100 = ______

⑪ 8.6 ÷ 100 = ______

⑫ 1.77 ÷ 10 = ______

A decimal ÷ 10

- Move the decimal point 1 place to the left.

e.g. 42.5 ÷ 10 = **4.25**

A decimal ÷ 100

- Move the decimal point 2 places to the left.

e.g. 32.4 ÷ 100 = **0.324**

Add zero(s) if necessary.

4.9 ÷ 100 = **0.049**

Find the quotients.

⑬ 6) 20.52

⑭ 7) 68.6

⑮ 8.9 ÷ 5 = ______

⑯ 21.28 ÷ 4 = ______

⑰ 5.46 ÷ 7 = ______

⑱ 33.03 ÷ 9 = ______

⑲ 46.4 ÷ 4 = ______

⑳ 50.72 ÷ 8 = ______

㉑ 21 ÷ 6 = ______

㉒ 10.16 ÷ 8 = ______

㉓ 2.58 ÷ 3 = ______

㉔ 1.18 ÷ 2 = ______

Division of Decimals:

1st Divide in the same way as whole numbers.

2nd Put a decimal point in the quotient directly above the one in the dividend.

e.g. 9.4 ÷ 4 = ____

```
    2.35
 4 ) 9.40  ← Add zero(s) if necessary.
     8
     14
     12
      20
      20
```

9.4 ÷ 4 = 2.35

Round each dividend to the nearest whole number to do the estimation. Then find the exact answer.

㉕ $4 \overline{)39.68}$

Estimate

㉖ $5 \overline{)54.5}$

Estimate

㉗ $8 \overline{)96.24}$

Estimate

㉘ $7 \overline{)84.49}$

Estimate

Solve the problems.

㉙ How much is a can of soup?

______ = ______

______

㉚ How much is a box of juice?

______ = ______ ______

㉛ How much is a muffin?

______ = ______ ______

㉜ How much is a piece of chicken burger?

______ = ______ ______

㉝ If a box of chicken burgers weighs 1.26 kg, how heavy is one piece?

______ = ______ ______

DATE: ____________

Day 51

Multiplication and Division of Decimals

Juice in all

$$\begin{array}{r} 1.44 \\ \times \quad 3 \\ \hline 4.32 \end{array}$$

1.44 L

1.44 L

Each mug holds 0.54 L of fruit punch.

$$\begin{array}{r} 0.54 \\ 8 \overline{)4.32} \\ 40 \\ \hline 32 \\ 32 \\ \hline \end{array}$$

Do the multiplication and division.

① 3.94×7

② 15.3×9

③ 5.06×8

④ 44.9×3

⑤ $6 \overline{)16.2}$

⑥ $7 \overline{)16.1}$

⑦ $5 \overline{)2.35}$

⑧ $8 \overline{)9.28}$

⑨ $3.6 \times 7 =$ ________

⑩ $6.45 \div 5 =$ ________

⑪ $9.24 \div 4 =$ ________

⑫ $11.44 \div 8 =$ ________

Fill in the missing numbers.

⑬ $\square.59 \times \square = 13.77$

⑭
$$\begin{array}{r} 3.\square \\ 5 \overline{)\square 7.\square} \\ \square\square \\ \hline 2\square \\ 25 \\ \hline \end{array}$$

⑮ $1\square.8 \times \square = 1\square 6.8$

Look at the pictures. Answer the questions.

⑯

a. If each watermelon weighs the same, how heavy are 6 watermelons?

____________ = ________

____

b. If Uncle Wayne cuts a watermelon into 8 equal slices, how heavy is each slice?

____________ = ________

____

⑰

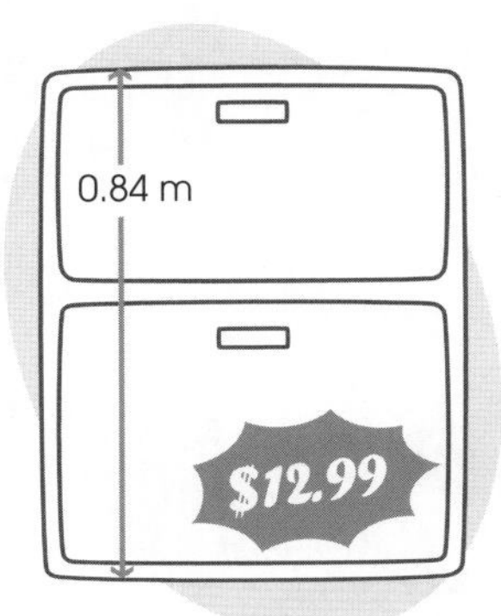

a. If Lucy and her 2 sisters buy a set of stackable drawers for their mother, how much does each girl pay on average?

____________ = ________

____

b. What is the total height of 4 sets of stackable drawers?

____________ = ________

____

⑱

a. Mrs. Hall buys 5 cartons of milk. How much milk does Mrs. Hall buy in all?

____________ = ________

____

b. Ted finishes a carton of milk in 4 days. How much milk does Ted drink every day?

____________ = ________

____

⑲

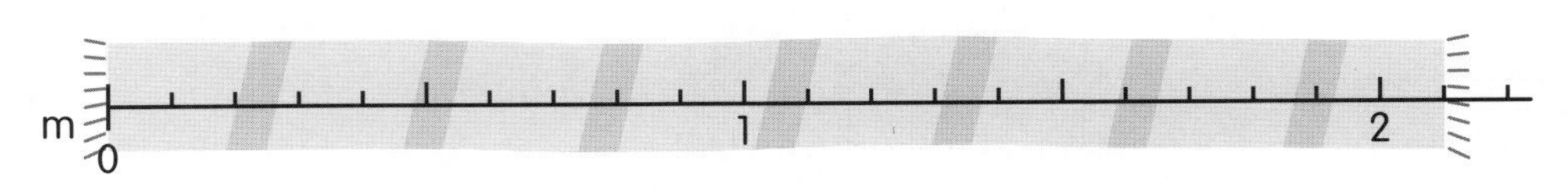

It took Mrs. Wood 7 days to weave the scarf. How much on average did she weave per day?

____________ = ________

____

The world's ***largest mug*** *weighs 3.5 tonnes. It is about 6.10 m high, with a diameter of 4.26 m.*

DATE: ____________

Day 52

Money (1)

Estimate the amount of money in each group. Then find the exact amount.

①

A Estimate: __________
Exact: __________

B Estimate: __________
Exact: __________

C Estimate: __________
Exact: __________

D Estimate: __________
Exact: __________

E Estimate: __________
Exact: __________

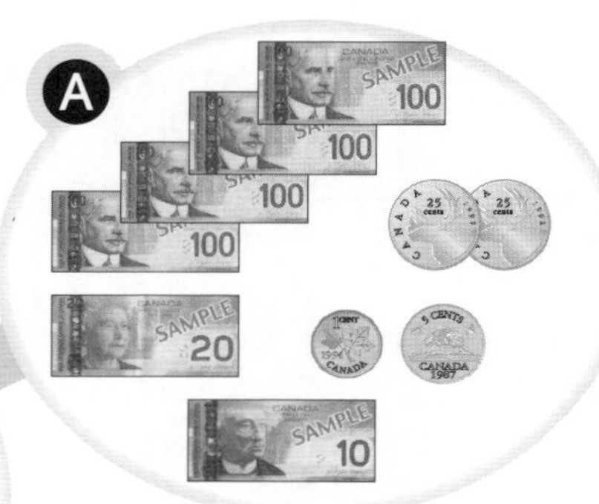

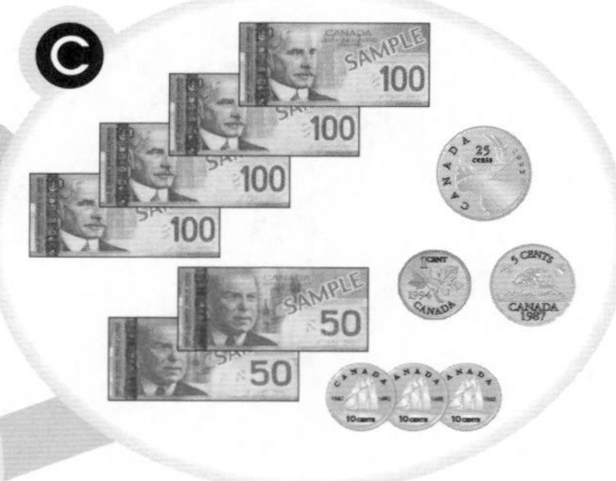

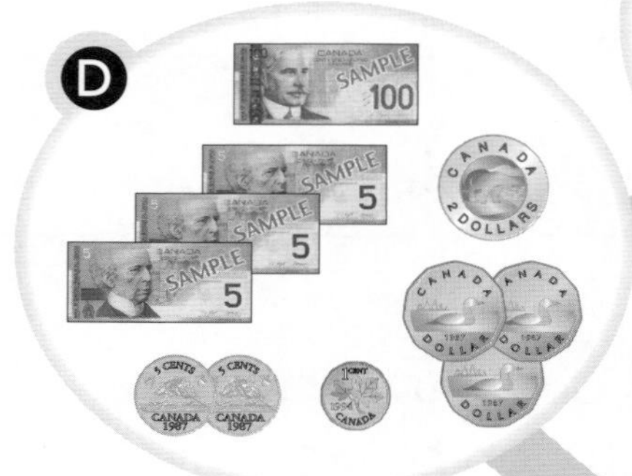

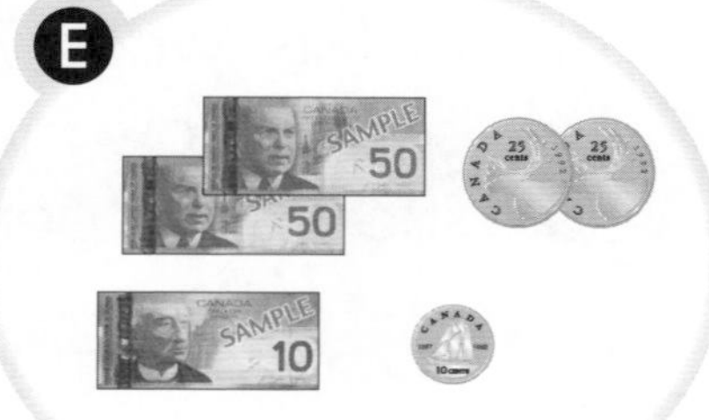

Write the amount in words. Then draw the fewest bills and coins to match the amount.

= $50

= $20

= $10

= $5

= $2

= $1

= 25¢

= 10¢

= 5¢

= 1¢

② $385.49: ____________________

③ $276.08: ____________________

④ $403.62: ____________________

⑤ $819.34: ____________________

Look at the price of each item. Put the items in order from most expensive to cheapest. Then answer the question.

⑥ In order: ________ , ________ , ________ , ________ , ________

⑦ What is the price difference between the most expensive item and the cheapest one?

____

DATE: ____________________

REVIEW

Add or subtract. Show your work. Write the answers in simplest form.

① $\frac{4}{9} + \frac{5}{9} =$

② $\frac{1}{8} + \frac{1}{8} =$

③ $\frac{6}{7} - \frac{1}{7} =$

④ $1 - \frac{7}{12} =$

⑤ $\frac{11}{15} - \frac{5}{15} =$

⑥ $\frac{9}{10} + \frac{7}{10} =$

Put the fractions in order from least to greatest.

⑦ $\frac{4}{6}$ $\frac{7}{18}$ $\frac{1}{3}$

____

⑧ $\frac{3}{5}$ $\frac{11}{15}$ $\frac{2}{3}$

____

⑨ $\frac{1}{4}$ $\frac{5}{12}$ $\frac{2}{6}$

____

Put '<' or '>' in the circles.

⑩ 2.46 ◯ 2.64

⑪ 1.09 ◯ 0.9

⑫ $\frac{41}{100}$ ◯ 0.4

⑬ $\frac{27}{100}$ ◯ 2.7

⑭ 3 tenths ◯ 27 hundredths

⑮ 1 tenth ◯ 15 hundredths

Find the answers.

⑯ 4.73 + 6.59 = ________

⑰ 18.9 – 2.44 = ________

⑱ 13.29 + 57.06 = ________

⑲ 51.81 – 33.77 = ________

⑳ 18.63 x 9 = ________

㉑ 17.04 ÷ 6 = ________

㉒ 264.6 ÷ 7 = ________

㉓ 25.78 x 8 = ________

㉔ 51.03 x 5 = ________

㉕ 170.4 ÷ 4 = ________

Draw the fewest bills and coins to show the given amount in each group.

$100 $50 $20 $10 $5 $2 $1 25¢ 10¢ 5¢ 1¢

㉖ $275.45

㉗ $486.83

Solve the problems. Write the answers in simplest form.

㉘ Jessica has a 1-kg bag of chocolate eggs. If she gives $\frac{1}{8}$ kg to James, how many kilograms of chocolate eggs will she have left?

_______________ = ________ ________

㉙ Each box of crackers weighs $\frac{8}{9}$ kg. If Anita buys 2 boxes of crackers, how many kilograms of crackers will she have in all?

_______________ = ________ ________

Look at the pictures. Answer the questions.

㉚

a. Mrs. Hall buys 6 bottles of detergent. How much does she need to pay? ________

b. If Mr. Wood has a bottle of detergent and uses 0.27 L, how much detergent is left? ________

㉛

a. A big bag of cookies costs $1.27 more than a box of cookies. How much does a big bag of cookies cost? ________

b. Jack buys a box of cookies and divides them equally into 3 groups. How much does each group of cookies weigh? ________

DATE: ____________________

Day 54

You Deserve A Break!

$1\frac{2}{3}$

23.83

$\frac{1}{5}$

4 hundredths

0.21

112.91

$\frac{1}{2}$

122.91

$\frac{3}{5}$

128.45

0.09

0.08

4 tenths

The picture contains answers to the questions below. Find and colour the sections with the answers to reveal the hidden animal.

① $\frac{5}{12} + \frac{1}{12}$ = Yellow

② $1 - \frac{4}{10}$ = Red

③ $\frac{5}{8} + \frac{7}{8}$ = Green

④ $\frac{7}{15} - \frac{1}{15}$ = Yellow

⑤ $115.68 - 2.77$ = Red

⑥ $9.88 + 29.75$ = Green

⑦ $17.58 \div 2$ = Yellow

⑧ 3.97×6 = Red

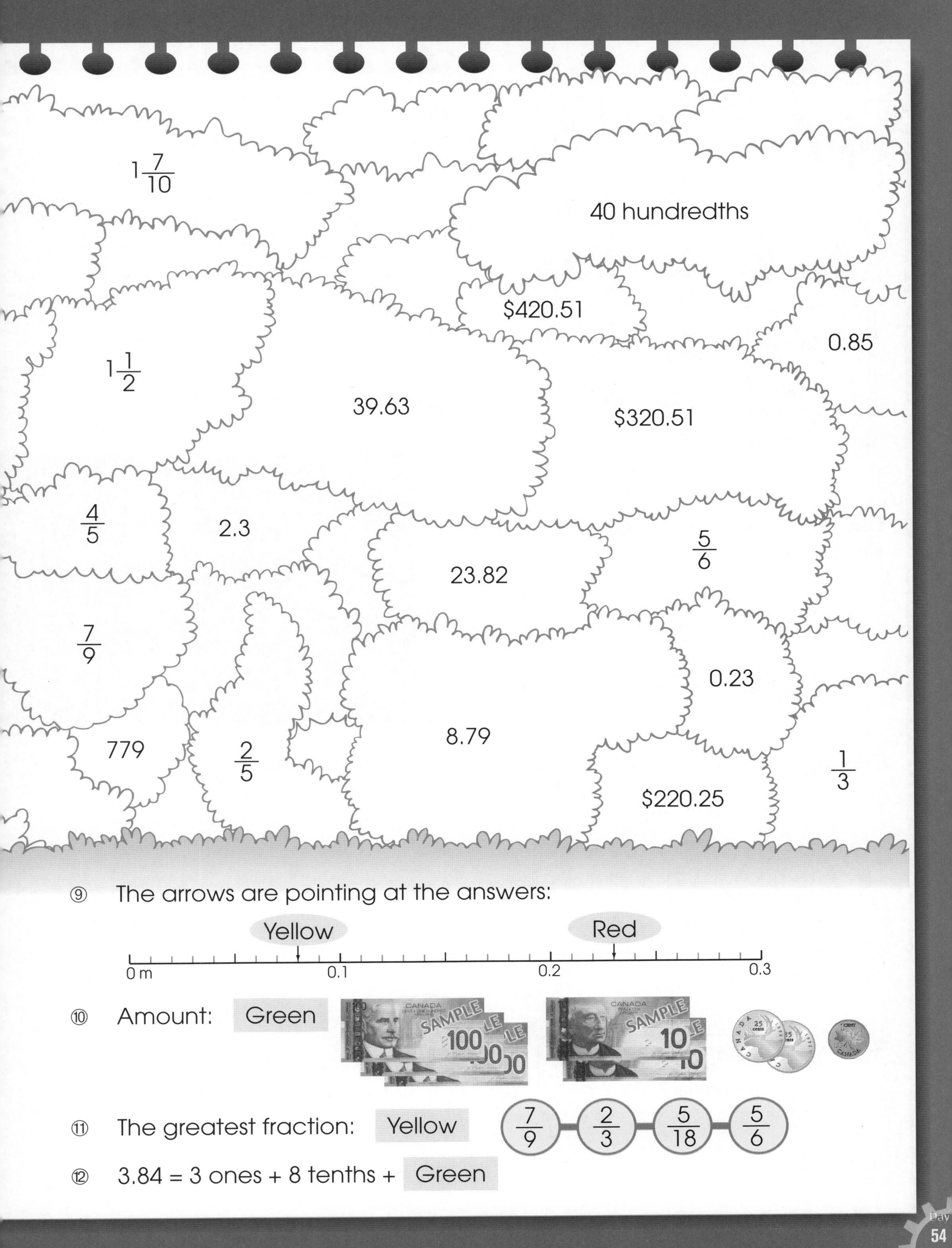

⑨ The arrows are pointing at the answers:

⑩ Amount: Green

⑪ The greatest fraction: Yellow

$\frac{7}{9}$ $\frac{2}{3}$ $\frac{5}{18}$ $\frac{5}{6}$

⑫ 3.84 = 3 ones + 8 tenths + Green

DATE: ______

Money (2)

When you add or subtract decimals, remember to align the decimal points.

e.g. $43.29 + $108.78 = ____

$$\begin{array}{r} \$\ \ 43.29 \\ +\ \$108.78 \\ \hline \$152.07 \end{array}$$

Align the decimal points.

$43.29 + $108.78 = <u>$152.07</u>

Find the total cost of each group. Then answer the questions.

①

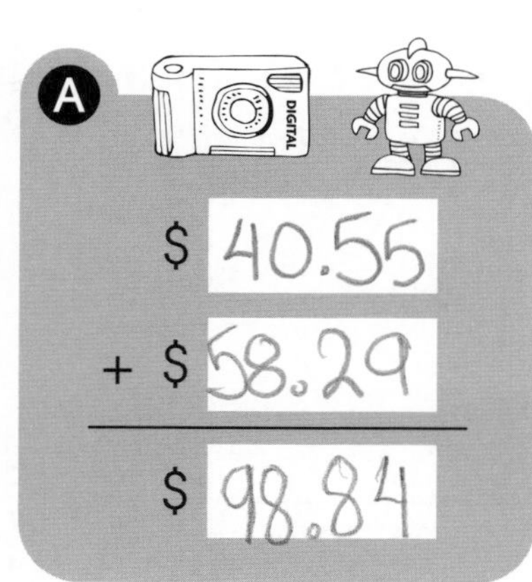

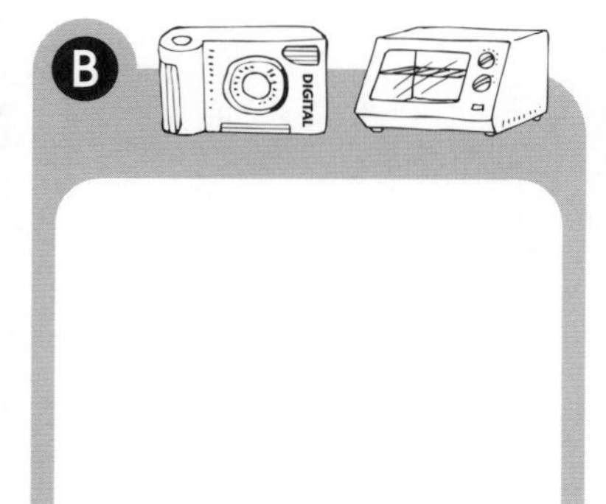

② *If I pay for A with a $100 bill, what is the change?*

______

③ *If I have $80 only, how much more do I need to buy C?*

______

Read the clues. Find and write the price of each item on the price tag. Then answer the questions.

④ • A gorilla costs   .

• A bear costs $9.86 less than a gorilla.

• A cat costs $12.74 less than a bear.

• A giraffe costs $8.16 more than a cat.

⑤ Lucy pays for a bear with a $50 bill. What is her change?

____

⑥ How much do a cat and a gorilla cost in all?

____

⑦ If Uncle Louis buys 2 bears, how much does he need to pay?

____

⑧ If the shopkeeper reduces the price of a giraffe by $8.88, how much does it cost now?

____

Day 56

DATE: ____________________

2-D Shapes

Didn't you see me having a walk?

Hexagon
6 vertices, 6 sides

Square
4 vertices, 4 sides

Rectangle
4 vertices, 4 sides

Trapezoid
4 vertices, 4 sides

Triangle
3 vertices, 3 sides

Name each shape. Then write the number of vertices and sides of each shape.

Polygon:
a flat shape with 3 or more sides

e.g. A rectangle is a polygon.

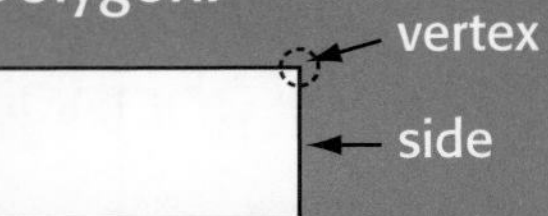

A rectangle has 4 vertices and 4 sides.

① square
4 vertices
4 sides

②
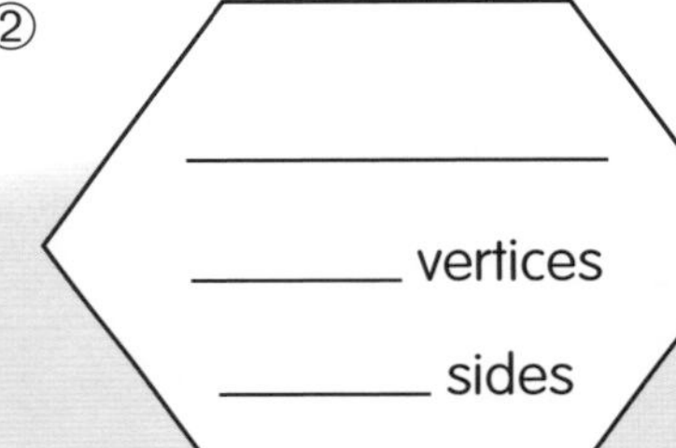
____ vertices
____ sides

③
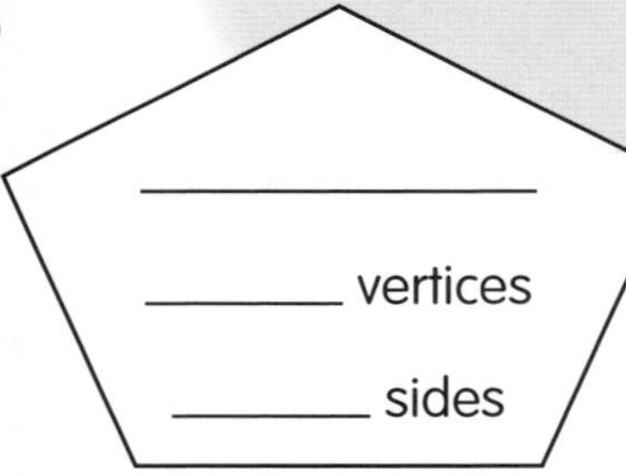
____ vertices
____ sides

④
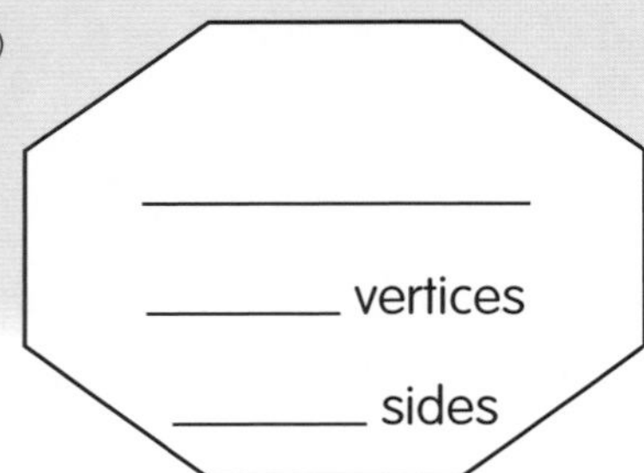
____ vertices
____ sides

⑤
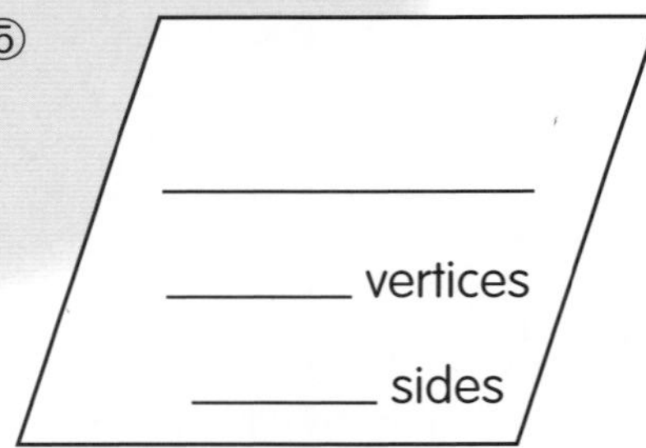
____ vertices
____ sides

Which shapes are quadrilaterals? Check the correct letters.

⑥
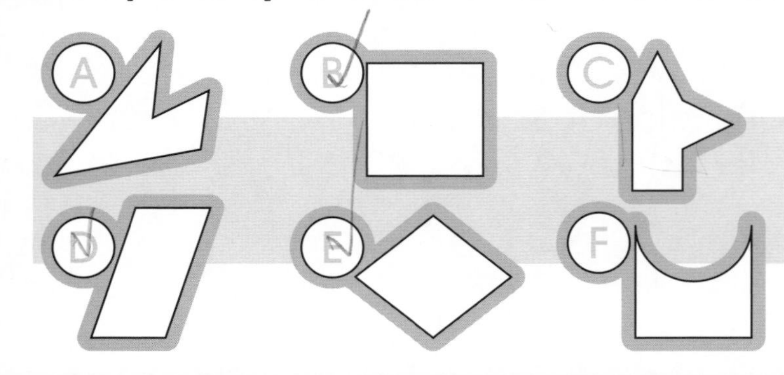

Quadrilateral:
a polygon that has 4 straight sides

e.g. 

A rectangle is a quadrilateral.

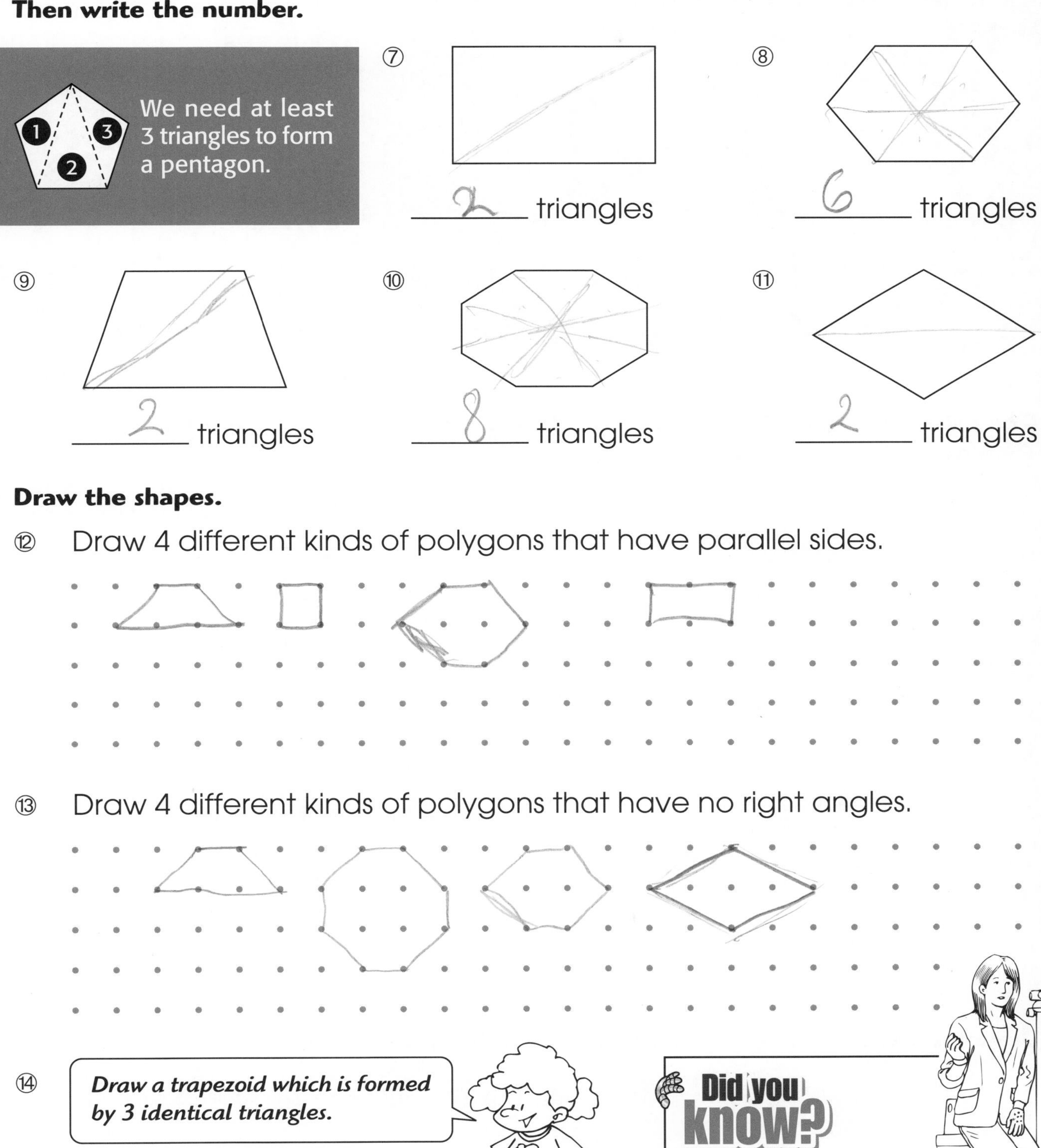

Draw lines to show the minimum number of triangles needed to form each shape. Then write the number.

We need at least 3 triangles to form a pentagon.

⑦ 2 triangles

⑧ 6 triangles

⑨ 2 triangles

⑩ 8 triangles

⑪ 2 triangles

Draw the shapes.

⑫ Draw 4 different kinds of polygons that have parallel sides.

⑬ Draw 4 different kinds of polygons that have no right angles.

⑭ *Draw a trapezoid which is formed by 3 identical triangles.*

Did you know?

An ultra-life like **robot** was introduced at the 2005 World Expo in Japan. Repliee Q_1 has 42 actuators in her upper body so that she moves and even appears to breathe like a human.

DATE: ______________

Lines of Symmetry

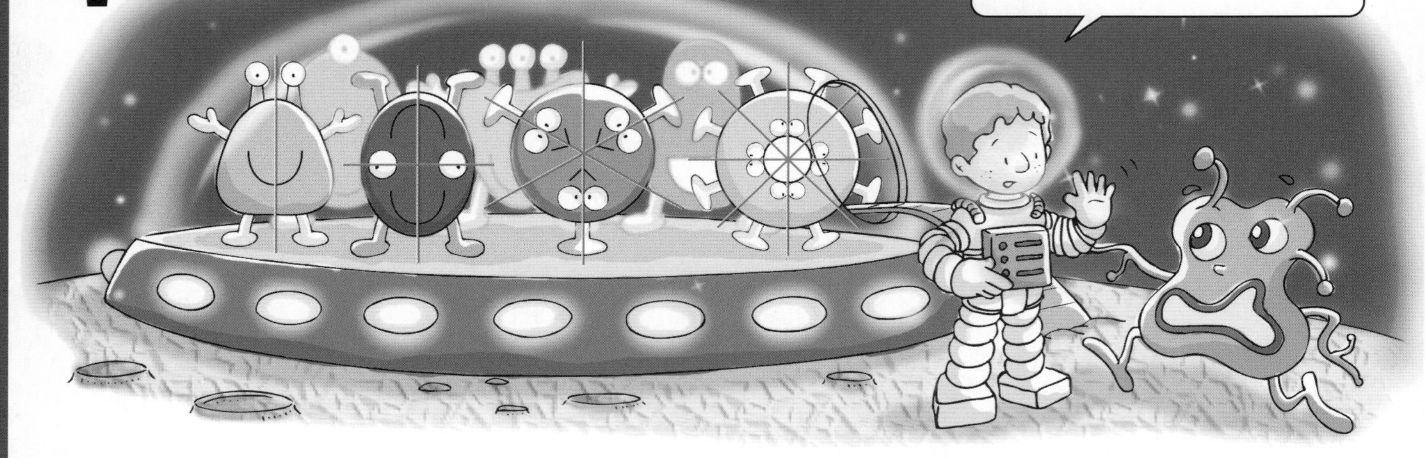

Draw the missing parts on each alien to match the number of lines of symmetry. Then draw the lines of symmetry.

① It has 4 lines of symmetry.

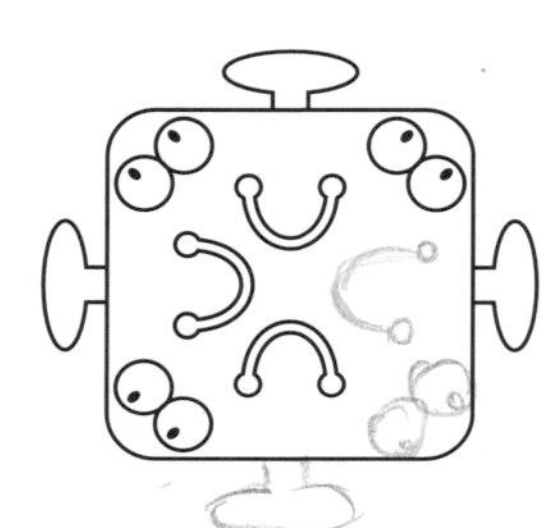

② It has 6 lines of symmetry.

③ It has 2 lines of symmetry.

④ It has 1 line of symmetry.

Draw the triangles with the given number of lines of symmetry.

⑤ No lines of symmetry

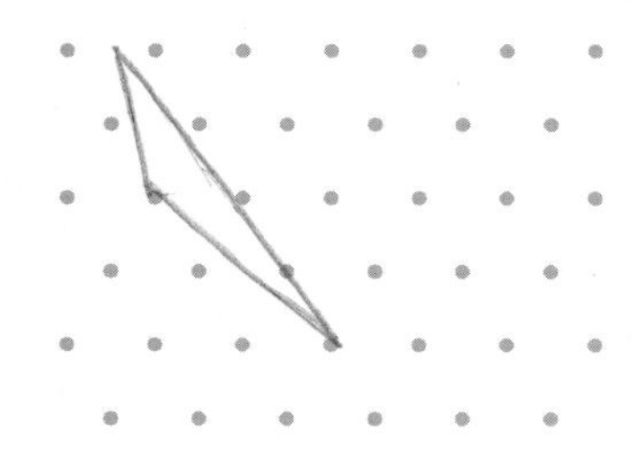

⑥ 1 line of symmetry

⑦ 3 lines of symmetry

Sort the shapes by the number of lines of symmetry. Write the letters.

⑧

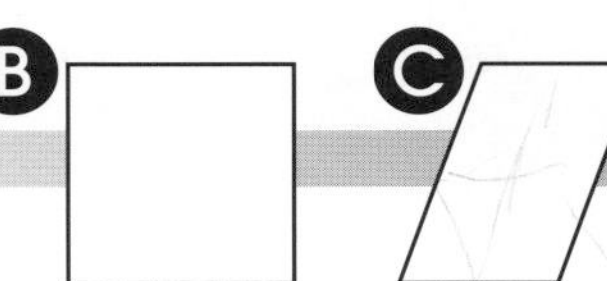
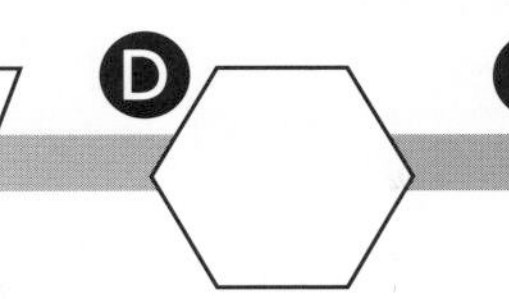
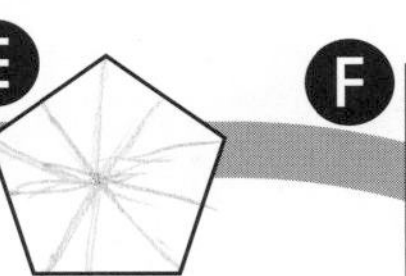

a. No lines of symmetry: ________

b. One line of symmetry: ________

c. Two lines of symmetry: ________

d. Three lines of symmetry: ________

e. More than three lines of symmetry: ________

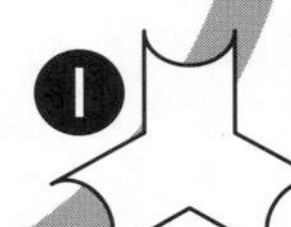

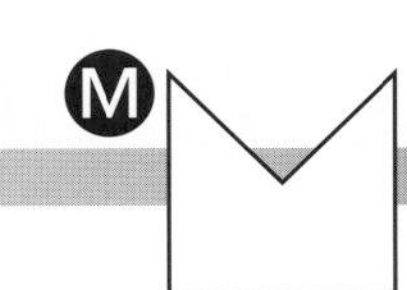
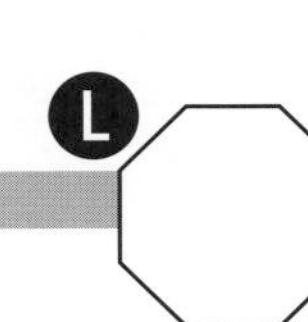

Draw from the lines of symmetry to complete the letters to find out the names of the aliens.

⑨

Draw a line of symmetry for each province or territory flag if it has any.

⑩

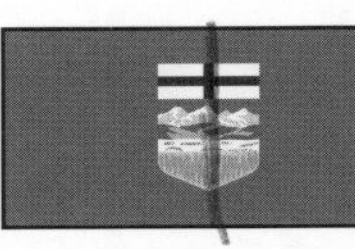

DATE: ____________________

Day 58

Tile Patterns

Draw lines to show the tile patterns.

①

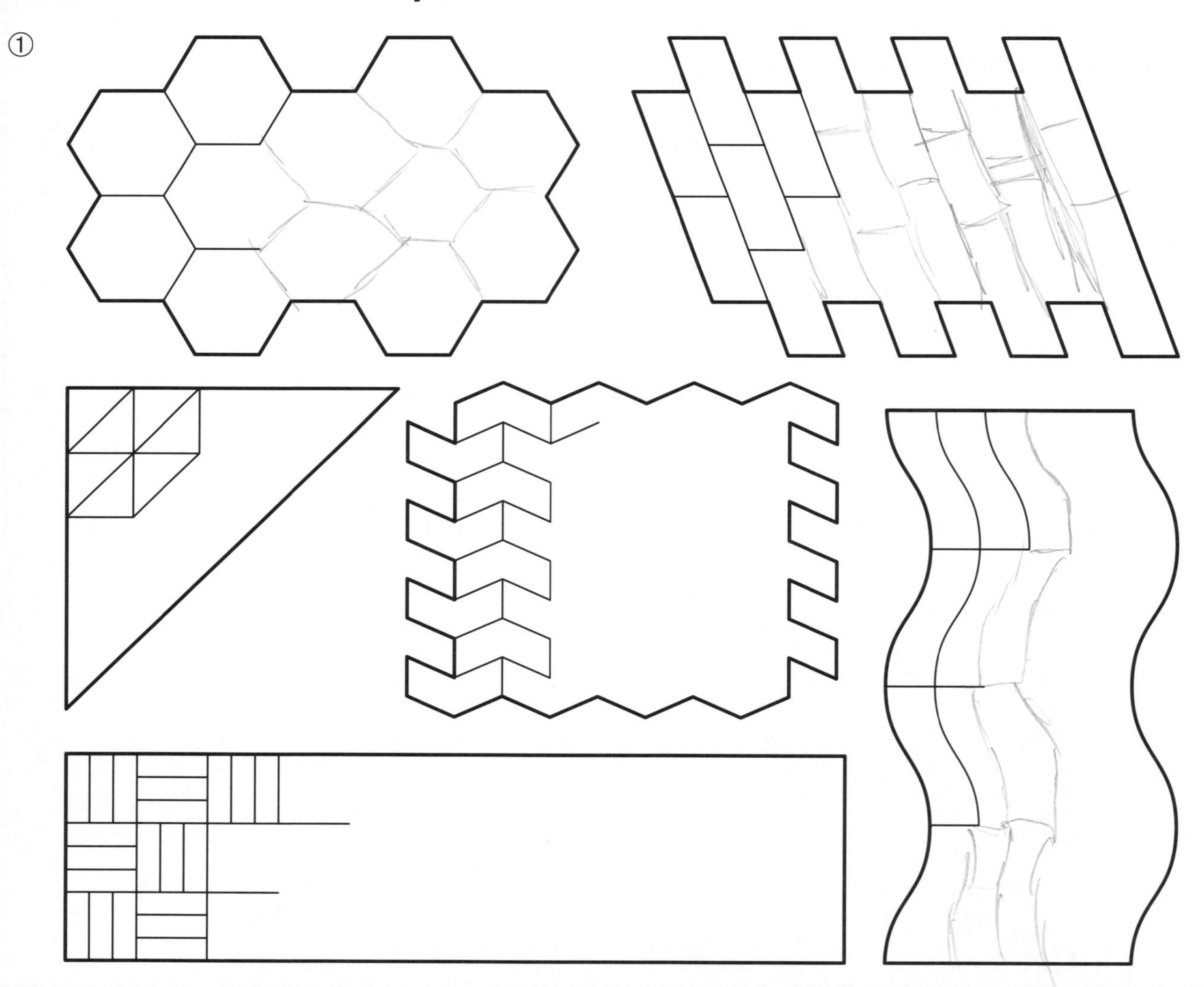

Trace the shapes with tracing paper. Then cut out the shapes to trace them on paper to test which shapes can form a tessellation. Check the shapes that can form tessellations.

②

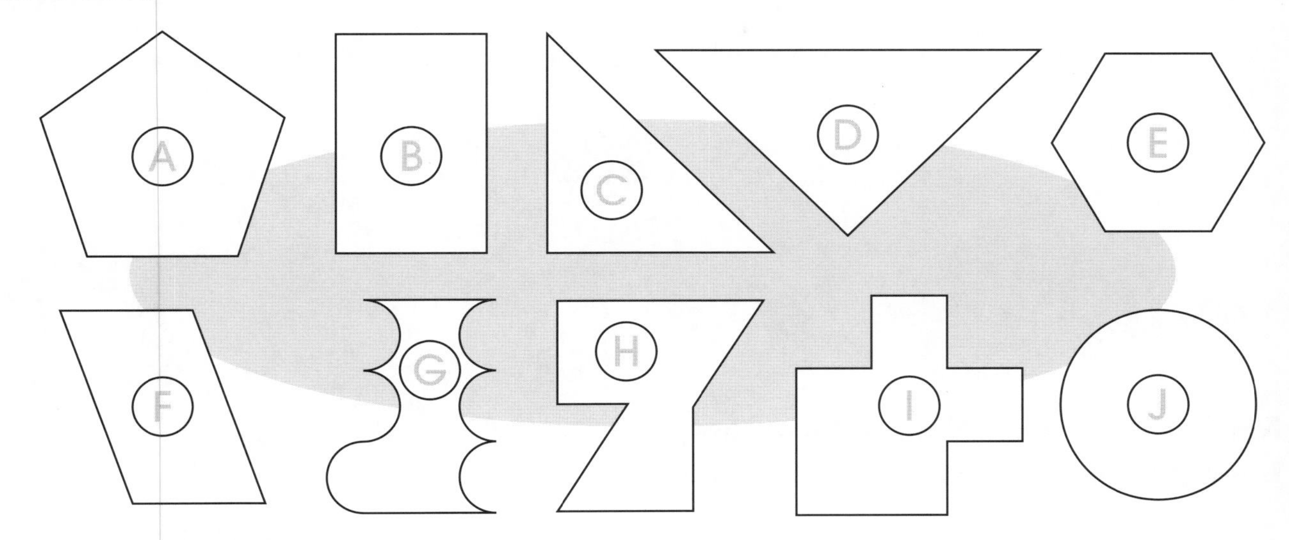

Name the shapes used in each pattern. Then complete the patterns.

③

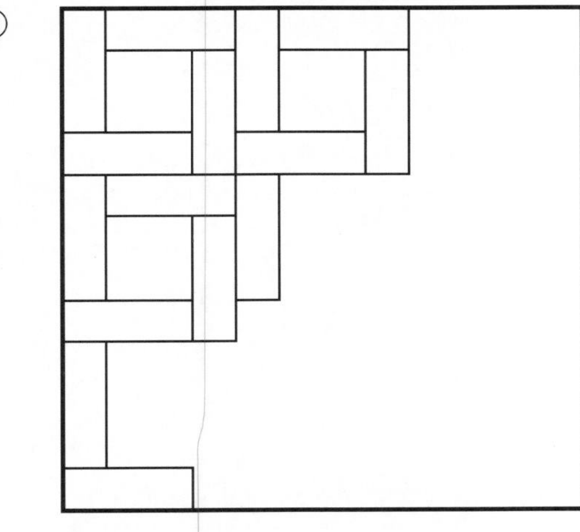

④

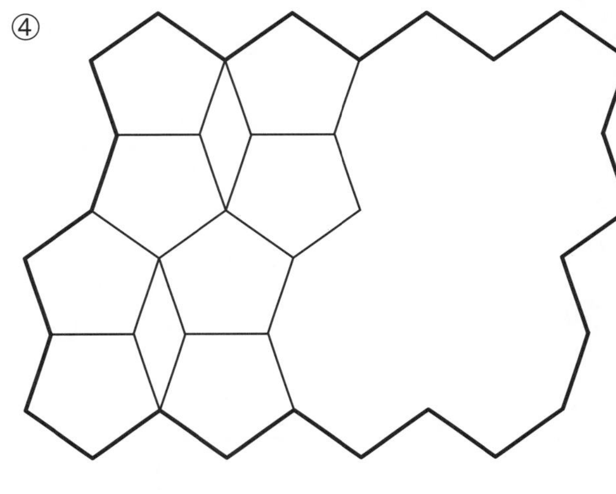

______________ ; ______________

______________ ; ______________

Use the same tile to create two other designs which are different from the given one.

⑤

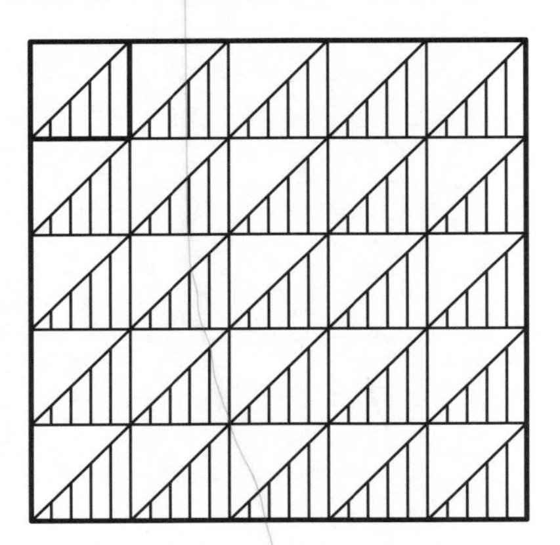

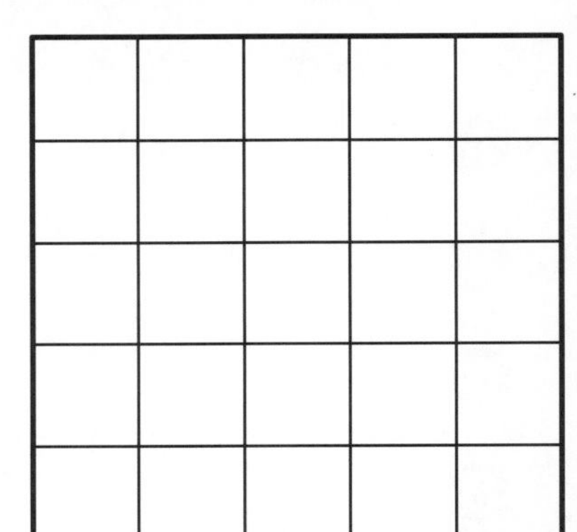

DATE: ____________________

Day 59

Sorting Angles

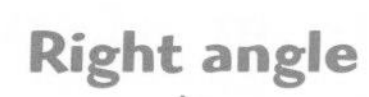

Name each angle. Then tell whether it is a right, an acute, or an obtuse angle.

①

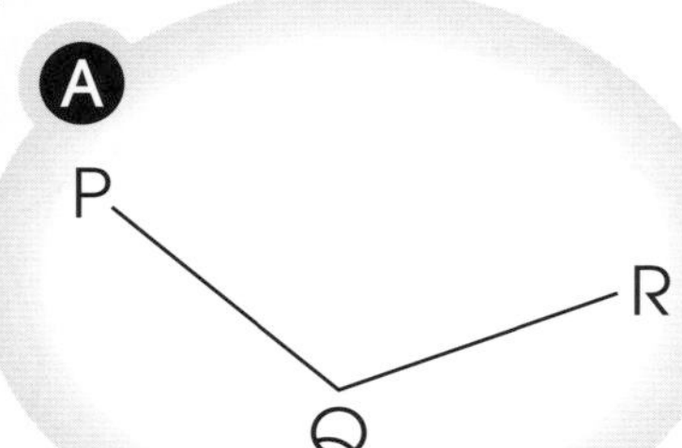

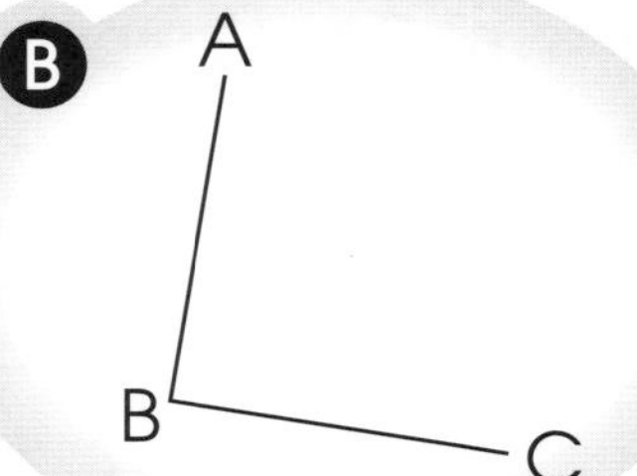

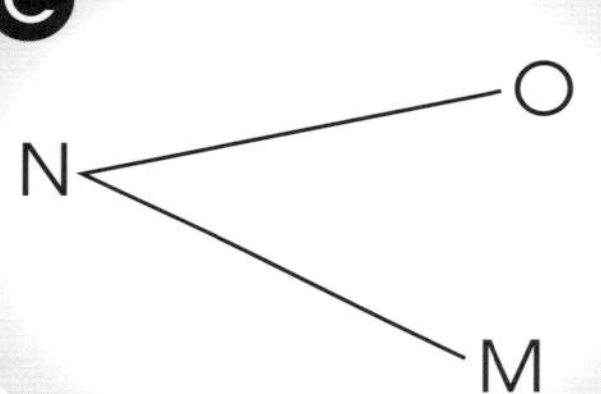

D
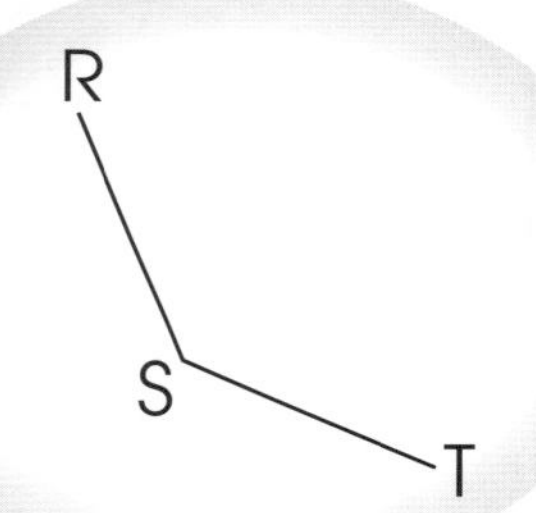

	Name	Type
A	or	
B		
C		
D		

Naming an angle:

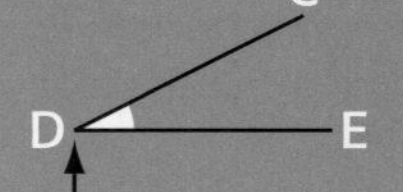

D is the vertex of the angle.

∠CDE or ∠EDC

Type of angle:

Acute angle:
an angle smaller than 90°
e.g.

Right angle:
an angle of 90°
e.g.

Obtuse angle:
an angle greater than 90°
e.g.

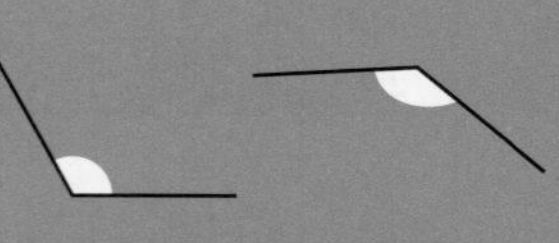

Sort the tools by their angles. Then circle the greatest ones for the groups of 'Acute Angle' and 'Obtuse Angle'.

②

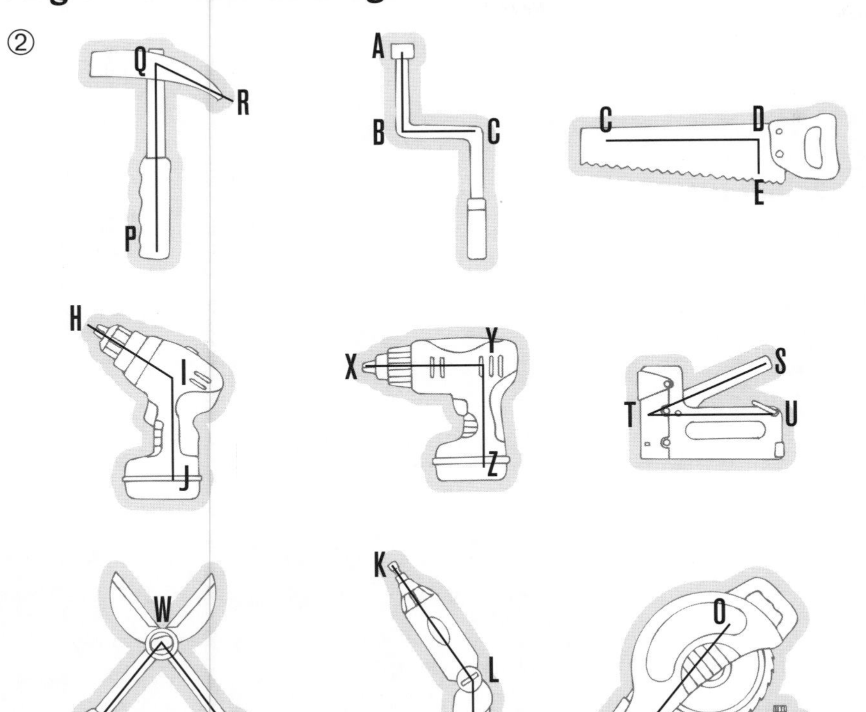

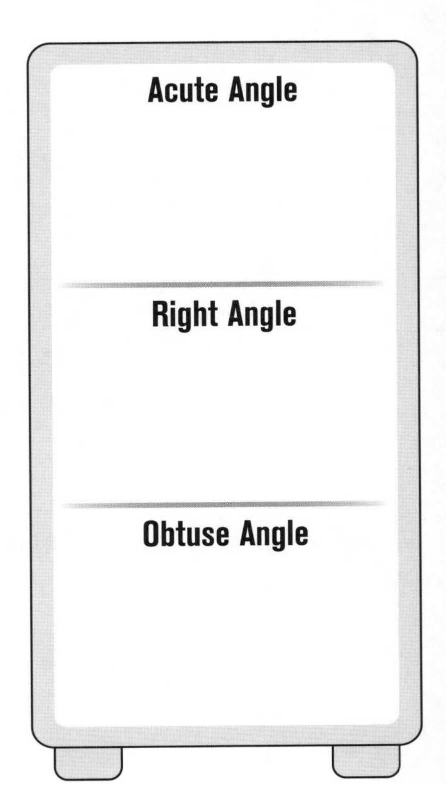

Put the labelled angles in order. Then draw an angle which is greater than all the angles in each group and name it.

③ A B C P Q R L M N

In order: ________ > ________ > ________

④ A B C D P Q R S L M N O

In order: ________ > ________ > ________

DATE:

Reading and Measuring Angles

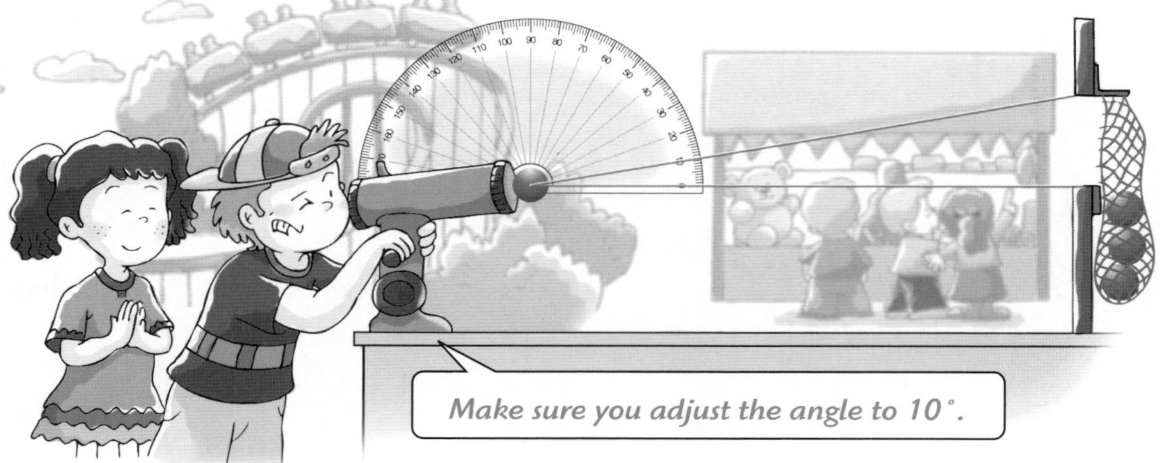

Measure the angles. Write the answers in the circles.

Measuring angles with a protractor:

Look at the numbers on both scales. If the angle is acute, use the smaller number. If it is obtuse, use the larger number.

e.g.

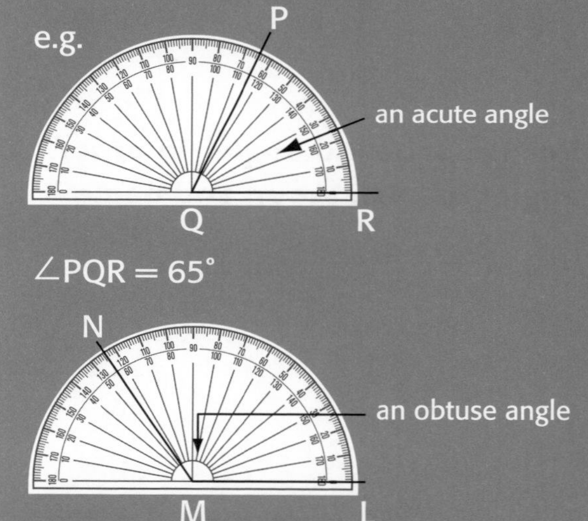

①

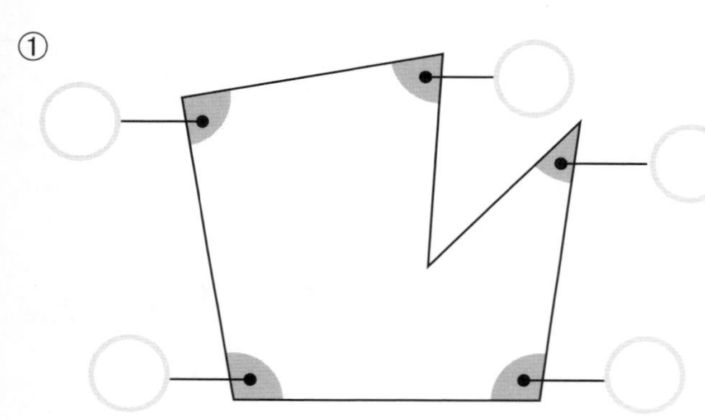

②

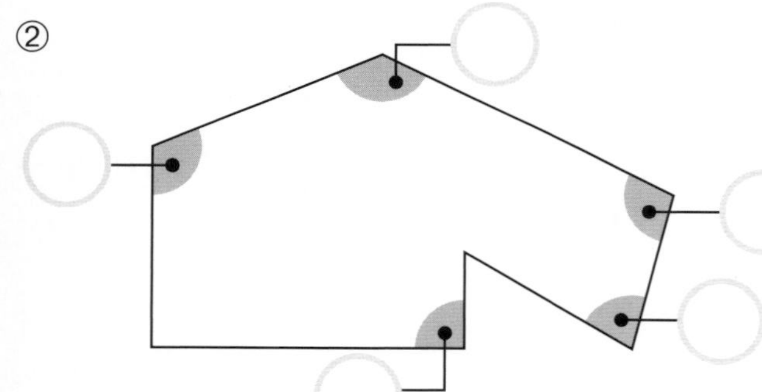

③

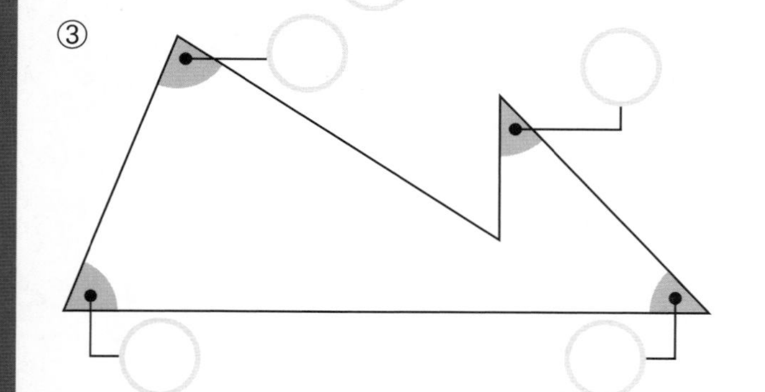

④

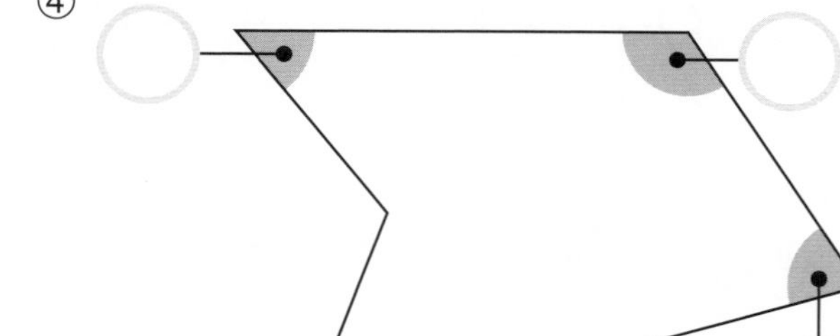

Look at the pictures. Check the correct answers.

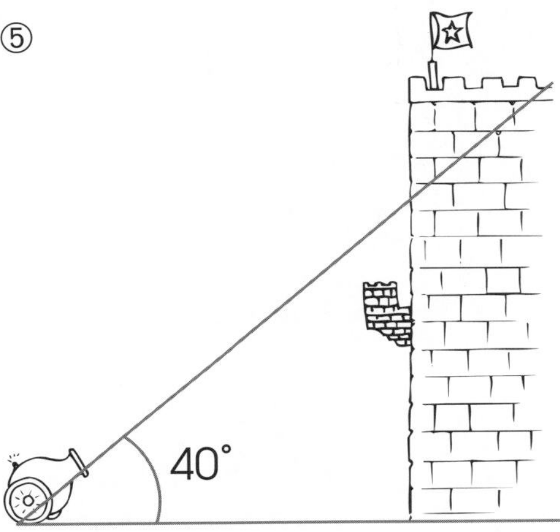

a. If Pirate Sam wants to hit the flag, how should he adjust the angle of the cannon?

Ⓐ To 50° Ⓑ To 40° Ⓒ To 15°

b. If Sergant Tim wants to hit the balcony, how should he adjust the angle of the cannon?

Ⓐ To 90° Ⓑ To 30° Ⓒ To 150°

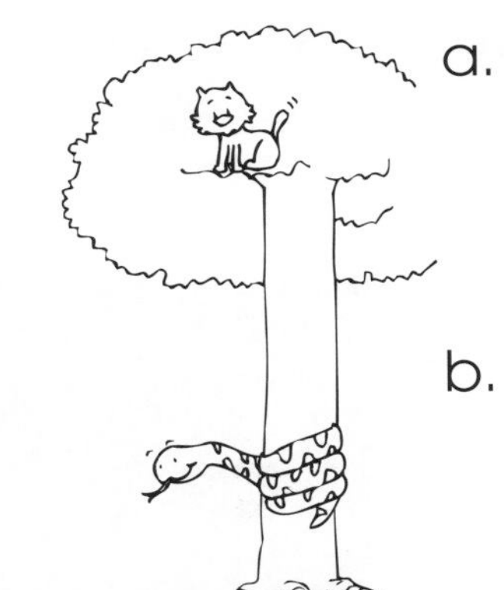

a. If Toby Dog wants to look at the animal at 40°, which animal will it be?

Ⓐ Bird Ⓑ Snake Ⓒ Cat

b. If Toby Dog wants to look at the animal at 75°, which animal will it be?

Ⓐ Bird Ⓑ Snake Ⓒ Cat

Find the angles in each triangle. Then find the sum of the angles for each triangle and fill in the blank to complete what Toby Dog says.

⑦

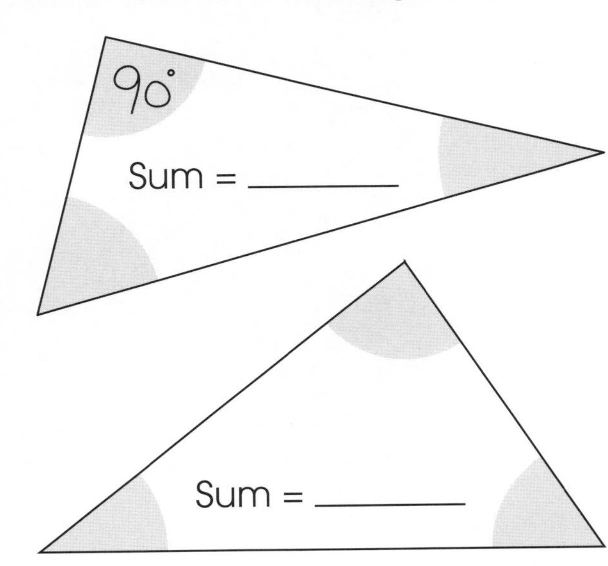

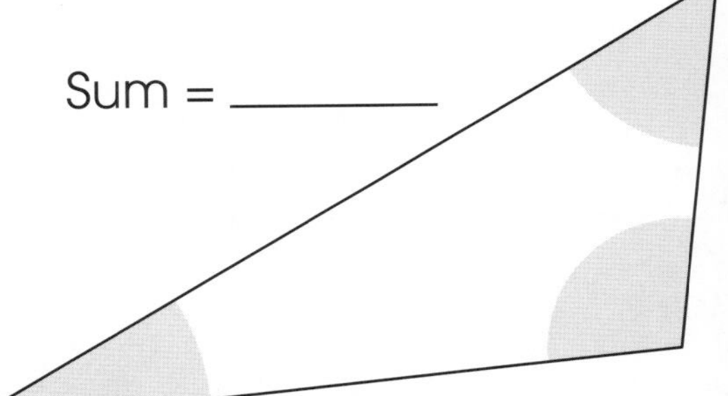

Sum = ________

The sum of the angles of a triangle is always ________ .

DATE: ______________________

Constructing Angles

George, bring the ladder and make an angle of 65° to rescue the boy up there!

Construct the angles.

① $\angle PQR = 68°$ $\angle KLM = 120°$
$\angle WXY = 45°$ $\angle ABC = 155°$
$\angle JKL = 102°$ $\angle STU = 24°$

Steps to construct angles using a protractor:

1st Draw a line and mark one end as the vertex.

2nd Put the protractor on the vertex and 0° on the line.

3rd Mark the angle to be constructed.

4th Remove the protractor and draw a line from the vertex to the point marked.

e.g. Construct $\angle ABC = 35°$.

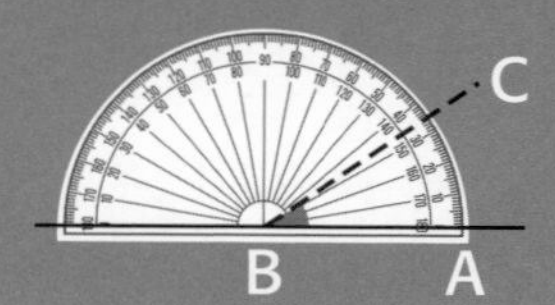

P ———— Q

W ———— X

S ———— T

A ———— B

Draw the hour hand to match the angle formed by the given minute hand and the drawn hour hand. Then tell the time.

②

____

③

____

Measure and record each given angle in the circle. Then draw the angle as instructed.

④

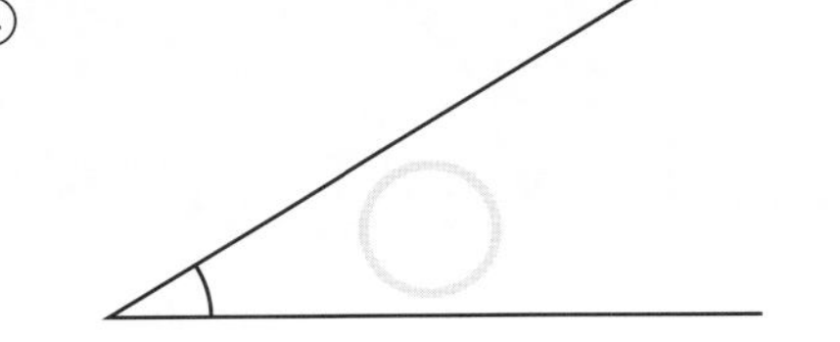

Draw an angle 30° greater than the given one.

⑤

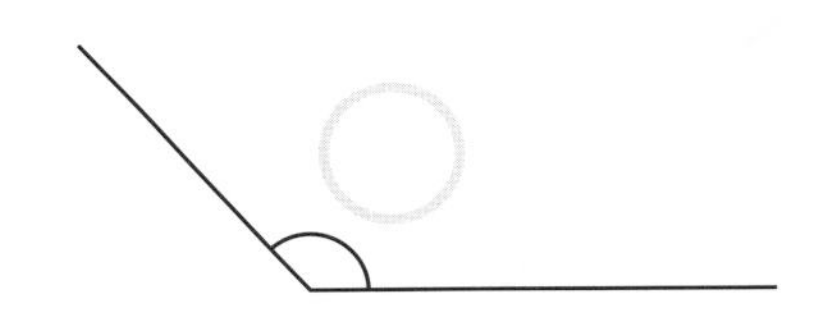

Draw an angle 45° less than the given one.

⑥

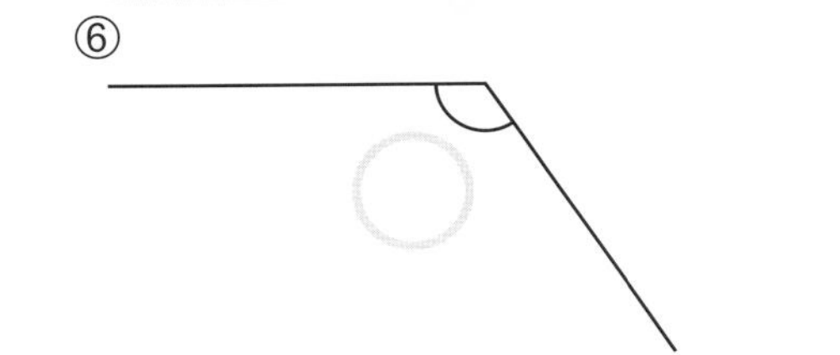

Draw an angle identical to the given one.

Construct a triangle with angles 60°, 60°, and 60°.

⑦

Did you know?

OXYGEN HEAT FUEL

The **fire triangle** is a simple model that illustrates the three key elements for ignition: heat, fuel, and oxygen.

DATE: ____________________

Day 62

Classifying Triangles

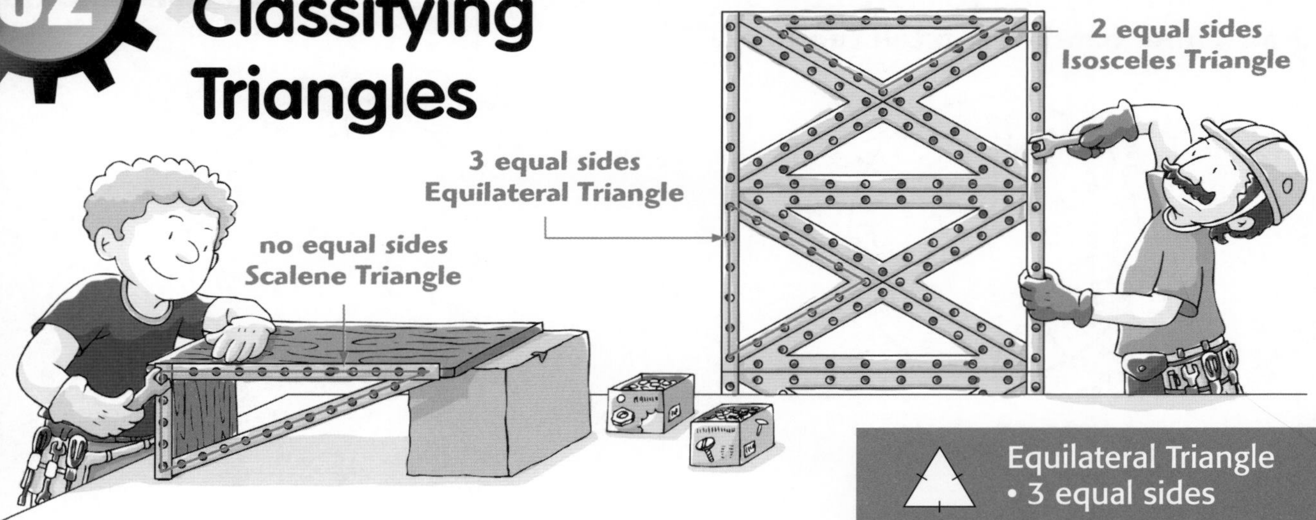

2 equal sides
Isosceles Triangle

3 equal sides
Equilateral Triangle

no equal sides
Scalene Triangle

Equilateral Triangle
• 3 equal sides

Isosceles Triangle
• 2 equal sides

Scalene Triangle
• no equal sides

Use a ruler to measure and record the sides of the triangles. Then name the triangles.

① ___ cm, ___ cm, ___ cm

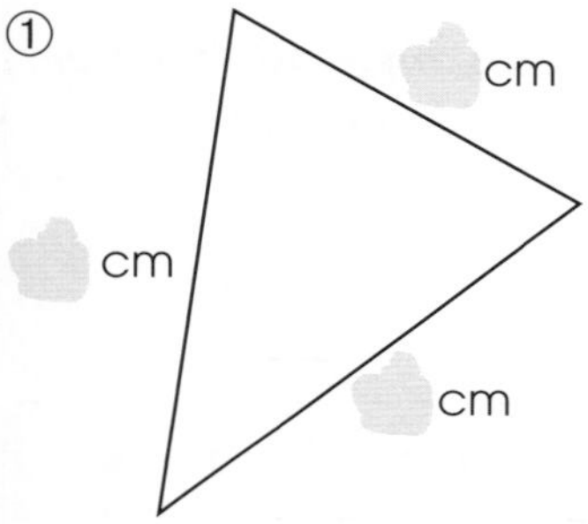

__________ triangle

② ___ cm, ___ cm, ___ cm

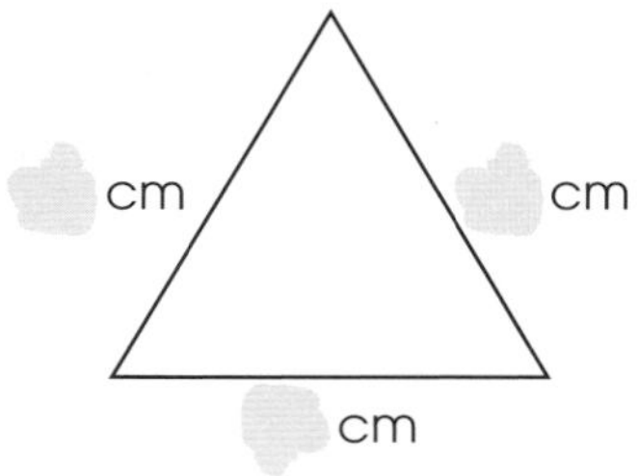

__________ triangle

③ ___ cm, ___ cm, ___ cm

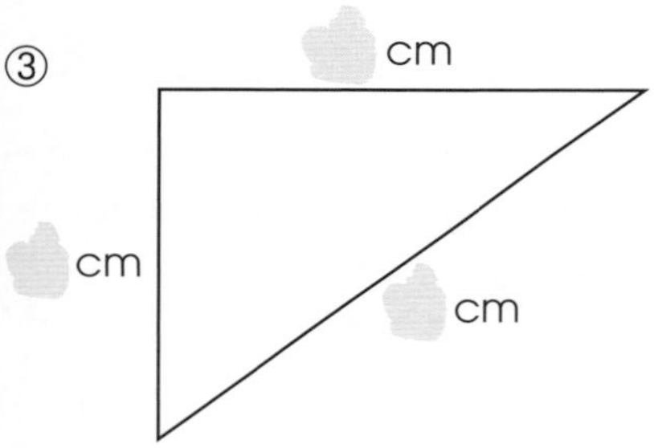

__________ triangle

④ ___ cm, ___ cm, ___ cm

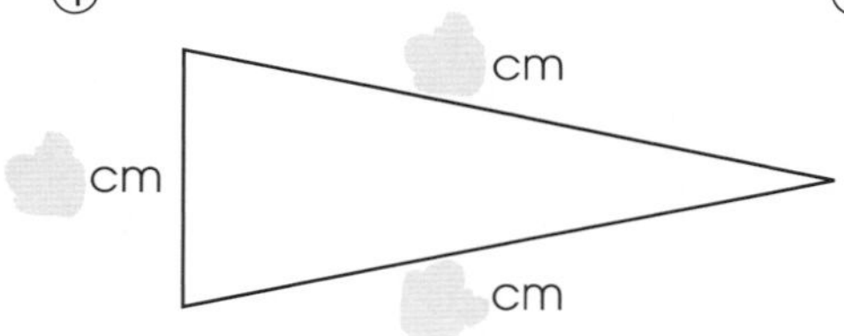

__________ triangle

⑤ ___ mm, ___ mm, ___ mm

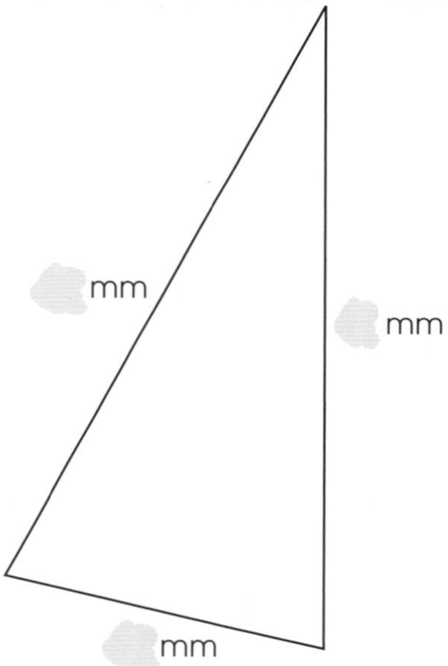

__________ triangle

Draw an equilateral triangle, an isosceles triangle, and a scalene triangle on the grid. Then label each triangle with its name.

⑥

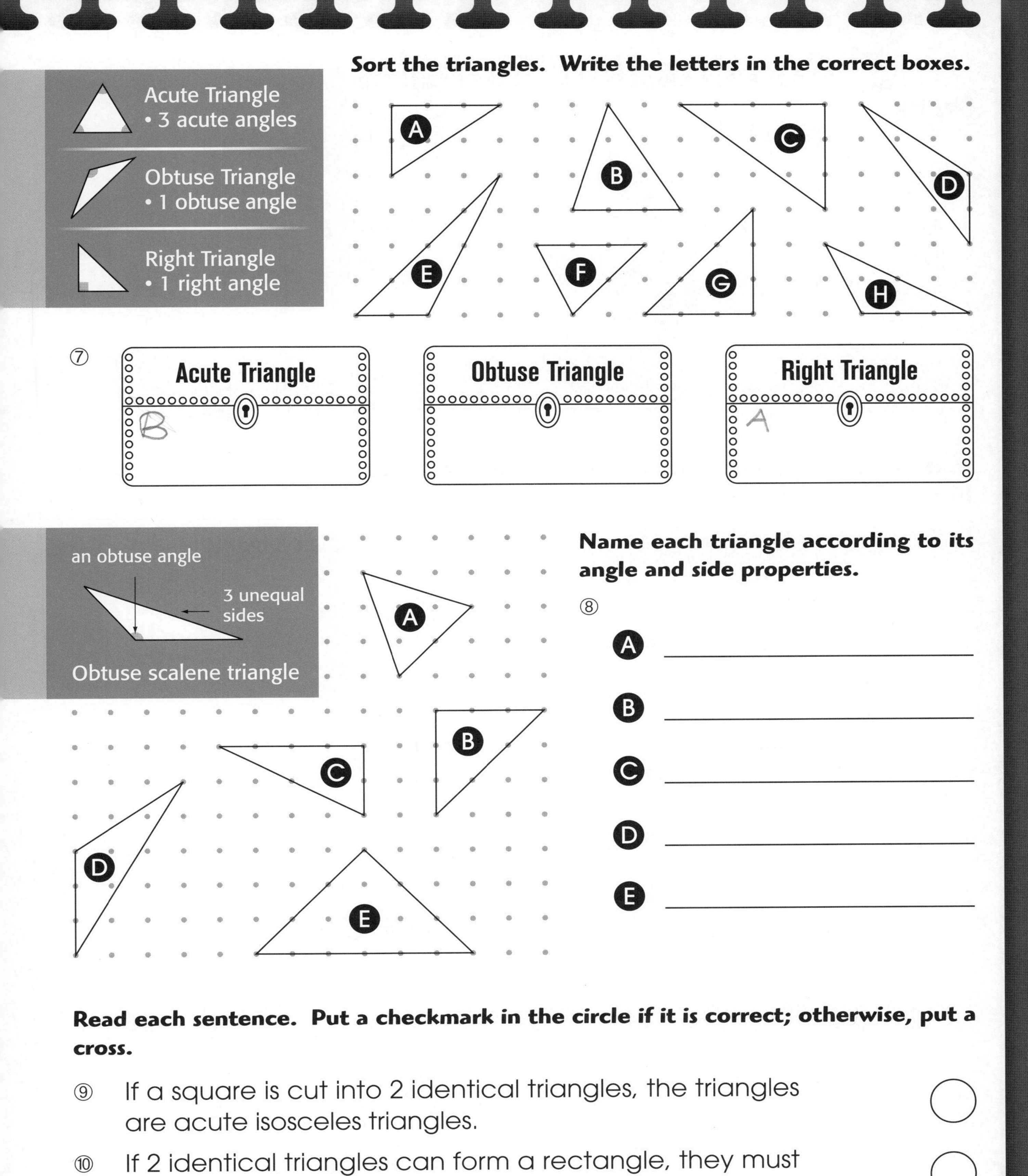

Sort the triangles. Write the letters in the correct boxes.

⑦ Acute Triangle | Obtuse Triangle | Right Triangle

Name each triangle according to its angle and side properties.

⑧

A ____________________

B ____________________

C ____________________

D ____________________

E ____________________

Read each sentence. Put a checkmark in the circle if it is correct; otherwise, put a cross.

⑨ If a square is cut into 2 identical triangles, the triangles are acute isosceles triangles. ◯

⑩ If 2 identical triangles can form a rectangle, they must be right scalene triangles. ◯

⑪ Two obtuse isosceles triangles can form a rhombus. ◯

DATE:

Day 63

Constructing Triangles

Draw the triangles and write the length beside each side. Then measure and record the angles of each triangle.

① A right scalene triangle

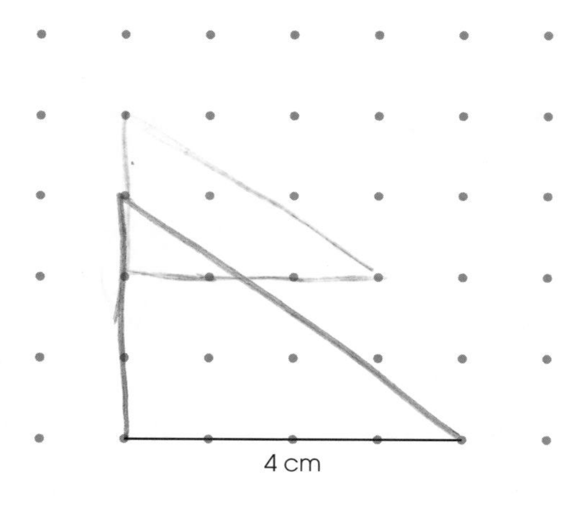

② A right isosceles triangle

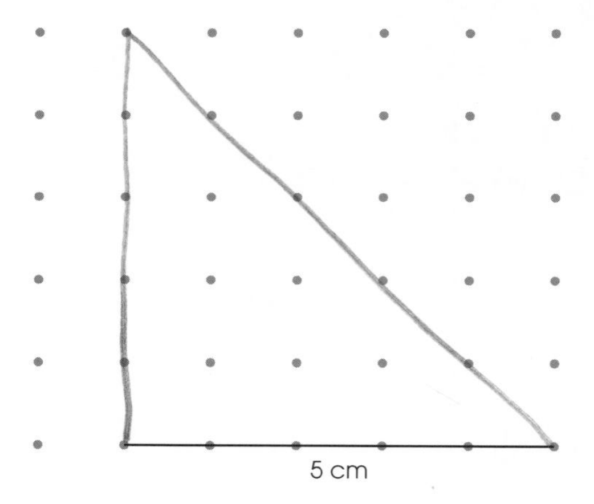

③ An obtuse scalene triangle

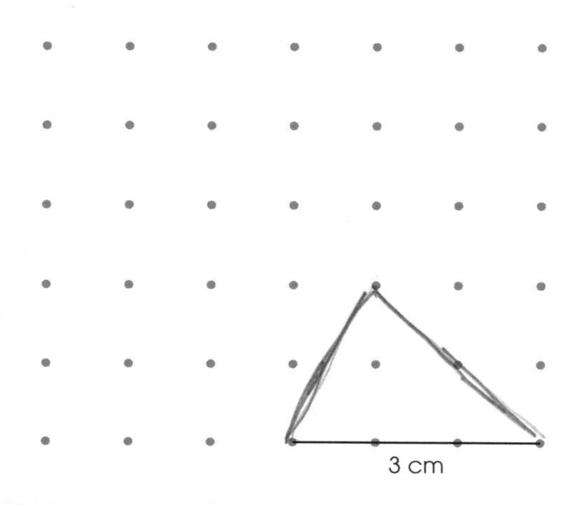

④ An obtuse isosceles triangle

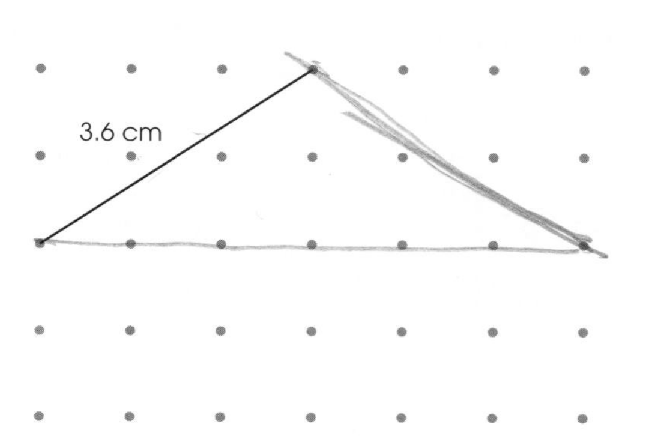

Each monster has a triangular face. Follow the instructions to draw their faces. Then fill in the blanks.

⑤ **Melissa Monster**

- Draw a horizontal line segment AB = 6 cm.
- Construct an angle of 45° at A and an angle of 45° at B.
- Extend the two lines until they meet at a point.
- Name the point C.

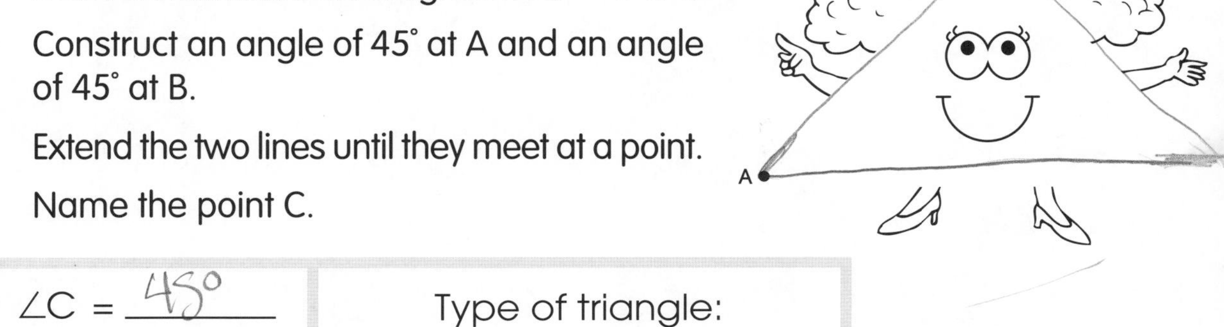

∠C = 45°	Type of triangle:
AC = 3cm	Right ________ triangle
BC = 3cm	

⑥ **Tiffany Monster**

- Draw a vertical line segment AB = 4 cm.
- Construct an angle of 70° at A and an angle of 60° at B.
- Extend the two lines until they meet at a point.
- Name the point C.

∠C = ________	Type of triangle:
AC = ________	
BC = ________	

Draw a triangle to match the description. Then name it.

⑦
- one angle of 30°
- one 4-cm side

DATE: ____________________

Day 64

Sorting 3-D Figures

Join the dots to complete the 3-D figures. Then sort the figures.

①

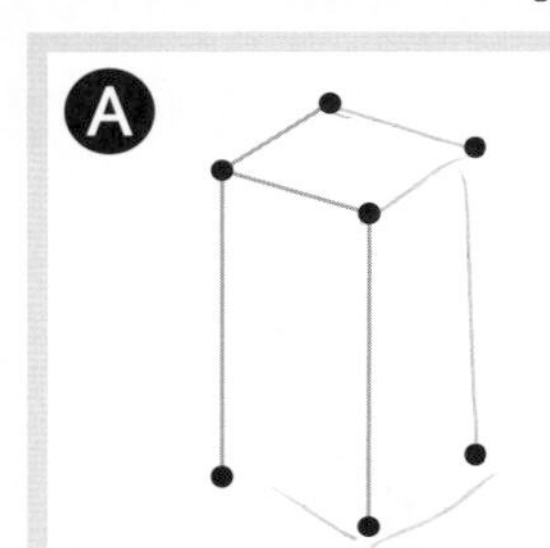

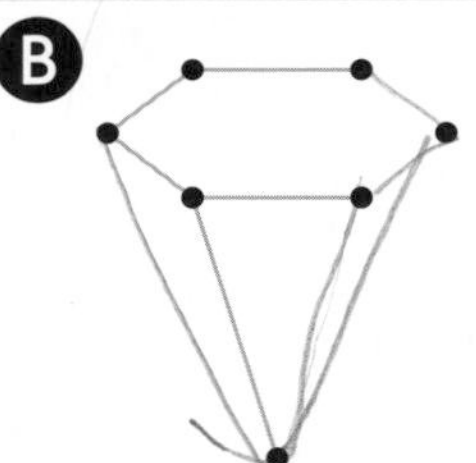

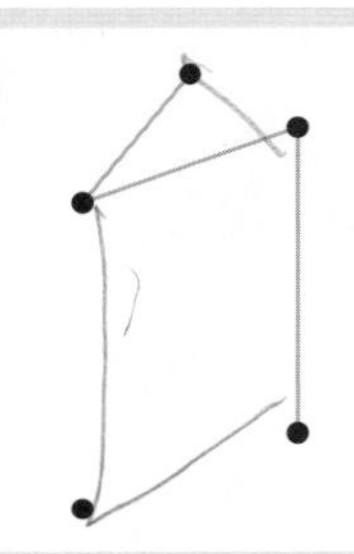

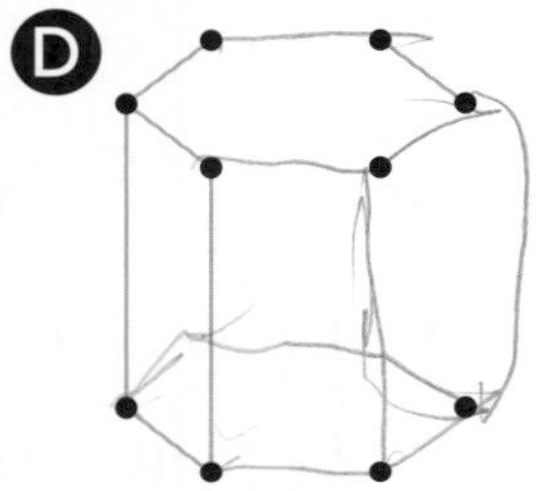

② With triangular faces: ____________________

Without triangular faces: ____________________

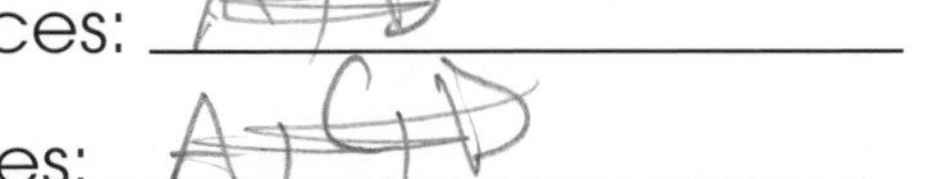

③ With rectangular faces: ____________________

Without rectangular faces: ____________________

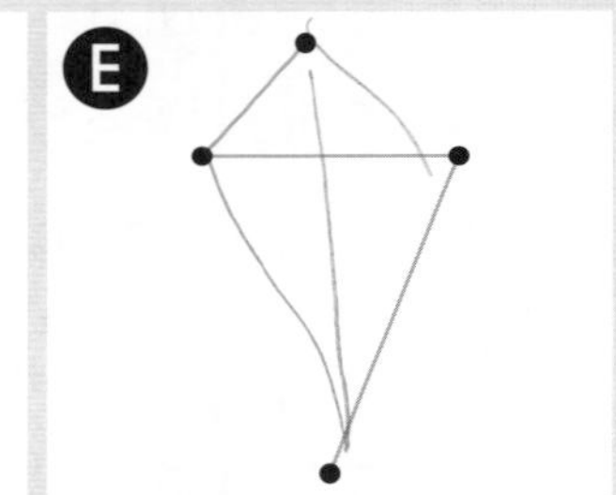

④ Can roll: ____________________

Cannot roll: ____________________

⑤ Can be stacked up: ____________________

Cannot be stacked up: ____________________

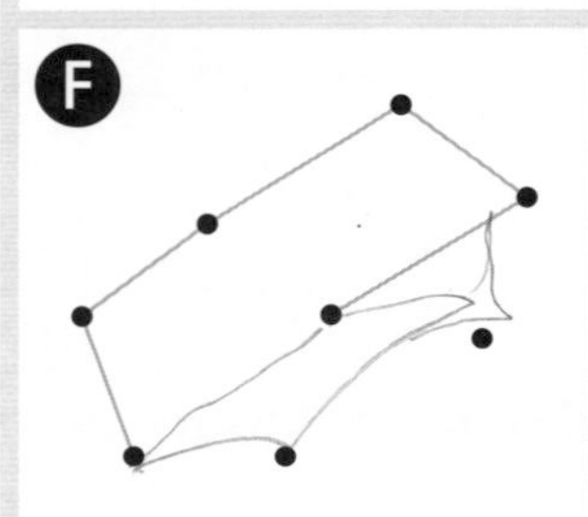

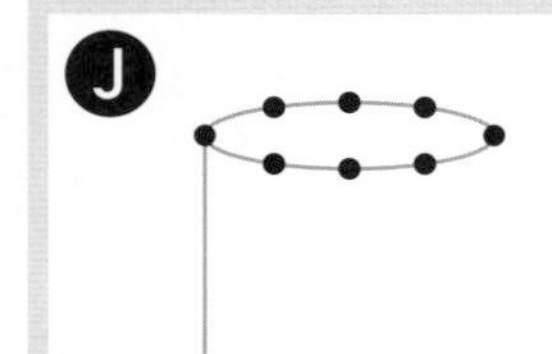

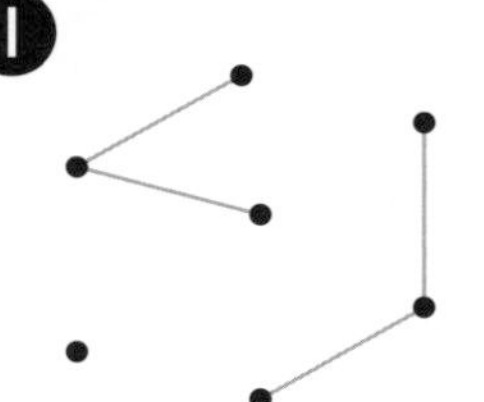

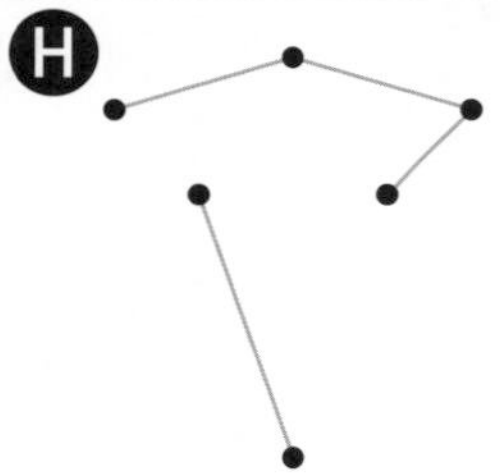

Which two 3-D figures can you see in each model? Name the 3-D figures. Then find a common thing in each group of models.

⑥ a.

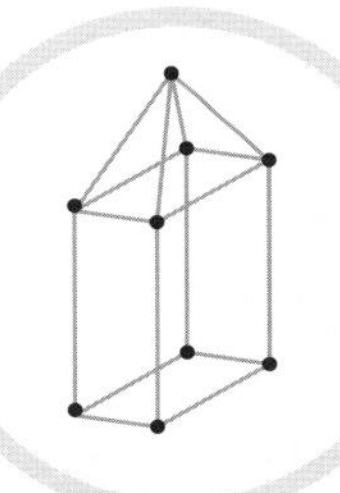

b.

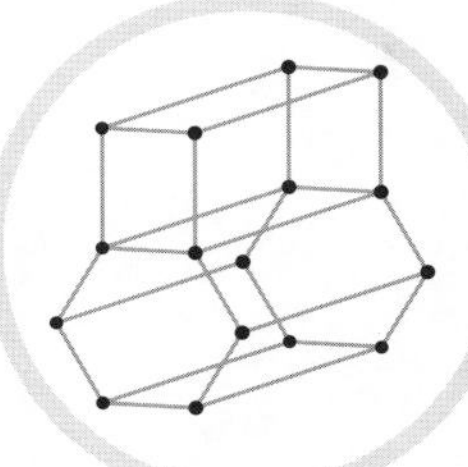

c.

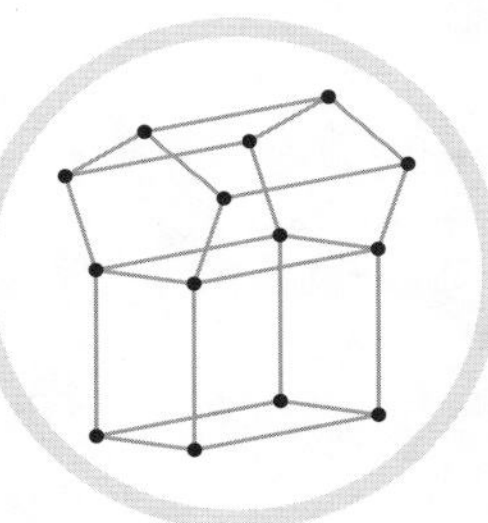

______________ ______________ ______________

______________ ______________ ______________

d. Thing in common: ______________

⑦ a.

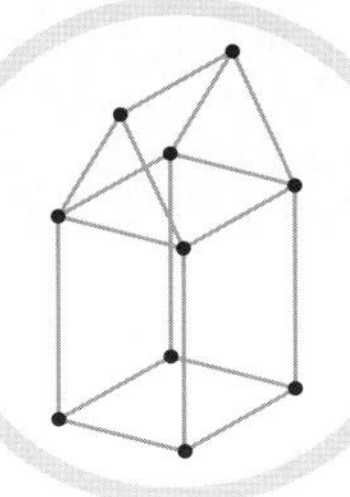

b.

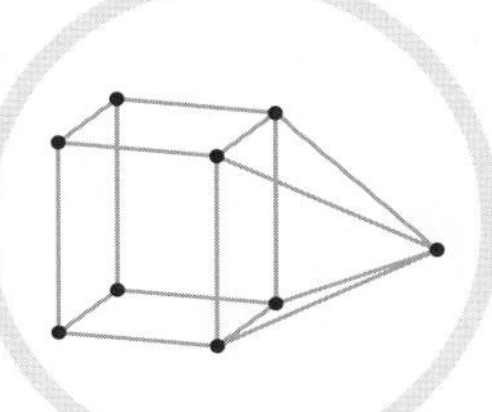

c.

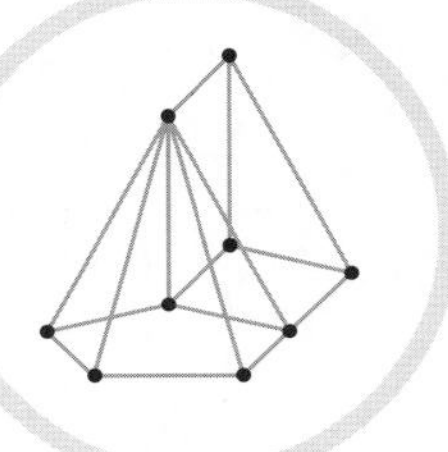

______________ ______________ ______________

______________ ______________ ______________

d. Thing in common: ______________

Draw two 3-D figures in each group to match each sorting rule.

⑧

With 5 or fewer faces	With more than 5 faces

⑨

With 6 or fewer vertices	With more than 6 vertices

DATE: ______________________

Day 65

Nets of 3-D Figures (1)

Choose the correct nets to match the 3-D figures. Write the letters.

A net is a 2-D layout for a 3-D figure.
e.g.

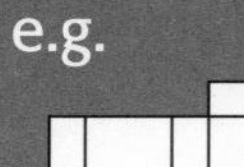
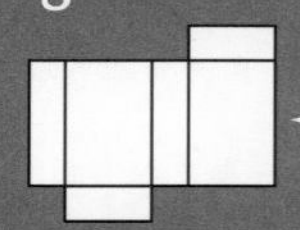

It is a net for a rectangular prism.

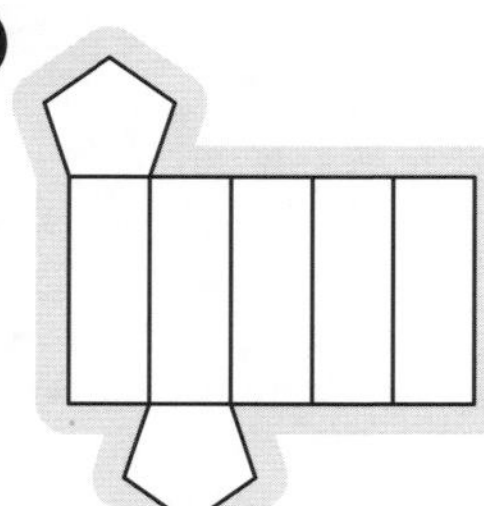

B

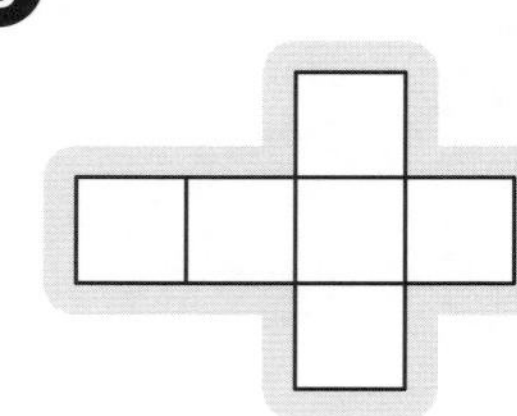

C

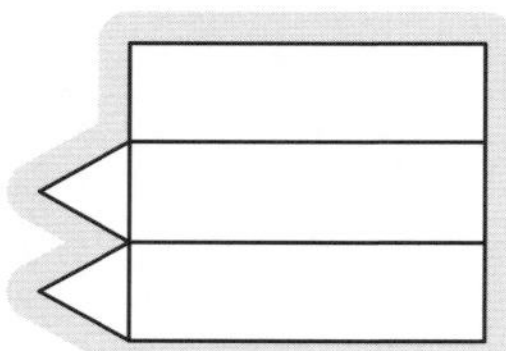

D

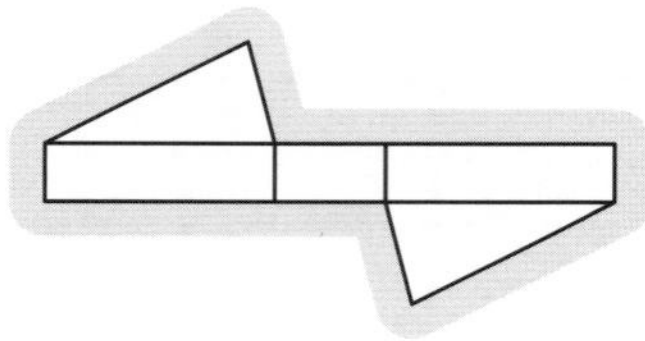

E

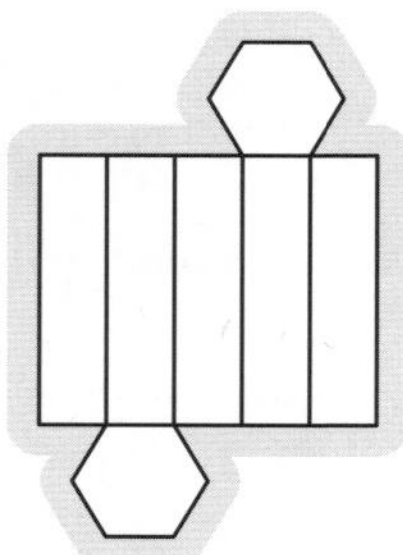

F

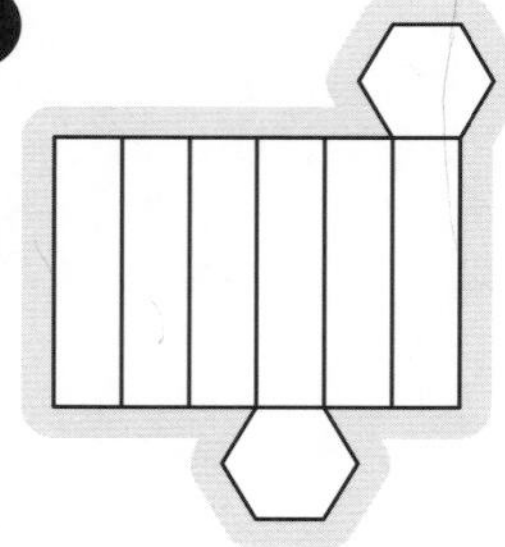

G

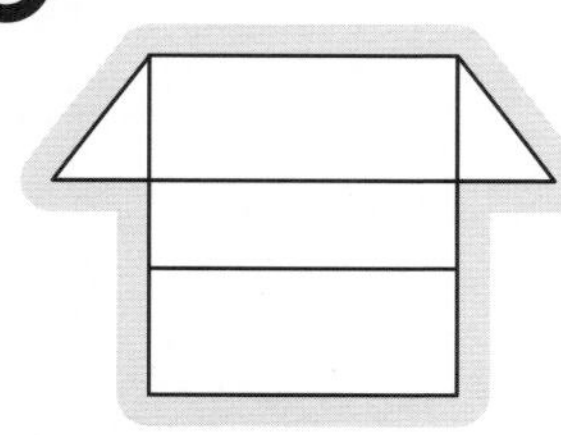

H

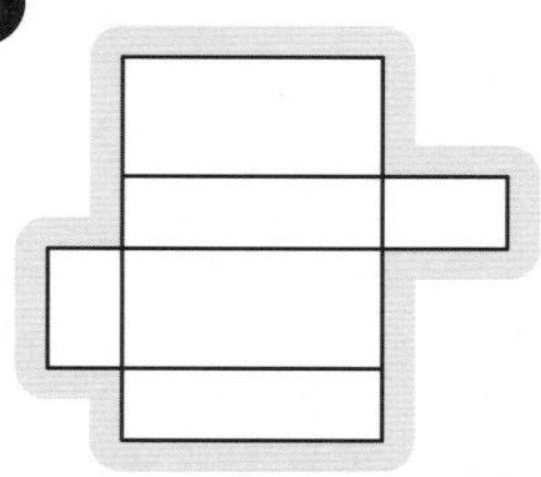

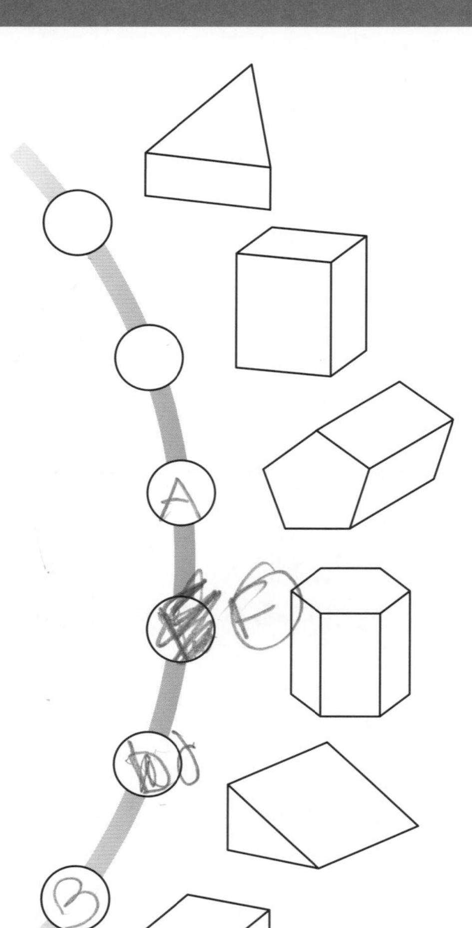

Draw the missing faces to complete the net for each prism.

②

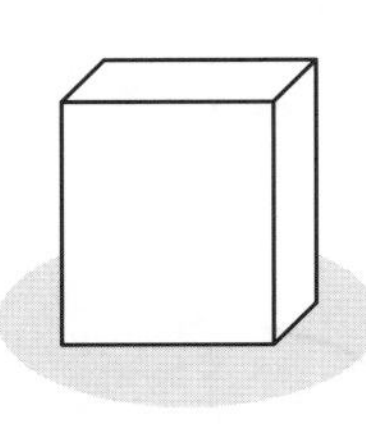

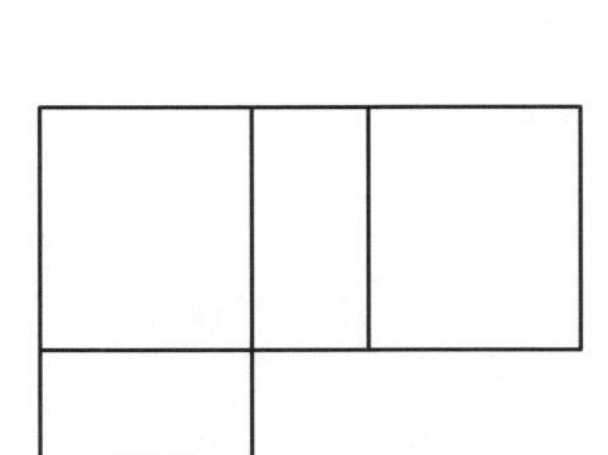

③

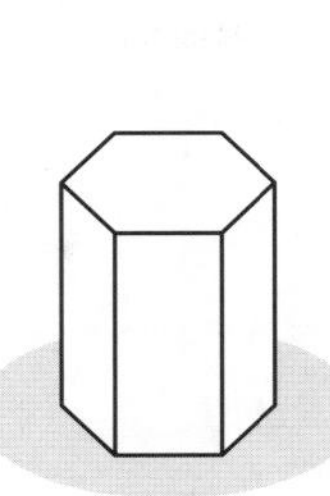

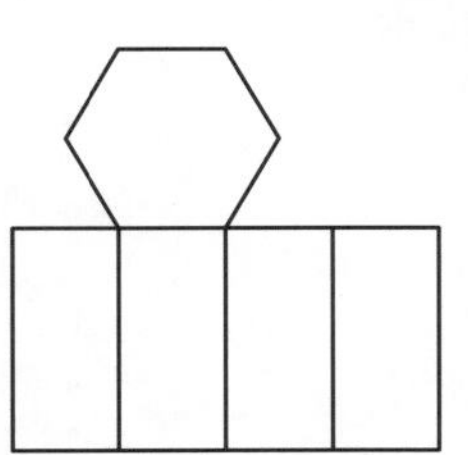

④

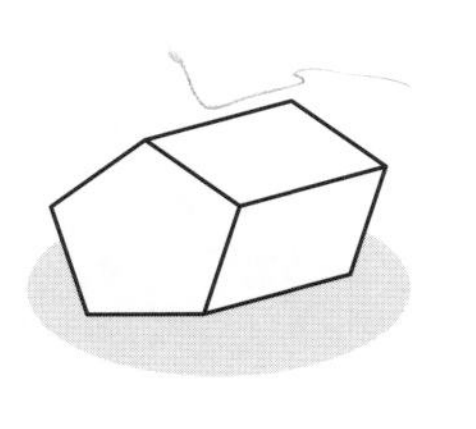

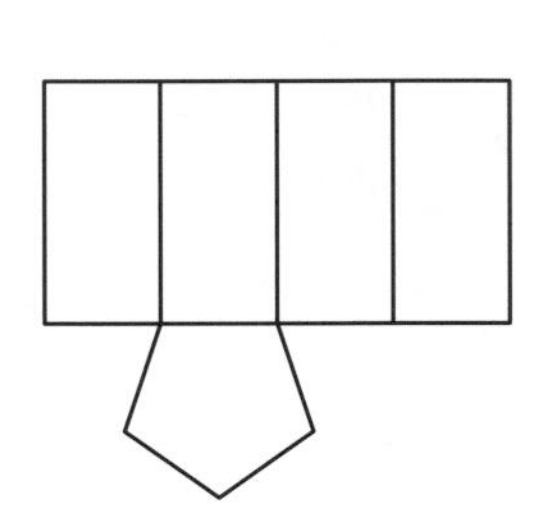

⑤

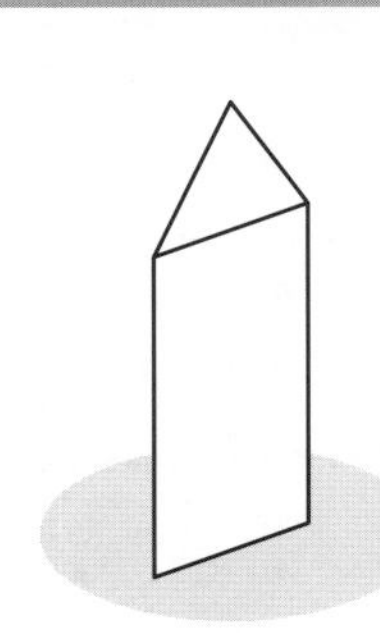

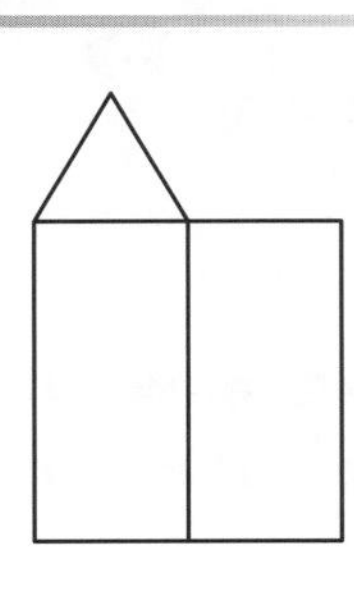

Colour the faces.

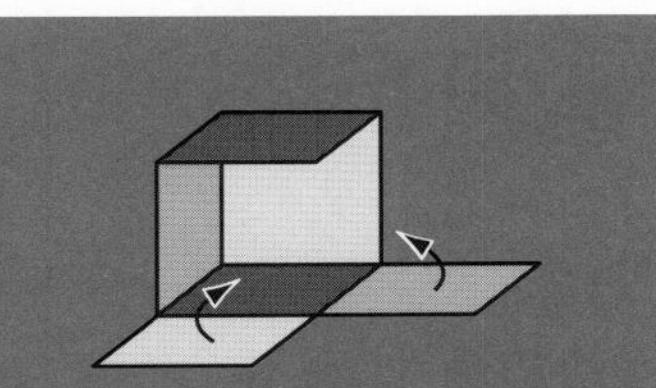

A cube has 3 pairs of opposite faces.

⑥

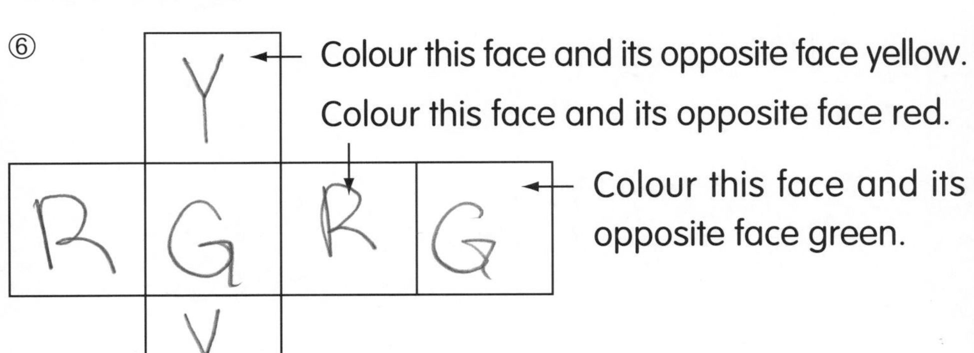

Colour this face and its opposite face yellow.

Colour this face and its opposite face red.

Colour this face and its opposite face green.

Put a checkmark in the circle if the nets can form a cube.

⑦

A 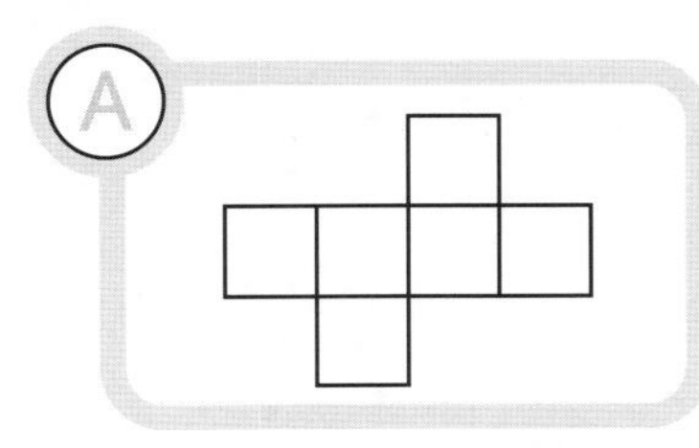

B 

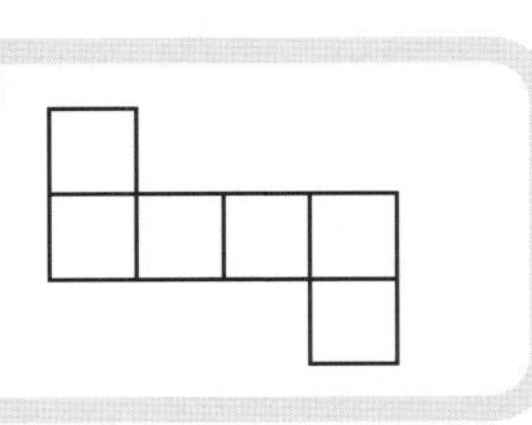

C 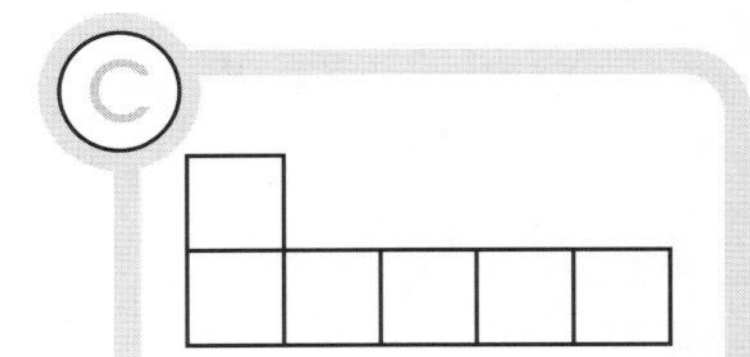

D 

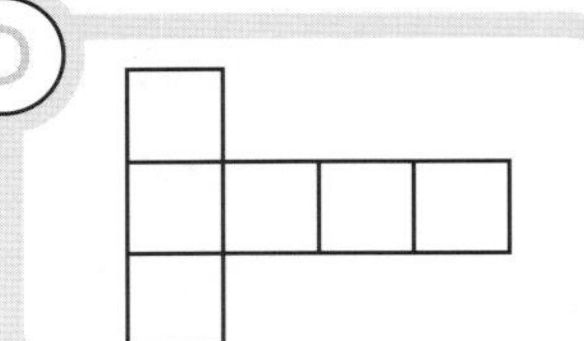

E 

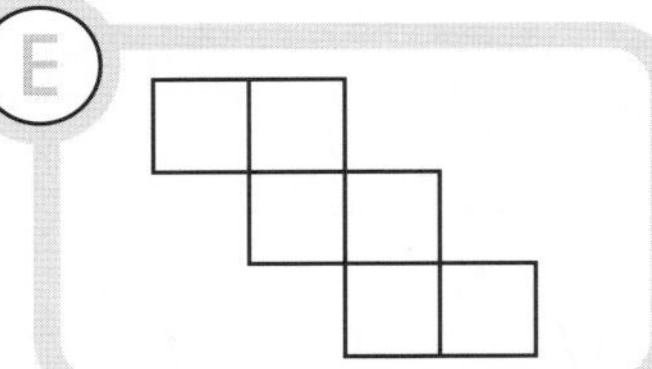

F 

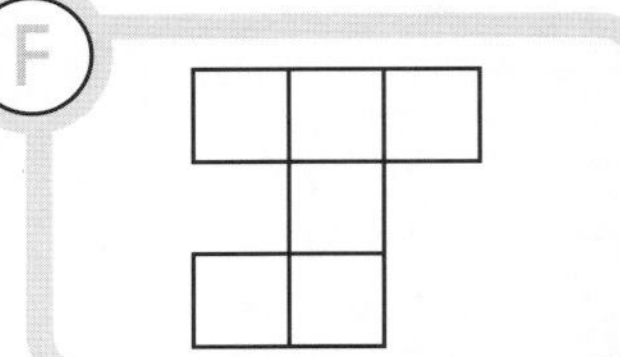

DATE: ____________________

Day 66

Nets of 3-D Figures (2)

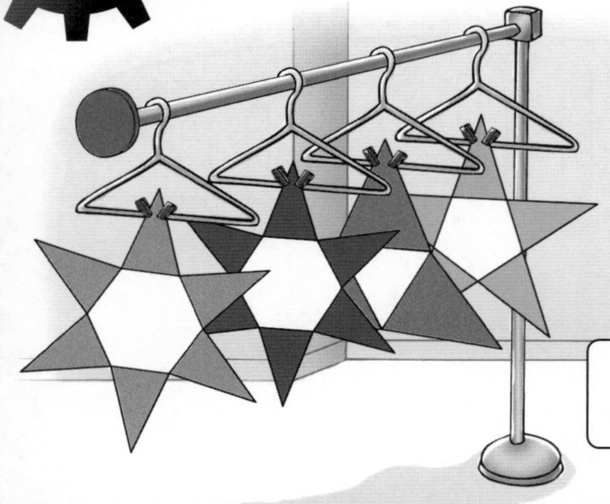

Which nets make the figures on the left?
Put a checkmark in the correct circles.

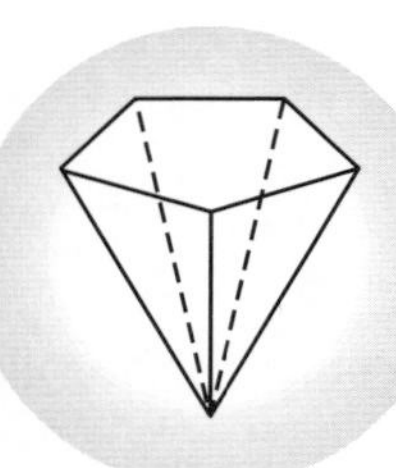

A 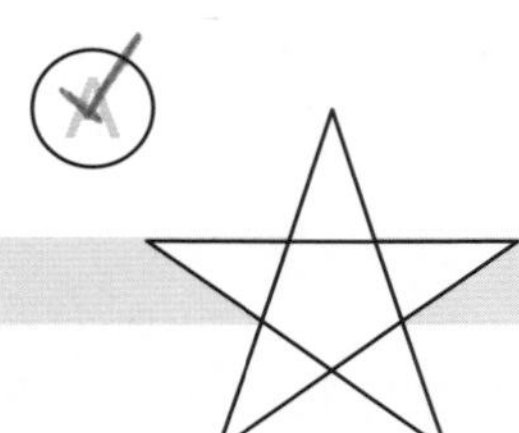

B 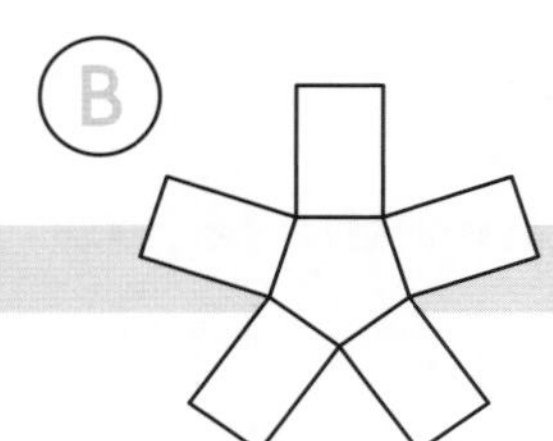

C  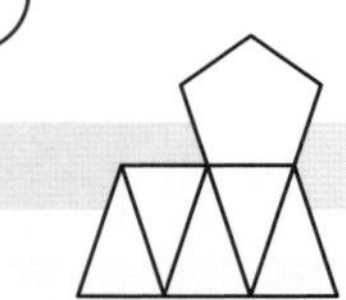

②

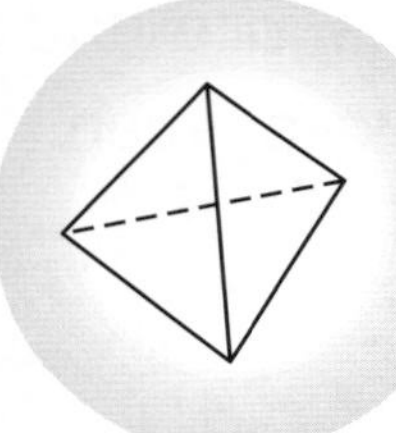

A 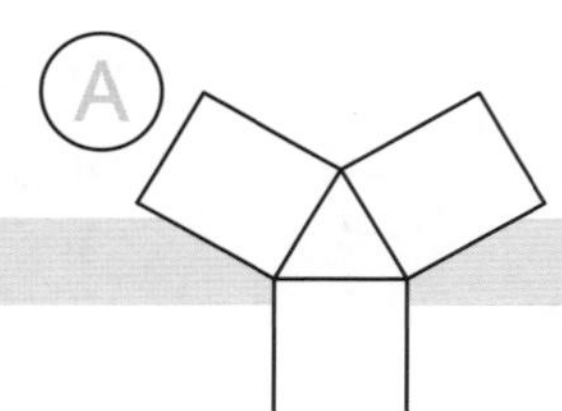

B 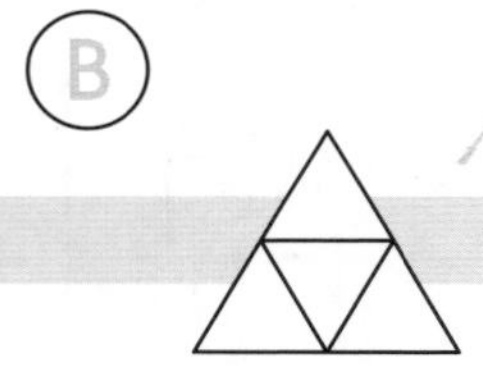

C 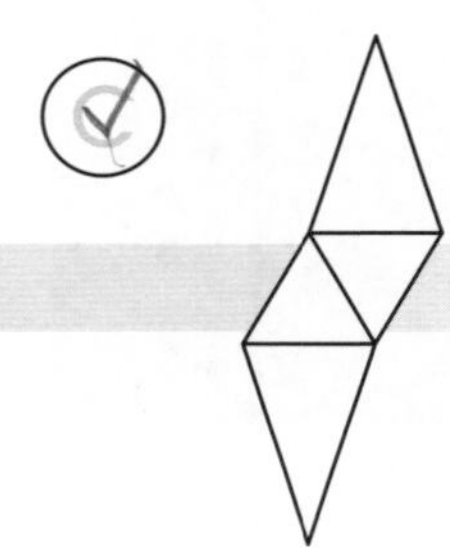

③

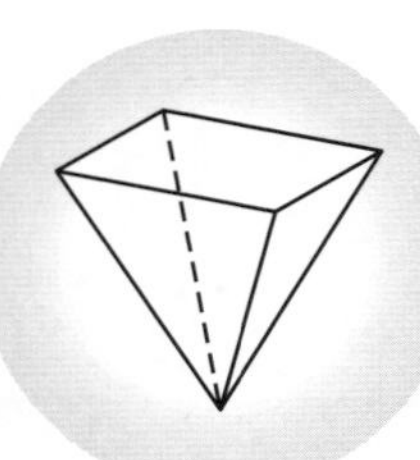

A 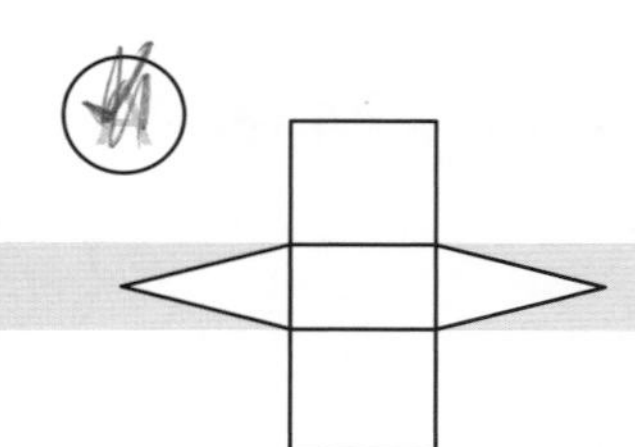

B 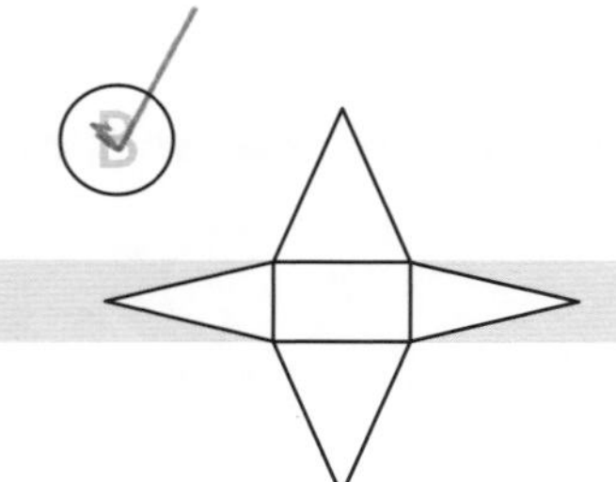

C 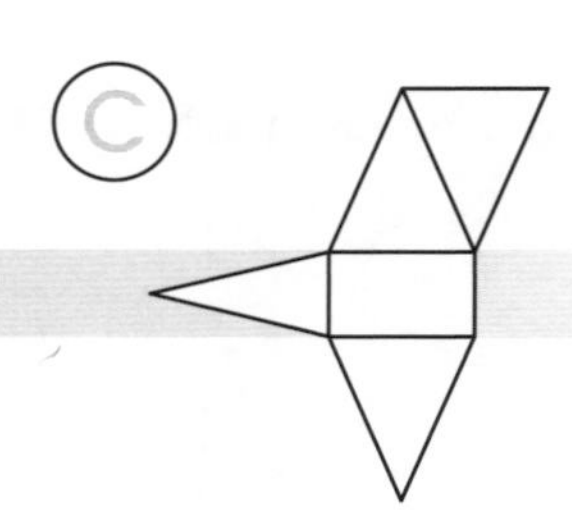

④

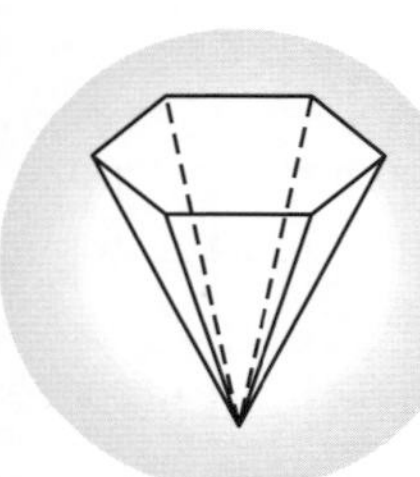

A 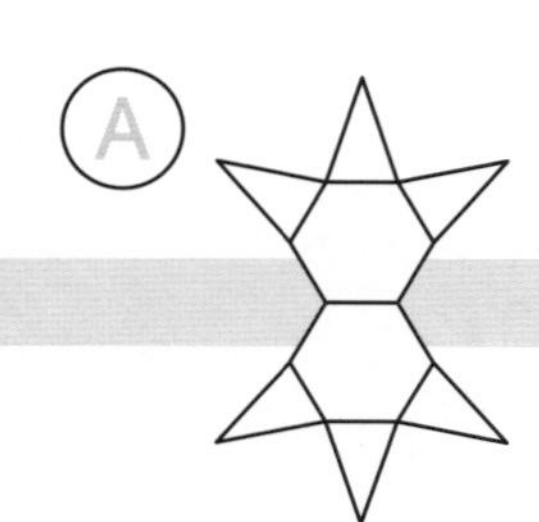

B 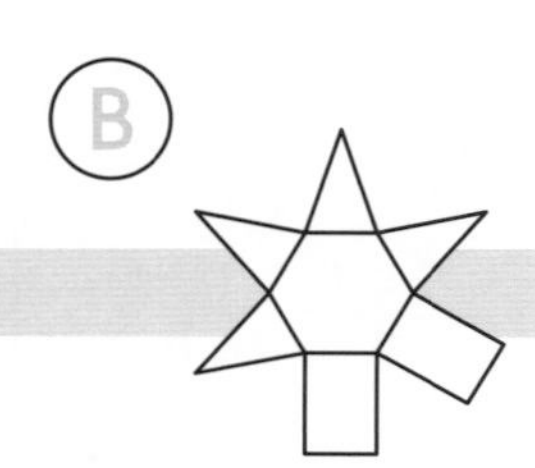

C 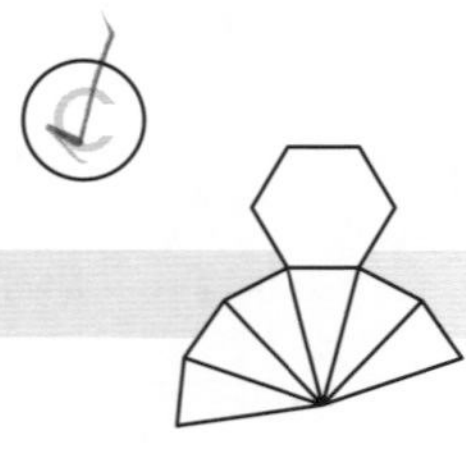

Draw the missing faces to complete the net for each pyramid.

⑤ Pentagonal pyramid

⑥ Triangular pyramid

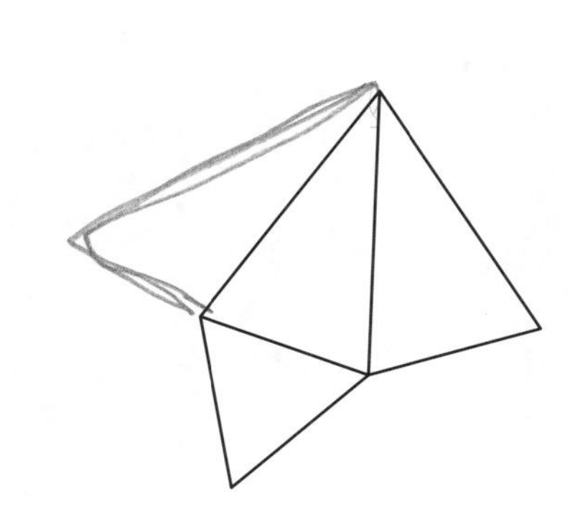

⑦ Hexagonal pyramid

Put a checkmark in the circles if the nets can form a rectangular pyramid.

⑧

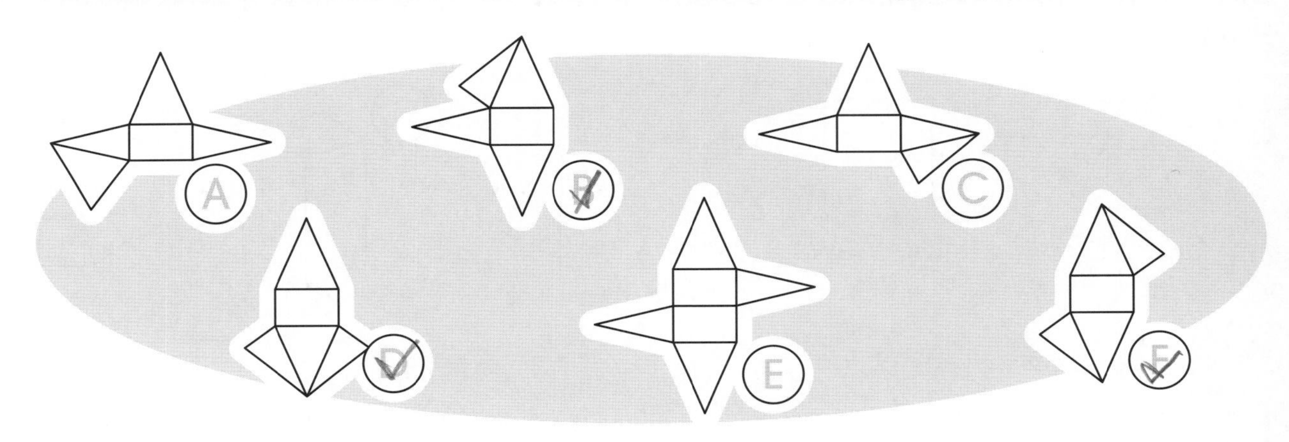

Draw 2 different nets for a triangular pyramid.

⑨

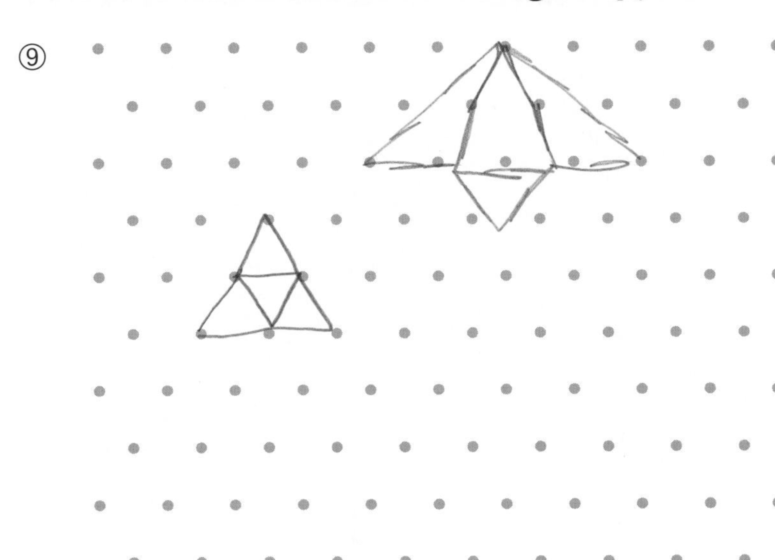

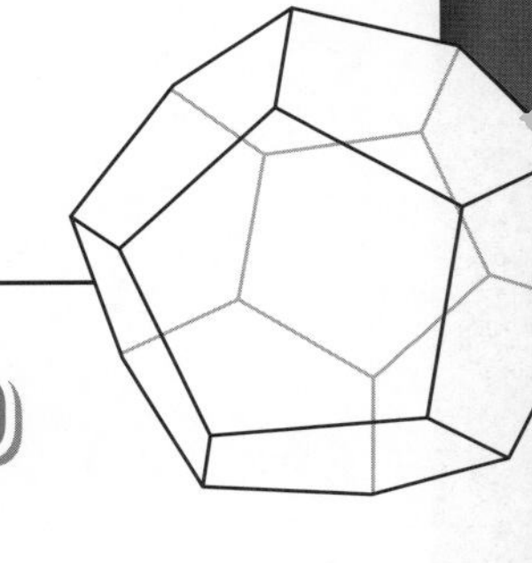

Did you know?

A ***dodecahedron*** (a 12-face polyhedron) can be created from 43 380 different nets.

DATE: ____________

Views of 3-D Figures (1)

The side view △, front view △, and top view ▭ are all very attractive.

Each child looks at a solid from two different views. Guess which solid each child is looking at. Check the letter.

① 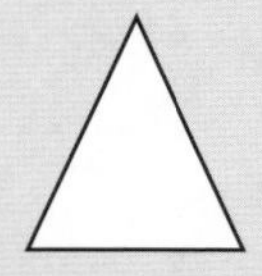 Side View  Top View

 A 
B 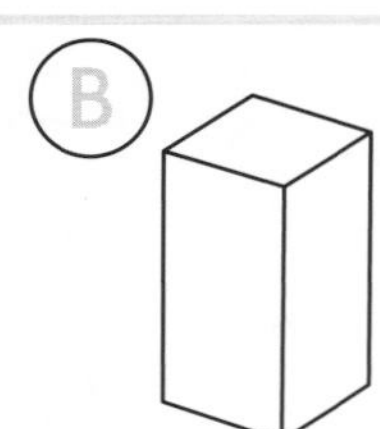
C 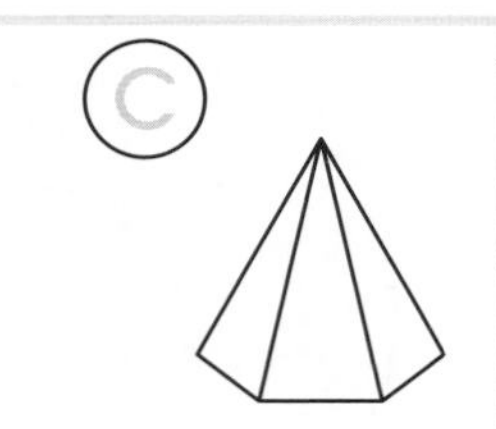

②  Front View 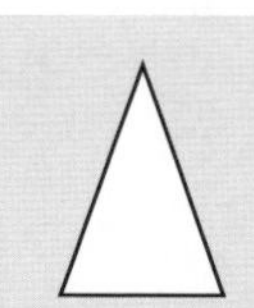 Side View

A 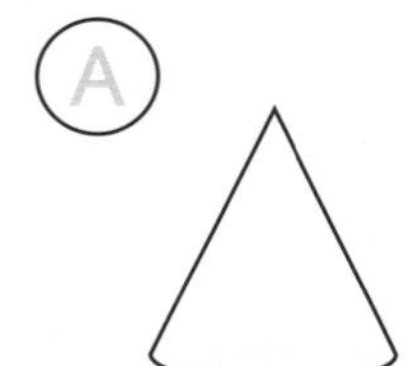
B 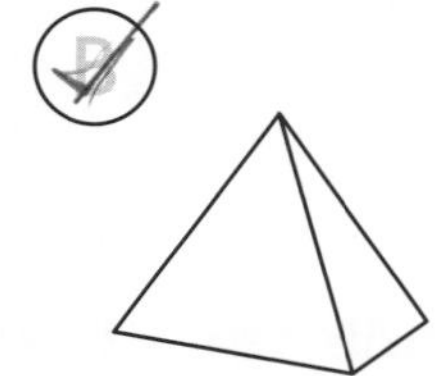
C 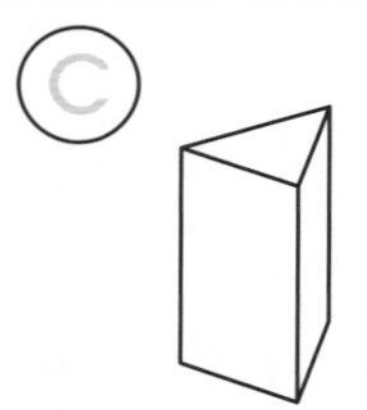

③ 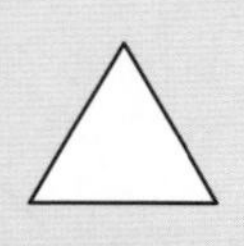 Top View  Front View

A 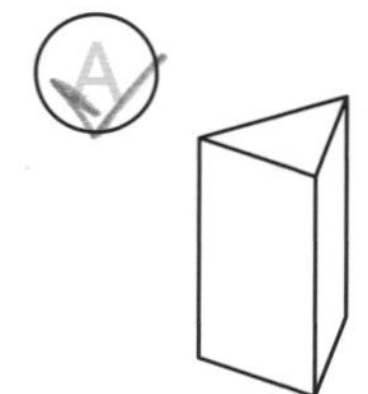
B 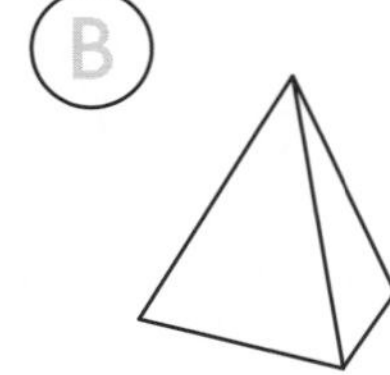
C 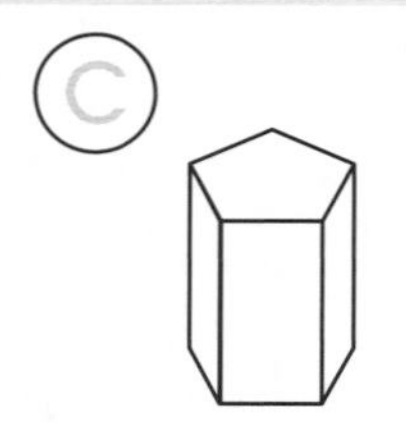

④ 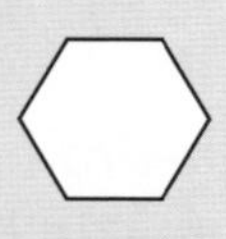 Top View 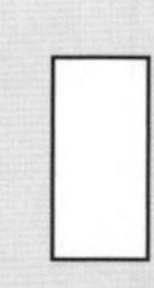 Side View

A 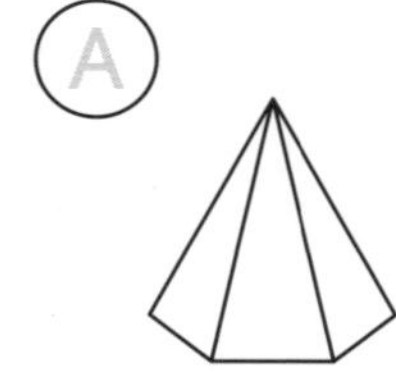
B 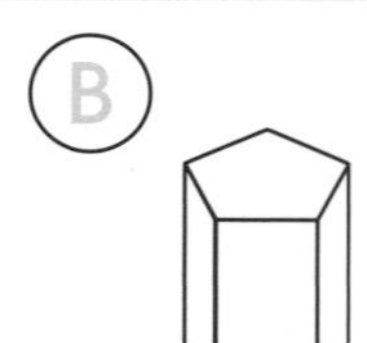
C 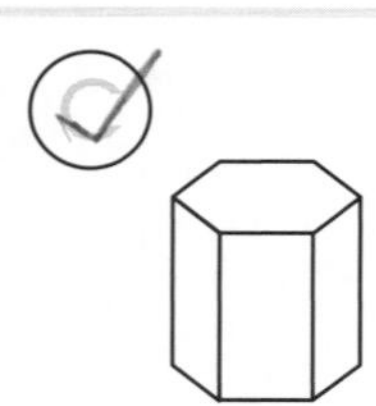

Draw the front view, side view, and top view of each solid.

⑤

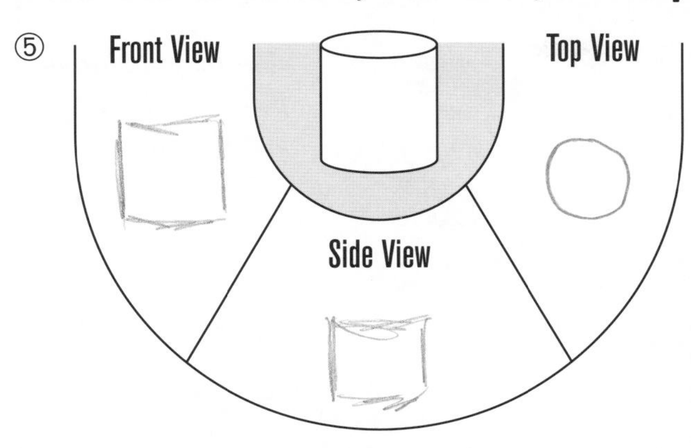

⑥

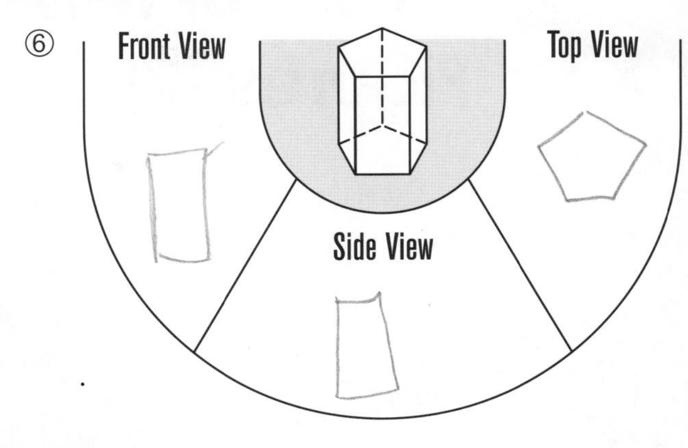

⑦

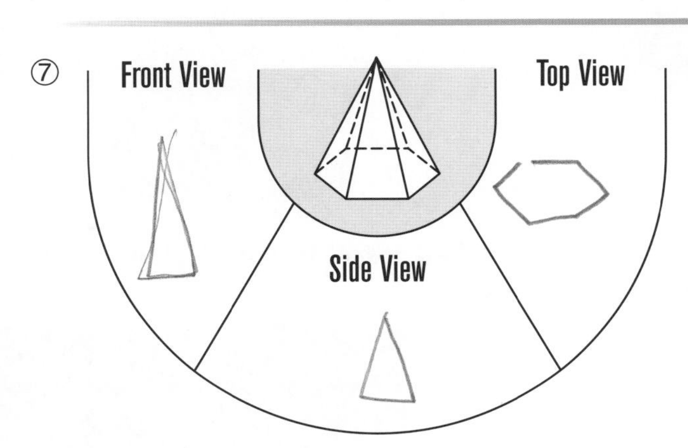

⑧

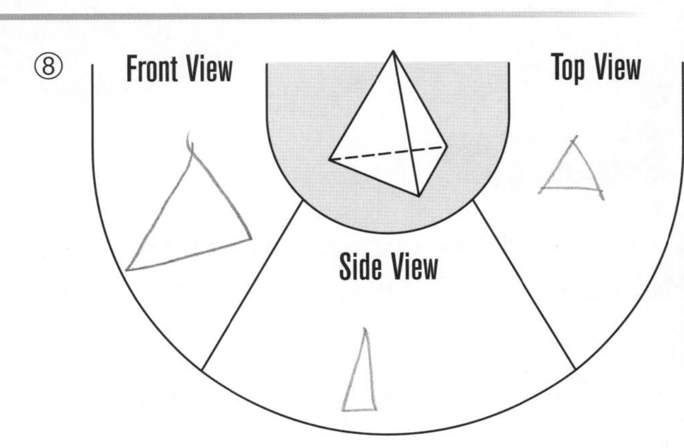

Answer the children's questions. Draw the answers in the circles.

⑨

The front view, side view, and top view of a solid are all in the shape of a rectangle. What solid is it?

⑩

The front view, side view, and top view of a solid are all in the shape of a square. What solid is it?

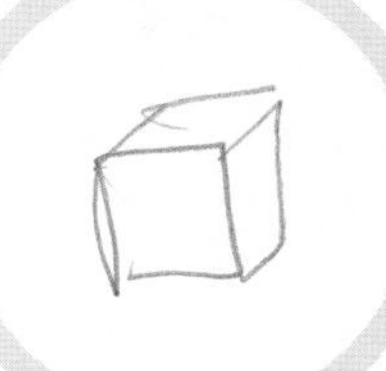

⑪

The top view of the solid is a circle and its side view is a triangle. What solid is it?

DATE: ____________________

Views of 3-D Figures (2)

Uncle Ray took pictures of the front view, side view, and top view of each structure. Help him match the pictures with the correct structures.

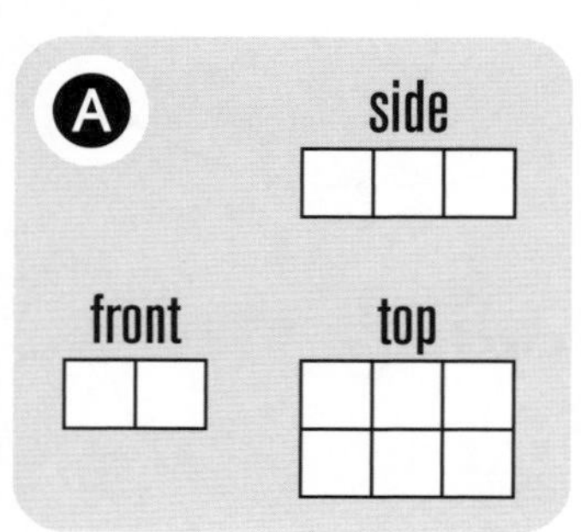

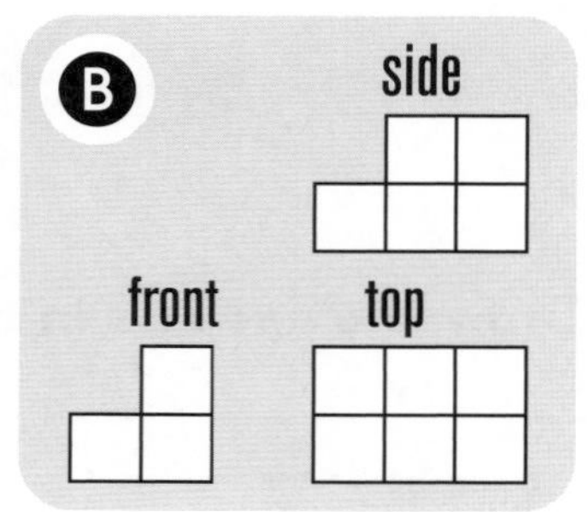

You can use cubes to build the structures and look at them from the top, front, or side. This can help you figure out the answers.

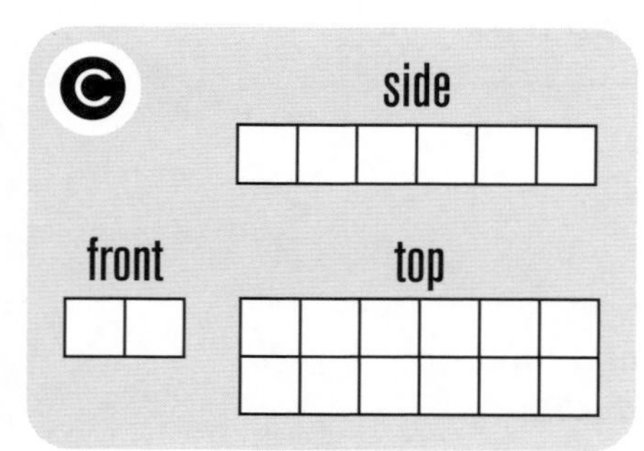

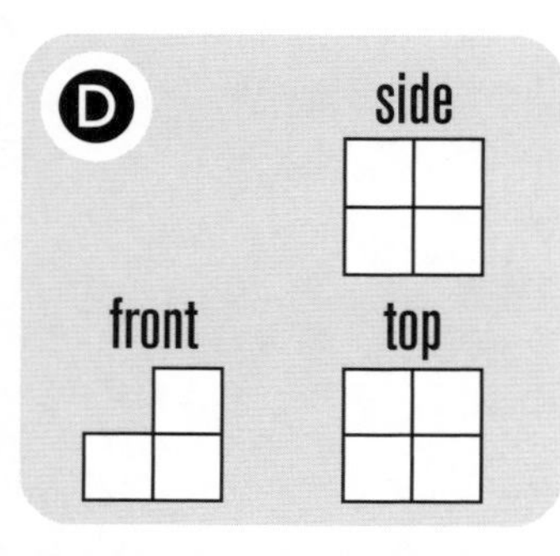

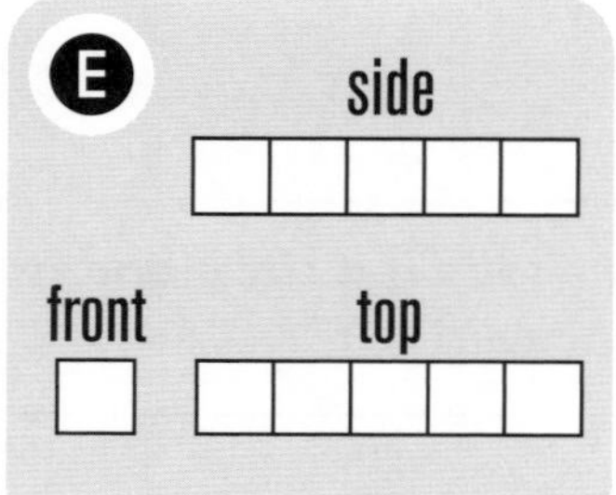

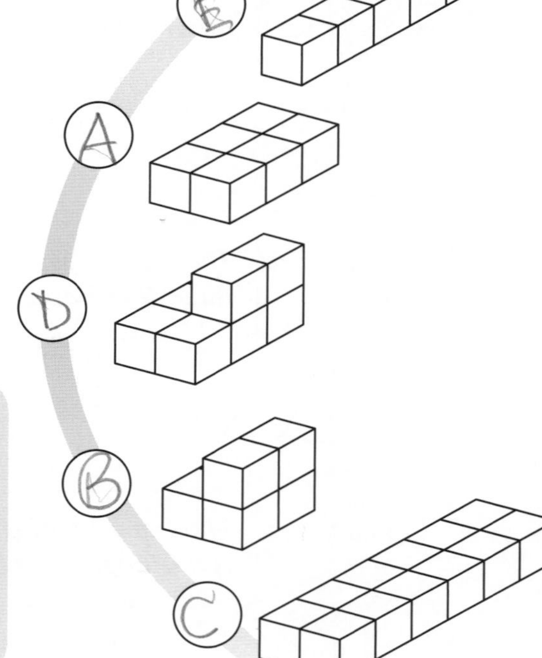

Draw the top view, front view, and side view of each structure.

	Structure	Top View	Front View	Side View
②	top view front view side view			
③				
④				
⑤				

Look at the coloured structure. Answer the questions.

⑥

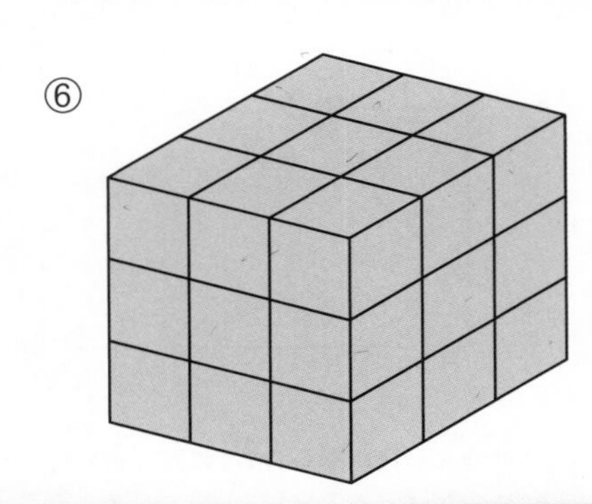

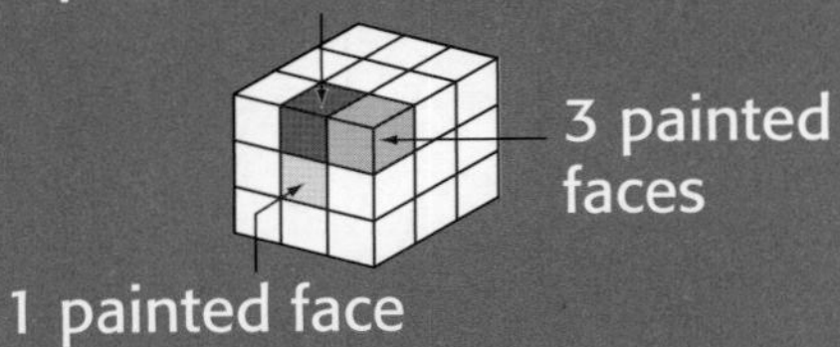

a. How many cubes have 2 painted faces?

6

b. How many cubes have 3 painted faces?

1

c. How many cubes have 1 painted face?

16

DATE: ____________

Day 69

Transformations (1)

Complete the translation images of the shaded shapes. Then describe the movements.

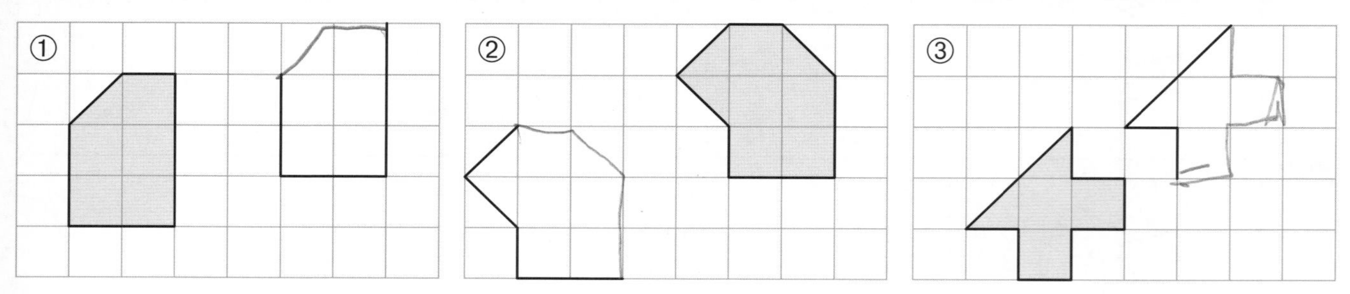

Complete the reflection images of the shaded shapes. Then draw the lines of reflection.

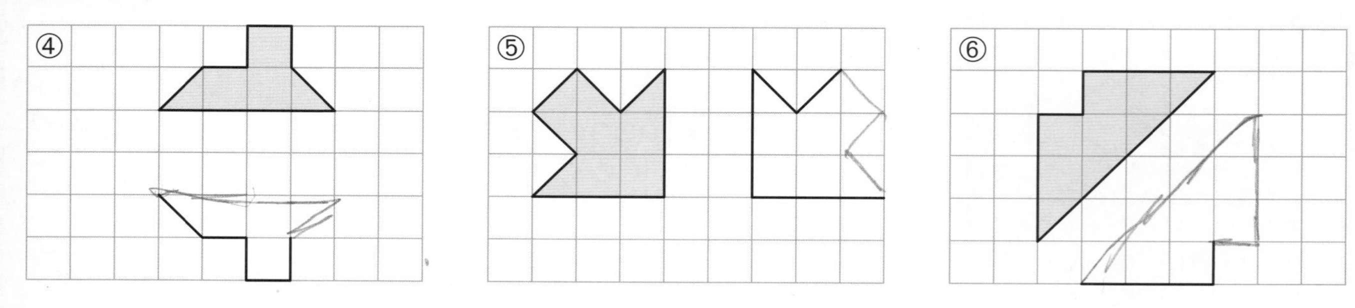

Complete the rotation images of the shaded shapes. Then draw the centres of rotation.

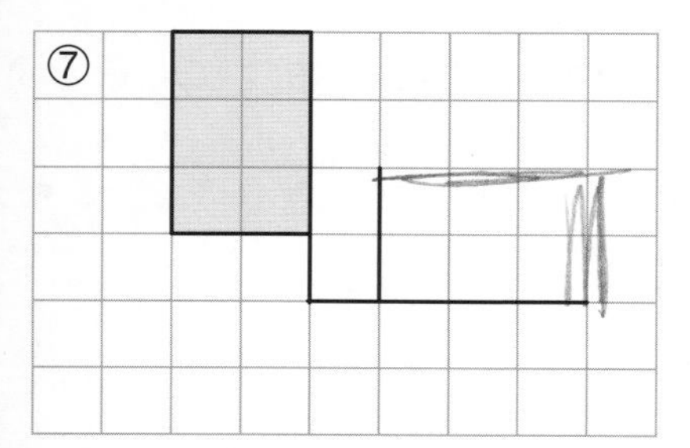

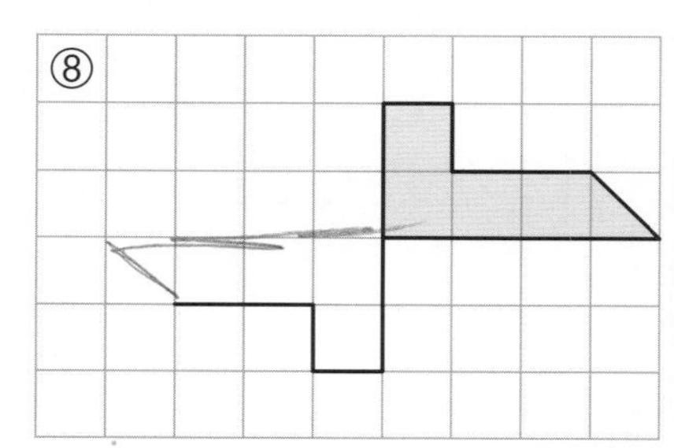

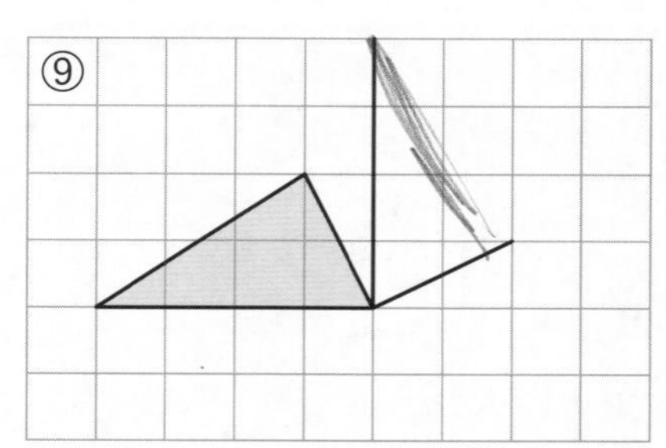

Read what the children say. Help them draw the pictures on the grid.

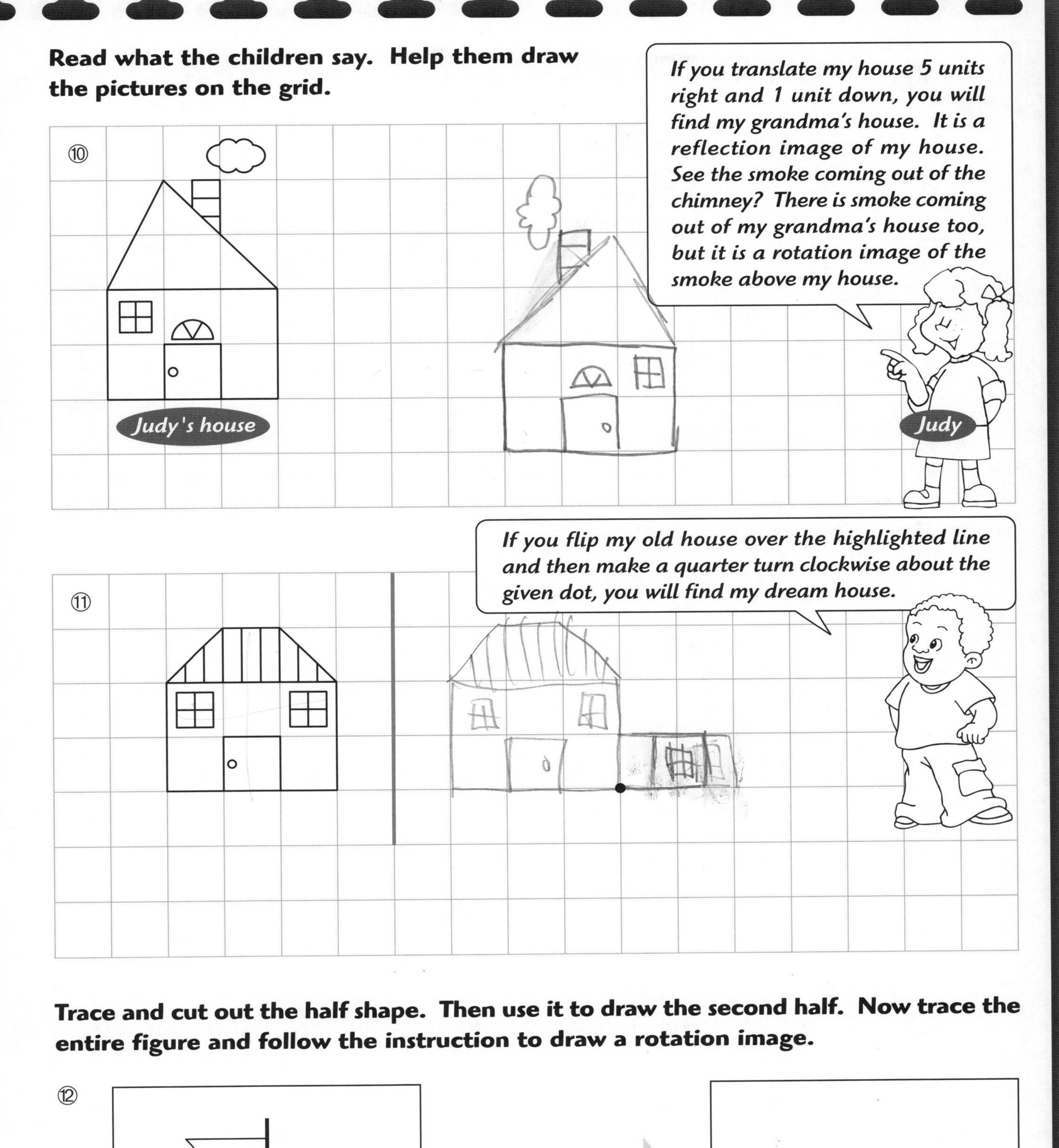

Trace and cut out the half shape. Then use it to draw the second half. Now trace the entire figure and follow the instruction to draw a rotation image.

⑫

Make a three-quarter turn in a clockwise direction.

DATE: ______________

Day 70

Transformations (2)

The children have used the shapes in the circles to make tessellating patterns. Tell which two transformations are used by writing 'translation', 'reflection', or 'rotation' on the lines. Then continue the pattern.

①

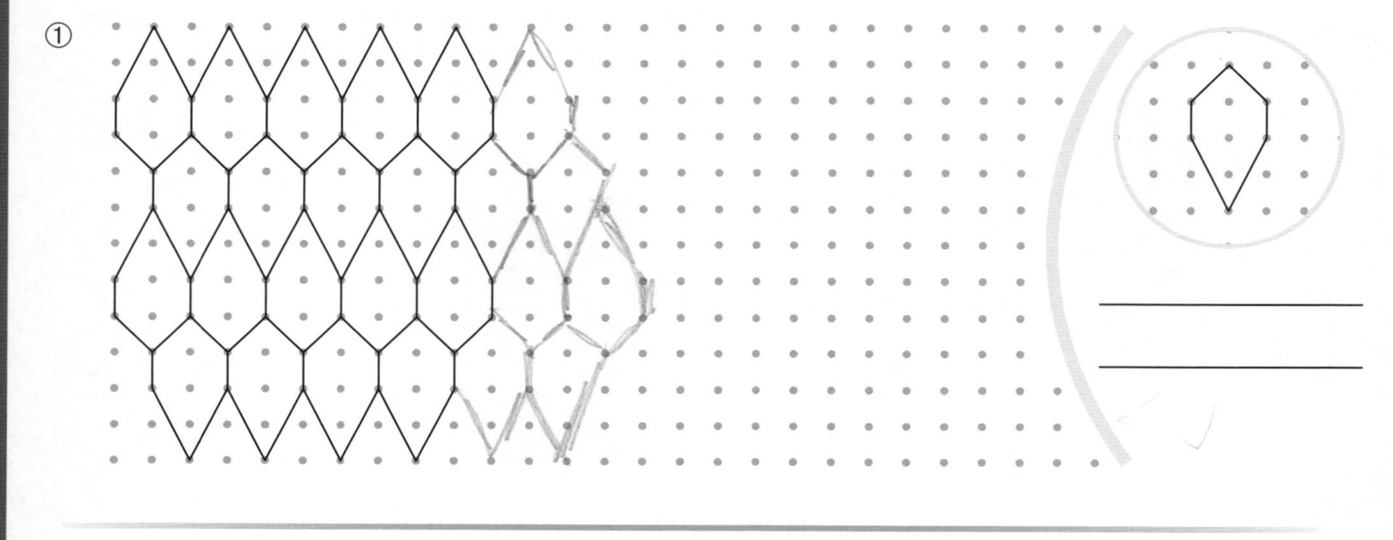

②

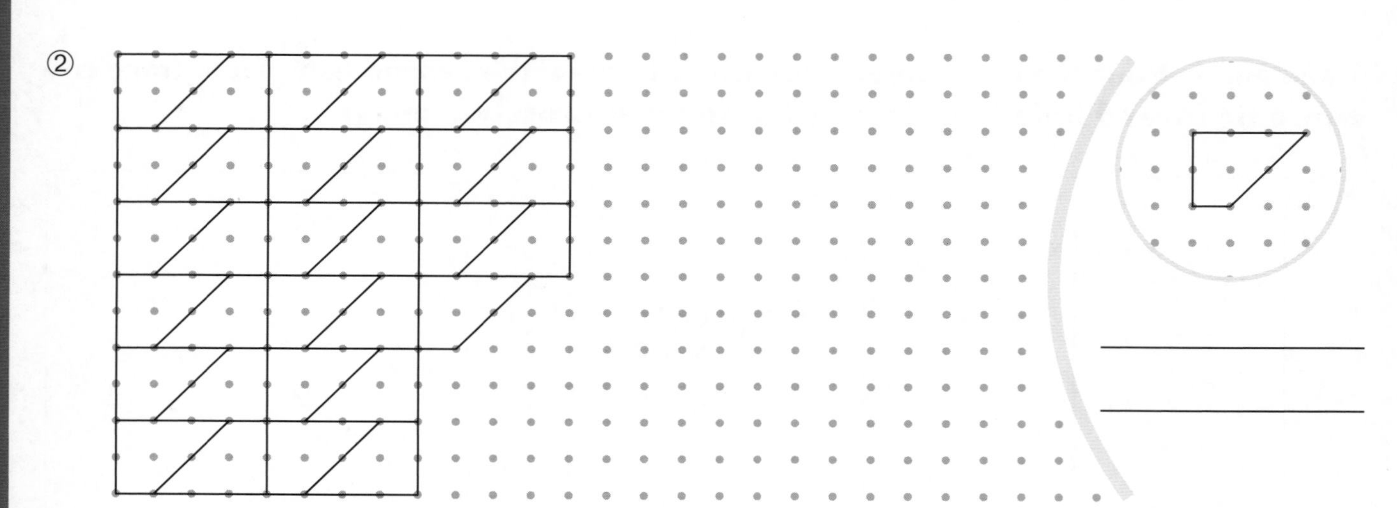

Use the two given transformations on each given shape to create your own tessellating pattern.

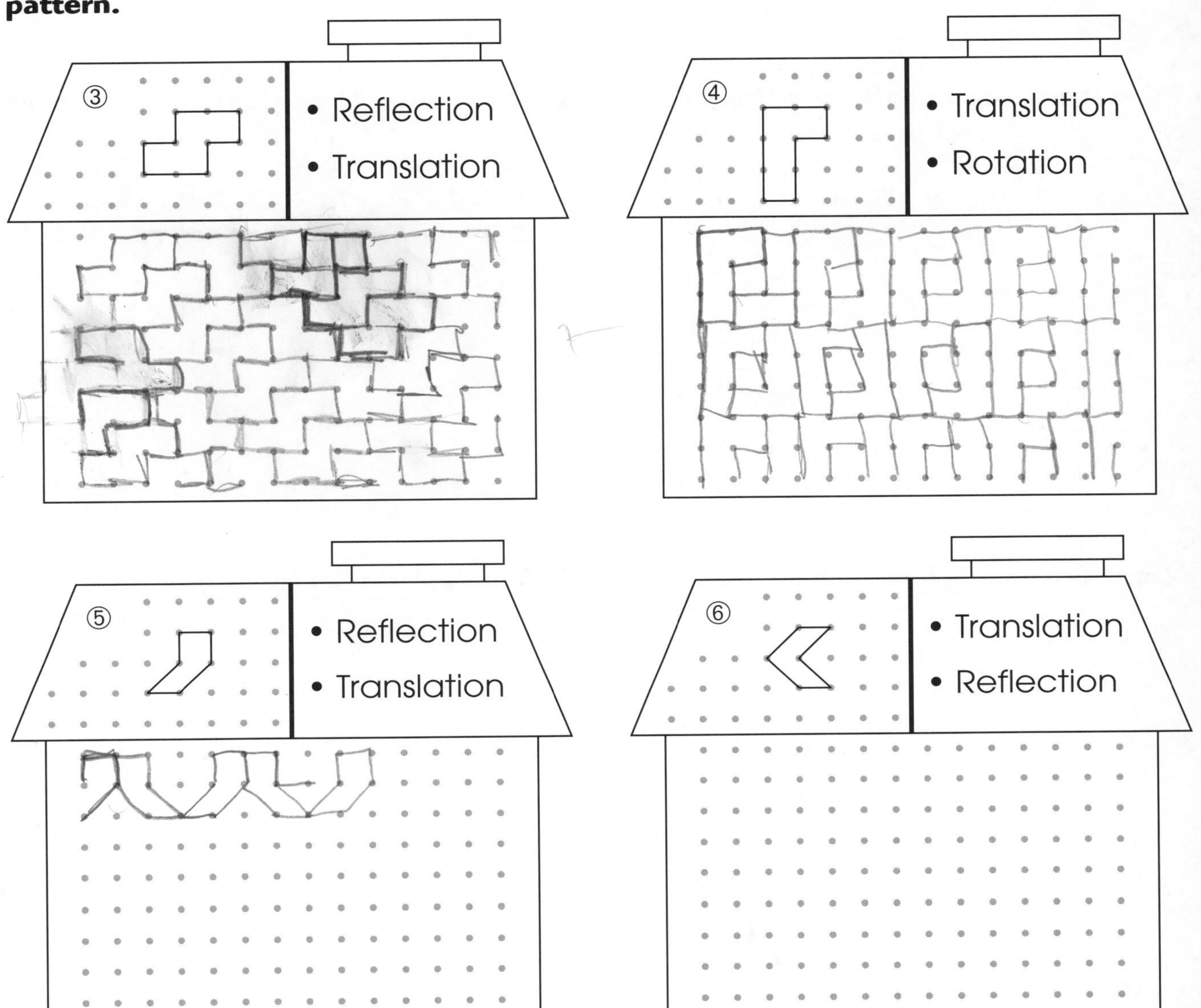

Use the tile in the circle to create two different tessellating patterns.

⑦

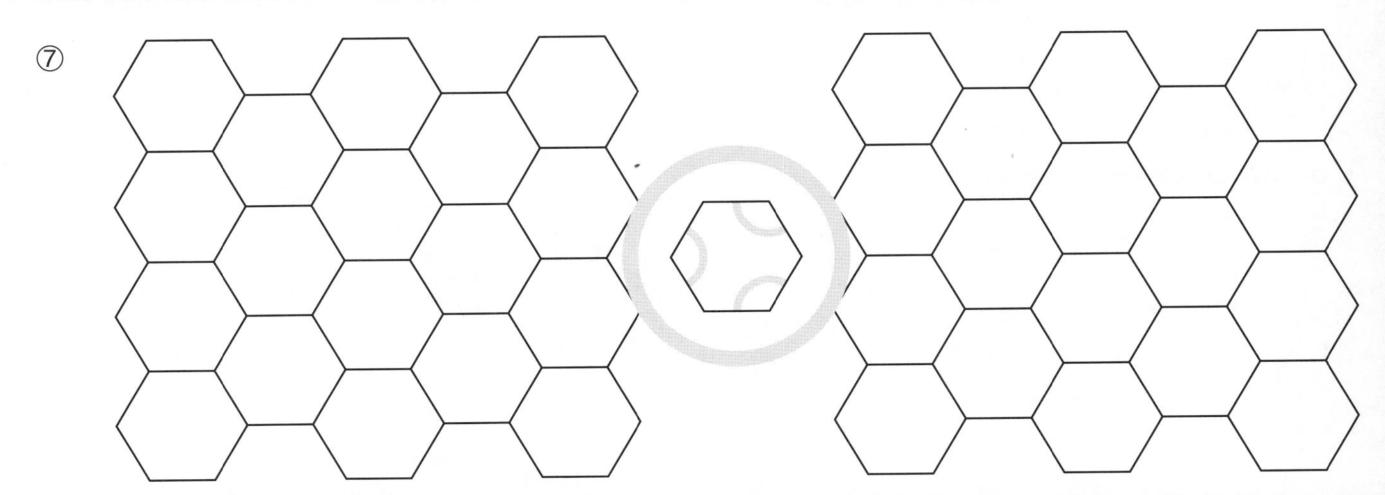

REVIEW

Draw the triangles and write the length beside each side. Then measure and record the angles of each triangle.

① An obtuse scalene triangle

3.4 cm

② A right isosceles triangle

4 cm

Name the solids. Then draw the missing faces to complete the net for making each solid.

③

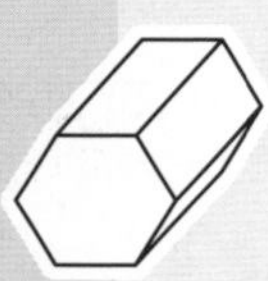

④

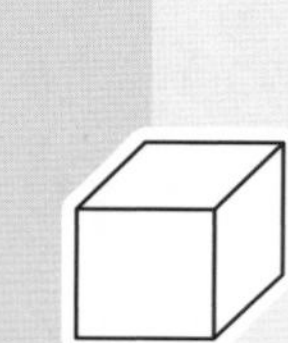

⑤

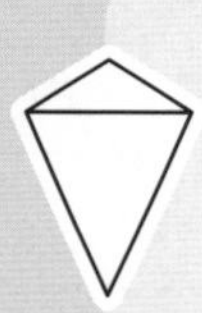

⑥

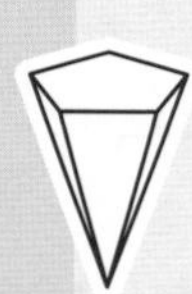

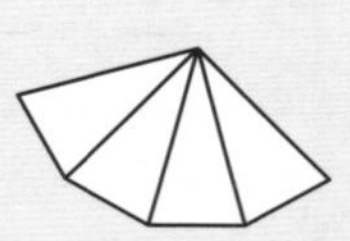

Complete the tile patterns.

⑦

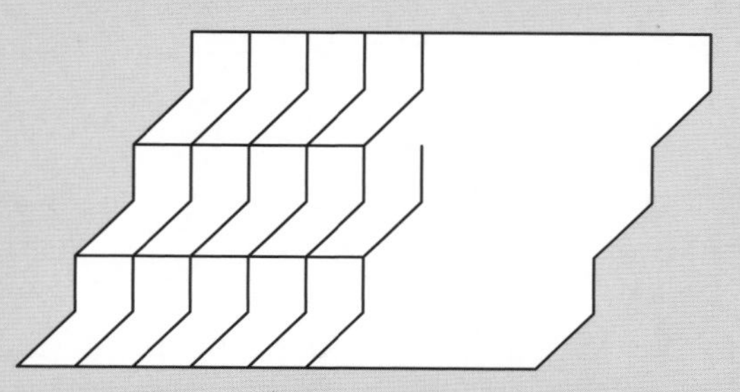

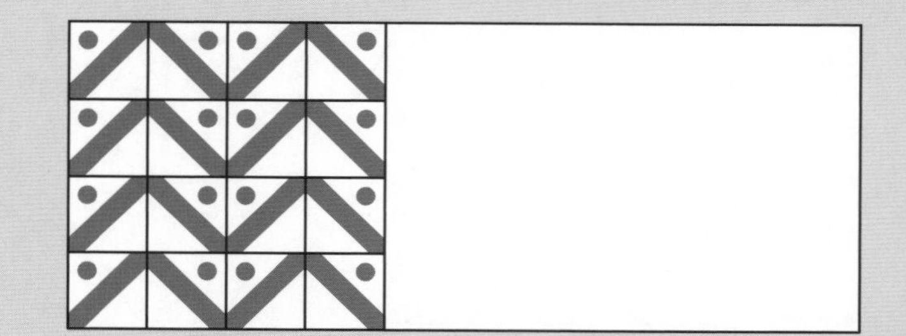

Draw the shapes.

⑧ Draw 4 different kinds of polygons that have parallel sides.

⑨ Draw 4 different kinds of polygons that have right angles.

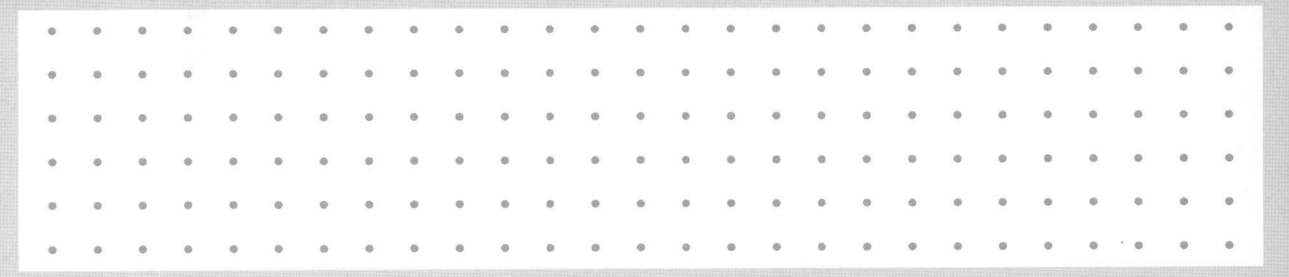

What transformations should be used to move the shaded shapes to the unshaded ones? Describe the transformations. Draw the lines of reflection or the centres of rotation if necessary.

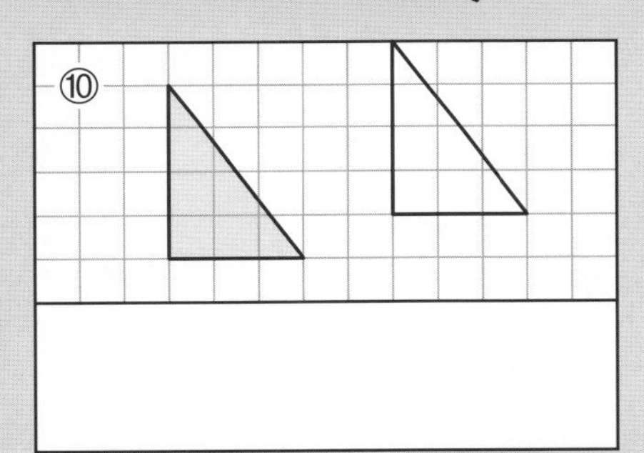

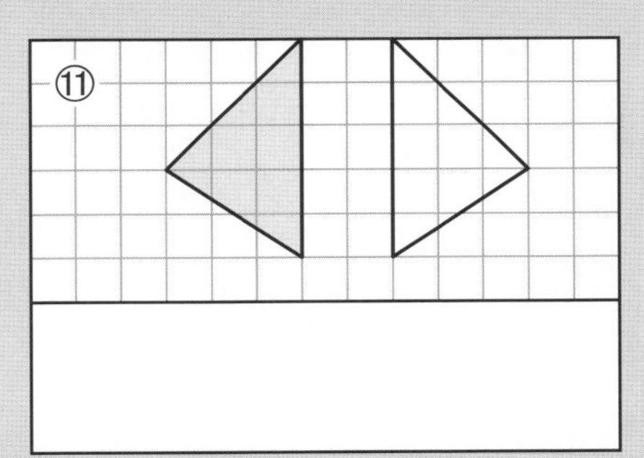

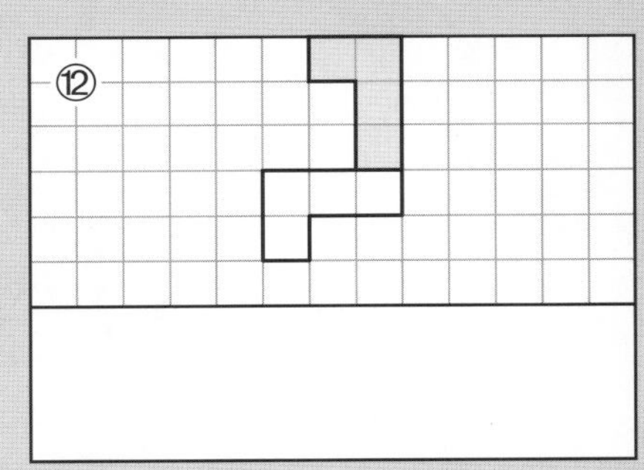

Answer the children's questions.

⑬

I have a solid. Its front, side, and top views are in the shape of a triangle. What solid do I have?

____

⑭

I have $58.64. If I buy my mom a gift that costs $39.89, how much will I have left?

____

DATE:
Day
72
You Deserve A
Break!
Help Billy Bee solve the problems. Then draw a line to show him his path to the flowers.
An obtuse scalene triangle
Name the triangle.
Top View of
An obtuse isosceles triangle
Name the solid that is formed by the net.
Rectangular Prism
Rectangular Pyramid

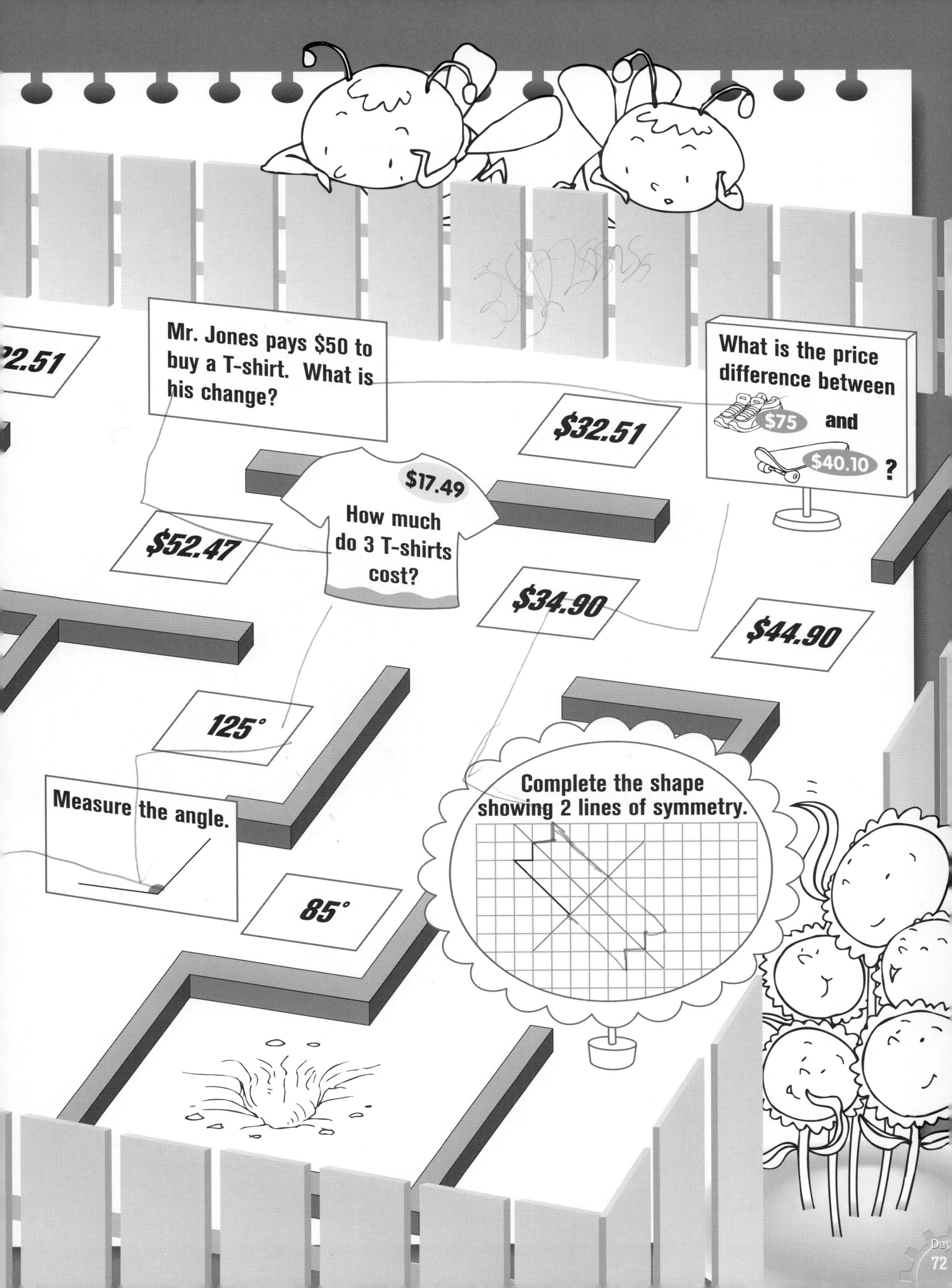

$22.51
Mr. Jones pays $50 to buy a T-shirt. What is his change?
$17.49
How much do 3 T-shirts cost?
What is the price difference between
$75
and
$40.10
?
$32.51
$52.47
$34.90
$44.90
125°
Measure the angle.
85°
Complete the shape showing 2 lines of symmetry.

DATE: ____________

Day 73

Coordinate Systems (1)

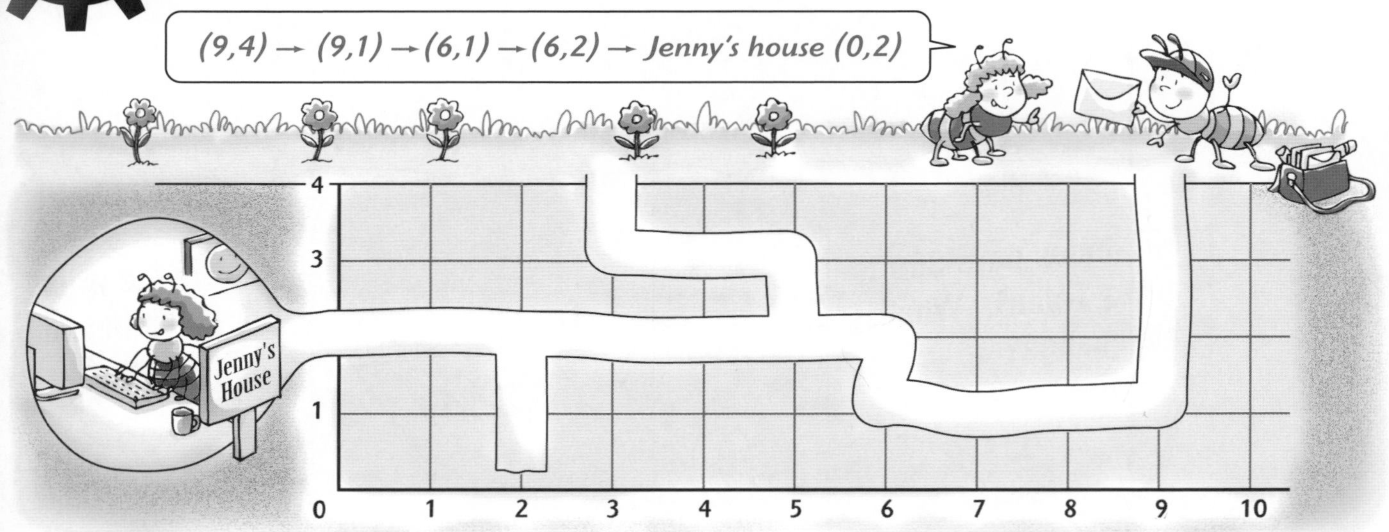

Look at the grid. Find the positions of the children and the snails. Then answer the questions.

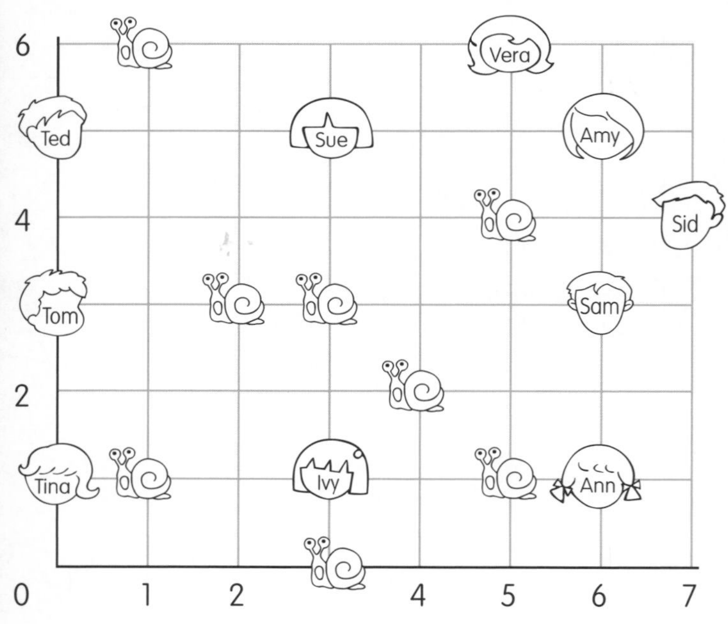

Ways to write ordered pairs:

(Number on the horizontal axis , Number on the vertical axis)

e.g.

★ (2,0)

★ (3,4)

① Amy 6,5 Ann 6,1

Ivy 3,1 Sam 6,3

Sue 3,5 Ted 0,5

Tina 0,1 Tom 0,3

Vera 5,6 Sid 7,4

②

Which child is surrounded by snails?

Ivy

The Prince is only allowed to move vertically and horizontally. Help him find the shortest and safest route to rescue the Princess. Draw the path on the grid and answer the questions.

③

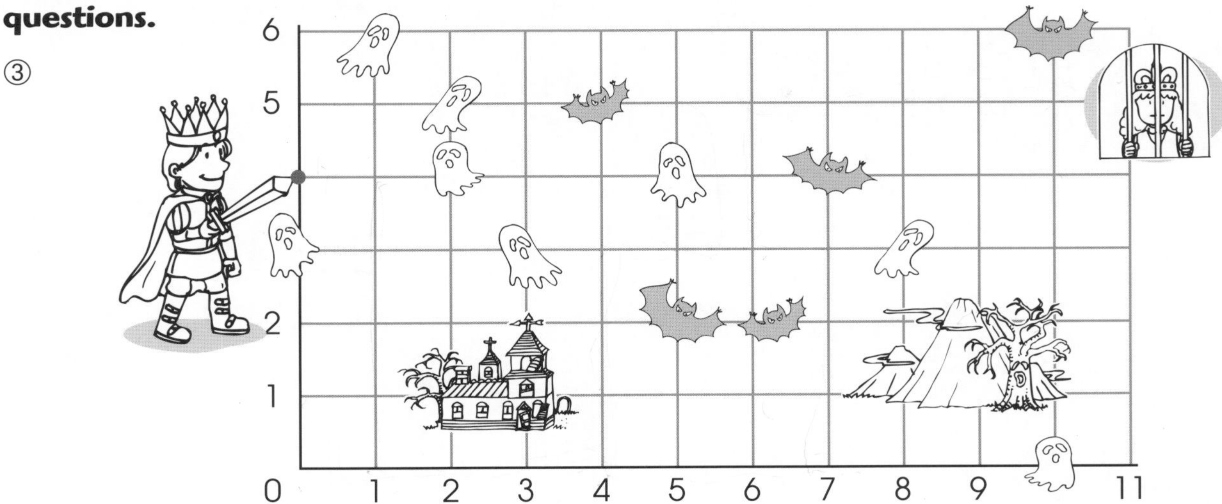

④ Write the coordinates of the points to show where the Prince should make a turn on his way to rescue the Princess.

⑤ If each unit on the grid represents 10 m, how far does the Prince need to go to rescue the Princess? 200m

⑥ a. What are the coordinates of the bats?

(4,5),(5,2),(6,2),(7,4),(10,6)

b. Which bat is the farthest away from the mountains? Write its coordinates.

⑦ a. What are the coordinates of the ghosts?

0,3,1,6,2,4,2,5,3,3,5,4,
8,3,10,0

b. Which ghost is the closest to the haunted house? Write its coordinates.

3,3

There are more than 11 000 known **ant species**. They range in size from 2 mm to 25 mm.

DATE: ____________________

Day 74

Coordinate Systems (2)

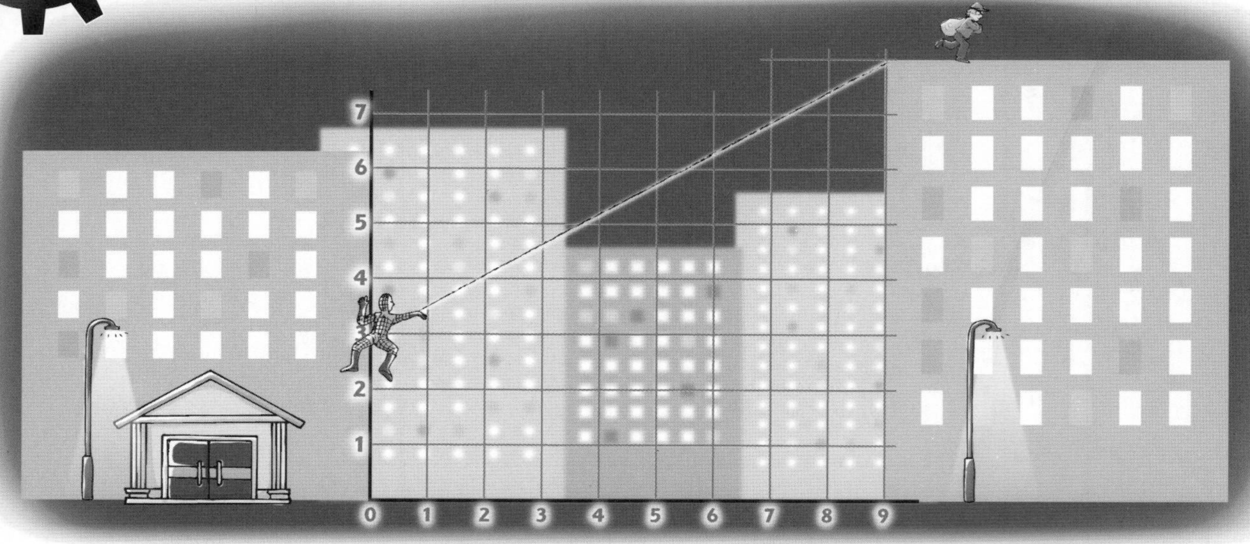

SUPERHERO IS GOING FROM (0,3) TO (9,8) TO CATCH THE THIEF.

Plot each group of points on the grid. Label each group with a letter. Then join the points to see what shape is formed. Name each shape.

①

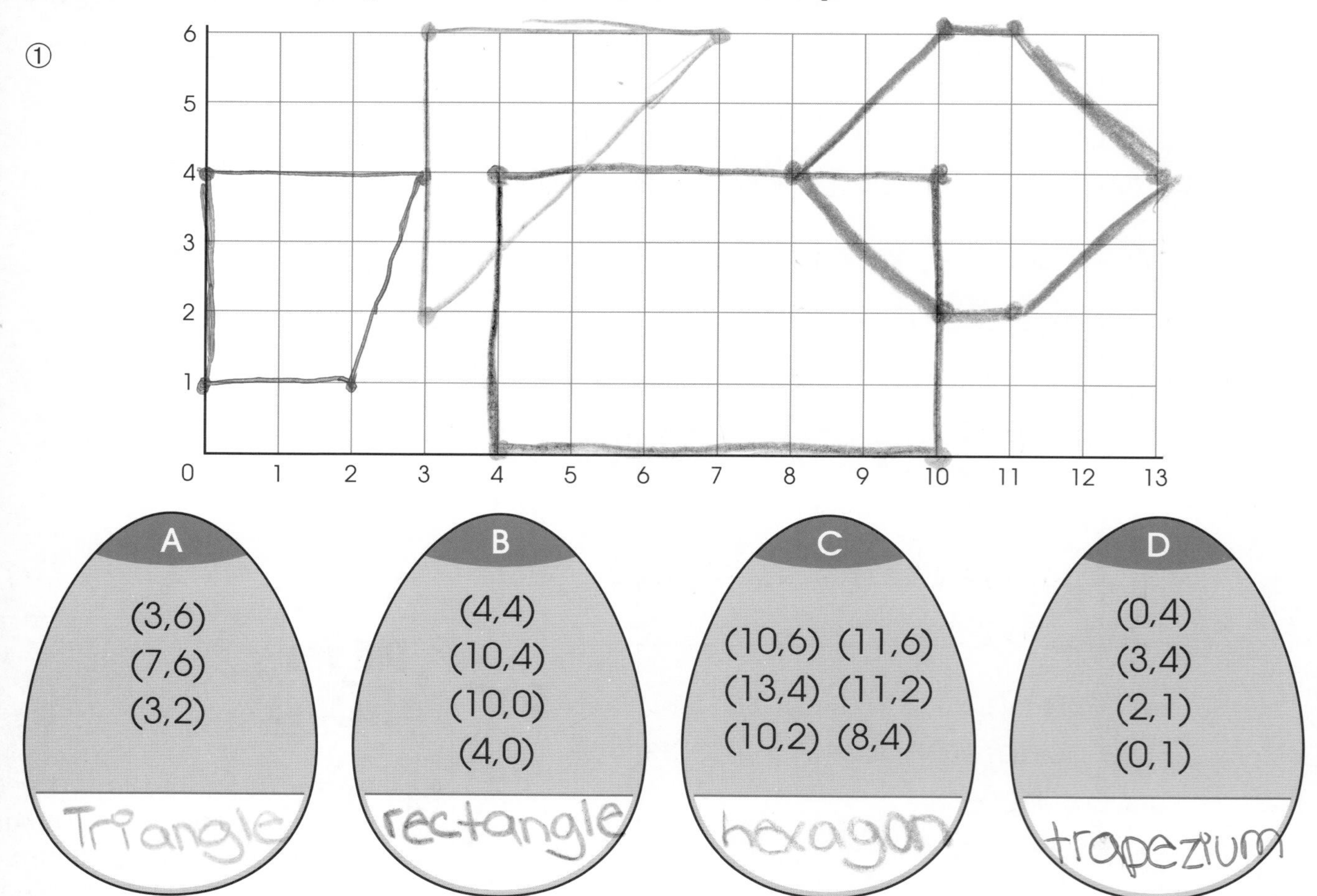

Read the clues to locate the places on the grid. Then answer the questions.

②
- A coffee shop is located between the convenience store and the museum, but it is not under the florist.
- The distance from Judy's house to the library is the same as that to the school.
- The distance from the museum to the convenience store is the same as that to the hospital.

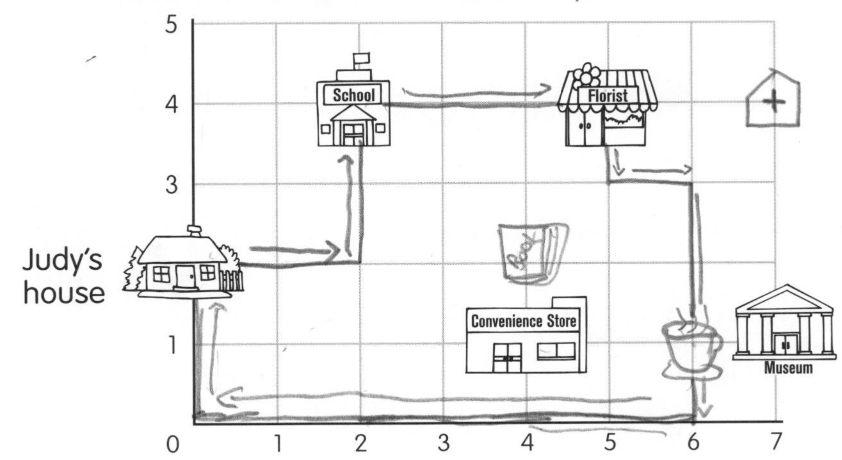

③ What is 2 units right and 3 units down from the florist? museam

④ What is 4 units left and 1 unit up from the convenience store? Judy's House

⑤ a. Draw lines on the grid to show the path that Judy's mom took to have her things done.

(0,2) ➔ (2,4) ➔ (5,4) ➔ (6,1) ➔ (2,0) ➔ (0,2)

b. List in order the places that Judy's mom passed by.

Judy's house, school, florist, coffee shop,

________________, 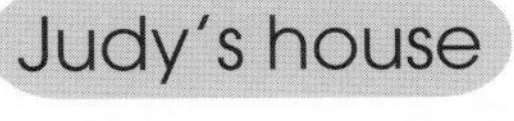

c. If Judy leaves the museum and goes to the convenience store, where will she have a chance to run into her mother?

coffe shop

*Alain Robert, nicknamed 'Spiderman', is a French **climber**. He has scaled more than 70 skyscrapers, including the Sear's Tower (443 m), with only his bare hands.*

DATE: ____________

Day 75

Number Patterns and Pattern Rules

x 2   + 1   x 2   + 1   x 2

5 10 11 22 23 46

Next two numbers: 47 , 94

Follow each pattern rule to fill in the missing numbers.

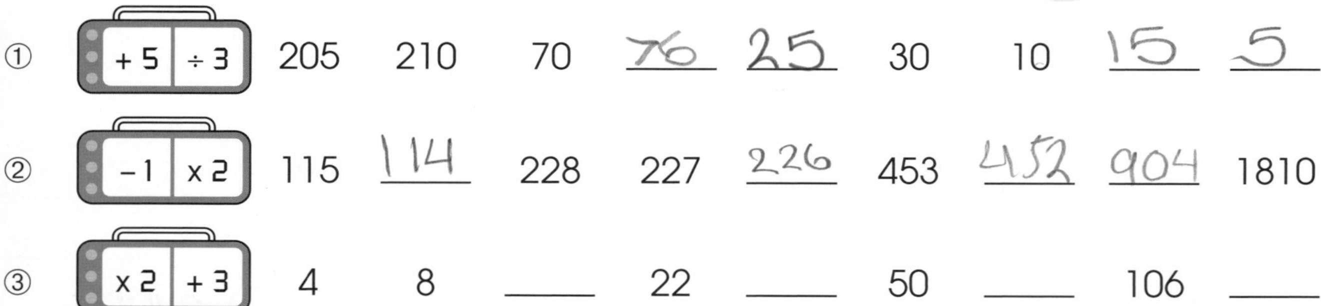

① [+ 5 | ÷ 3] 205 210 70 76 25 30 10 15 5

② [− 1 | x 2] 115 114 228 227 226 453 452 904 1810

③ [x 2 | + 3] 4 8 ____ 22 ____ 50 ____ 106 ____

④ [÷ 2 | + 10] 900 ____ ____ 230 240 ____ 130 ____ 75

Find out the pattern rule for each number pattern. Then find the next 3 numbers.

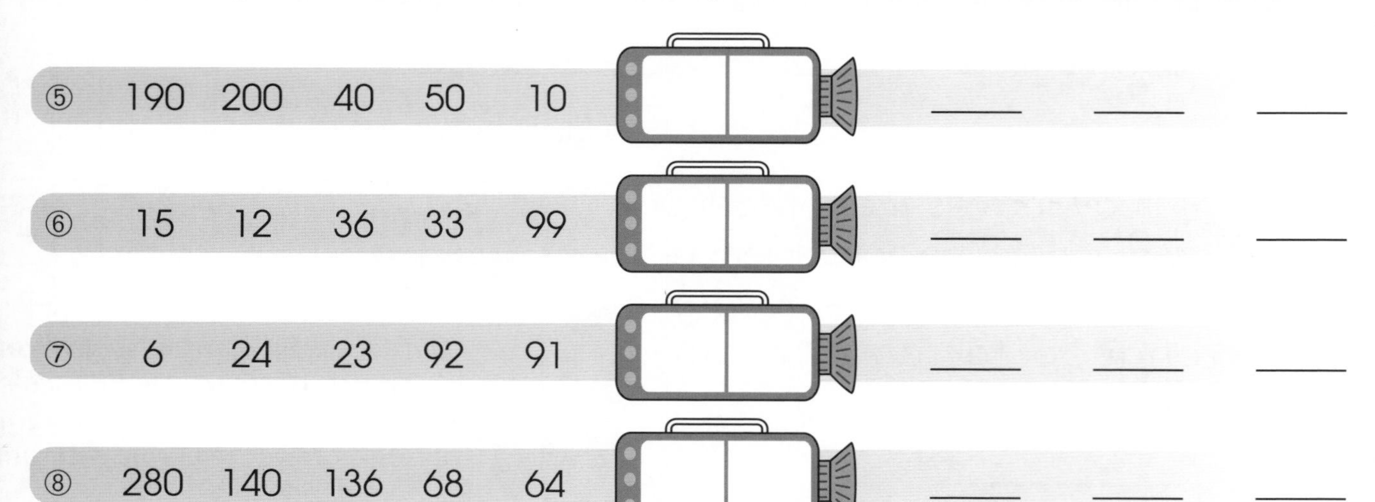

⑤ 190 200 40 50 10 [|] ____ ____ ____

⑥ 15 12 36 33 99 [|] ____ ____ ____

⑦ 6 24 23 92 91 [|] ____ ____ ____

⑧ 280 140 136 68 64 [|] ____ ____ ____

Follow each number pattern to find the next 4 numbers. Then apply the same pattern rule on the given number to create another set of numbers.

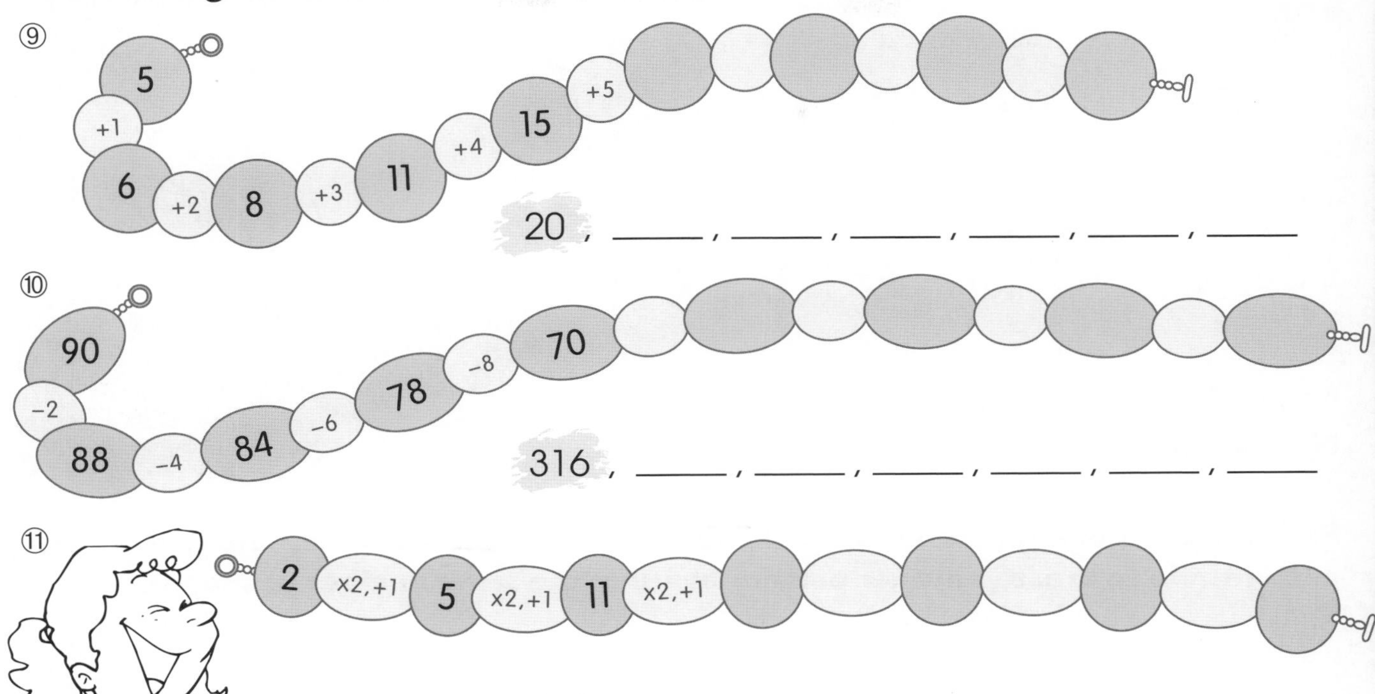

⑨ 20 , ______ , ______ , ______ , ______ , ______ , ______

⑩ 316 , ______ , ______ , ______ , ______ , ______ , ______

⑪ 9 , ______ , ______ , ______ , ______ , ______ , ______

For each group of numbers, write the rule that you can use to obtain the 2nd number from the 1st number. Then follow the rule to write two more pairs of numbers.

1st number	1	2	3	4	5
2nd number	4	7	10	13	16

1 x 3 + 1 2 x 3 + 1 3 x 3 + 1

Rule: Multiply the 1st number by 3; then add 1.

⑫

1st number	2	4	10		
2nd number	2	3	6		

Rule: ______________________

⑬

1st number	5	8	10		
2nd number	9	18	24		

Rule: ______________________

Did you know?

The Chauvet Cave in France contains the oldest known **cave paintings**, dated about 32 000 years ago. More than 260 animal paintings of 13 different species were found there.

DATE: ____________

Day 76

Creating Patterns

No. of Eyes: Increase by 2 each time

No. of Legs: Increase by 1 each time

Follow each shape pattern to draw the next two pictures. Then apply the same pattern rule to create another pattern by using the same number of shapes.

①

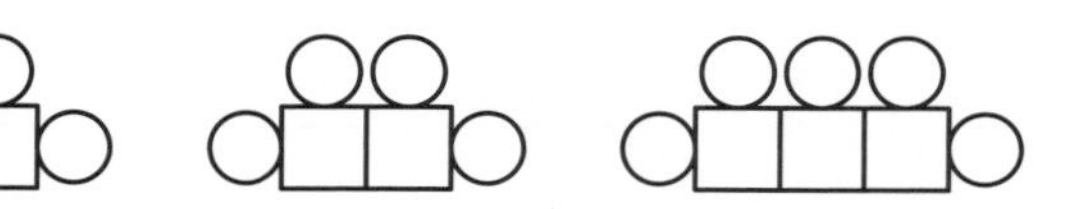

②

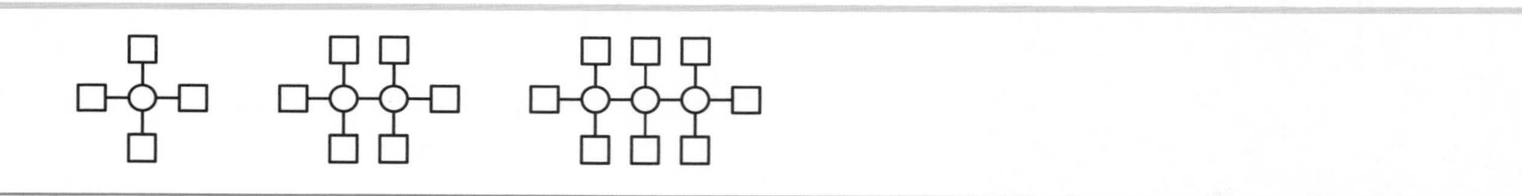

③

Use the given operations and numbers in each group to make four different pattern rules. Then create a set of numbers for each pattern rule.

④

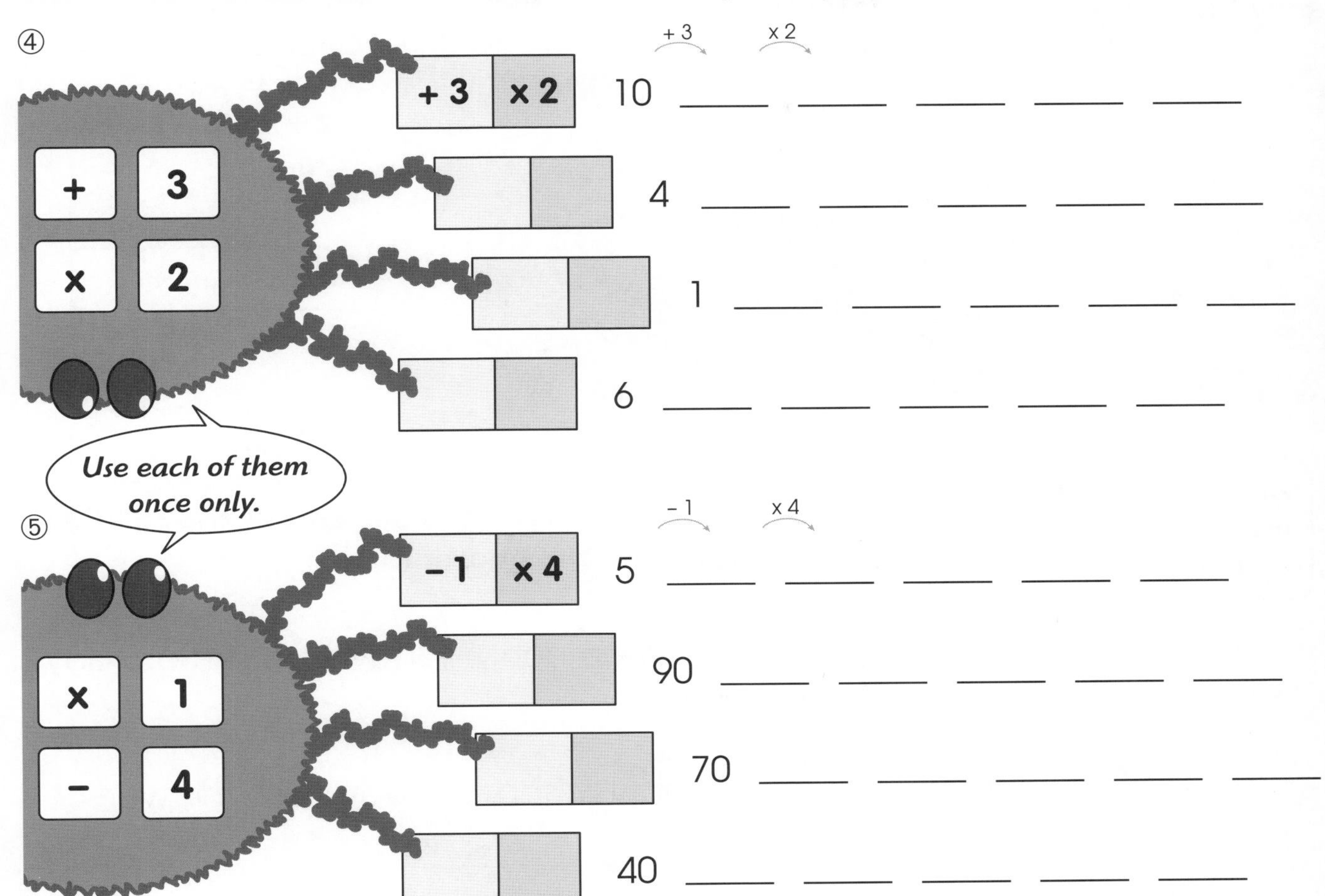

⑤

– 1 x 4

– 1 | x 4 5 ___ ___ ___ ___ ___

x 1

– 4

90 ___ ___ ___ ___ ___

70 ___ ___ ___ ___ ___

40 ___ ___ ___ ___ ___

Follow each bead pattern to draw the next picture and write the matching number sentences.

⑥

1 x 1 = 1 2 x 2 = 4 3 x 3 = 9 ___________

⑦

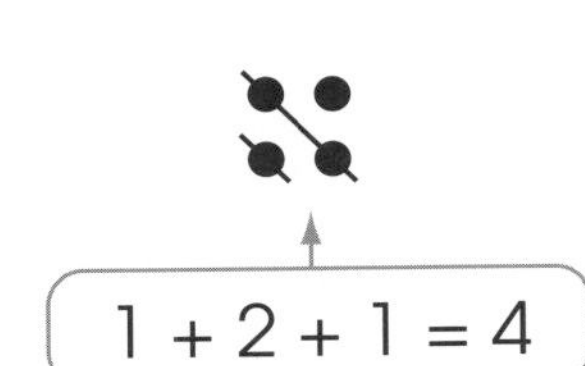

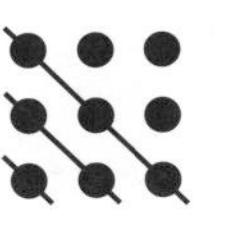

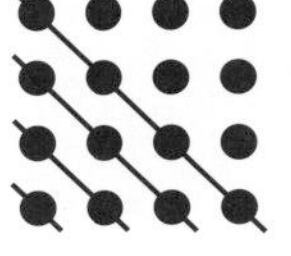

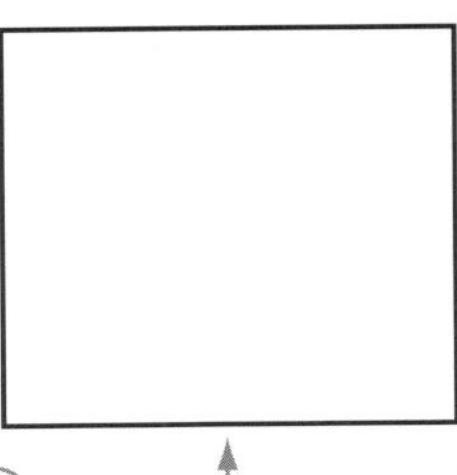

1 + 2 + 1 = 4

1 + 2 + 3 + 2 + 1 = 9

1 + 2 + 3 + 4 + 3 + 2 + 1 = 16

DATE: ______________

Problems Involving Patterns

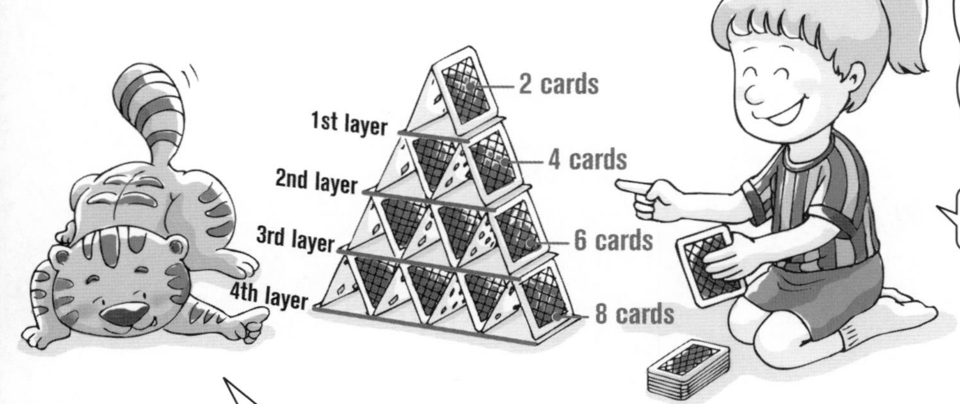

Complete the tables to show the patterns of the children's savings. Then answer the questions.

① a.

Judy's Savings

Day	Savings (¢)
Sun	20
Mon	40
Tue	60
Wed	80
Thu	
Fri	

b. How much will Judy save on Saturday?

____

c. How much will Judy save this week?

____

d. On which day will Judy put $2 into her piggy bank?

____

② a.

Maria's Savings

Day	Savings (¢)
1	400
2	375
3	350
4	325
5	
6	

b. How much will Maria save on Day 7?

____

c. On which day will Maria put $2 into her piggy bank?

____

d. If Maria saves quarters only, how many quarters will Maria save on Day 12?

____

Tommy played a computer game with his friends. Look at their scores and follow the patterns to complete the table. Then answer the questions.

③

Game	1st	2nd	3rd	4th	5th	6th	7th
Tommy	20	40	60	80	100		
Wayne	40	50	60	70	80		
Sean	85	80	75	70	65		
Peter	10	20	40	80	160		

④ Describe the patterns of the children's scores.

a. Tommy: He got ______ points in the 1st game. Then he got ______ points more each time.

b. Wayne: ______________________

____

c. Sean: ______________________

____

d. Peter: ______________________

____

⑤ How many points will each boy get in the 8th game?

Tommy: ______ points Wayne: ______ points

Sean: ______ points Peter: ______ points

⑥ If Wayne doubles the points that he got in the 1st game, will he beat Tommy in the 7th game? ______

⑦ If Peter gets only half of his score in the 1st game, will he still beat all the boys in the 7th game? ______

DATE: ____________________

Day 78

Simple Equations

We've got 300 points!

Each of us has got 100 points.

Use the 'guess-and-test' method to find the unknowns.

Solving equations:

e.g. $12 \times y = 60$

1st Think:

What number multiplied by 12 is 60?

2nd

Guess	Test
3	12 x 3 = 36 (not 60) ✘
4	12 x 4 = 48 (not 60) ✘
5	12 x 5 = 60 ✔

$y = 5$

① $m + 28 = 40$

Guess	Test

$m =$ ______

② $n - 17 = 53$

Guess	Test

$n =$ ______

③ $k \times 6 = 72$

Guess	Test

$k =$ ______

④ $a \div 5 = 27$

Guess	Test

$a =$ ______

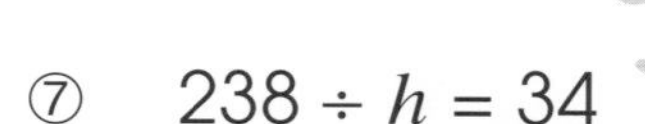

⑤ $91 - y = 16$

Guess	Test

$y =$ ______

⑥ $23 \times b = 184$

Guess	Test

$b =$ ______

⑦ $238 \div h = 34$

Guess	Test

$h =$ ______

Find the unknowns.

⑧ $36 - m = 4$

$m =$

⑨ $x + 11 = 49$

$x =$

⑩ $n \div 6 = 36$

$n =$

⑪ $15 \times h = 300$

$h =$

⑫ $y - 47 = 28$

$y =$

⑬ $150 \div k = 15$

$k =$

$y - 5 = 7 + 16$ ← simplify 7 + 16 first

$y - 5 = 23$ ← Think: What number minus 5 is 23?

$y = 28$

Simplify the equations. Then find the unknowns.

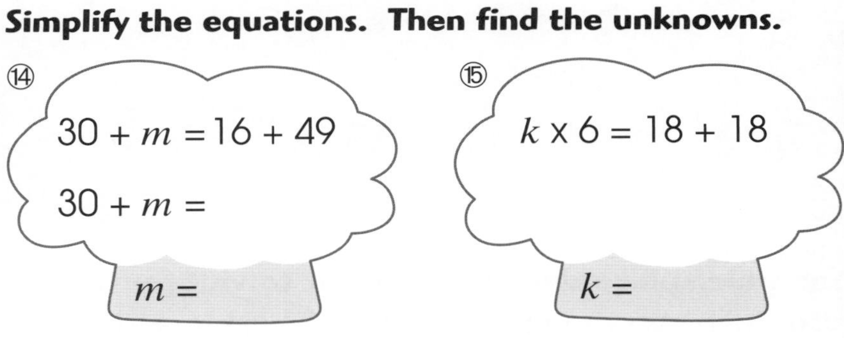

⑭ $30 + m = 16 + 49$

$30 + m =$

$m =$

⑮ $k \times 6 = 18 + 18$

$k =$

⑯ $24 \div y = 16 - 12$

$y =$

⑰ $52 - a = 25 \times 2$

$a =$

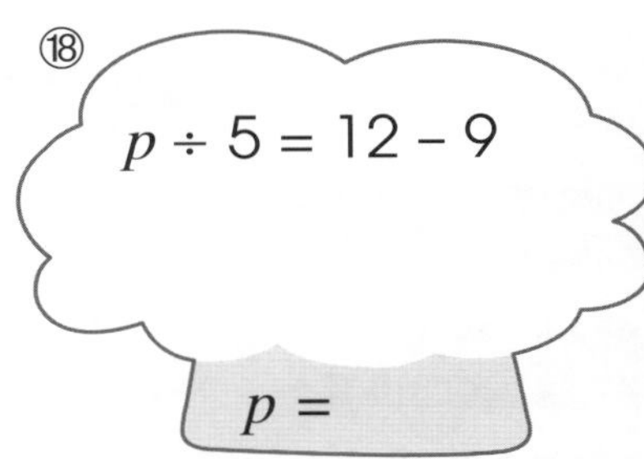

⑱ $p \div 5 = 12 - 9$

$p =$

Read what the children say. Check the correct equations. Then find the answers.

⑲

If I eat 4 candies, the number of candies left will equal the total number of candies in the bag and in the box. How many candies do I have at first?

Helen

Ⓐ $4 - y = 15 + 8$ Ⓑ $y - 4 = 15 + 8$ Ⓒ $4 = y + 15 + 8$

Helen has ______ candies.

⑳

If the total cost of 4 balls equals the total cost of a bear and a top, how much does a ball cost?

Ⓐ $4 + k = 9 + 3$ Ⓑ $4 \times k = 9 \times 3$ Ⓒ $4 \times k = 9 + 3$

A ball costs $ ______ .

DATE: ____________________

Day 79

Pictographs

See which place the children want to visit for their next outing.
Use the pictograph to complete the table and answer the questions.

Places to Visit (one figure = 20)

Niagara Falls
CN Tower
Algonquin Park
ROM

Remember to check the legend of each graph.

e.g. (one figure) = 10

Each picture represents 10 people.

①

	Niagara Falls	CN Tower	Algonquin Park	ROM
No. of Children				

② If 72 girls want to visit CN Tower, how many boys want to go there?

_______ boys

③ If one third of the children who want to visit Niagara Falls are girls, how many boys want to go there?

_______ boys

④ How many children want to have activities outdoors?

_______ children

See what kind of food the people in the food court of Maple Mall have for lunch. Use a pictograph to show the data. Then answer the questions.

Look at the data.

Then decide what scale should be used to present them.

Food	No. of People
Pizza	150
Salad	100
Spaghetti	250
Sandwich	500
Fried Chicken	450

⑤

⑥ If each order of salad costs $7.99, how much do the people pay in all for salad? ____________

⑦ If there are 175 orders of forest ham sandwiches, how many orders of sandwiches are not forest ham? ____________

⑧ What do most people have for lunch? ____________

⑨ There are usually about 200 orders of fried chicken each day, but the number of fried chicken orders today is a lot different from normal. What do you think could be the reason?

____

⑩ Mr. Jones wants to open a foodstall in Maple Mall. If you were Mr. Jones, what type of food would you sell? Why?

____

____

____

Did you know?

*Most octopuses can only live for one or two years. However, the **Giant Pacific Octopus** can live for about 4 years.*

DATE: ____________________

Reading Bar Graphs

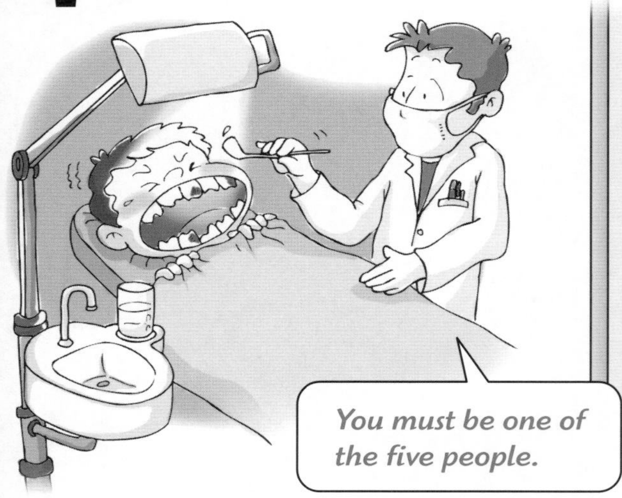

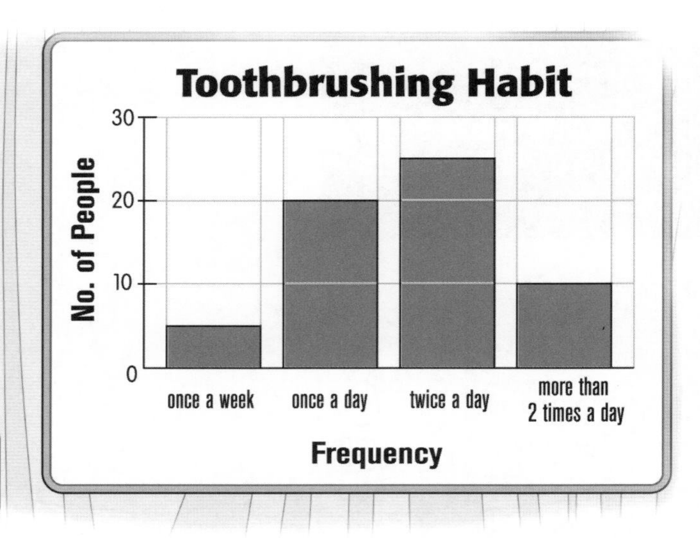

Read the graph showing the number of packs of toothbrushes sold last week. Then complete the table and answer the questions.

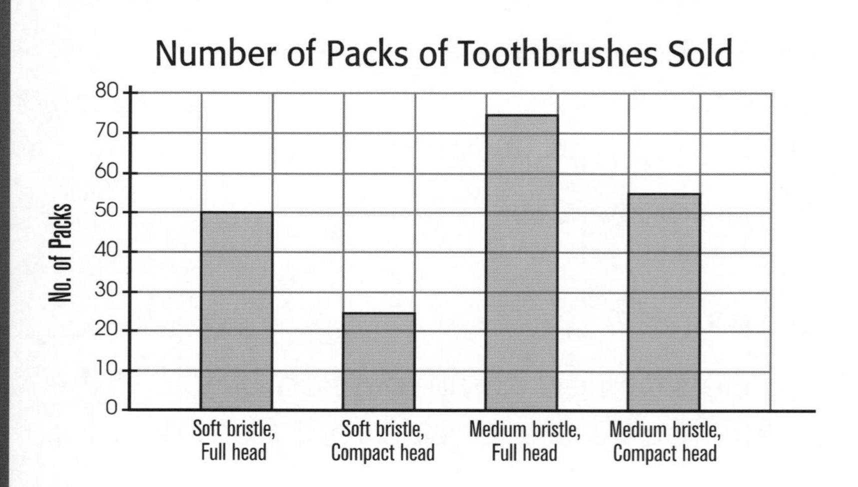

①

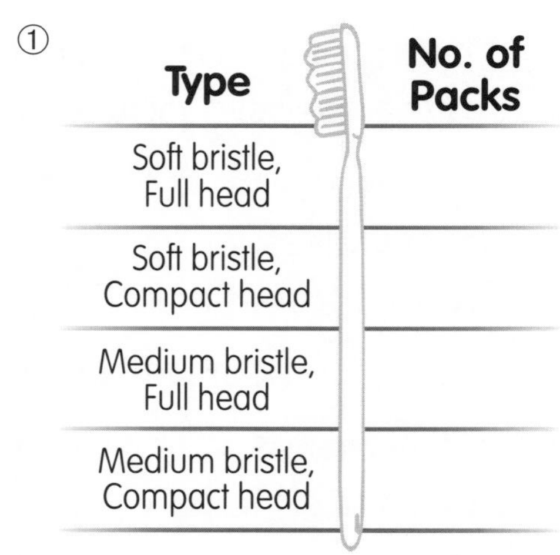

Type	No. of Packs
Soft bristle, Full head	
Soft bristle, Compact head	
Medium bristle, Full head	
Medium bristle, Compact head	

② How many packs of soft-bristle toothbrushes were sold in all? ________ packs

③ How many packs of compact-head toothbrushes were sold in all? ________ packs

④ If there are 8 toothbrushes in each pack, how many soft-bristle and compact-head toothbrushes were sold in all? ________ toothbrushes

⑤ If each pack of toothbrushes costs $12, how much was earned selling the medium- bristle and compact-head toothbrushes? $ ________

Look at the bar graph. Complete the table and answer the questions.

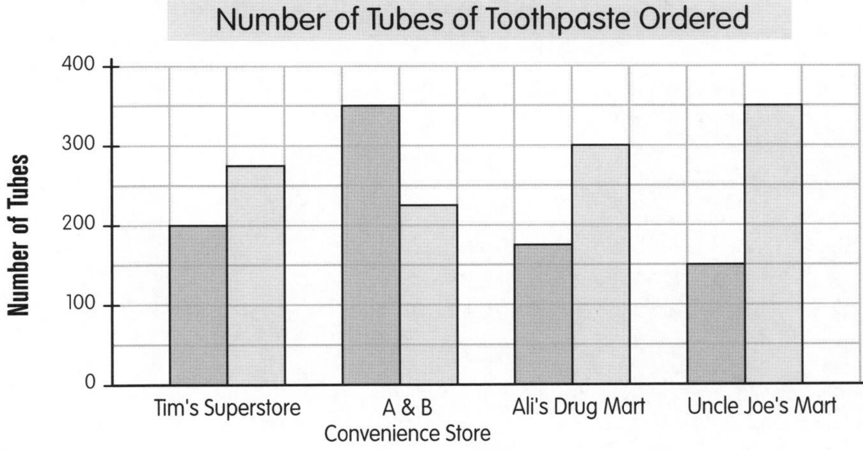

⑥

	Tim's Superstore	A & B Convenience Store	Ali's Drug Mart	Uncle Joe's Mart
Winterfresh Gel	tubes	tubes	tubes	tubes
Whitening Paste	tubes	tubes	tubes	tubes

⑦ How many tubes of toothpaste did A&B Convenience Store order in all? ________ tubes

⑧ Which store ordered the most Winterfresh Gel toothpaste? ______________

⑨ Which store ordered the most Whitening Paste toothpaste? ______________

⑩ If there are 25 tubes of toothpaste in a box, how many boxes of toothpaste did Ali's Drug Mart order in all? ________ boxes

⑪ If a tube of toothpaste costs [two 25-cent coins], how much will Uncle Joe's Mart need to pay for the order?

$ ________

Did you know?

Human grows 2 sets of teeth. Children have 20 **milk teeth**, while the permanent set is formed between the ages of 6 and 12.

DATE: ____________________

Day 81

Making Bar Graphs

Read how much each child has and make a bar graph to show the data. Then answer the questions.

①

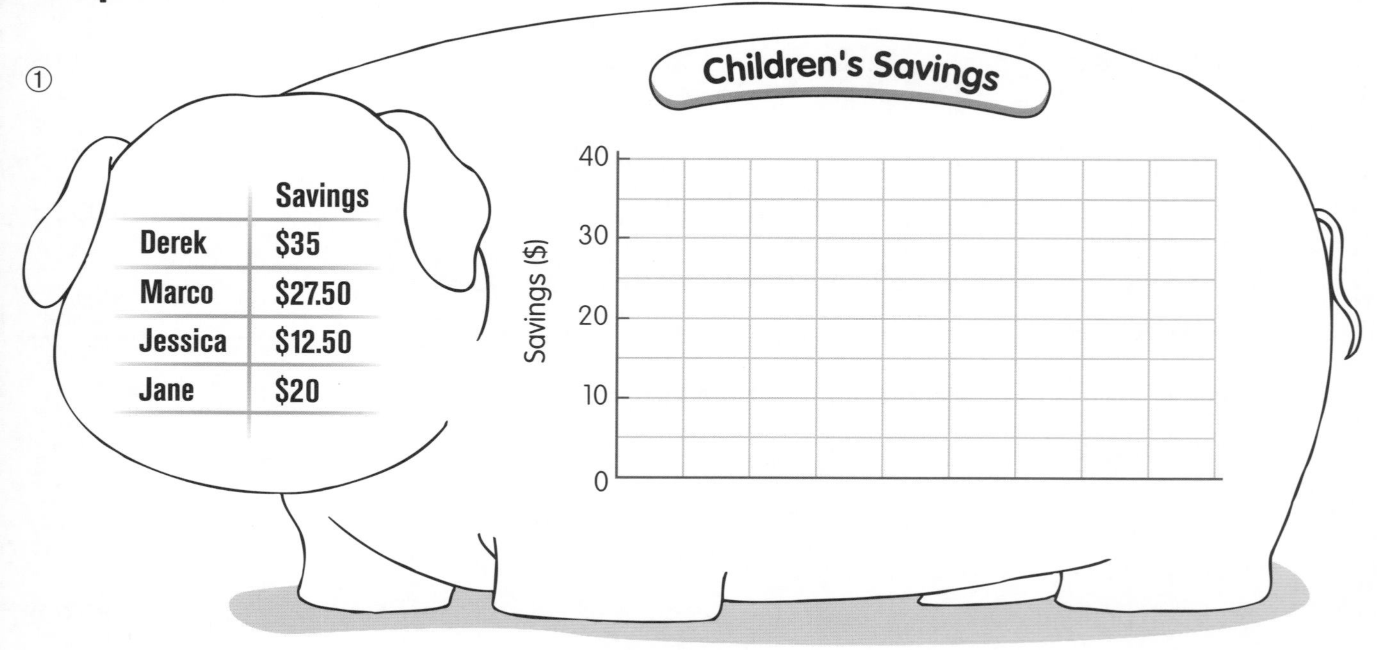

	Savings
Derek	$35
Marco	$27.50
Jessica	$12.50
Jane	$20

② How much more did Derek have than Jessica? ____________

③ If a rolls of stickers costs $9, what is the maximum number of roll of stickers Marco can buy with his savings? ____________

④ If Marco wants to have the same amount of money as Jessica, how much should Marco give her? ____________

The children have collected different containers for their recycling campaign. Help them use a bar graph to show the data. Then answer the questions.

⑤

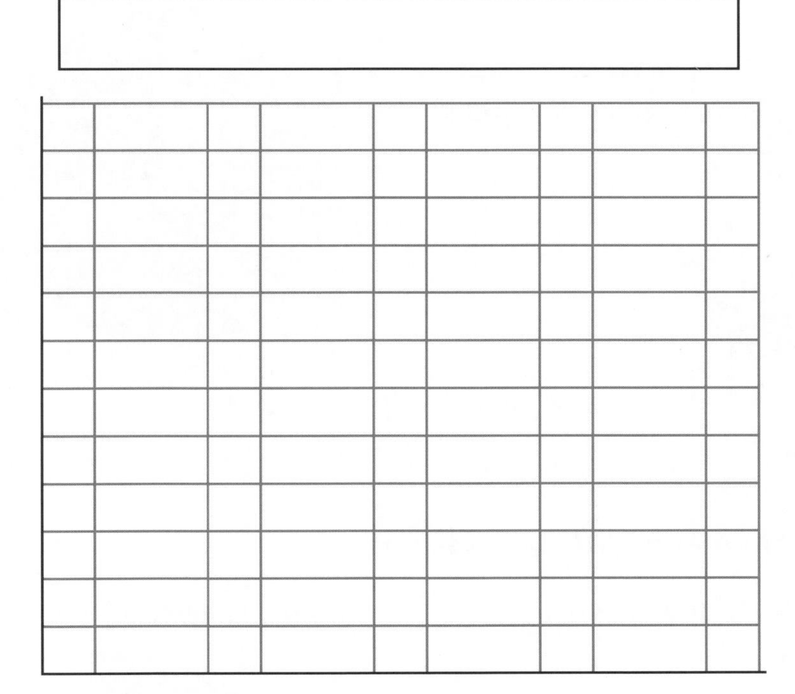

No. of Containers

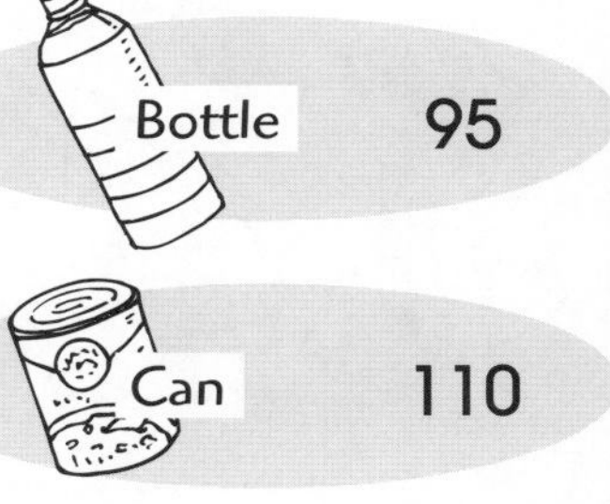

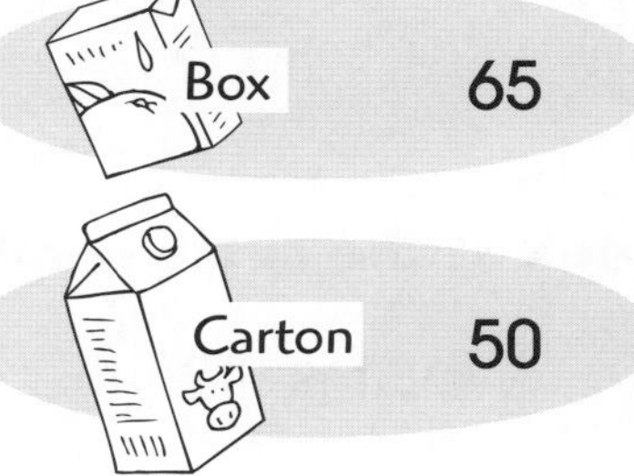

⑥ Which type of container is most collected? ____________

⑦ Which type of container is least collected? ____________

⑧ How many fewer boxes are collected than bottles? ____________

⑨ How many containers are collected in all? ____________

$$\text{Average} = \frac{\text{Total}}{\text{Number of Addends}}$$

⑩ If there were 64 children participating in the campaign, how many containers were collected by each child on average?

____

⑪ *Each box holds 70 items.*

How many recycle boxes are needed to hold all the containers collected?

____

DATE: ____________________

Reading Circle Graphs

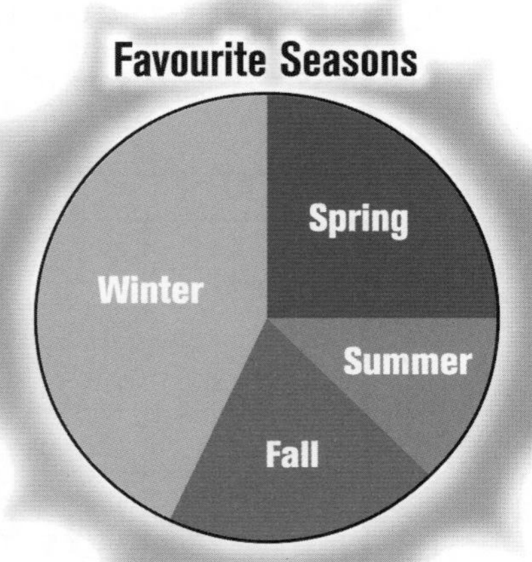

Look at the circle graph. Then answer the questions.

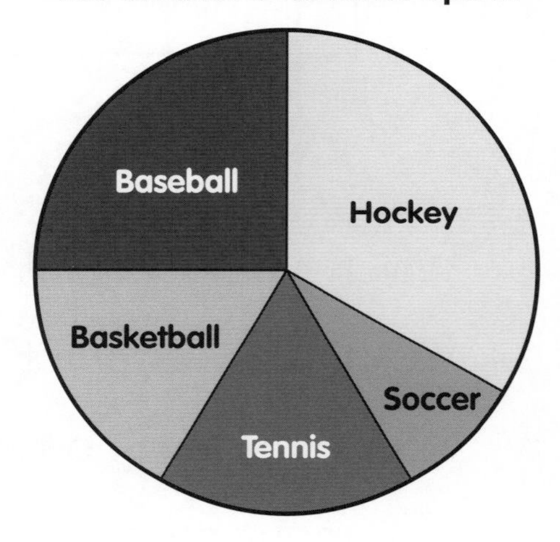

① What is the title of the graph?

____

② How many kinds of sports are shown? What are they?

____

____

③ Which sport do most children like?

____

④ Which sport do fewest children like? __________

⑤ Which sport is a bit less popular than hockey? __________

⑥ About what fraction of the children like hockey? __________

⑦ If 10 children like soccer, about how many children like basketball? __________

⑧ If 40 children like tennis, about how many children like soccer? __________

See what the children in Mrs. Smith's class have for breakfast. Use the circle graph to answer the questions.

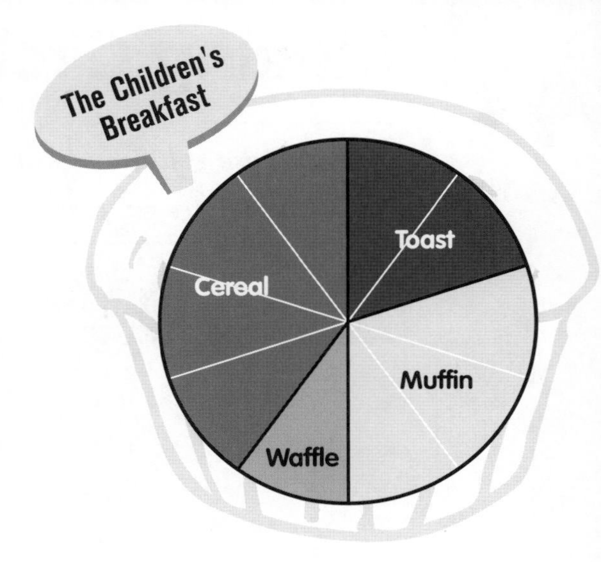

⑨ Which is the least popular food for breakfast? ______________

⑩ Which is the most popular food for breakfast? ______________

⑪ What fraction of the children like

a. toast? ______________ b. muffin? ______________

c. waffle? ______________ d. cereal? ______________

⑫ How many children like

For question ⑫, find out how many children each part represents first.

a. toast? ______________

b. muffin? ______________

c. waffle? ______________

d. cereal? ______________

⑬ If $\frac{1}{3}$ of the children who have muffin choose cereal for breakfast, which circle graph shows the new data?

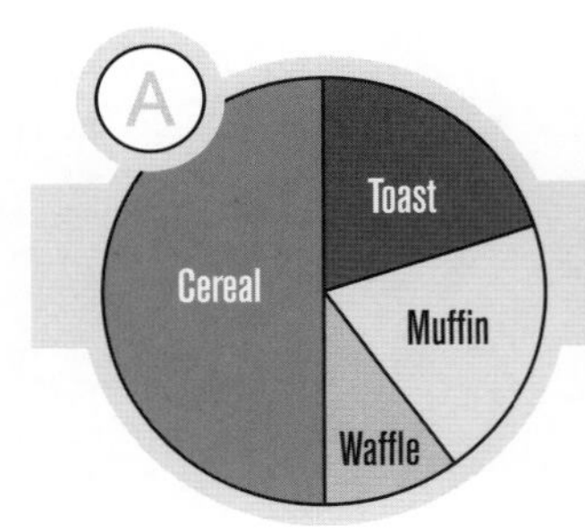

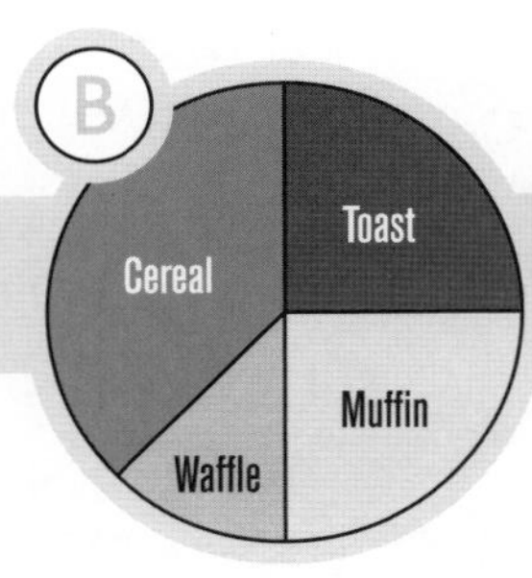

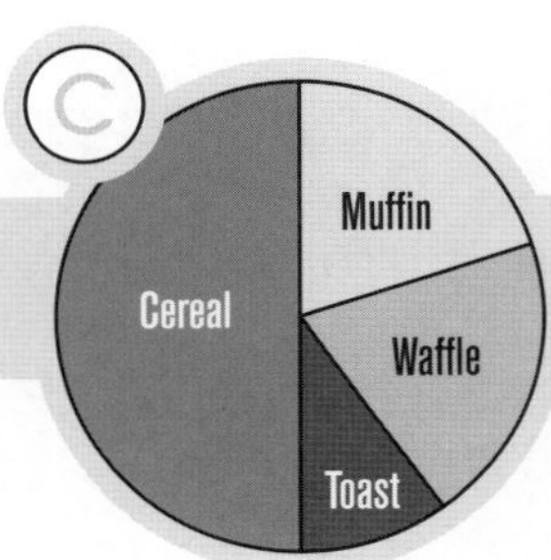

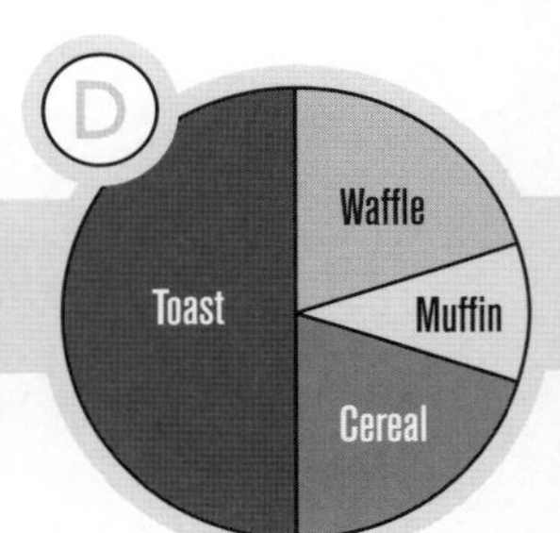

DATE: ____________

Day 83

Making Circle Graphs

$\frac{1}{3}$ *of us are goldfish;* $\frac{1}{4}$ *are mollies; and the rest are guppies.*

Fish in The Tank

Molly

Goldfish

So $\frac{5}{12}$ *of the fish are guppies, right?*

Modify the circle graph below to make it more well-organized. Then answer the questions.

①

Fruits in the Basket

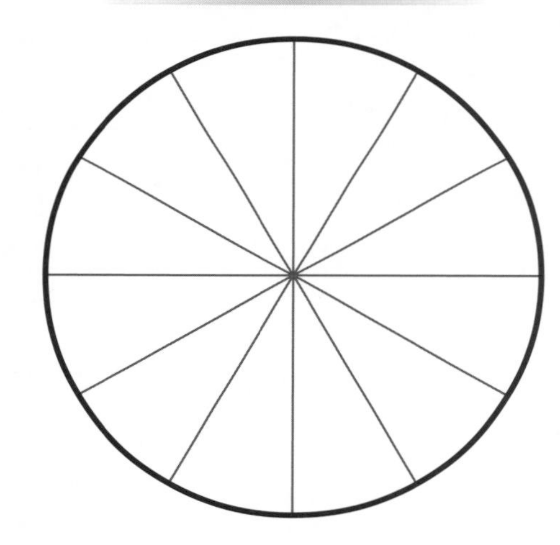

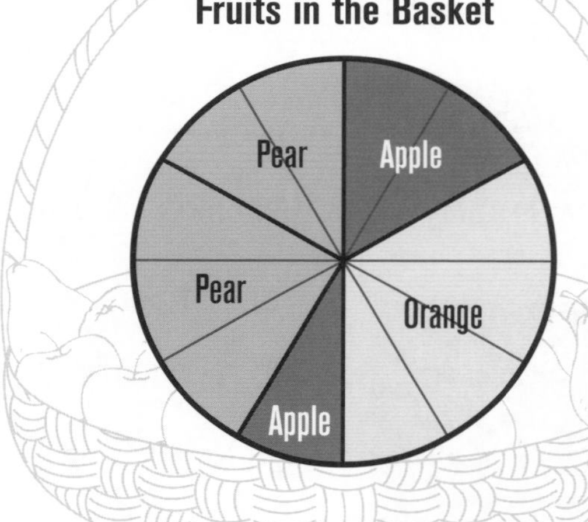

② What fraction of the fruits are

a. apples? ______ b. oranges? ______ c. pears? ______

③ Which kind of fruit is in the greatest portion? ____________

④ There are 24 fruit items in the basket.

a. How many pears are there in the basket? ____________

b. If $\frac{1}{2}$ of the pears are rotten, how many pears are not rotten? ____________

Mary's mother has made some cookies. Use a circle graph to show the data. Then answer the questions.

Fraction of the total number of cookies

Peanut butter: $\frac{1}{8}$

Chocolate chip: $\frac{5}{16}$

Oatmeal raisin: $\frac{1}{2}$

White chocolate: $\frac{1}{16}$

⑤

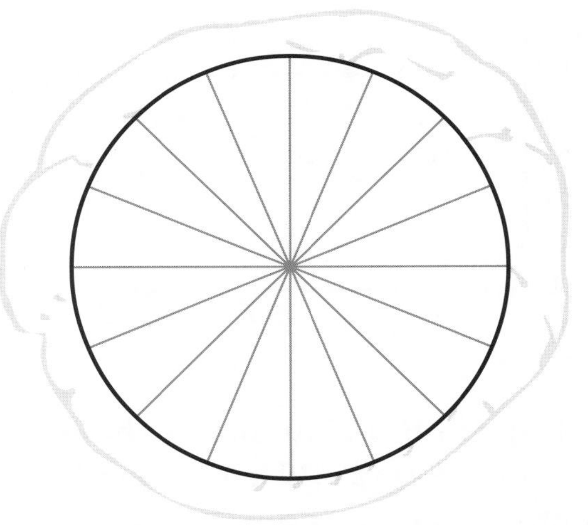

⑥ Most cookies are ______________ flavoured.

⑦ The number of peanut butter cookies is ________ times the number of white chocolate cookies.

⑧ The number of oatmeal raisin cookies is ________ times the number of peanut butter cookies.

⑨ Mary's mother has made 16 cookies. There are ________ peanut butter cookies, ________ chocolate chip cookies, ________ oatmeal raisin cookies, and ________ white chocolate cookie.

⑩ Mary gives all the oatmeal raisin cookies to her grandma. Help her use a circle graph to show the cookies left.

DATE: ____________

Day 84

Reading Line Graphs

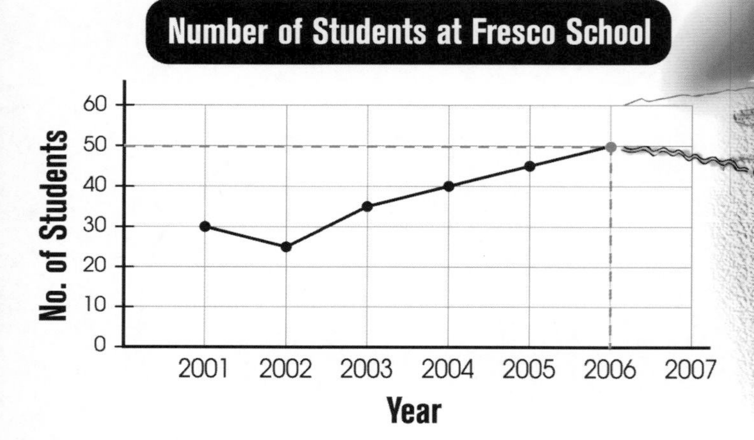

Fresco School

We have 50 students in 2006.

The line graph below shows the number of cartons of eggs sold in the past 6 weeks. Use the graph to answer the questions.

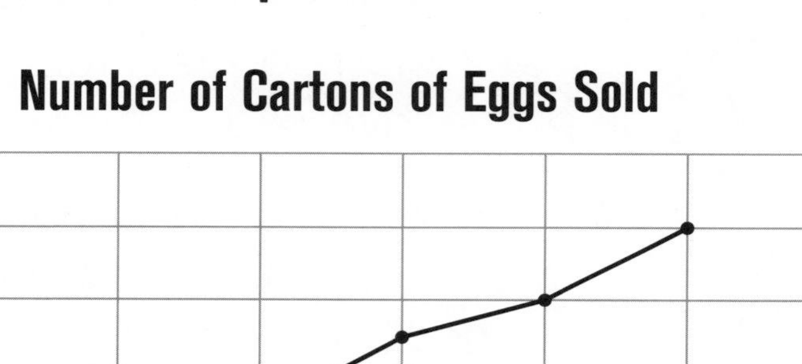
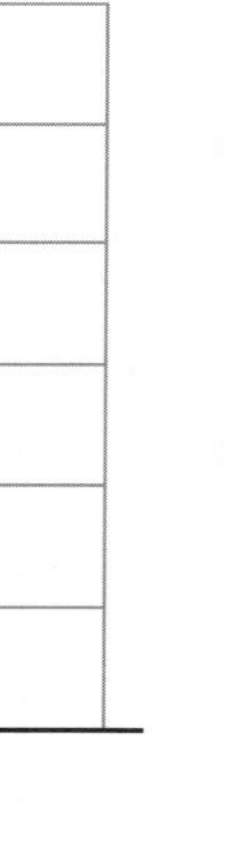

① How many cartons of eggs were sold in week 2? ________ cartons

② How many more cartons of eggs were sold in week 5 than in week 3? ________ more

③ How many eggs were sold in week 1? ________ eggs

④ How many cartons of eggs were sold each day on average in week 4? ________ cartons

⑤ How much was collected from selling the eggs in week 3? $ ________

The line graph below shows the savings of Jason and Katie. Use the graph to answer the questions.

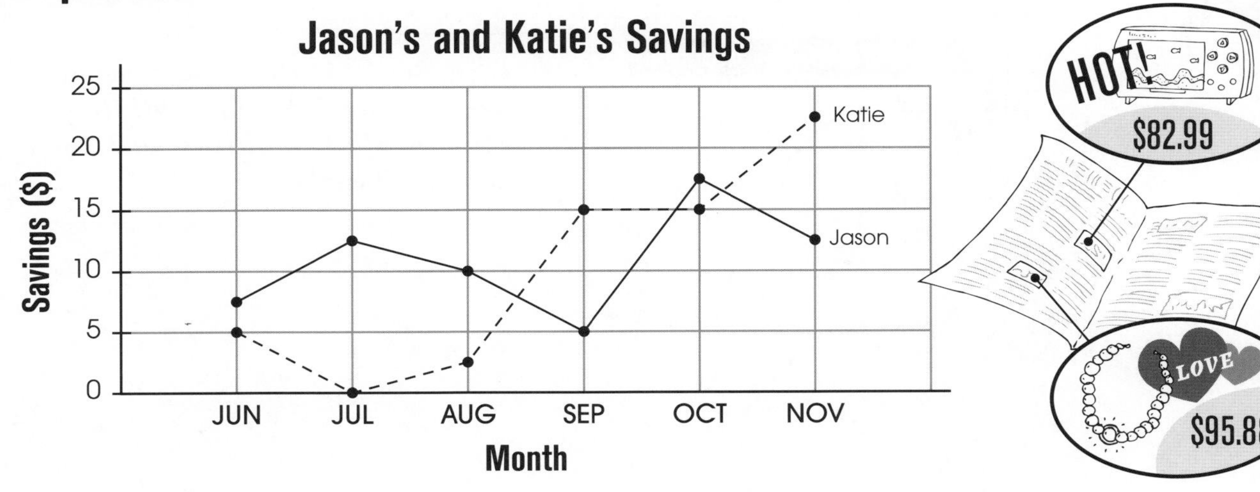

⑥ How much did Katie save in August? __________

⑦ How much did Jason save in November? __________

⑧ How much more did Jason save than Katie in October? __________

⑨ In which months did Katie save more than Jason? __________

⑩ How much did Jason save in the six months? __________

⑪ How much did Katie save in the six months? __________

⑫ How much did Katie save each month on average? __________

⑬

How much do I need to save in December so that I can have enough money to buy a video game as a Christmas gift for Katie?

____

For question ⑭, find the total savings of Jason and Katie first. Then use subtraction to find the answer.

⑭

I want to buy a necklace as a Christmas gift for Mom and I'll ask Jason to share the cost. After buying the necklace, how much will Jason and I have left?

____

DATE: ____________

Day 85

Making Line Graphs

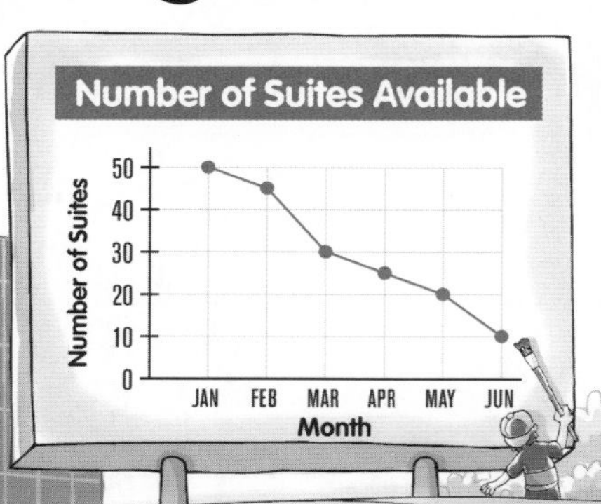

Look, Boss! More and more people are moving into our building. Maybe all the suites will be occupied by July.

See how much Joseph spent on cards. Help him show the data with a line graph. Then answer the questions.

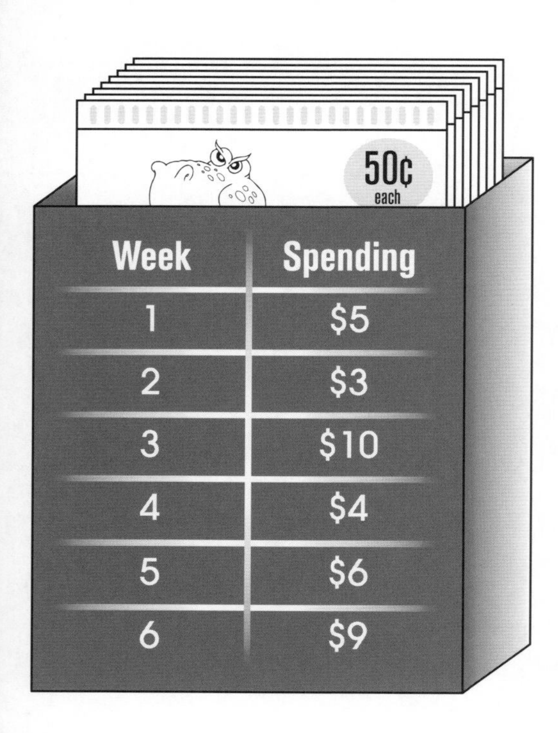

Week	Spending
1	$5
2	$3
3	$10
4	$4
5	$6
6	$9

① ____________

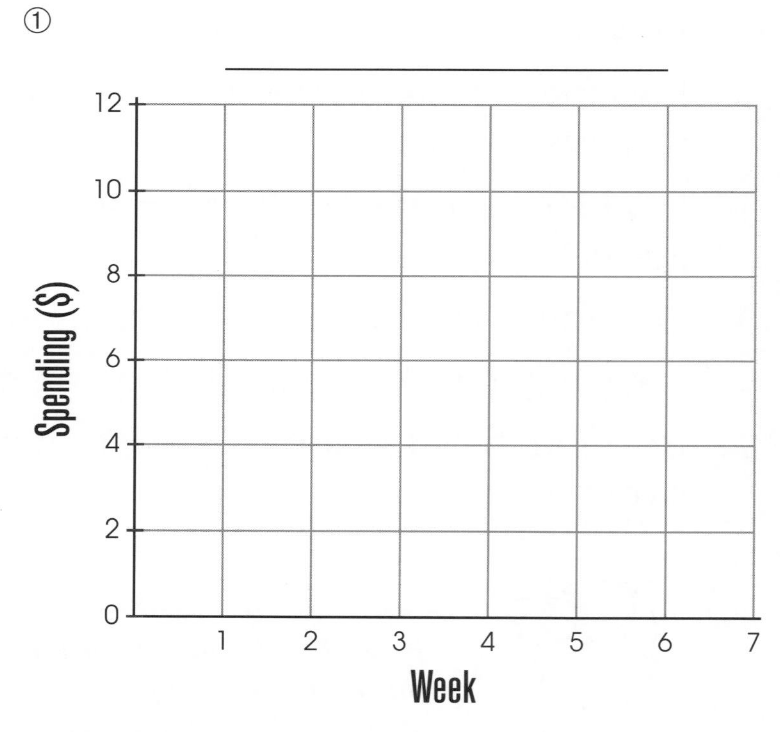

② How much more did Joseph spend in week 6 than in week 1? ____________

③ How many cards did Joseph buy in week 4? ____________

④ How much did Joseph spend in all in the six weeks? ____________

⑤ If Joseph buys 2 more cards in week 7 than in week 6, how many card does Joseph buy in week 7? ____________

Molly recorded the number of adult and children's tickets sold for a clown show. Help her complete the line graph to show the data. Then answer the questions.

	JAN	FEB	MAR	APR	MAY	JUN	JUL	AUG	SEP	OCT	NOV
No. of Adult Tickets	260	200	280	200	220	240	440	480	280	300	320
No. of Children's Tickets	140	180	200	200	300	140	380	420	120	200	180

When you draw a graph with more than 1 line, remember to label each line on the graph.

⑥

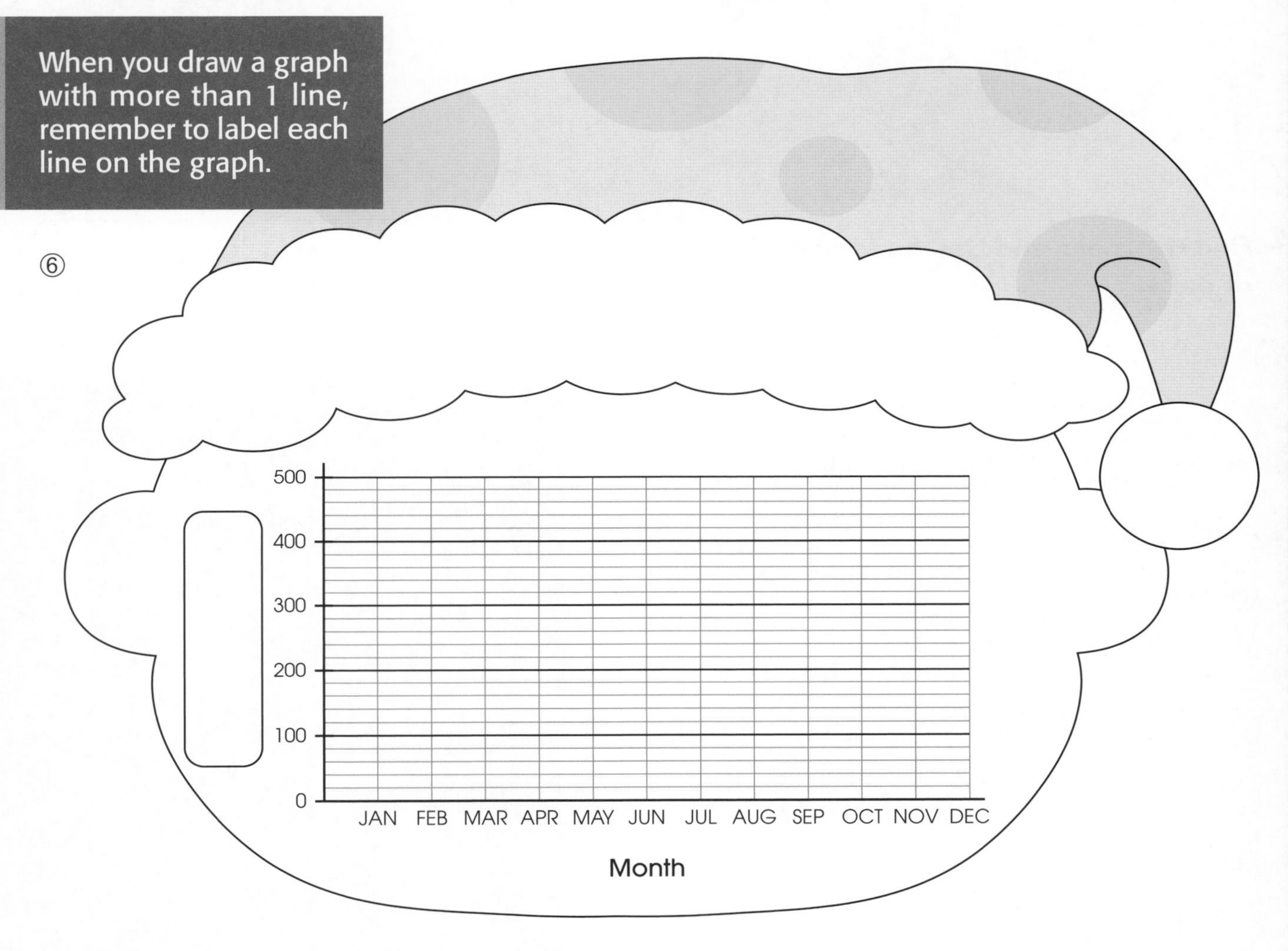

⑦ How many tickets were sold in June? ____________

⑧ In which month was the most tickets sold? Suggest a reason why it was so.

____

⑨ What do you expect the ticket sales to be in December, compared to the sales in November? Explain your answer.

____

DATE: ________________

Mean and Mode

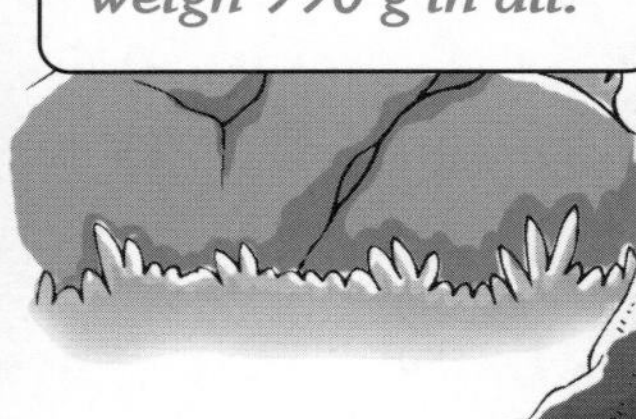

Mean: 990 g ÷ 6
= 165 g
Mode: 150 g

Yes! I know their mean is 165 g and their mode is 150 g. I can't wait to take a bite.

Find the mean and the mode of each group of data.

①

6.4 kg 5.8 kg
3.9 kg 4.5 kg
5.8 kg 3.6 kg

Mean: ________

Mode: ________

②

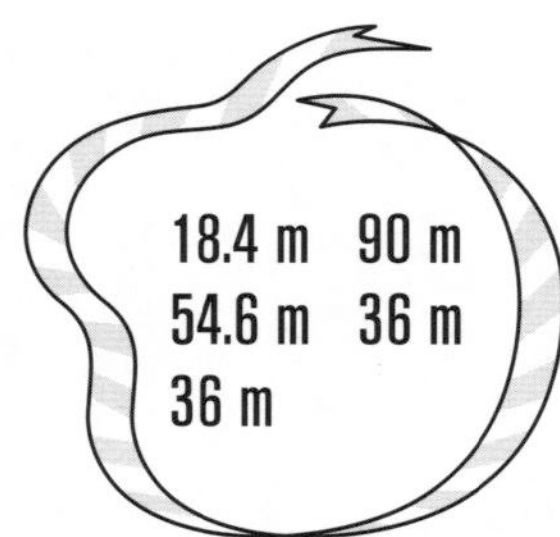

Mean: ________

Mode: ________

③

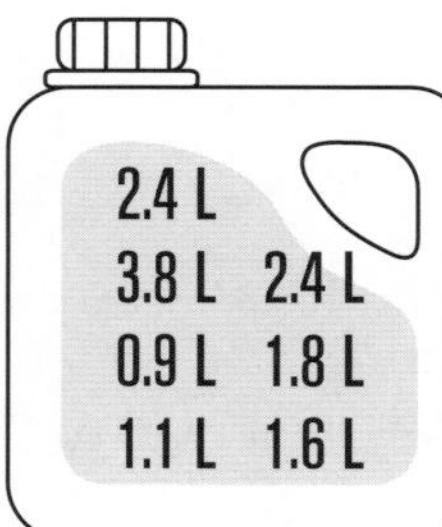

Mean: ________

Mode: ________

Mean:
the sum of a set of numbers divided by the total number of addends

Mode:
the number in a group which occurs most often

e.g. The number of children in each group:

16 24 16 8 11

Mean: (16 + 24 + 16 + 8 + 11) ÷ 5
= 15
Mode: 16

The mean number of children in each group is 15; the mode number is 16.

④

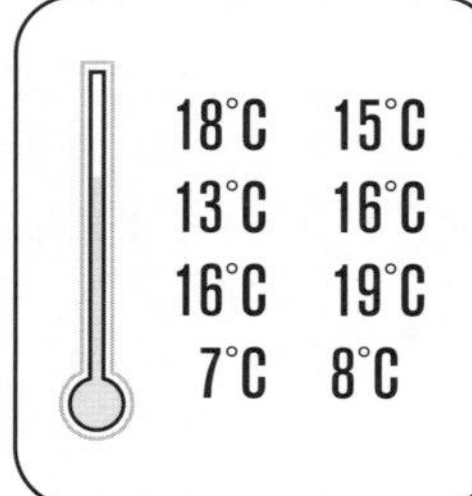

Mean: ________

Mode: ________

⑤

16.4 cm² 13 cm²
16.4 cm² 25 cm²
28 cm² 6.8 cm²

Mean: ________

Mode: ________

Read what the children say. Help them find the means and the modes.

I have 4 bags of candies. They weigh 43.2 g, 56.9 g, 43.2 g, and 44.7 g. What are the mean weight and the mode weight of my candies?

The mean is ________ and the mode is ________ .

I have 3 big boxes each with 64 marbles and 2 small boxes each with 54 marbles. What are the mean number and mode number of marbles in the boxes?

The mean is ________ and the mode is ________ .

I have 2 red apples and 4 green apples. Each red apple weighs 182 g and each green apple weighs 3 g less than the red ones. What are the mean weight and the mode weight of the apples?

For question ⑧, find the weight of a green apple first. Then use multiplication and addition to find the total weight of the apples.

The mean is ________ and the mode is ________ .

⑨

The mean savings are ________ and the mode savings are ________ .

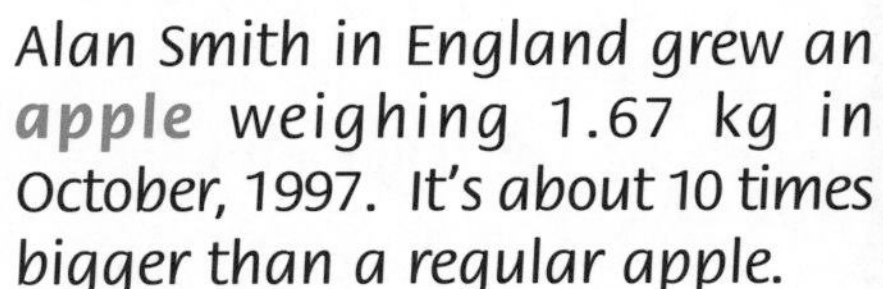

Did you know?

Alan Smith in England grew an **apple** weighing 1.67 kg in October, 1997. It's about 10 times bigger than a regular apple.

DATE: ____________

Probability (1)

There are only 3 of us. The probability of each of us being eaten is 1 out of 3.

Probability:

a number showing how likely it is that an event will happen

$$\text{Probability} = \frac{\text{No. of outcomes of a particular event}}{\text{Total no. of outcomes}}$$

no chance to happen → 0 — other events — 1 ← certain to happen

The more probable the event, the greater the fraction.

Write fraction in simplest form to describe the probability of each event.

Marbles
5 green
3 red
2 yellow

① What is the probability of picking

a. a green marble? ______

b. a red marble? ______

c. a yellow marble? ______

② What is the probability of choosing

a. a boy? ______

b. a girl? ______

c. a boy with glasses? ______

③ What is the probability of landing on

a. 'crackers'? ______

b. 'chips'? ______

c. 'lollipop'? ______

d. 'candy'? ______

The children are going to spin one of their teachers' spinners below to see what snacks they can have. Help them write fraction in simplest form to describe the probability of each event. Then answer the questions.

④ Mr. Winter's Spinner

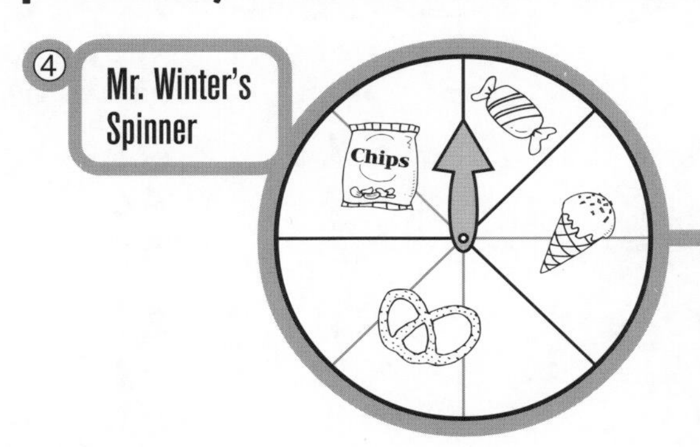

The probability of landing on

a. (chips) : ______ b. (candy) : ______

c. (pretzel) : ______ d. (lollipop) : ______

⑤ Mr. Hall's Spinner

The probability of landing on

a. (cake) : ______ b. (ice cream cone) : ______

c. (cherry candy) : ______ d. (doughnut) : ______

⑥ Mrs. Wood's Spinner

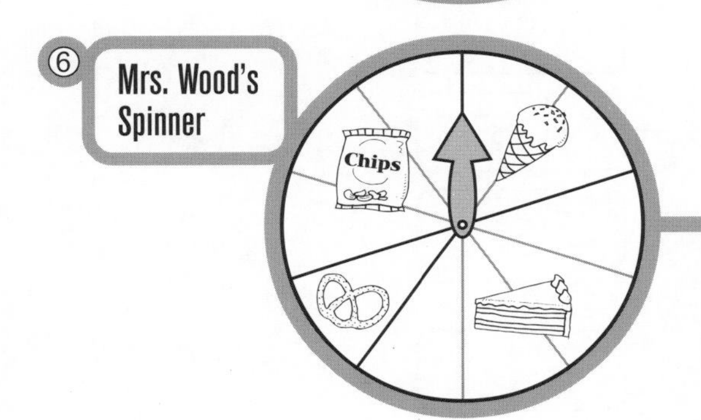

The probability of landing on

a. (ice cream cone) : ______ b. (pretzel) : ______

c. (cake) : ______ d. (candy) : ______

⑦ Which spinner should Jane choose to spin? Explain.

____

____

I want to have an ice cream cone.

Jane

⑧ Which spinner should Mary choose not to spin? Explain.

____

____

I love candies.

DATE: ______________

Day 88

Probability (2)

See what bread and what fillings are available. Complete the tree diagram to show all the choices. Then answer the questions.

①

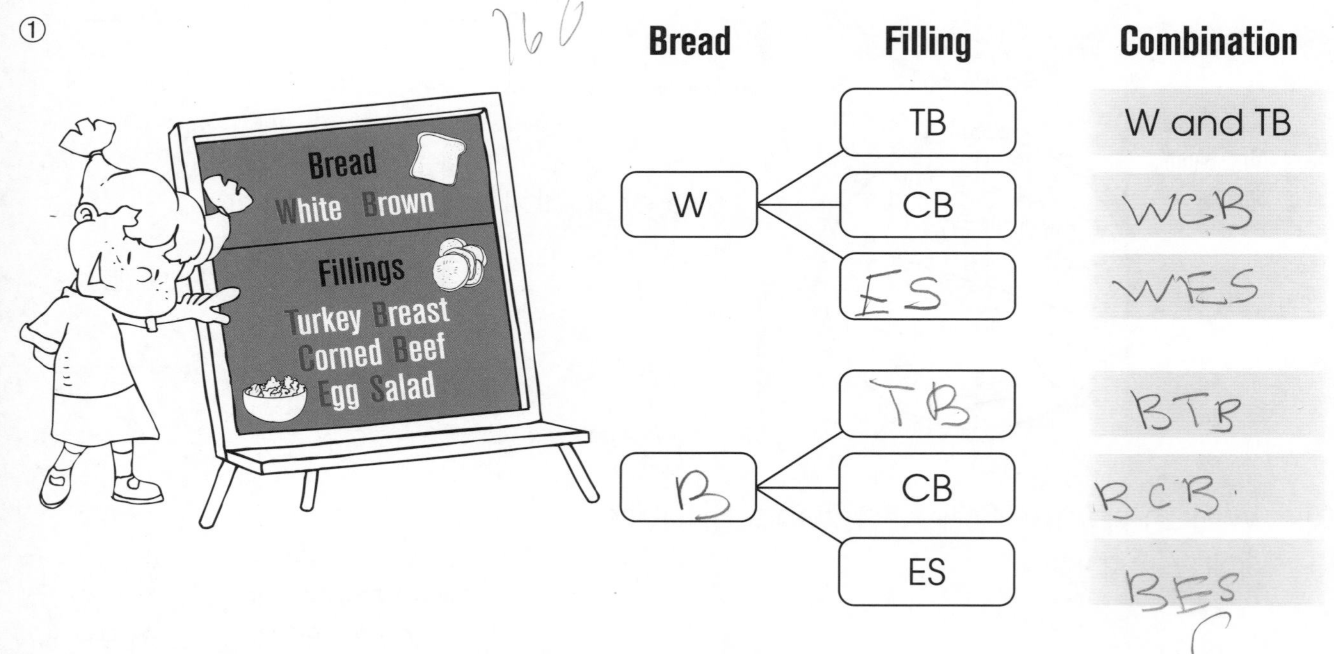

② How many possible combinations are there? 6

③ What is the probability that a customer will order a sandwich of

a. white bread with corned beef? 1/6

b. brown bread with meat? 1/3

c. white bread? 1/2

d. brown bread with cheese? 0/6

Each child can spin twice. Use a tree diagram to show all the combinations. Then answer the questions.

④

⑤ How many possible combinations are there? 16

⑥ What is the probability of getting

a. 2 toys? 9/16

b. 2 different toys? 1/4

c. only 1 toy? 1/4

d. no toys? 1/16

e. 2 tops? 1/16

f. 1 top and 1 puppet? 1/16

⑦ If 160 children play this game, about how many children will get 2 identical toys? 40

DATE: ____________________

Day 89 REVIEW

Find the mean and the mode of each group of data.

①
45 cm 30 cm
18 cm 30 cm
57 cm

Mean:
Mode:

②
23 kg 18.9 kg
23 kg 23 kg
6.6 kg 18.9 kg

Mean:
Mode:

③
24°C 20°C
20°C 20°C

Mean:
Mode:

④
4.5 mL 4.5 mL
16.7 mL 26.7 mL
16.7 mL 16.7 mL

Mean:
Mode:

See how many flowers are in Aunt Lisa's flower shop. Help Aunt Lisa make a bar graph to show the data. Then fill in the blanks.

⑤

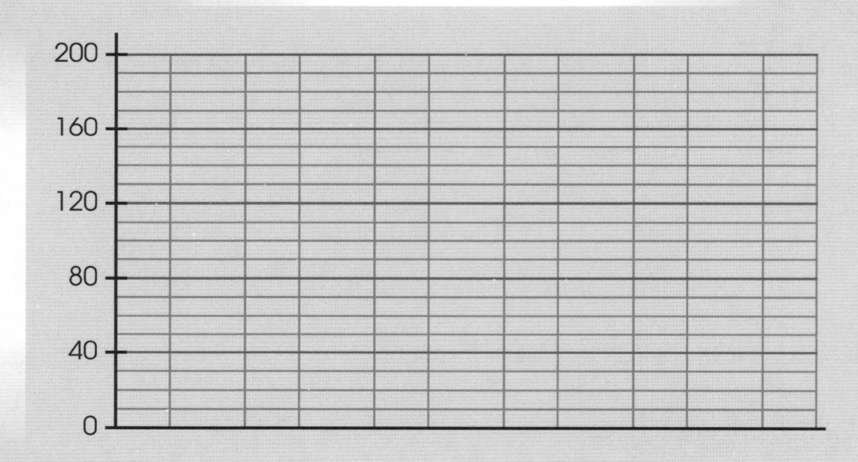

	Number
Rose	170
Carnation	90
Gladiolus	60
Lily	120
Calla	160

⑥ There are ________ kinds of flowers in Aunt Lisa's flower shop; ________ is the most in number.

⑦ There are ________ more callas than carnations.

⑧ The number of lilies is ________ times the number of gladiolus.

⑨ The average number of each kind of flower is ________ .

⑩ If the cost of ten roses is $8, the total cost of all the roses is $ ________ .

Find the pattern rule for each number pattern. Then find the next 3 numbers.

⑪ 9 7 35 33 165 163 Rule ______ ______ ______

⑫ 780 390 388 194 192 96 Rule ______ ______ ______

⑬ 5 15 16 48 49 147 Rule ______ ______ ______

Simplify the equations. Then find the unknowns.

⑭ $18 + k = 16 \times 3$

⑮ $y \div 4 = 11 - 2$

⑯ $a - 7 = 60 \div 3$

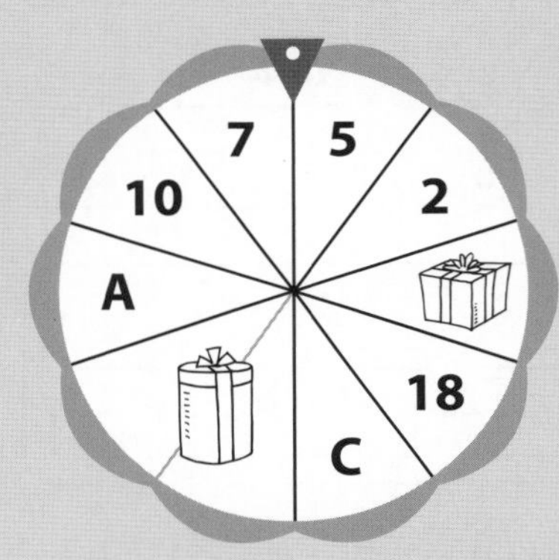

Look at the spinner. Then write fraction in simplest form to describe the probability of each event.

⑰ The probability of landing on

a. (gift) : ______

b. letters: ______

c. numbers: ______

d. even numbers: ______

e. gifts: ______

f. 'sorry': ______

⑱ **Draw lines on the grid to show the path that Molly has taken to walk to school.**

(0,3) → (1,1) → (4,1) → (4,5) → (5,4) → (5,3) → (7,3)

Molly

DATE: ____________

Day 90 You Deserve A Break!

The children are trying their luck in a game. Help them answer the questions.

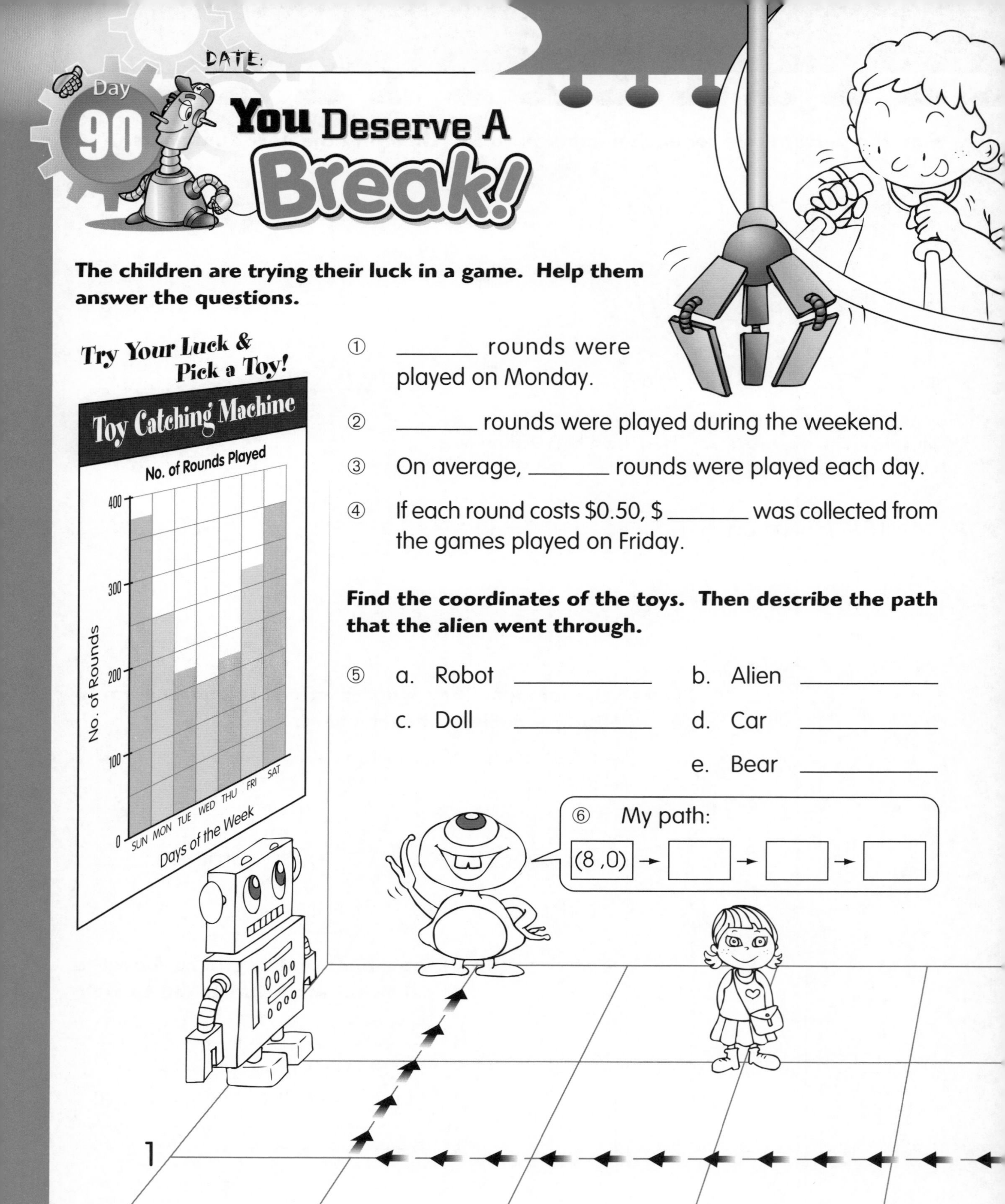

① ______ rounds were played on Monday.

② ______ rounds were played during the weekend.

③ On average, ______ rounds were played each day.

④ If each round costs $0.50, $ ______ was collected from the games played on Friday.

Find the coordinates of the toys. Then describe the path that the alien went through.

⑤ a. Robot __________ b. Alien __________

c. Doll __________ d. Car __________

e. Bear __________

⑥ My path:

(8 ,0) → ☐ → ☐ → ☐

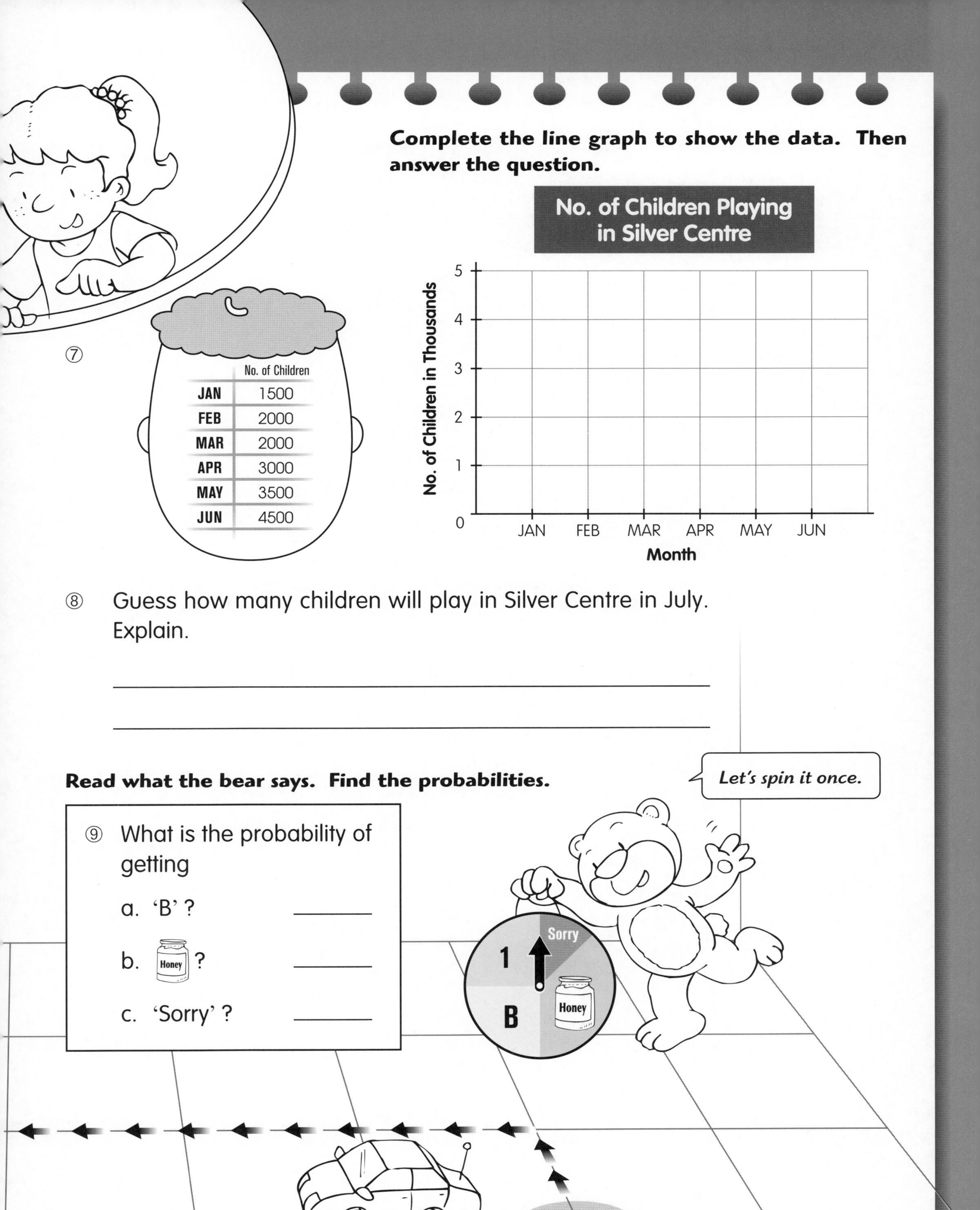

Complete the line graph to show the data. Then answer the question.

⑦

	No. of Children
JAN	1500
FEB	2000
MAR	2000
APR	3000
MAY	3500
JUN	4500

⑧ Guess how many children will play in Silver Centre in July. Explain.

____

____

Read what the bear says. Find the probabilities.

⑨ What is the probability of getting

a. 'B' ? ________

b. Honey ? ________

c. 'Sorry' ? ________

Daily Smart

English

Contents

GRADE 5

Date : ____________________

Canoe Travel in Early Canada

Early Canadian explorers travelled into the wilderness on canoes. They learned to travel this way from the native tribes – aboriginal peoples of Canada. This was a convenient way to travel then but slow and difficult compared to present day. Because Canada had many lakes and connecting rivers, it was a faster way to travel at that time than on land.

The explorers or paddlers would usually start from a larger trading post or a fort, paddling in their canoes along the connecting rivers and lakes until they reached their destinations, which were smaller trading posts or native villages. They would begin their journey by packing their supplies, goods, and passengers.

For days, they would paddle, then unpack, and carry their belongings including their canoes over connecting foot trails. These connecting foot trails between lakes and rivers are called "portages". At the end of each portage they would repack the canoes and start paddling along another river or lake again.

This system of packing, unpacking, and paddling would be repeated numerous times until they reached their final destination. After trading was conducted, they would rest for a few days and begin the same process again but this time, to go home. Hence, the common term "portaging" is used today when referring to camping and canoeing in the Canadian wilderness.

Paddlers that travelled into the wilderness numerous times earned the privilege of wearing a feather in the cap or hat. The early French Canadian boatman or canoeman employed by the early fur-trading companies was called a "voyageur". The independent French or Metis woodsman or fur trader not usually employed by the companies was called a "coureur de bois", which meant "runner of the woods". One company that employed these voyageurs was the Hudson's Bay Company, which is the present day "The Bay".

A. Write "T" for the true statements and "F" for the false ones.

1. A "portage" would be done only once.
2. Canada has many lakes and rivers, making canoe travel convenient.
3. Land trails connecting rivers and lakes are called "portages".
4. The paddlers would travel with empty canoes.
5. At the "portage" everything would be carried over on horseback.
6. The Hudson's Bay Company employed a lot of voyageurs.

B. Circle the nouns and underline the verbs in these sentences.

1. They learned to travel this way from the native tribes.
2. These connecting foot trails between lakes and rivers are called "portages".
3. At the end of each portage they would repack the canoes and start paddling along another river or lake again.

C. Find the word.

- Letters 3, 5, 6, and 7 together means wild, uncontrollable anger.
- Letters 1, 2, and 4 together is a container used for cooking.

Date : ______________________

Nouns

A **noun** names an animal, a person, place, or thing. It can be classified into one of the following types:

Countable common nouns – house, cat
Uncountable common nouns – water, air
Proper nouns – Trudeau, Michael
Compound proper nouns – Canadian Opera Company, National Ballet of Canada

A. Read the passage and write the nouns in the table. Determine if they are countable common (CC), uncountable common (UC), proper (P), or compound proper (CP).

Gabriel prayed he wouldn't stumble in his final clarinet solo with the Toronto Symphony Orchestra. He reached into his pocket for his tranquilizer, but found that it had dissolved in his handkerchief. He scraped out what he could and swallowed it with some water. It tasted rather strange. Gabriel went on to play an impressive solo. As he walked down the hall later, he felt something in his pocket – it was his tranquilizer. Why was it still there? Then he remembered: what he had swallowed earlier was his own phlegm! Just then, Gabriel woke up. Relieved that it was only a terrible dream, he went to get dressed. But this time, he made sure his pocket was empty.

1. Gabriel	P	2.		3.	
4.		5.		6.	
7.		8.		9.	
10.		11.		12.	

B. **Match the common nouns with the proper nouns by writing the letters in the correct circles.**

A country

B street

C person

D hotel

E city

F arena

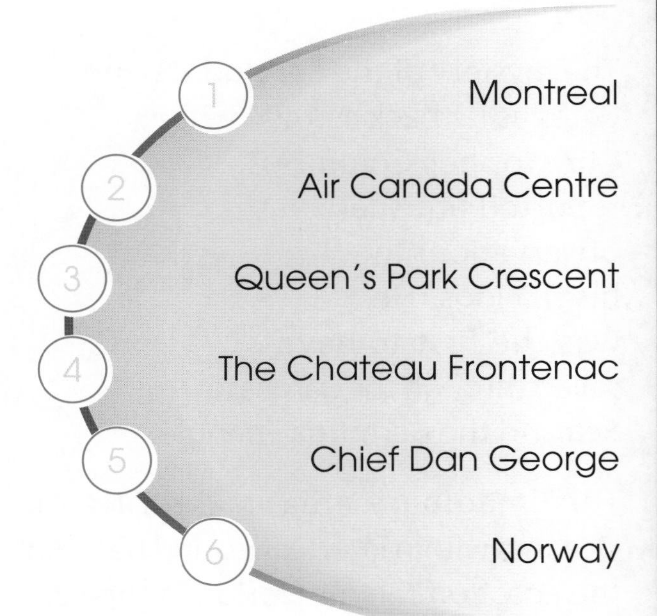

C. **Use the given endings to change the following verbs, adjectives, and adverbs into nouns.**

1. able ____________
2. humble ____________
3. promote ____________
4. remember ____________
5. attend ____________
6. televise ____________
7. together ____________
8. tolerate ____________
9. competent ____________
10. kind ____________
11. good ____________
12. solid ____________

Did You Know?

Some surnames derive from the father's given name. For example, "Robinson" means "the son of Robin".

Date : ______________________

The Mysterious Bermuda Triangle

The mystery of the Bermuda Triangle dates as far back as 1492 when Christopher Columbus reported unusual observations in his sea logs. He was the first to have sailed through the Sargasso Sea and the Bermuda Triangle.

Bermuda

Miami

Puerto Rico

This imaginary area in the Atlantic Ocean is within Puerto Rico and Bermuda and the coast off Miami, Florida in the United States. Even though Columbus was the first to write detailed accounts of experiencing calm seas one minute and tumultuous seas in the next as well as strange glowing lights in the distance, the numerous peculiar events were not taken seriously until 1918 when the traceless sinking of the USS Cyclops prompted further investigation. Since then, more ships, small boats, and aircraft have been lost without a trace. Among supernatural explanations, some theories were born. One theory was "magnetic variation".

Strangely enough, the Bermuda Triangle is one of two places on Earth where a magnetic compass points towards true north. Normally, the compass would point towards magnetic north. The magnetic variation is the difference between the two and it can be as much as 20 degrees. Because of this variance, failure for a navigator to compensate will result in veering off course and getting lost.

Another theory was a combination of the swift and turbulent character of the Gulf Stream with an unpredictable Caribbean-Atlantic weather pattern, resulting in sudden magnetic storms and hurricanes. During these storms, navigational errors may have caused the fatal disappearances of these ships or aircraft.

Numerous witnesses have described experiencing severe "jolts and pulses" while in the boat or aircraft, and ceased electronic equipment, and seeing the bending of space. Nevertheless, there are still those who believe that in spite of plausible scientific theories, ironically the most reasonable explanation is still the paranormal. Thus, these events that have happened in the Bermuda Triangle still remain a mystery.

A. **Circle the correct answers.**

1. What is the passage about?

   A. Sea storms and hurricanes

   B. Supernatural explanations

   C. Theories for explaining the disappearances of ships and aircraft

2. Which sentence below describes the main idea?

   A. Christopher Columbus saw the first ship disappear into the Atlantic Ocean.

   B. The Bermuda Triangle is a defined area in the Atlantic Ocean.

   C. The scientific theories for the vanishing ships and aircraft have not been proven.

3. Which theory was cited in the passage?

   A. Vortex kinesis

   B. Magnetic variation

   C. Unpredictable weather patterns

B. **Match the words with their meanings.**

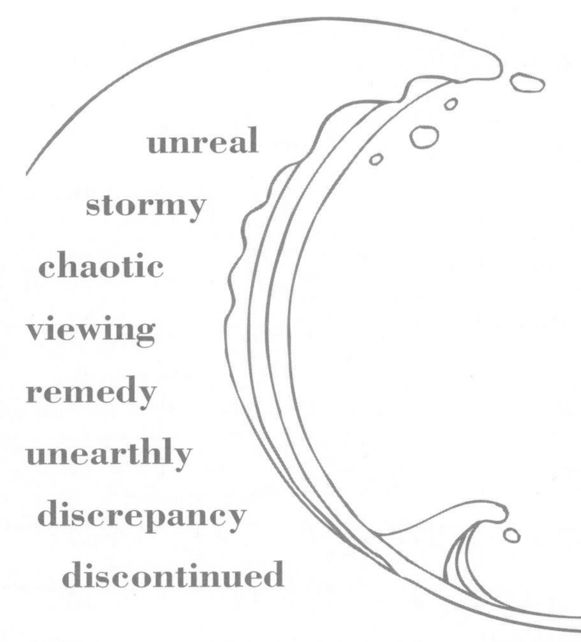

1. observations ____________________
2. imaginary ____________________
3. tumultuous ____________________
4. supernatural ____________________
5. variation ____________________
6. compensate ____________________
7. turbulent ____________________
8. ceased ____________________

Date : ____________________

Direct and Indirect Objects

A **direct object** is the receiver of the action of the verb.
Example: Casey mailed the package.
An **indirect object** is to whom or what the action of the verb is directed.
Example: Casey mailed Walter the package.

Happy Birthday

A. Determine if each underlined object is direct "D" or indirect "I".

1. The pianist played a wonderful song. ______
2. Lucy ate the entire cake in the kitchen. ______
3. May told her mother about the latest horror film. ______
4. Bobby sends his buddy a postcard from Amsterdam. ______
5. Janice lent Wendy her scooter. ______

B. Circle "D" if the sentence contains a direct object, "I" if it contains an indirect object, and "N" if it contains neither. You may circle "D" and "I" in some cases.

1. Carly wore a pretty dress in the evening. D I N
2. Mrs. Robinson told Carly not to go out late at night. D I N
3. Sean read his daughter a bedtime story. D I N
4. Mr. Robinson wrote his wife a postcard. D I N
5. Lynn ordered some gifts from an online company. D I N
6. Emma gives her dog delicious treats from time to time. D I N
7. The sweet music is playing in the lounge. D I N
8. Jenny bought a new pet turtle on Tuesday. D I N
9. Emma's dog catches the frisbee with his big mouth. D I N
10. Bert lives a few blocks away. D I N

C. **Write the underlined words in the correct columns. You will find that most of the answers in the column for indirect objects are pronouns.**

It was a dark and rainy night. Emily had just finished reading her book and wanted to get a snack from the kitchen. Other than her cat and the occasional field mouse, the house was empty. When Emily reached the bottom of the staircase, she saw a mouse scurrying around the corner. Normally, this would not have given her the creeps. But on this particular night, Emily had an eerie feeling that the mouse was trying to tell her something. What had it just seen? She felt a wisp of air over her head. "Deliciously scary" was how her best friend had always described this house. Emily turned around to see what had brought home the wind. To her disappointment, it was her cat. It had lept from the staircase railing, wearing the cape that Emily had put on it earlier. "My house is never scary enough," she sighed, and opened the cabinet to get some cookies.

Direct Objects	Indirect Objects
book	

Did You Know?

"Object" comes from a Latin word for "thrown in". In grammar, the object is a word or string of words "thrown in" after the verb to complete a sentence.

Date : ____________________

Bats

Bats! Just the word itself might send cold shivers down the back of anyone! Bats have been portrayed as strange, malicious, and disgusting creatures flying mysteriously about in the night for the sole purpose of frightening people and animals. Horror movies of all kinds have cast bats in the role of "bad guys".

Bats are the only mammals on Earth that fly. They have skin attached to the long arm skeleton and ankles, making each wing kite-like. Their wings have no feathers. The problem this creates is that bats cannot easily take off from level ground. They have to be at higher locations so that they can drop-launch themselves into flight.

Bats mostly fly at night foraging for food. There are two types of bats: the insect-eaters and the fruit-eaters. Insect-eating bats can be found anywhere in the world except the polar regions. Fruit-eating bats are found mainly in the sub-tropical and tropical regions. Both types of bats also feed on syrup, nectar, blood, and small animals, but their predominant diet would either be fruits or insects.

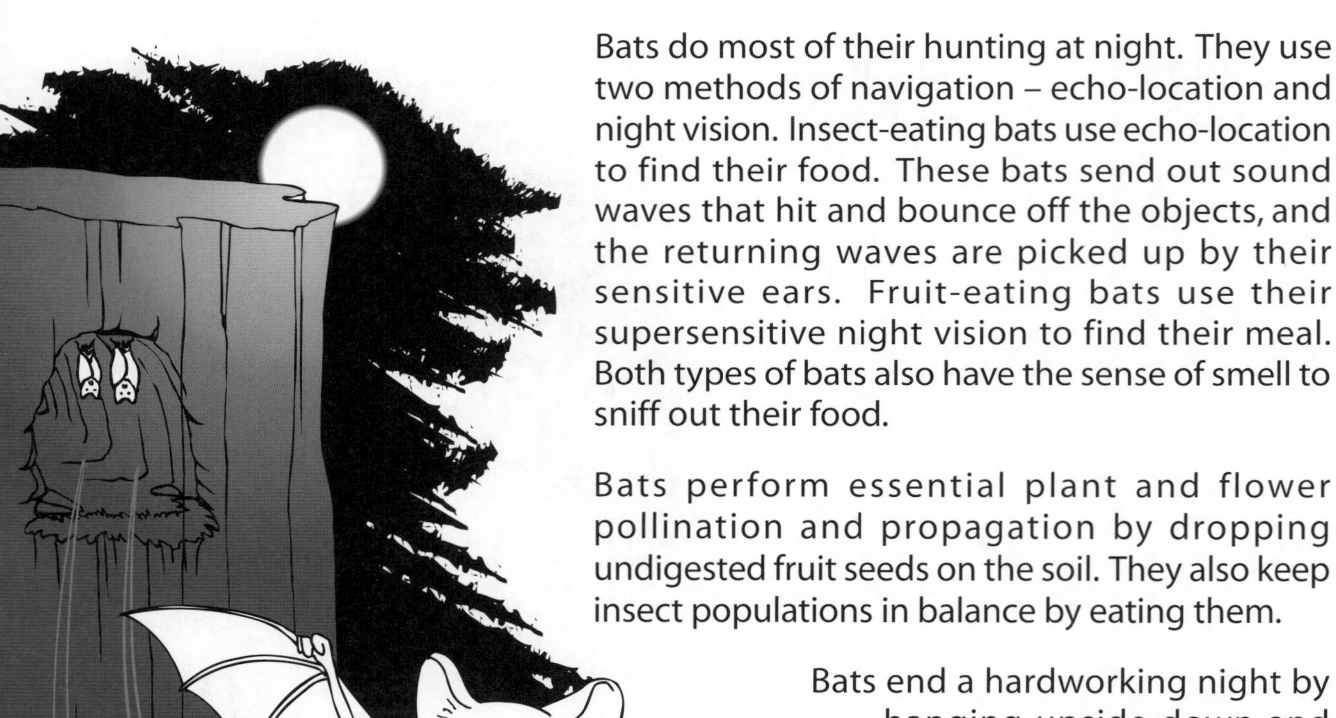

Bats do most of their hunting at night. They use two methods of navigation – echo-location and night vision. Insect-eating bats use echo-location to find their food. These bats send out sound waves that hit and bounce off the objects, and the returning waves are picked up by their sensitive ears. Fruit-eating bats use their supersensitive night vision to find their meal. Both types of bats also have the sense of smell to sniff out their food.

Bats perform essential plant and flower pollination and propagation by dropping undigested fruit seeds on the soil. They also keep insect populations in balance by eating them.

Bats end a hardworking night by hanging upside down and folding their wings around the body to go to sleep. So bats are a lot more interesting and important to our ecology than how the movies portray them.

A. Circle the correct answers.

1. Bats are ____ .

   A. mammals that can swim
   B. birds that cannot fly
   C. mammals that can fly

2. Bats also feed on ____ .

   A. syrup and nectar
   B. blood and small animals
   C. all of the above

3. Bats hang upside down to ____ .

   A. sleep
   B. wait for their prey
   C. prepare for take-off

B. Put the following sentences in order. Write the letters.

How insect-eating bats hunt for food:

- A They note the location of the food.
- B Bats send out sound waves.
- C Their ears pick up the returning sound waves.
- D The sound waves hit and bounce off the object.

1. ______ 2. ______ 3. ______ 4. ______

C. Answer the following questions.

1. Why do you think there are no insect-eating bats in the polar regions?

____

____

2. Why aren't bats as bad as people might think?

____

____

Date : ______________________

Pronouns: Subject, Object, and Reflexive

In a sentence or paragraph, the **subject pronoun** takes the place of the subject noun, and the **object pronoun** takes the place of the object noun. A **reflexive pronoun** is a type of object pronoun. We use it when the subject's action turns back on the subject.

Example: Susan likes apples. She likes them because they are sweet. She usually washes herself after a day at the farm.

A. Determine if each underlined pronoun is a subject (S), an object (O), or a reflexive (R) pronoun. Write the question numbers in each group.

1. Maggie taught herself how to roller-skate.
2. Danny made a big breakfast for himself.
3. "Could you take a picture of me next to this sculpture?" Sylvia asked Ted.
4. Archie missed school yesterday because he was sick.
5. My mother is a teacher. She teaches Drama and Music.
6. We saw Stephen at the park yesterday, but he didn't see us.
7. "Look at all these presents!" Tom exclaimed. "They're for us!"
8. "Did you make these cards yourself?" Mrs. Robinson asked her son.

B. Choose the appropriate reflexive pronoun for each sentence.

1. I wash ________________ when I get up.
2. Aaron got ________________ into trouble.
3. Megan set ________________ an impossible task.
4. The little mice hid ________________ behind the piano.
5. After we fell, we picked ________________ up.

themselves
ourselves
yourselves
herself
himself
myself
yourself
itself

C. Fill in the blanks with the appropriate pronouns.

We often make the mistake of using "me" when we should be using "I", and vice versa. So pay close attention to the structure of the sentences as you do this exercise.

1. There is a squirrel in the backyard.

   ________________ is burrowing its food in the ground.

2. Jenny asked Carol, "Do you want to meet Betty and ________________ at the restaurant? We could have dinner there together."

3. Carol said, "Linda and ________________ will be seeing a movie tonight. Sorry I won't be able to join you this time."

4. "You don't have to thank me," said Jane to Darren. "These cookies are my thanks to ________________ , actually."

5. Little Gordon and little Terry are very tired. ________________ have gone to bed.

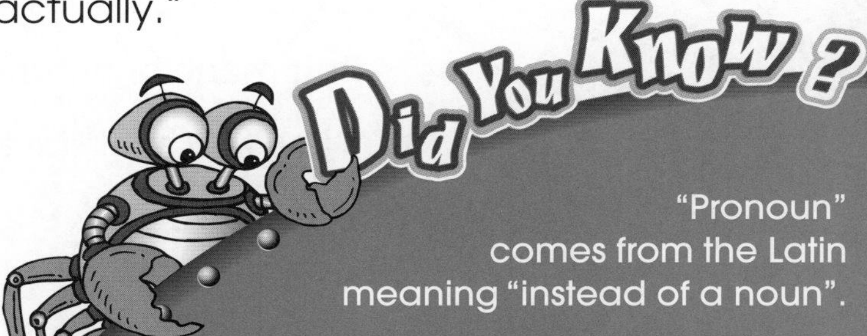

"Pronoun" comes from the Latin meaning "instead of a noun".

Date : ____________________

Boomerangs – Shapes that Fly

A boomerang is a flat, curved, wooden throwing stick that spins during flight, changes direction, and returns to the thrower. It is a native tool and weapon of the Australian Aborigines. What makes it unusual is that no other native culture in the world has a boomerang as its tool. Most things that are thrown stay away but not the boomerang. Why? Well, because the unique bent construction of the boomerang makes it so.

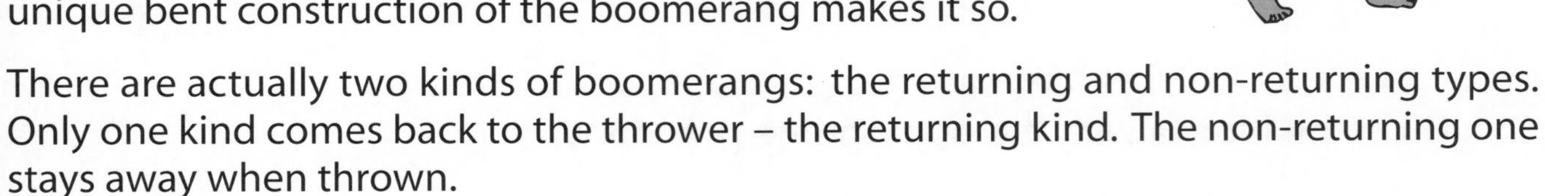

There are actually two kinds of boomerangs: the returning and non-returning types. Only one kind comes back to the thrower – the returning kind. The non-returning one stays away when thrown.

Returning boomerangs are flat and curved, held at one end and thrown towards a target; mid-way during flight the stick changes direction, curves back, and returns to the thrower. It is this change of direction during mid-flight that makes the "returning boomerang" so unusual of all the throwing tools in the world. Returning boomerangs are used mostly for games, fun, and ceremony; occasionally, they are also used for hunting.

Non-returning boomerangs are more like regular sticks – once thrown they do not return to the user. They are also much deadlier and simpler in design. They tend to be straighter and heavier at one end than the curved boomerang. They are also more accurate and travel in a straighter line. This tool is used for hunting and also as a weapon. Boomerangs can be as long as 75 centimetres and can travel as far as 45 metres.

Go to a toy, game, or hobby store and check out what boomerang kits are available. Go to the library and find out more information about boomerangs and, if possible, instructions on how to make one. Make one yourself.

When you have a boomerang, ask yourself these questions:

- How long is the boomerang?
- Is it a returning or non-returning boomerang?
- What shape does it have: C, V, U, or L?
- Is it made of natural or synthetic material?
- How far can it travel?

So, there you have it about boomerangs, an experiment in shapes that fly away or fly back to you!

A. **Complete the chart below to compare returning and non-returning boomerangs.**

Returning Boomerang

Shape: ______________________

Movement: ______________________

____

Use: ______________________

____

Non-Returning Boomerang

Shape: ______________________

Movement: ______________________

____

Use: ______________________

____

B. **Put the following characteristics about boomerangs in order by writing the letters in the circles.**

A change direction in mid-flight

B return to the thrower

C spin during flight

D are flat, curved, wooden throwing sticks

C. **Find the synonyms for these words from the passage.**

1. device ______________
2. normal ______________
3. special ______________
4. bent ______________
5. turns ______________
6. directions ______________

Date : ____________________

Demonstrative Pronouns

When we want to identify people or point to physical objects, we use "**this**", "**that**", "**these**", or "**those**". When we want to refer to someone or something that has already been mentioned, or is known, in the sentence, we use "**one**" or "**ones**".

Examples: This ice cream cone looks really good.
"That's no excuse," said Mother.
These flowers over here are pretty.
My budgie looks cuter than those over there.
"I don't like jackets with zippers," says the customer. "Do you have one with buttons?"

A. Fill in the blanks with the appropriate demonstrative pronouns.

1. "I brought you ______________," said Adam as he held out a bag of grapes.
2. "Look at ______________ one," said Natalie, holding a grape between her fingers. "It's as big as a ping-pong ball!"
3. "______________ was an interesting story you just told, Dad!" Michael said.
4. "Let's go to the ice cream parlour," suggests Leo. "______________'s a good idea!" Tina replied.
5. "Are the new dresses longer than the old ______________?" Clara asks.
6. "The shirts on sale at this store are not the same ______________ we saw at the other store," said Mrs. Polansky to her husband.
7. "Who's ______________?" Amanda asked the person on the line.
8. "Was ______________ Aunt Meg on the phone?" Mother asked Amanda.
9. "______________ are my children – Jonathan and Emma," says Mrs. Lau, pointing at the kids playing in the sand far away.

B. Some of the sentences below contain incorrect demonstrative pronouns. Circle them and write the correct ones on the lines.

1. "That is my favourite vegetable," says Lily, clutching a big ball of cabbage.

   ____

2. "Thai mangoes are better than that of Indonesia," says Grandma to Lily.

   ____

3. "Those are the women who look after the gallery," says Ms. Homer of the group of ladies at the other end of the room.

   ____

4. "This is where I used to live," says Grandma, standing in front of the house with a green roof.

   ____

5. "Those are the bracelets that your great-grandmother gave me when I was very young," Grandma says as she shows Lily the treasures in her jewellery box.

   ____

6. "These apples over there look really ripe," says Lily to Grandma.

   ____

7. "Wow! These carrots from your garden are much bigger than the one from mine," says Grandma to her neighbour.

   ____

Date : ____________________

Glass – from Sand to Almost Anything

Look around you at home, school, and anywhere else and you'll find glass or glass products. Glass is a brittle, mostly transparent substance. It comes in many shapes and colours. It is often heavier than plastic and can break easier than plastic or metal.

What is glass used for? Just about everything. Glass can be used to hold things, look at, look through, protect, and just plain be. Play a game and try to identify glass products wherever you go and write each down on a small sheet of paper. Look at its use, shape, colour, and size and imagine how it's made.

Glass is made from sand that is heated, very hot, until it melts into a syrup-like or water-like consistency. It can then be blown or poured into a mould. When melted glass is syrup-like, a long blowpipe is dipped into the glass and air is blown through the pipe to make different shapes. When melted glass is water-like, it is poured into a mould and allowed to set like "jello" dessert but much harder and firmer. It can be made into soda glass, flint glass, heat-resistant glass, optical glass, and fiberglass, all for different uses.

Soda glass can be used for windows, cups, bowls, mirrors, and many other items. Flint glass is used for expensive crystal glassware. Heat-resistant glass is used for laboratory equipment and cooking ware. Optical glass is used in cameras, binoculars, telescopes, and spectacles. Fiberglass is used to strengthen other materials by mixing with them.

Glass is most beautiful to look at when it is blown like a balloon into different shapes and colours. When you get a chance to travel around town or the world, keep your eyes out for ornamental glass works like stained glass windows in old churches, glass sculptures, and crystal glass.

Next time you are building a sandcastle at the beach, imagine where that sand might end up. If you are lucky, you may find a jewel in the sand called "beach glass". Beach glass is broken glass washed up onto shore with its sharp edges eroded and sometimes we mistake it for a strange pebble or smooth stone.

A. **Answer the following questions.**

1. How is sand made to become glass?

2. How can glass be made into different shapes?

3. Which kind of glass is not "pure" glass?

4. Which do you think is the most commonly-used glass?

5. Name a kind of unusual glassware not mentioned in the passage.

B. **Match the words with their meanings on the window. Write the letters on the lines.**

1. transparent ______
2. brittle ______
3. identify ______
4. eroded ______
5. spectacles ______
6. expensive ______
7. consistency ______
8. ornamental ______
9. mould ______
10. stained ______

A. spot
B. density
C. costly
D. tinted
E. pre-made shape
F. eyeglasses
G. see through
H. worn smooth
I. decorative
J. hard but easily broken

Did You Know?

Glass never wears out. It takes 1 000 000 years to decompose!

Date : ____________________

Day 10

You Deserve A Break!

The letters on each vehicle make up a word to do with driving. Unscramble them and write the word on the correct road sign. Then colour Bernie's favourite cars.

So, Bernie, which ones are your favourite cars?

Nouns

____

____

____

____

r v i e d

u r c a e f l

e a b r k s

k r a p

a e f s

g h i s l t

My favourites are the ones that have a word with the long "a" sound.
Verbs
Adjectives
a s p s
s o w l
e w h e l
p o t s
g r n e s a s s e p
R
k c u s t

Date : ____________________

Interrogative Pronouns

An **interrogative pronoun** is one that is used to ask a question.

Examples: What kind of tea is that, sir?
Which is your favourite ice cream flavour?
Who spilled the soup?
Whom did you call?
Whose shirt is this?

It can also be used indirectly.

Examples: Can you find out what it is?
I'll see who's there.

A. Underline the appropriate interrogative pronoun for each question.

1. (Who / Whom) wants more pasta?
2. (Whom / Whose) shoes are these?
3. (What / Which) have you been up to?

Use "who" in the question if the answer involves a subject pronoun.

Use "whom" in the question if the answer involves an object pronoun.

4. (Who / Whom) just called?
5. (Who / What) book are you reading?
6. (Whose / Whom) gloves did you borrow?
7. Owen asked me (which / whom) pair of socks I liked better.
8. (What / Which) could be sweeter than honey?
9. My friend wanted to know (what / which) I had decided to do.
10. Did Mrs. Slade ask you (which / whose) topic you've chosen?
11. I asked Sydney (which / what) he was leaving the city for.
12. To (who / whom) did you give this note?

B. Mike the Monkey is chatting with Ben. Match Ben's questions with Mike's answers by writing the correct letters on the lines.

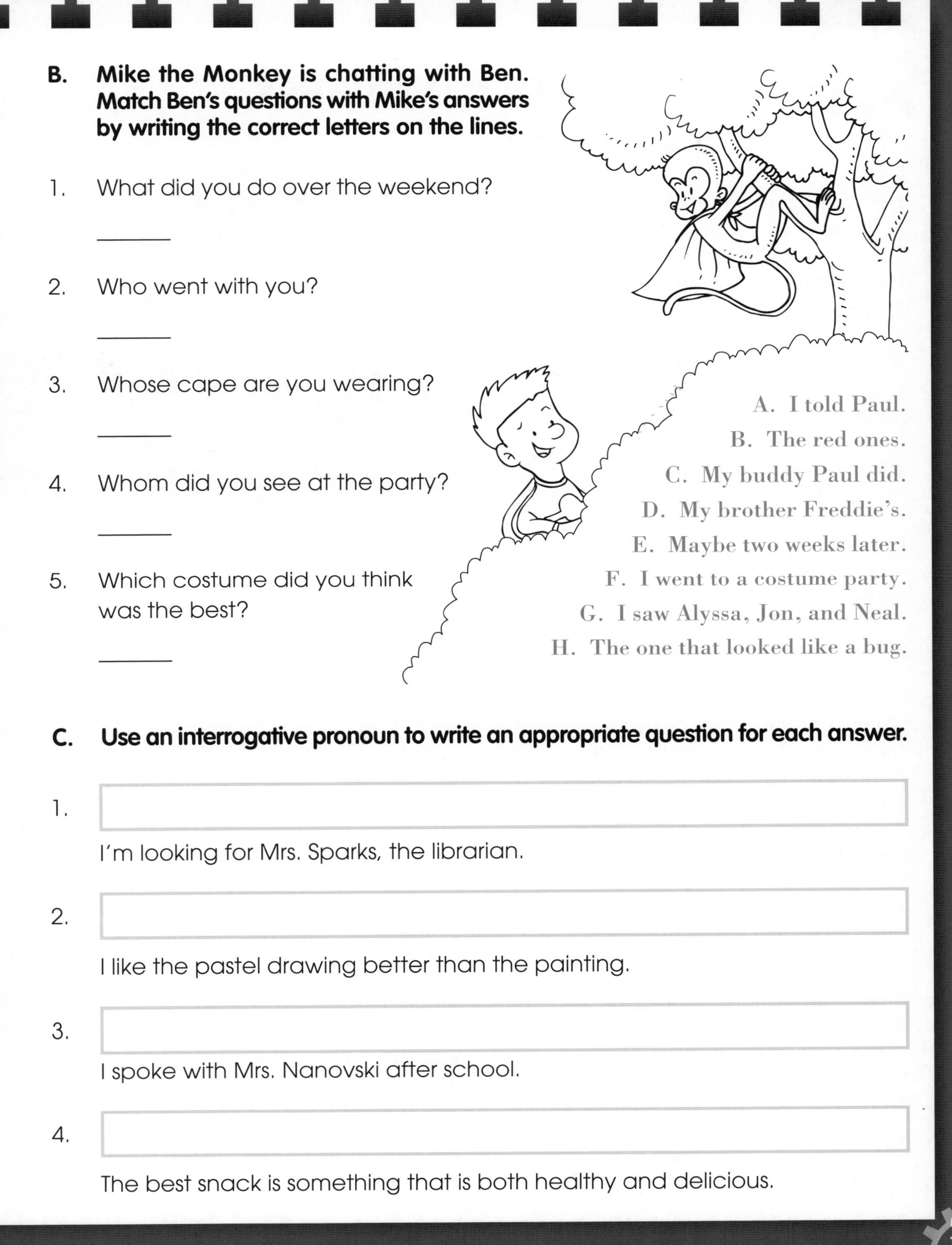

1. What did you do over the weekend?

   ______

2. Who went with you?

   ______

3. Whose cape are you wearing?

   ______

4. Whom did you see at the party?

   ______

5. Which costume did you think was the best?

   ______

A. I told Paul.

B. The red ones.

C. My buddy Paul did.

D. My brother Freddie's.

E. Maybe two weeks later.

F. I went to a costume party.

G. I saw Alyssa, Jon, and Neal.

H. The one that looked like a bug.

C. Use an interrogative pronoun to write an appropriate question for each answer.

1. ______

   I'm looking for Mrs. Sparks, the librarian.

2. ______

   I like the pastel drawing better than the painting.

3. ______

   I spoke with Mrs. Nanovski after school.

4. ______

   The best snack is something that is both healthy and delicious.

Date : ____________________

To See Mars – a Chance in a Lifetime

Never in our lifetime will we see Mars as close to the Earth as it was from October 2005 to January 2006. During this time, they were 70.25 million kilometres apart at their closest. Mars is the brightest object in the sky next to the moon and easy to spot with the naked eye. There won't be another encounter like this until 2287!

In 2003, the two planets were 55 758 006 km apart from centre to centre and that was the closest they had been in 60 000 years. What happened to allow this approach? It had everything to do with their orbits. The Earth and Mars both orbit around the sun and because the Earth is closer to the sun, it completes its orbit faster. By the time Mars makes one trip, the Earth will have made two. At times, the two planets will be on opposite sides of the sun while at other times, the Earth will pass relatively close to Mars. Sometimes, Mars and the sun will be on opposite sides of the Earth: As the sun is setting in the west, Mars is rising in the east. The reverse will happen as the two planets continue along their orbits. When they are on opposite sides of the sky, scientists say that Mars is in "opposition".

The orbital paths of the Earth and Mars are elliptical (oval-shaped) and that is why the Earth is a little closer to the sun at one end than at another. Also, when observing the sky at the same time each night, you will notice that Mars is moving from west to east but that every 26 months, it seems to change direction and moves from east to west. How is this possible?

It's only an illusion! Because the Earth moves past Mars every 26 months, the "passing" makes it seem as though Mars is moving backward. But as the two planets continue moving and we view Mars from a different angle, the illusion disappears and Mars will be seen moving forward again. This seemingly backward movement is called "retrograde". It also happens with other planets that orbit farther away from the sun.

So concentrate your sights on the southeastern skies at night and see if you can spot the Red Planet. Better yet, try to view it through a telescope.

A. **Circle "T" for the true statements and "F" for the false ones.**

1. Between October 2005 and January 2006, the Earth was the closest it would ever be to the sun in our lifetime. T F

2. "Retrograde" is the illusion that a planet is moving backward for a short period of time when it is actually moving forward. T F

3. At some point in their orbits, the sun and Mars are on opposite sides of the Earth. T F

4. Mars and the Earth orbit at different rates around the sun. T F

5. Venus was the brightest object in the sky in 2005. T F

6. The Earth always orbits around the sun faster than Mars. T F

B. **Choose the correct answer to complete each sentence.**

20 000
orbital
elliptical
southeastern
southwestern
opposition
retrograde
illusion
60 000

1. When Mars and the Earth are on opposite sides of the sky, they are in ______________ .

2. Before 2003, the Earth and Mars were the closest ______________ years ago.

3. Mars can be seen with the naked eye in the ______________ sky.

4. Another word for "oval-shaped" is ______________ .

5. It is an ______________ that Mars seems to change direction every 26 months.

Date : ____________________

Relative Pronouns

Relative pronouns are those that relate to a previously occurring noun in the sentence.

Examples: This is the building where I work.
Let's meet on a day when we're both free.
This is the person whom I met.
This is the person who took me around the city.

A. Complete each of the following sentences with the appropriate relative pronoun.

1. I want to see a movie ____________ features polar bears.
2. This is the place ____________ we live.
3. My cousins live in Iqaluit, ____________ is the capital city of Nunavut.
4. My brother is the person ____________ help I always seek.
5. Let's meet up for lunch at a time ____________ the restaurant is not crowded.
6. The illustrator of this picture book is the one ____________ I told you about.
7. Susie wants to read a book ____________ will blow her away.
8. My grandma is the one in the family ____________ always tells me stories.

B. Read what the children say and fill in the blanks with "which" or "that".

We use "which" when we already know enough about the previously occurring noun, but want to give further information about it.

1. Mr. English collects crystal figurines, ______________ he buys whenever he travels to other countries.
2. The building looks more like a globe than a dome, ______________ is supposed to be half a globe.
3. Leonard wants to go to a school ______________ is closer to his house.
4. Mrs. Fells likes snacking on corn chips ______________ are unsalted.

We use "that" when we don't yet know enough about the previously occurring noun, and need to tell about it.

Try this intuitive method: For any given sentence, use "that" first. If it doesn't sound right, then use "which".

5. Licorice is the kind of candy ______________ Hilary's parents love.
6. I want to read the book *Rusty Paradise,* ______________ my friend David told me about.

C. Sometimes we can omit the relative pronoun altogether. In 1 to 3, put a line through the relative pronoun where it can be omitted. Then rewrite 4.

1. Indian cuisine is the kind of food that Kelly would like to try.
2. *War and Peace* is the book that Kevin would never want to read.
3. Tom is the friend whom I trust the most.
4. This is the person with whom I work.

____

____

____

Did You Know?

"Dome" comes from *domus*, meaning "house" in Latin. It is a word related to "domestic", which means "belonging to the household".

Date : ____________________

Mars Rovers and Landers

Because of the extreme Martian environment and the difficulty of humans travelling into deep space, it has not yet been possible to send astronauts to Mars. However, sophisticated robots have been programmed to collect samples, process information, and send data back to the Earth. Thanks to numerous robotic missions, we now know that water vapour and ice exist on the Red Planet. New technologies and innovations continue to bring back data to a hungry scientific community.

We often think of robots as mechanical men made of metal that can be programmed to do simple things. Some may think of the Terminator: human-like because it speaks but unlike a human because it is indestructible and possesses phenomenal strength. But none of this describes the Mars rovers and landers.

A robot is a complex series of procedures. The Mars rover or lander is a collection of several systems, with three major components: sensors, processors, and actuators.

Sensors are used for determining and gathering data about the environment. Cameras and touch sensors are common examples. Some robots also use temperature and humidity sensors. Opportunity, the rover that explored the surface of Mars, sent back signals whenever it encountered something, such as when it came across a huge, deep crater. The robot's processors then "decided" to examine it. The processors would instruct the actuators to power a robotic arm to collect samples, or wheels to move the whole robot into the crater. You can see how the processors take input from the sensors, make a decision, and then command the actuators to respond.

When all these components work well together from such a great distance as that between the Earth and Mars, astronauts do not have to risk their lives in space for the purpose of research. And until astronauts are able to land on Mars, these rovers and landers will continue to be the next best thing.

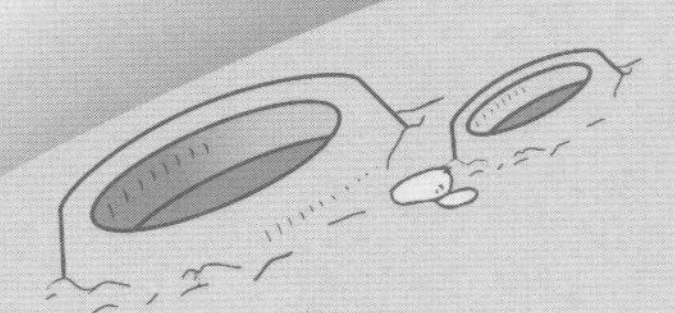

A. **Read the clues and complete the crossword puzzle with words from the passage.**

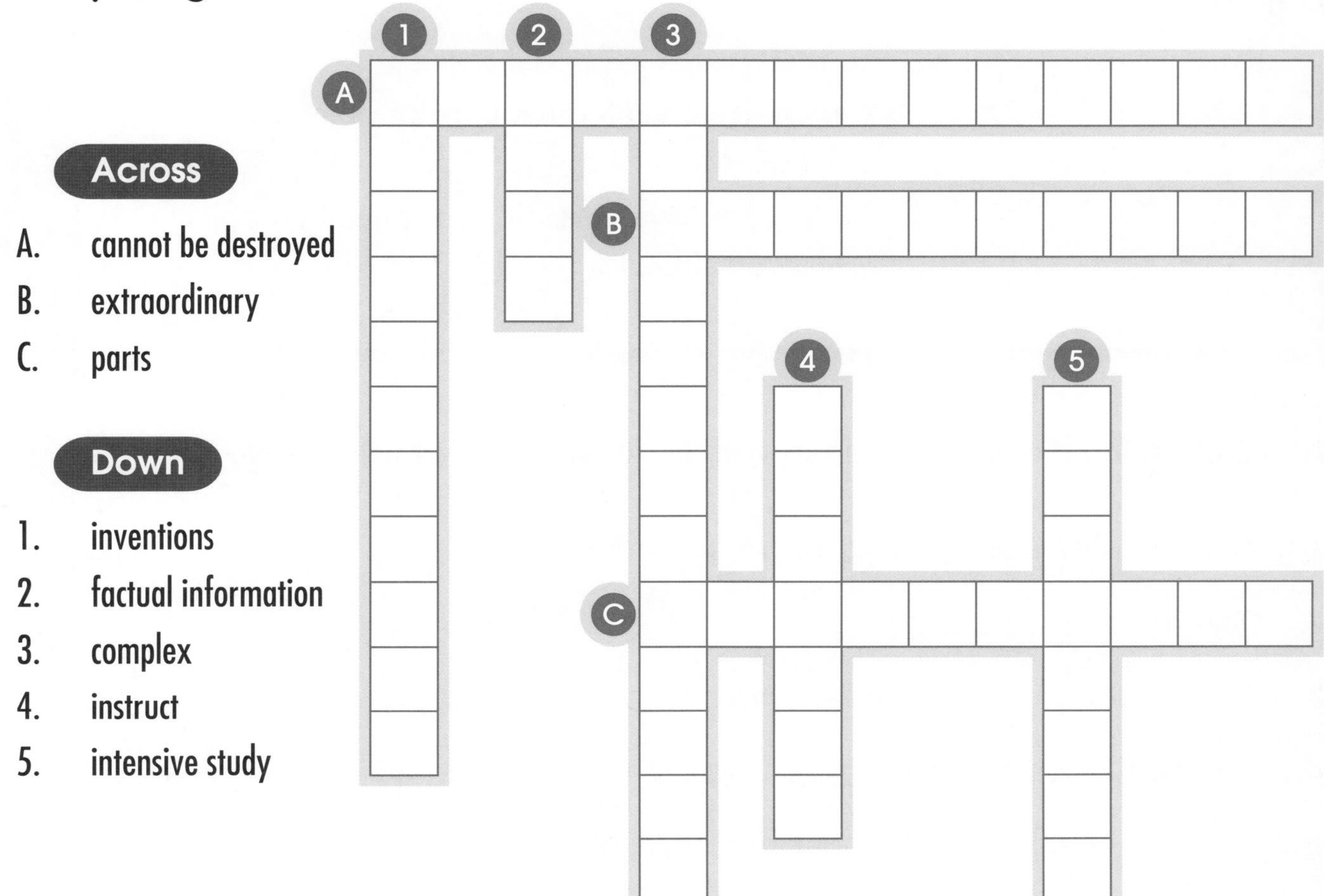

Across

A. cannot be destroyed
B. extraordinary
C. parts

Down

1. inventions
2. factual information
3. complex
4. instruct
5. intensive study

B. **Write "T" for the true statements and "F" for the false ones.**

1. There is vapour and air on Mars. ______
2. No astronauts have ever set foot on Mars. ______
3. Not all robots are human-like machines. ______
4. Sensors, processors, and actuators form the three major parts of the Mars lander. ______
5. Opportunity crashed into a deep crater on the Mars surface and was destroyed. ______
6. The robotic arm on the Mars lander is controlled by the actuators. ______
7. The robotic arm's sole function is to collect rock samples. ______
8. The processors send commands to the actuators. ______

Date : ____________________

Transitive and Intransitive Verbs

A **transitive verb** must take an object.

Example: Mitchell took a nap.

An **intransitive verb** does not need an object.

Example: Mitchell snored.

A. Determine if each underlined verb is transitive "T" or intransitive "I".

1. Joey's sister likes to sleep in the basement. ______
2. Tommy's dog can dance. ______
3. The students asked their teacher not to erase the board yet. ______
4. The bank wants to maximize its profit this year. ______
5. Mr. and Mrs. Russo murmur over their salad. ______

B. Choose the appropriate verbs for the sentences. Then determine if they are transitive or intransitive by writing "T" or "I" in the parentheses.

It is Katie's birthday. Her brother has 1. ______________ ( ) her a very cute toy – a stuffed kangaroo that hops! Katie is so excited that she 2. ______________ ( ) and 3. ______________ ( ). Her brother cannot 4. ______________ ( ) his excitement and skips along as well. The two of them are so happy that when their parents come home with the birthday cake, they do not 5. ______________ ( ) their faces! But as soon as Mom takes out the candles, they gather around the cake and Katie 6. ______________ ( ) her tenth birthday wish.

bought
makes
jumps
giggles
contain
recognize

C. Unscramble the letters and write the missing verb in each sentence. You will find synonyms of your answers on the pizza.

1. "There are so many types of food to (vosura) ____________ in this restaurant," says Rachel.
2. Spring is coming and the snowman is beginning to (lemt) ____________ .
3. No matter what the boy says, he still cannot (desarupe) ____________ his parents to buy him a new car.
4. "I wonder if it is better to stay in the country," Gabrielle (derspon) ____________ .
5. Several police cruisers have come out to (roltap) ____________ the streets.

enjoy
guard
convince
dissolve
thinks

D. Some verbs can be either transitive or intransitive. Use the following verbs in sentences of your own to show they can be used both ways.

1. sing
   a. ____________________
   b. ____________________
2. eat
   a. ____________________
   b. ____________________
3. play
   a. ____________________
   b. ____________________
4. drink
   a. ____________________
   ____
   b. ____________________
   ____

Did You Know?

One type of transitive verb is the ditransitive verb, which takes one subject and two objects. In "Bobby sends his buddy a postcard", "send" is a ditransitive verb.

Date : ____________________

Hybrid Cars

The recent searing summer and an increase of abrupt climate change have caused environmentalists, world leaders, and the general public to intensify their discussions about global warming. A major pollutant is car emission, whereby carbon dioxide is produced as a by-product. The increase in carbon dioxide levels is a primary factor in the rise of greenhouse gases. As a result, more car owners are considering driving cars that use alternative fuels instead of relying solely on fossil fuels such as gasoline.

The hybrid is one such car: it uses electricity in combination with gasoline. In fact, any vehicle that combines two or more sources of power is a hybrid. Submarines are also hybrids because they use nuclear and electric power or diesel and electric power.

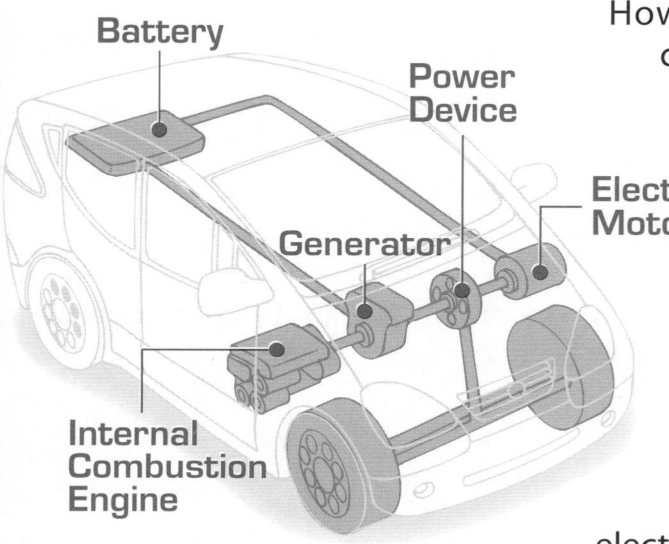

How do the two sources of power work in combination to provide the power needed? The fuel tank supplies gasoline to the engine, which is smaller than the one in an average car because advanced technology is used to reduce fuel emissions and improve efficiency. The gasoline also turns a generator; it never directly powers the engine. The generator can either supply battery power to accelerate the car or slow it down and return the energy to the batteries. The electric motor has advanced electronics that allow it to act as a motor as well as a generator. The batteries store the energy that the electric motor uses. The transmission performs the same function as the transmission in a conventional car, which is to turn the wheels.

When the ignition is turned on, the car starts with its electric motor. As it drives and the speed reaches 64 kilometres per hour or over, the gasoline engine kicks in and provides the acceleration needed to reach the desired higher speed. Power is drawn from the batteries. During braking, the electric motor transforms the car's momentum into electrical energy, which is then stored in the batteries. To conserve fuel, the gas-powered engine is shut off during stops. The two main goals of improving mileage and reducing emissions are met.

At present, there are several models of hybrid cars built by popular car manufacturers but the selection is slim. More manufacturers need to incorporate hybrid cars as part of their consumer selection. But in the meantime, are you doing your part in reducing greenhouse gases?

A. Check ✔ the main idea of this passage.

☐ Hybrid cars are simpler in structure than conventional cars.

☐ Hybrid cars work better than conventional cars.

☐ Hybrid cars are better for the environment.

☐ Hybrid cars save energy and can only travel up to 64 km per hour.

B. Find answers from the passage.

1. One possible effect of global warming:

____

2. One possible cause of global warming:

____

3. One possible effect of reducing carbon dioxide production:

____

4. How we can help reduce global warming:

____

____

5. Why submarines are hybrids:

____

Did You Know?

Before its current usage to mean hybrid propulsion, the word "hybrid" was used in the U.S. to mean a vehicle of mixed national origin, for example, a European car fitted with American mechanical parts.

Date : ____________________

Subject-Verb Agreement

The **verb** in a sentence must **agree** with its **subject** in number and be in the right tense.

Examples: The girls are very happy.
The children were still playing when the bell rang.
Because their play was a success, the actors wanted to celebrate.

A. Circle the appropriate verb for each sentence.

1. The street festival yesterday (were / was) packed with people.
2. Caitlin and Maya (is / are) at the ceremony.
3. Kathy's brother said that he (would / will) help assemble the new table.
4. Once the table is assembled, the dining room (would / will) be complete.
5. On stage, the dancer is very flamboyant. Off stage, she (was / is) very subdued.
6. She never used to watch the show *Gilmore Girls*, but now she (finds / found) herself glued to the TV whenever it is on.

B. Choose the most appropriate subject for each sentence.

Sara
rabbit
Mr. Selby
Sara's parents
The tourists

1. The ____________________ likes to hide in the bushes.
2. ____________________ is usually in her best mood in late afternoon.
3. ____________________ are fascinated by the cobblestones on the streets.
4. ____________________ have decided to give more money to the hospital.
5. ____________________ often tells his class stories of prominent Canadians.

C. **Read what the children say and choose the appropriate subject for each sentence.**

Some nouns look plural but should be treated as singular subjects.

Classics

Family Studies

Mathematics

Physics

news

1. The ______________________ is on.
2. ______________________ is an interesting subject that is related to Science.
3. ______________________ is a subject that combines Mathematics and Science.
4. ______________________ is a popular subject among students of literature because it deals with the languages, literature, and history of ancient Greece and Rome.

Some nouns are collective subjects. They look singular but may be treated as singular or plural subjects.

family

group

staff

team

band

5. The ______________ had just won their first game.
6. The ______________ that cheered for Tom were friends from his class.
7. The ______________ are concerned there may be a strike.
8. The ______________ does not want to move yet.

Did You Know?

In Philosophy, the word "subject" is often used as a synonym for "human being", or the "consciousness" of a human being.

Date : ______________________

Cool Sweat in Hot Times

Hot summer days! Keep me cool! Where is the air conditioner? I need ice cream, a cold drink, ice cubes, anything! Do these things really keep you cool during a heat wave? They all help but what really keeps you cool is your healthy skin sweating and the evaporation of that sweat.

The skin is the largest organ of the human body. It stops bugs, bacteria, and chemicals from entering most of our body. The skin also protects us from the ultra-violet rays of the sun that can harm us. Below the skin surface are many sweat glands that open up into pores on the skin surface. We have millions of sweat pores all over the body. For a summer heat wave, the healthy skin sweats efficiently.

Evaporation keeps us cool. It works best when there is a breeze with low humidity. Low humidity allows for easier sweat evaporation because of the greater difference in wetness between the skin surface and the surrounding air. In high humidity there is much less difference in wetness, and evaporation is not as great. Therefore, on a hot day any situation that has a cool temperature, a light breeze, and low humidity will keep you cool and comfortable. That is what an air conditioner does.

Sweat is made up of mostly water and some undissolved solids. These solids can clog sweat pores. So frequent washing keeps the pores open and free of clogging, making it easier to sweat. It will keep your skin healthy and clean too.

So when we sweat, it's not that yucky; it's more helpful than we imagine.

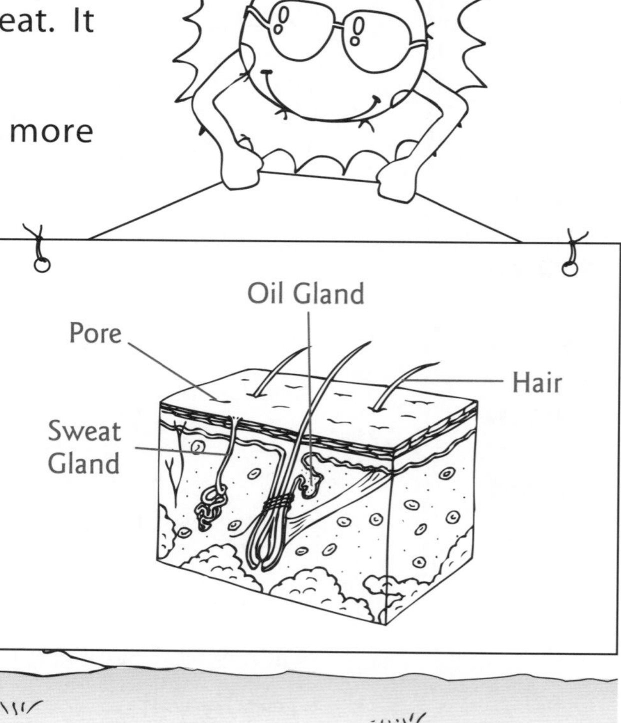

A. **Circle "T" for the true statements and "F" for the false ones.**

1. The skin is an organ. T F
2. It is the hair on the skin that helps keep us cool. T F
3. Low humidity makes it easier for sweat to evaporate. T F
4. Sweating comes from oil-pores in the skin. T F
5. Ultra-violet rays are harmful to our bodies. T F
6. Sweat is mostly water and undissolved solids. T F

B. **Fill in the blanks with words from the passage.**

1. Put on sunblock to protect yourselves against the ____________________ when you sunbathe.
2. The water in the pail dried up due to ____________________ .
3. Humidity determines the ____________________ of our surroundings.
4. The garbage will ____________________ up the drains and cause floods when there is heavy rain.

C. **Answer the following questions.**

1. How does our body keep us cool on a hot summer day?

____

____

2. How does humidity affect evaporation?

____

____

____

Did You Know?

We shed about 600 000 particles of skin every hour, or 0.7 kg a year, which means that by 70 years of age, we will have lost almost 49 kg of skin!

Date : ____________________

Present Tense: Simple and Progressive

We use the **simple present tense** when talking about a habit or a simple truth.

Example: Jim has a glass of milk every morning.

We use the **present progressive tense** when talking about an action that is going on, or an action that will take place in the near future.

Examples: Jennifer is wrapping presents for her friends.

Shelby is coming tomorrow.

A. Fill in the blanks with the present progressive tense of the verbs in parentheses.

1. Nicki (show) ______________ Jack her new running shoes.

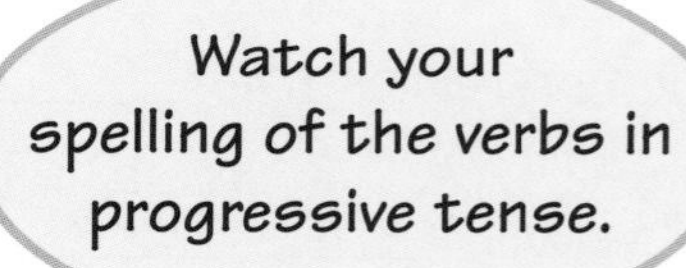

2. The children (run) ______________ towards the ice cream truck.
3. The breeze (blow) ______________ through the trees.
4. The dog (chew) ______________ on a new toy in the family room.

5. Jack (go) ______________ down the stairs on his pogo stick.
6. Mom and Dad (prepare) ______________ dinner together this evening.
7. The soup (simmer) ______________ in the pot.
8. A firefly (shine) ______________ in the dark.
9. The fire (burn) ______________ brightly in the fireplace.

B. **Fill in the blanks with the simple present tense or the present progressive tense of the verbs in parentheses.**

1. Bernie (sing) ____________________ a pretty song every morning.
2. I (arrive) ____________________ by train tonight.
3. Shelby (look) ____________________ after her baby sister whenever her mother is out.
4. Janice (like) ____________________ her aunt's beautiful vase.
5. Sara (plan) ____________________ to visit Calgary this summer.
6. Janice (think) ____________________ about what to include on her party menu.
7. Mrs. Watt (read) ____________________ her son a bedtime story every night.
8. Bobby (give) ____________________ his dog a bath once every three weeks.

C. **Use the keywords correctly to write one sentence in the simple present tense and one in the present progressive tense.**

1. farmers milk cows now day

   a ____

   b ____

2. children lie meadow afternoon

   a ____

   b ____

3. Daphne Sophia fall asleep television night

   a ____

   b ____

Date :

You Deserve A Break!

A. Which of these words have their "y" dropped before you add "ies" to their plural form? Write their plural form on the tower. Then write Matt's special words on the board.

airplane

hobby

doily

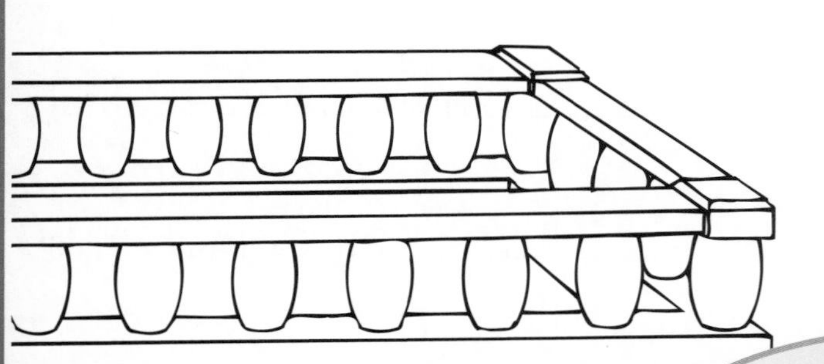

Matt, you said some of these words are special. How come?

They're special because they rhyme with your name, Keri.

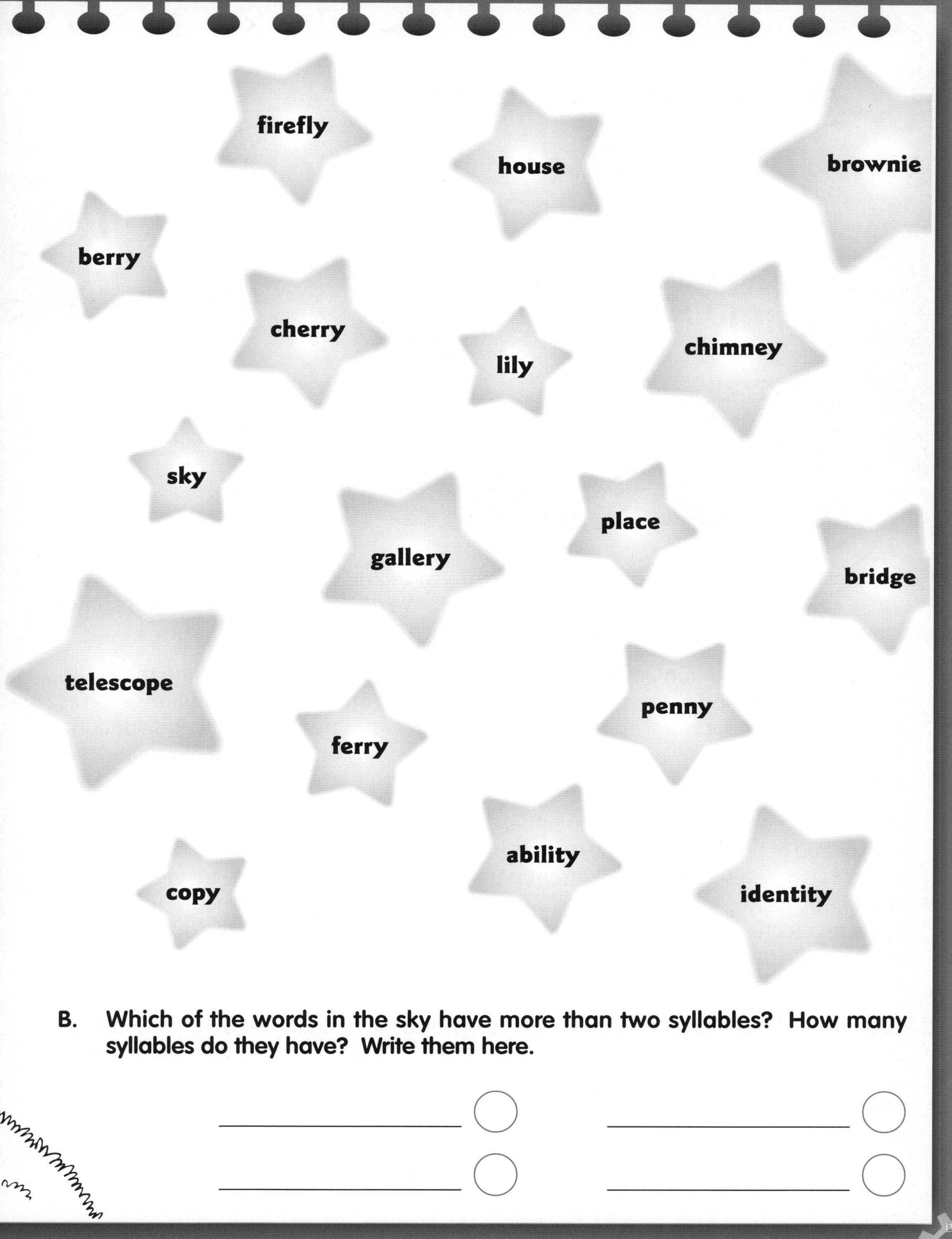

B. Which of the words in the sky have more than two syllables? How many syllables do they have? Write them here.

Day 21

Weather or Climate?

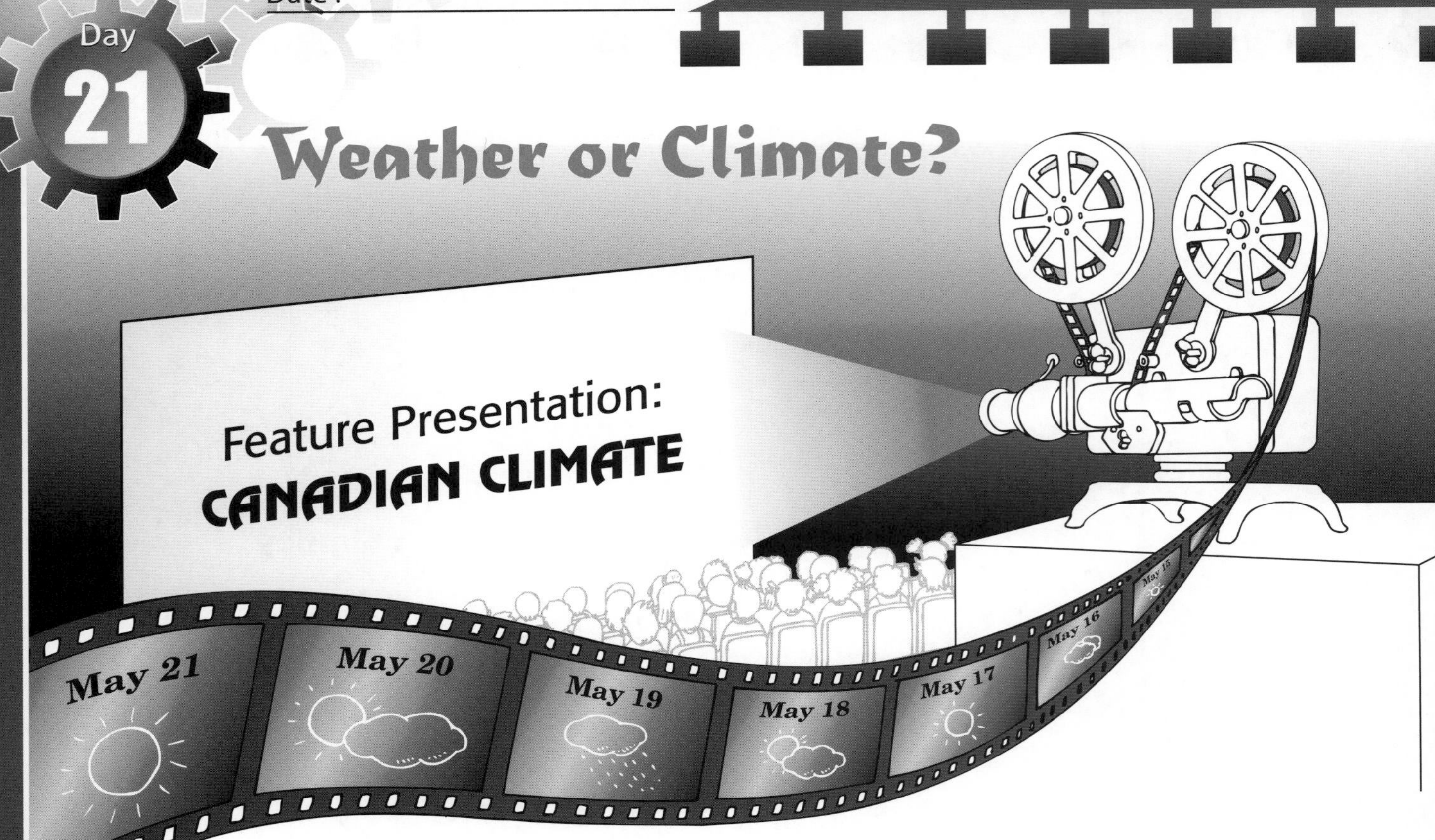

Lying on a picnic blanket looking at the beautiful summer sky, we often say, "What beautiful weather for a picnic!" We do not say, "Oh! What a beautiful climate for a picnic!" Hmm. What is the difference?

Weather is the condition of the atmosphere (the layer of gases surrounding the Earth) at a specific time and place. It includes observation of atmospheric conditions such as temperature, air pressure, humidity, wind, cold or warm fronts, clouds, and sunlight. So when we say the day is cold or hot, sticky or dry, sunny or cloudy, "rain or shine", we are talking about the weather.

Climate, on the other hand, is the weather of a place observed and recorded over a very long period of time. Climate covers large areas of land: regions in a country or continents of the Earth. It also varies in different parts of the world. Examples are wet tropical, humid tropical, desert, highland, and alpine. Each of these types of climate is influenced by factors such as altitude, distance from the equator, distance from the ocean, natural features like mountain barriers, and the movement of the atmosphere. All of these things are studied by scientists over long stretches of time.

To better understand the difference between weather and climate, let us use the analogy of a movie, in which weather is one of the many scenes, and climate is the plot. Think of weather as a snapshot, and climate as the entire film. It is useful to remember that what concerns us from day to day is the weather, but what concerns us from year to year is our climate.

So, weather or climate? Now you know the difference.

A. **Read the clues and complete the crossword puzzle with words from the passage.**

Across

A. the layer of air surrounding the Earth

B. the height above sea level

Down

1. how hot or cold it is
2. a synonym for "characteristics"
3. the amount of water in the air
4. an imaginary line around the Earth between north and south

B. **Circle the correct answers.**

1. Some weather conditions of the atmosphere are ____ .

   A. air pressure B. humidity C. animal migration D. A and B

2. Some factors that influence climate are ____ .

   A. crop circles B. altitude C. mountain barriers D. B and C

3. The huge land masses on Earth are called ____ .

   A. countries B. continents C. mountain barriers D. regions

4. If weather is a snapshot, then climate is the ____ .

   A. analogy B. plot C. camera D. B and C

Date : ____________________

Past Tense: Simple and Progressive

We use the **simple past tense** when talking about something that happened habitually or at a particular time in the past.

Examples: Craig woke up early yesterday.
Wendy lived in Montreal for five months last year.

We often use the **past progressive tense** when talking about something that continued to happen over a period of time.

Example: Aidan was watching TV when the doorbell rang.

A. Choose the appropriate verb for each sentence and decide whether to use it in the simple past or past progressive tense.

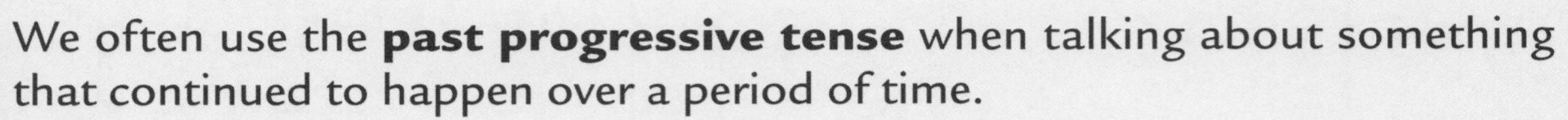

1. The boys were trying to fly a kite when their mother ____________________ them in for lunch.
2. Tina ____________________ some stain off her shirt when the waiter came to take her order.
3. The audience ____________________ when the curtain suddenly fell and all the children laughed on stage.
4. As soon as Leslie ____________________ me after school yesterday, she ____________________ .
5. Mother was making dinner when the power ____________________ off.
6. The drama teacher was getting a drink when the parents came over and ____________________ her on a successful student production.
7. Our team ____________________ by three points when it started to rain.

B. **Fill in the blanks with the simple past or past progressive tense of the verbs in parentheses.**

1. Fabio (fly) ____________________ in his dream when his cat woke him up.
2. Sally's friends often (talk) ____________________ to her when she was trying to study.
3. Martin (walk) ____________________ to the library when he bumped into an old friend from kindergarten.
4. Margaret (rehearse) ____________________ with her choir when she was called to the office.
5. Wayne often (play) ____________________ catch with his buddies last summer.
6. The telephone rang when I (take) ____________________ a shower.
7. The teachers (have) ____________________ a meeting yesterday.
8. Keith was debating whether to get a banana split or a strawberry sundae when he (spot) ____________________ a chocolate fudge sandwich on the menu and (decide) ____________________ to order that instead.

C. **Each of the following may or may not have the correct past tense. Circle any wrong verbs and write the correct form on the lines.**

1. Mother drunk a glass of water to wash down her food. ______________
2. Calvin drawed a picture of his new dog. ______________
3. After nearly an hour, Team A was still leading Team B by fourteen points. ______________
4. Laura bended her body in a wide arc to see if she was flexible enough for gymnastics. ______________

Date : ____________________

Aurora Borealis

Aurora borealis, or northern lights, can be seen in the near north latitudes and the Arctic. At 100 to 1000 kilometres above the Earth's surface, they are seen mostly at night and may last for hours.

The northern lights appear as a stream of luminous diffused lights, starting at the horizon and floating upwards to a point directly overhead. It is a spectacular event that is hard to describe. There could be colours of green, orange, and pink one day, and then yellow and white the next. On some nights they look like curtains, and on others they resemble a series of searchlights.

Very little air or gas exists in the Earth's upper atmosphere; the condition there is almost like a vacuum. When atomic particles from the sun hit the Earth's upper atmosphere, energy is released, creating the northern lights. Neon lights work in the same way: a neon light is a tube of near vacuum-like conditions with gas particles inside. An electrical current agitates the gases and light is given off.

There are actually two light shows on Earth: aurora can be seen both near the North and South Poles. The name for southern lights is *aurora australis*. In Roman mythology, "Aurora" is the goddess of dawn. In Latin, "australis" means "of the south wind", while "borealis" means "of the north wind".

It is too bad that the northern lights are not predictable. One seldom orders up a display of aurora like ordering a hamburger at a fast food joint. However, it has been suggested that the lights are more common after major solar flares and sunspot activities on the sun's surface.

According to some old legend, good fortune will beset you if the goddess likes you and puts on a display in the sky.

A. Match the words with their meanings.

1. sunspots ______ A. bursts
2. flares ______ B. dark spots on the sun
3. latitudes ______ C. small portions of matter
4. luminous ______ D. giving off light
5. particles ______ E. distances from the equator

B. Arrange the following into one sentence by writing 1, 2, 3, 4, and 5.

	from solar flares
	collide with the gases
	in the Earth's upper atmosphere
	light energy is released
	when atomic particles

C. Read the clues and unscramble the words.

1. of the south wind (iaaulssrt) ____________________
2. of the north wind (aeioblsr) ____________________
3. the goddess of dawn (uoaArr) ____________________
4. the polar region in the north (Aiccrt) ____________________
5. collection of tales (holymotyg) ____________________

Did You Know?

Fairbanks, Alaska is a good place for watching aurora since it is along the ring-shaped region in the North Pole where northern lights occur.

Date : ____________________

Future Tense: Simple and Progressive

We use the **simple future tense** when talking about something that will happen.

Examples: It will be warm and sunny tomorrow.
Richard will rest after mowing the lawn.

We use the **future progressive tense** when talking about something that will happen over a period of time.

Examples: Richard will be napping for the rest of the day.
The sun will be shining for the entire afternoon.

A. Change the verb in parentheses to the tense indicated for each sentence.

1. Many of us (watch) ____________________ the Olympics on TV.
   Simple future
2. The phone (ring) ____________________ in five minutes.
   Simple future
3. Vinnie's cousin (visit) ____________________ for the summer.
   Future progressive
4. There (be) ____________________ a new radio program on Monday morning.
   Simple future
5. Shelley (ride) ____________________ her bicycle to school this year.
   Future progressive

B. Fill in the blanks with the simple future or future progressive tense of the verbs in parentheses.

1. Marty (attend) ____________________ a different school for some time.
2. William (turn) ____________________ eleven years old this March.
3. Catherine's children (play) ____________________ one more game.
4. Since the day is so hot, we (swim) ____________________ until sunset.

C. **Choose the appropriate word for each sentence and determine whether to use it in the simple future or future progressive tense.**

go find snap look see sound

1. Richard ______________________ five movies over the course of the film festival.

2. "If we don't take the burning sausage out of the frying pan now, the smoke detector ______________________ off!" said Jack.

3. "Watch," says Timothy to Robertson. "In a few minutes, the magician there ______________________ his fingers and all the frogs will disappear."

4. Kiefer hid his sister's favourite doll and knows she ______________________ all over for it throughout the day.

D. **Read what Jimmy says to find out what "future in the past" is. Then choose the appropriate phrase for each sentence.**

would have gone
would go
would be going
would have been going

We use the tense "future in the past" when we want to say that, at some point in the past, something was yet to happen in the future.

1. David decided yesterday that he ______________________ to the baseball game today.

2. David decided last year that he ______________________ to many games this year.

3. If David's friends had not been able to go with him today, he still ______________________ to the game himself.

4. If David had not won a season's worth of baseball game tickets, he ______________________ to hockey games this year instead.

Date : ____________________

Boxing

Boxing is a sport where two athletes wearing regulation-sized gloves exchange punches and blows according to rules agreed upon. Points are awarded by a panel of ringside judges, and the referee controls the conduct of the fight. A boxer wins by a knockout or technical knockout, or if the opponent is disqualified. As a sport, boxing can be played in one of two sets of rules: amateur Olympic rules or professional rules.

Pugilism – the art of fighting with fists and hands – goes back to the beginning of civilization. Records from the Sumerian times (around 4000 B.C.) and Babylonian times (around 2700 – 538 B.C.) reveal that boxing existed as an art as well as a practice.

Ancient Greeks had urns with pictures of boxers wrapping their hands with thongs, or strips of leather. But besides boxing, the ancient Olympics featured an event called "pankration" (*pan* meaning "all" and *kratos* meaning "strength"), which was a combination of boxing, wrestling, and "all-in-all-out mayhem". It was not a pleasant sport.

Ancient Rome had gladiators and slave boxers in various boxing events. Ancient Romans even continued the Greek pankration tradition, but spelled it "pancratium" in Latin. During the times of the gladiatorial games, boxing was such a savage sport that boxers would wear cestuses (thongs with metal knobs and plates) for their matches.

The modern square boxing ring got its name from the circular arena where ancient Roman boxers fought. These matches got so vicious that they were banned and outlawed throughout the rest of the Roman Empire.

Boxing did not reappear until late 1600s in England, where boxers fought with bare knuckles. Still a brutal sport, it was also tied to gambling. Around the 1860s, the Marquess of Queensbury introduced 12 rules that made the sport more civilized. These rules, with modifications, have been used for most boxing matches since 1872.

In spite of the roughness of its origin, modern boxing can be very beneficial. Young boxers learn how to have a good boxing stance and how to box with a jab, a hook, a cross, a straight, and an upper-cut punch. They also learn how to defend themselves by ducking, clinching, slipping, parrying, feinting, or blocking. Above all, the young boxer learns about good sportsmanship, benefits from hard work, and gains self-confidence.

A. Give one-word answers to the following questions.

1. What did ancient Greeks use to cover their hands for boxing? ____________
2. What did ancient Roman boxers wear for their boxing matches? ____________
3. What does "kratos" mean? ____________
4. Which country started the Olympics? ____________
5. In 1600s England, boxing was associated with something else. What was it? ____________

B. Read the clues and complete the crossword puzzle with words from the passage.

Across

A. chaos

B. what you may gain from learning boxing

C. the art of fighting with fists and hands

D. an ancient Greek event of boxing and wrestling

E. a defence technique

F. a type of punch

Down

1. trained fighters in ancient Rome

2. changes

Date : ____________________

Comparative and Superlative Adjectives

We use **comparative adjectives** to compare two people, animals, things, or groups. We use **superlative adjectives** when the comparison is among three or more.

Examples: The giraffe's neck is longer than Susie's.
The giraffe has the longest neck among animals.

A. Complete the table by writing the comparative and superlative forms of each adjective.

	Adjective	Comparative	Superlative
1.	safe		
2.	happy		happiest
3.	forgetful	more forgetful	
4.	great		
5.	big	bigger	
6.	friendly		
7.	sad		
8.	nice		
9.	important		most important
10.	thin		
11.	influential		
12.	easy		
13.	tiny		
14.	marvellous		

B. Use the following keywords to write sentences with comparative or superlative adjectives.

1. Doris bustling Toronto Canada thinks city

___

2. Jill Jack careful than person

___

3. Kelly Dana usually than fast

___

___

4. beautiful Rome Paris city than

___

___

C. Determine if the comparative or superlative adjective in each sentence is in the correct form. If not, write the correct form on the line.

1. Marie's room is the most tidy. ___
2. We had the splendidest dinner in Little Italy. ___
3. Kim's mother makes the smoothest cheesecake. ___
4. There is another restaurant further down the street. ___

D. Some adjectives have irregular comparative and superlative forms. You saw one in (C). Think of two more and write them down along with their comparative and superlative forms.

1 ___ : ___ ; ___

2 ___ : ___ ; ___

Date : ______________________

Campfire

A campfire is one of the most enjoyable aspects of a camping trip. The old woodsman travelling in the wild depended totally on the campfire to cook his food, boil his water, provide warmth and light, and give protection against wild animals.

Most modern campsites have designated concrete fire pits. These concrete fire pits make lighting a campfire safer than in the wild forest but even so, proper fire safety rules must be followed. A safe campfire must be only large enough to easily control and to prevent it from spreading.

The steps in making a campfire have remained the same. First, we must pick or prepare a safe fire pit. In a modern camp it is usually there already. Second, we must collect firewood and separate it into groups of different sizes – from small twigs, called kindling, to large sticks and logs. Third, we must have a fire starter. In the old days we would have made one, but nowadays we have all kinds of fire starters like gasoline-soaked wood chips and others. Fourth, we need fire fighting tools like a shovel and bucket to beat the stray fire; or, we could smother the sparks with dirt. Fifth, we need a poker to arrange the burning wood.

Making a campfire is really about starting a very small fire and building it up slowly by adding increasingly larger sized firewood until the desired size is reached. Let us leave out the huge bonfires. These types of fire are very hard to control safely in most campfire pits.

Start by building a teepee or square of medium sized sticks. Leave a hole or space in the centre to place the kindling and fire starter. Then light them with a burning match or steel and flint. Gently fan the small fire. When it starts to get bigger and burns the teepee or square, slowly add more firewood to build it into a size that you want. Add firewood gently so as not to smother the fire.

By now the marshmallows, camp songs, and scary stories are ready for all to enjoy. Happy camping!

A. Circle "T" for the true statements and "F" for the false ones.

1. To start a campfire, bury firewood in a hole, cover it with dirt, and light the dirt with a match. T F
2. The old woodsman depended on the campfire for survival. T F
3. Fire safety rules are laxer in modern campsites because the pits are made of concrete. T F
4. In order to build a fire, it is important to add larger sized wood slowly and gently. T F

B. Sequence the following steps by writing 1, 2, 3, 4, and 5 on the lines.

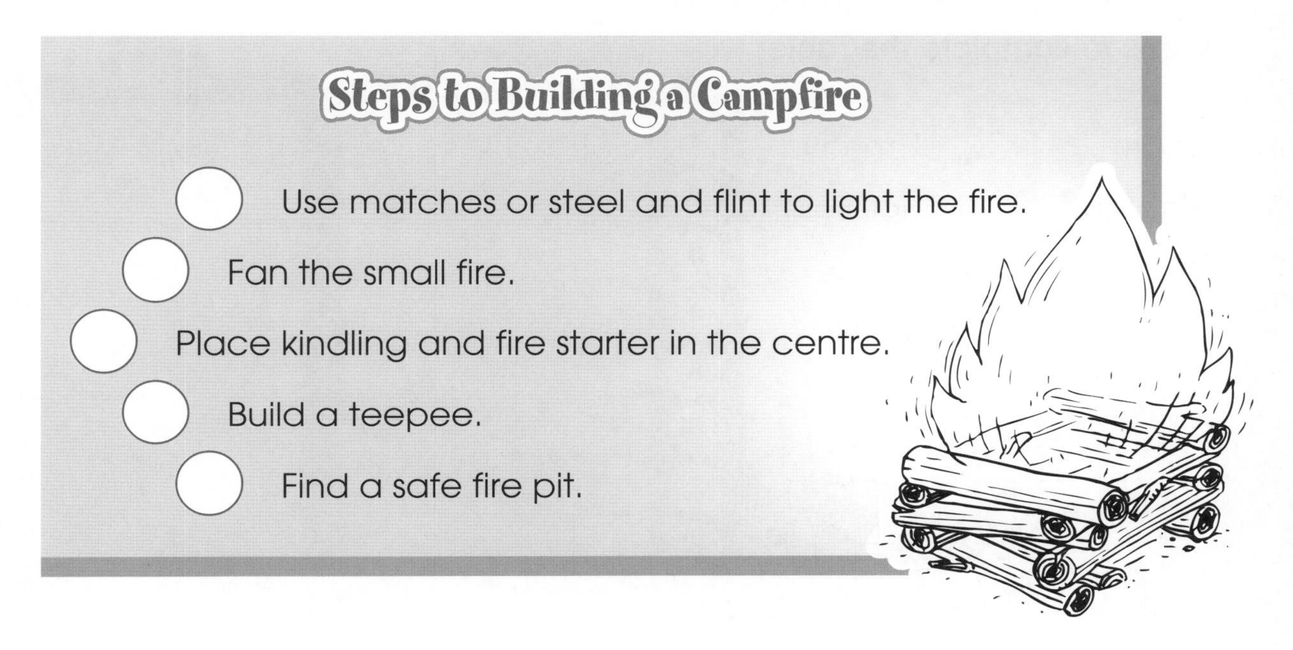

C. There are some compound words in the passage. Find and write them on the lines.

____

____

____

____

____

____

Date : ______________________

Creating Adjectives from Verbs

Many verbs can become adjectives when we add "**-ing**" or "**-ed**" to them. In general, "-ing" adjectives describe the effect of someone or something, while "-ed" adjectives describe someone's feelings.

Examples: Lori's skipping ability is amazing.
Her friends were amazed when they were skipping during recess.

A. Create adjectives from the following verbs to complete the table.

1.	charm	2.	annoy
3.	frighten	4.	interest
5.	embarrass	6.	bore
7.	welcome	8.	move

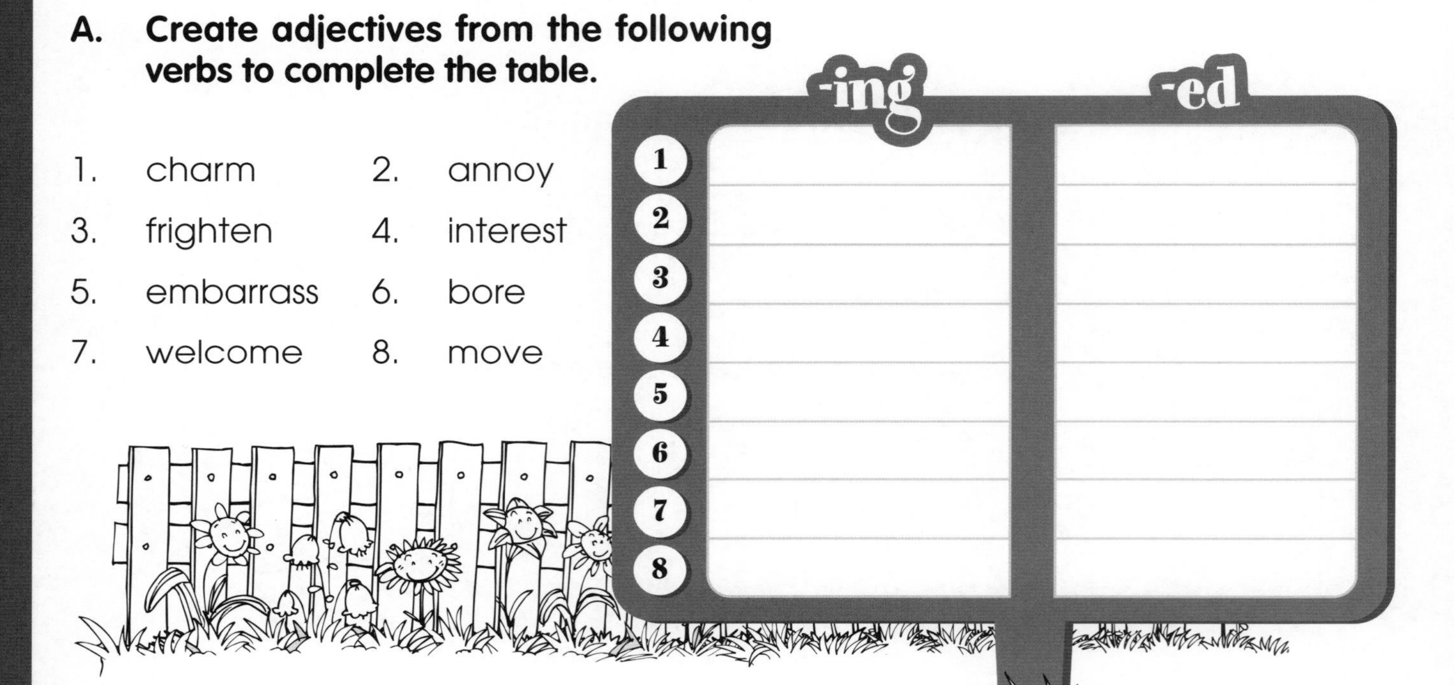

	-ing	-ed
1		
2		
3		
4		
5		
6		
7		
8		

B. Choose an appropriate adjective from the table above to complete each sentence.

1. Clara looked ______________________ when she saw a bat.
2. The student was so ______________________ that he fell asleep.
3. My little sister whines in an ______________________ voice.
4. Richard lives in a ______________________ house with a cute fence.
5. Many in the audience wept at the end of the film because the story was so ______________________ .

C. **Choose an appropriate verb to make a comparative or superlative adjective for each sentence.**

exercise surprise
depress interest convince
confuse touch bore

1. Tom said, "These are some of the ____________________ books I've ever read.
2. Carol's argument was ____________________ than Walter's.
3. Though Henry and Clare went to see one film after another, they ended up even ____________________ than they had been.
4. After the main character dies in the novel, Wanda sighs, "This is the ____________________ story I've read this month."
5. The more he explained, the ____________________ it became.

D. **Complete the following sentences with appropriate verb-turned adjectives.**

solve *please* *satisfy* *disappoint* *prepare* *thrill*

1. The skater's huge smile shows he is very ____________________ with his performance.
2. Gregory is always ____________________ to talk on the spot.
3. Molly was ____________________ that the monsters in the movie were not real.
4. Mrs. Goodall was ____________________ to hear that her grandson was engaged.
5. Our teacher was very ____________________ with our work.

Date : ____________________

Erica's Journal

Erica was tired when she got home but thank goodness it was Friday. She made herself a snack of celery and cream cheese and ran upstairs to write in her journal.

"Dear Journal,

This morning, we played Dodge Ball in the yard and then the bell rang because it started to rain. We quickly lined up outside Room 210 and Ms. Chang let us in. We got ready to do silent reading after the announcements. That was when I saw Celia talking to Ms. Chang. Celia didn't look happy. Ms. Chang was listening and looked serious. She told us that she had to deal with a problem outside and reminded us to continue reading. They went into the hall, closed the door, and then came in together after a while.

Standing by the whiteboard, Ms. Chang interrupted silent reading and said that there was a problem. She talked about vandalism and graffiti. It seemed that someone had gone into Celia's desk and wrote unkind comments on a list of her favourite TV shows. She wanted to know if anyone knew about it. No one put up their hand. Then Ms. Chang continued to talk about honesty and respect for other classmates' property. Still, no one said anything. She then said if anyone knew anything and would like to meet her privately after school, she would keep it confidential.

She got up and asked us to get ready for spelling. As she walked around, she collected our journals. She went back to her desk and started to read them. It looked like she was comparing the printing of each student with Celia's list. Then she called Daniel to her desk. Daniel said a lot but I couldn't hear him. He sat down suddenly on the chair beside Ms. Chang's desk and started to cry.

After sitting there for a long time, Daniel confessed that he was the one who wrote the comments. I heard Ms. Chang asking him why and he said that Celia was always bothering him whenever he was reading. Ms. Chang said that what he did was inappropriate and that there were other ways to deal with a problem. If Daniel didn't want Celia to bother him, he should have told her. Ms. Chang also talked to Celia about the importance of leaving others alone. In the end, Celia and Daniel apologized to each other, but because Daniel went into Celia's desk, he would have to miss a basketball home game."

A. Circle the correct answer for each question.

1. Who approached Ms. Chang with a problem?

   A. Celia and Erica B. Daniel

   C. Celia D. Erica

2. A student wrote something unkind on ____ .

   A. Celia's desk B. Erica's chair

   C. Daniel's notebook D. Celia's list

3. The student most likely wrote the unkind comments on ____ .

   A. Friday B. Tuesday

   C. Thursday D. Monday

B. Give your own point of view.

1. Do you think Daniel's writing on Celia's list was graffiti? Why?

   ____

2. If you were Ms. Chang, would you have talked with Daniel while the rest of the class was there?

   ____

3. If someone was always bothering you at school, what would you do?

   ____

   ____

4. Ms. Chang said if anyone knew anything about Celia's problem and wanted to tell her, she would keep it confidential. Why do you think she should?

   ____

   ____

   ____

   ____

   ____

   ____

Did You Know?

The first pencil was invented in 1560 after a large tree was uprooted in a storm and a black substance called graphite was discovered beneath its roots.

Date : ____________________

Day 30 You Deserve A Break!

Lori and the potatoes are singing a song about musical instruments that have other words in their names. Find out what they are and write them in the boxes.

In this instrument's name there is...

a tub

a bone

a horn

a net

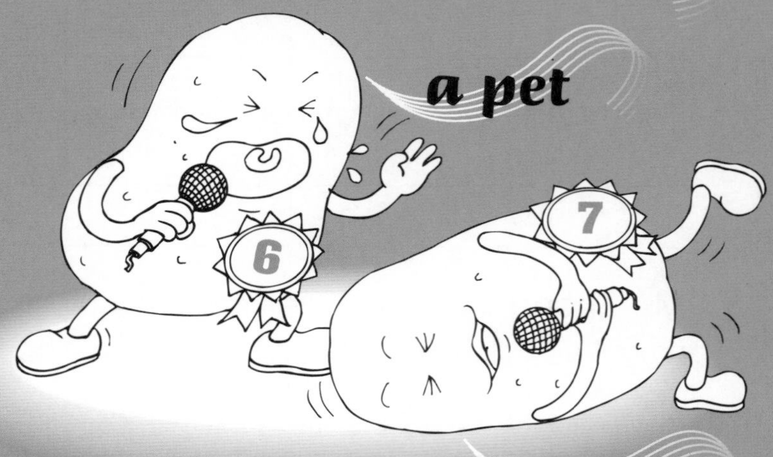

a pet

a bar

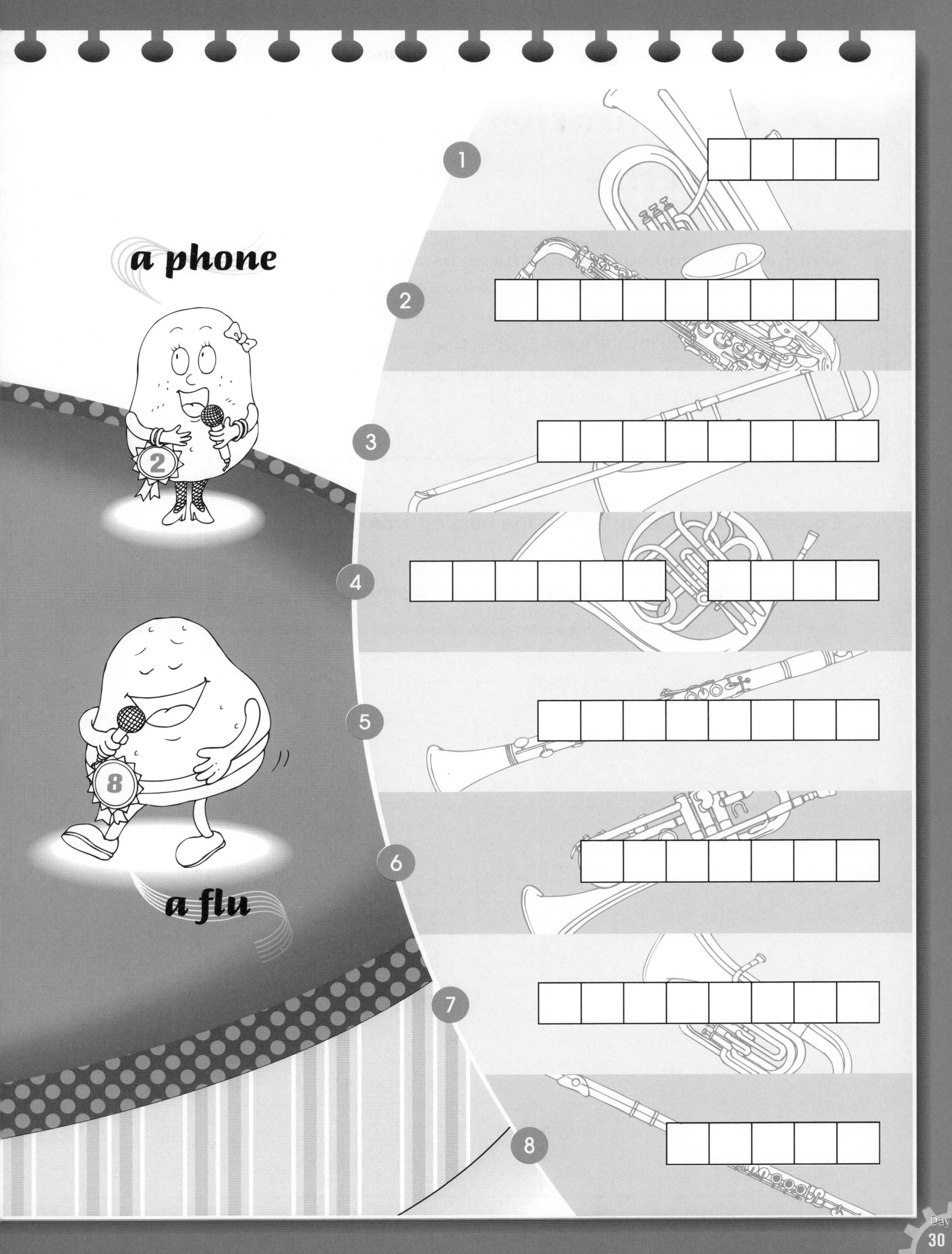

a phone
2
8
a flu
1
2
3
4
5
6
7
8

Date :

Comparative and Superlative Adverbs

Comparative and **superlative adverbs** are formed and used in the same way as comparative and superlative adjectives.

Examples: The audience arrived sooner than expected.
The dancer performed more comfortably on the old stage than on the new one.

A. Complete the table by writing the missing words.

	Adjective	Adverb	Comparative	Superlative
1.	clear			
2.		seriously		
3.			more carefully	
4.				most beautifully
5.			more strongly	
6.		commonly		
7.	quiet			
8.		gently		
9.			more rationally	
10.				most importantly
11.			more easily	
12.		happily		
13.	simple			

B. Choose the most appropriate adverb from the flower and use it in the comparative or superlative form for each sentence.

soon
early
usually
frequently
often
late

1. The ________________ we arrive, the less time we will have to explore the city.
2. Sam is like a bird. He is always the one to get up ________________ than everyone else.
3. Terry has been visiting his grandpa ________________ over the past two weeks.
4. The ________________ Marla gets better, the faster she could resume training.

C. Find a synonym from the cookie for each adverb. Then use the synonym to compose a sentence.

daringly
benevolently
inventively
lovingly
truthfully

1. affectionately ________________

____

____

2. bravely ________________

____

____

3. kindly ________________

____

4. creatively ________________

____

5. candidly ________________

____

Date : ____________________

Secret Writing

Spies throughout the ages have used secret writing to pass messages to one another. They use previously agreed upon codes and symbols known only to themselves to write these messages, thereby preventing their enemies from knowing their plans.

Secret writing known also as a cryptogram or cryptograph is used by many people besides spies and secret agents: scientists who want to guard their research against others, diary writers who want their private thoughts and feelings kept confidential, or lovers who wish to keep their situation a secret.

Basically, anything can be written as secret messages. You can write your e-mail, snail mail, and even your classroom notes in code.

For hundreds of years, maybe even thousands, messages were handwritten and delivered by postmen of some kind or private couriers. Letters in envelopes could be easily stolen, cut open, and the messages read. Secret writing or a cryptogram makes a stolen letter harder or impossible to read. This gives spies time to change their plans, if needed, once the theft is known.

An example of secret writing is to use a numbering system for the letters of the English alphabet. For instance, "A" is 01, "B" is 02..., "M" is 13..., "Y" is 25, and "Z" is 26. Let us call this Code One. So, in order to write "This is Code One", we would write 20080919 0919 03150405 151405.

To make the code more difficult, you can group the numbers into fours or eights or whatever you like, but make sure you remember which code system you use or you won't be able to decode your own message! That is why secret writers make code books and code tables to simplify the "coding and decoding".

Another way is to use a "reverse alphabet" system, like "A" is Z, "B" is Y, "C" is X..., "Y" is B, and "Z" is A. "This is Code Two" would become GSRH RH XLWV GDL. Yet another way is to use numbers for the first half of the alphabet and reverse alphabet for the second half. "This is Code Three" would be 07SR06 R06 X02WV 07S05VV.

A. Circle "T" for the true statements and "F" for the false ones.

1.	Only secret agents in the olden days wrote secret messages.	T	F
2.	Reverse alphabet is one way of writing coded messages.	T	F
3.	Secret writing makes stolen letters harder to read.	T	F
4.	The cryptogram and cryptograph are two coding systems.	T	F
5.	Code books are used to decode encrypted messages.	T	F
6.	Three types of coding were described in the passage.	T	F
7.	A secret message may consist of both letters and numbers.	T	F
8.	The harder it is to decode a message, the more time there is for spies to alter their plans.	T	F

B. Try the following.

1. Write "cryptogram" using Code One.

____

2. Decode "XIBKGLTIZN" into plain English using Code Two.

____

3. Use Code Three to write a secret message. Provide the answer.

____

____

4. Create and describe a "Code Four". Then use it to write a secret message.

____

____

____

____

____

Did You Know?

Some spies became great novelists by turning their experiences into stories. Ian Fleming, creator of James Bond, was an example.

Date : ____________________

Conjunctions

A **conjunction** is a word that joins together words, phrases, or sentences.

Example: Mr. Saber is a happy and fun-loving farmer. Although he is well into his fifties, he is like a kid at times. His wife wants him to grow up, but he prefers to be young at heart.

A. Circle the conjunctions in the following sentences.

1. Marie and Joseph arrived before Mrs. Saber had time to clean up the house.
2. Mrs. Johnston waited at the station until the sun went down.
3. The children left the beach only after it had started to rain.
4. Mrs. Morgan called to her son, "You're not going to be on time unless you hurry up!"
5. To get to Vancouver from Toronto, we can travel by plane or train.
6. The little kid said to his dad at the park, "Catch me if you can!"
7. Although the seats were not too comfortable on the train, Mrs. Simmons did not complain.
8. Mr. Saber is in a very good mood today because his favourite hen has laid a few eggs.
9. Mr. Saber has been a farmer since he was fifteen years old.
10. Mrs. Simmons arrived at the train station and was so happy to see Mrs. Johnston.

B. Fill in the blanks with the appropriate conjunctions.

because *unless* *therefore*
while *still* *than* *although*
so *since* *but* *when* *if*

1. Marie and Joseph did not want to leave ______________ they would miss the animals on the farm.
2. Mrs. Saber did not like the roast she prepared, ______________ everyone else enjoyed it.
3. Mr. and Mrs. Saber will not move to the city ______________ there is a very good reason to do so.
4. ______________ Marie and Joseph are city dwellers, they ______________ visit their parents' farm every now and then.
5. The hen went back to sleep ______________ Mr. Saber was not looking.

C. Some conjunctions are used in pairs. Complete each sentence with the appropriate pair.

either...or *neither...nor* *not only...but also*
both...and *whether...or* *though...yet*

1. Canada is ____________ a big country ____________ very cold in winter.
2. Carly said to Mel, " ____________ you are mistaken ____________ I am."
3. The students in Mrs. Peters's class ____________ love ____________ respect her.
4. The Simpsons do not mind ____________ they stay ____________ move to another house.
5. "Things are ____________ good ____________ bad; only thinking makes them so," a teacher said to Bob, who had a puzzled look on his face.

Date : ________________

Moon Phases

The full moon is one of the brightest objects in the night sky. It outshines all the stars and planets when seen with the naked eye. The bright full moon lights up everything in its path – trees, grass, night animals, ponds, and everything else. It casts a unique dreamy, sleepy, almost cozy glow.

The moon's appearance and disappearance from the night sky was so important to many early civilizations that they set their calendars to the moon cycle, and not the sun cycle. Our calendar today is set according to the sun cycle.

The observation of the phases of the moon has been done since ancient times. The cycle starts from a new moon (waxing crescent) growing fuller into a first quarter (half moon). Then it becomes a gibbous moon (more than a half, but less than full) before finally becoming a full moon.

On the return cycle, the full moon becomes a gibbous moon and then enters the last quarter (a half moon) before changing into the waning crescent (old moon). There is complete darkness for a little while and then the cycle starts again. The whole cycle takes about 29.5 days. That is how the name for "month" came about, from the moon.

The sun's rays light up the moon surface so that we can see it from the Earth. There are really two key positions of the moon, the Earth, and the sun that make the observation of the moon phases clearer. First, when the moon is directly between the Earth and the sun, we see only the dark night sky, or the dark side of the moon surface (sun → moon → Earth = dark). Second, when the Earth is between the sun and the moon, we see the bright full moon (sun → Earth → moon = full moon). All the other phases are between these two key positions – full moon versus dark night.

A. **Circle "T" for the true statements or "F" for the false ones.**

1.	The full moon is the brightest object in the night sky seen with the naked eye.	T	F
2.	It takes about thirty days for the moon to rotate around the Earth.	T	F
3.	Ancient civilizations set their calendar to the Earth cycle.	T	F
4.	Today we use the solar calendar.	T	F
5.	We see a bright full moon when the Earth is between the sun and the moon.	T	F

B. **Read the clues and complete the crossword puzzle with words from the passage.**

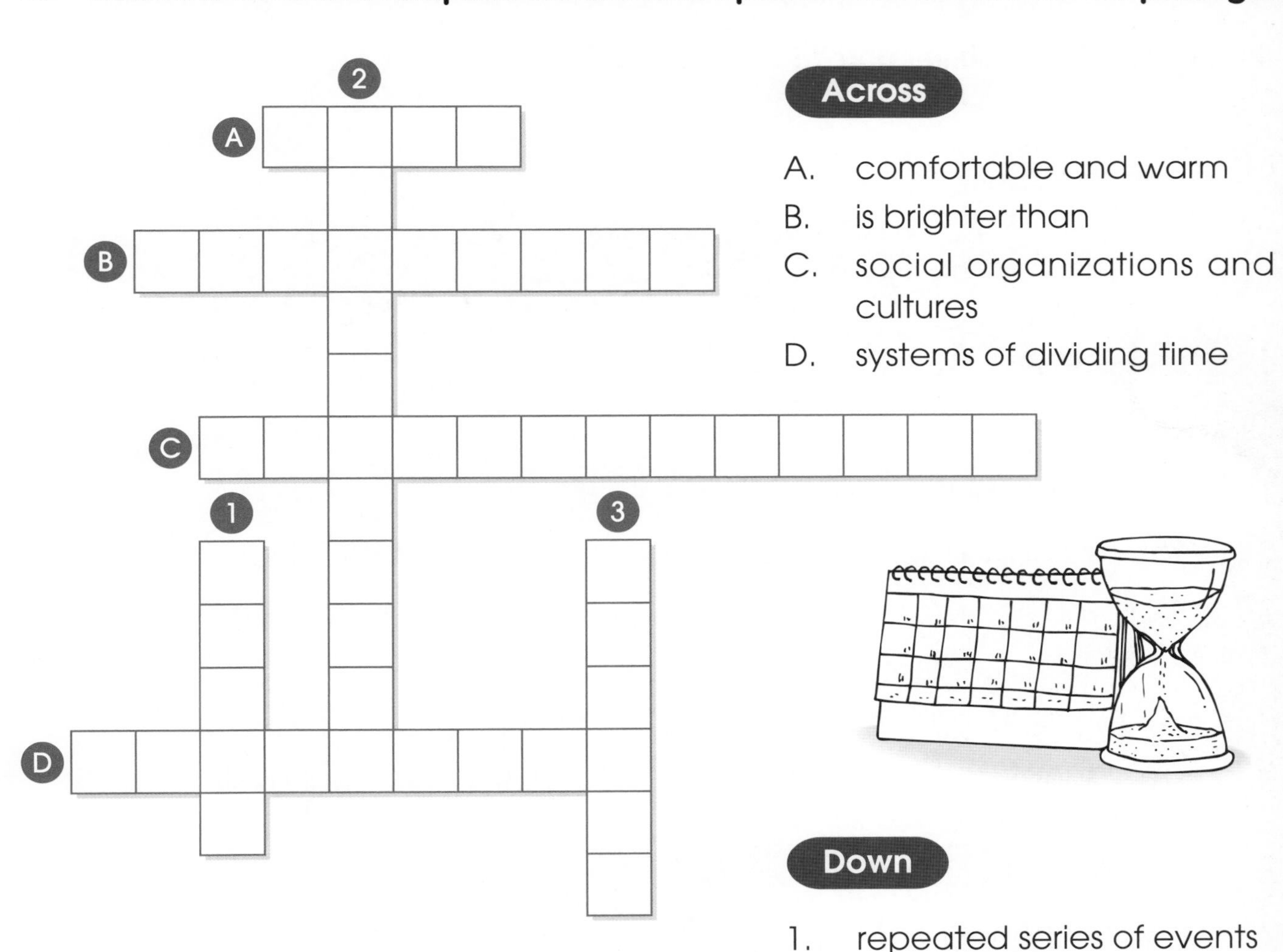

Across

A. comfortable and warm

B. is brighter than

C. social organizations and cultures

D. systems of dividing time

Down

1. repeated series of events
2. watching carefully
3. stages

Date : ____________________

Modal Verbs: Can and Could

Can

We use "can" to talk about ability in the present or future.

Examples: Patrick can play the piano, but Lucy cannot.
"I can't babysit your brother today," says Shelley. "But I can tomorrow."

We also use "can" to give or ask for permission in the present or future.

Examples: "Can we have a snack before we go to bed, Mom?" ask the children.
"Okay. You can have a few cookies," says Mother.

A. Write "A" for ability and "P" for permission.

1. Beavers can build amazing dams. ______
2. "You're kidding me, Richard!" says Tom. "Beavers can't sing!" ______
3. "Sure, you can use my computer to surf the Web," says Michael to Todd. ______
4. Sydney's dog can read his owner's mind. ______
5. Bob cannot go to the baseball game tonight because he is grounded for a week. ______
6. Frankie is only five but he can already swim quite well. ______
7. "No, you cannot eat all the cookies in the jar," says Mother. ______
8. You can drive to Germany from France, but you cannot do that from Australia. ______

Could

We use "**could**" to talk about ability or permission in the past.

Examples: Leila could talk when she was barely two.
Julie could not talk until she was almost three.
The teacher just told the class that they could do some silent reading.

We also use "**could**" to talk about possibility.

Examples: "Why isn't Tim in class today?" asks Jon.
"He could be sick," said Lewis.
"Look how dark it is outside," says Bob. "It could start raining any minute."

B. Determine whether each of the following is about ability, permission, or possibility. Write the correct question numbers in the spaces provided.

1. "The bell could ring any minute now," says Mr. Graham.
2. Grandpa could read four newspapers in one afternoon back in the days when he was young.
3. "Could you help me untie this knot?" Sheila asks her sister.
4. Melissa said I could borrow her books when she finished reading them.
5. The line-up was so crowded yesterday that nobody could move even an inch.
6. Christopher could juggle three balls when he worked at the circus.
7. I doubt the corner store will close down, but of course I could be wrong.
8. There could be a storm tomorrow, as forecast by the weather network.

Ability ________

Permission ________

Possibility ________

Date : ____________________

Origami

Origami is a visual or sculptural art form that has crossed over from the East to the West and is now practised and enjoyed by many all over the world.

Although the word *origami* is Japanese in origin – *oru* means "to fold" and *kami* means "paper" – the art form may have originated in China. Paper was invented in China and was then introduced by Buddhist monks to Japan in the late 6th century. Paper folding was invented shortly after and origami was born. The monks used origami in their Shinto ceremonies, a religion in Japan where white serrated strips of paper were used to mark sacred objects. They can still be seen in shrines today. Origami was also referred to as folding of certificates or documents. The ancient custom of special folding was to prevent unauthorized copying of important diplomas for Tea Ceremony masters or masters of swordsmanship.

Because paper was rare, paper folding became a pastime of the nobility during the Heian Period (794–1185). Set shapes were used only for ceremonies such as weddings. Origami became a form of entertainment for the common people around the Edo Period (1600–1868). Its popularity declined around the 19th century with the modernization of Japan. But Master Yoshizawa Akira, the grandmaster of origami, published books with new design models in the 1950s. Together with Sam Randlett, an American, they developed a standard set of origami diagram symbols that are still used today.

A girl named Sasaki Sadako is remembered for associating the crane (*tsuru*) design with peace. As a victim of the atomic bombing in Hiroshima, Sadako wanted to make 1000 cranes to wish for her own recovery. She was following a tradition that believes a wish would come true for every crane completed. Even though she did not complete the 1000 cranes because she died after making 644, her friends continued on her behalf and dedicated them to her at her funeral. Following this tradition, each year on Peace Day (August 6), thousands of origami tsuru are sent to Hiroshima. So the next time you make an origami tsuru, make a wish for peace.

A. Circle the correct answers.

1. Origami was popular around ____ .

   A. the Heian Period
   B. the Edo Period
   C. the late 19th century
   D. the 20th century

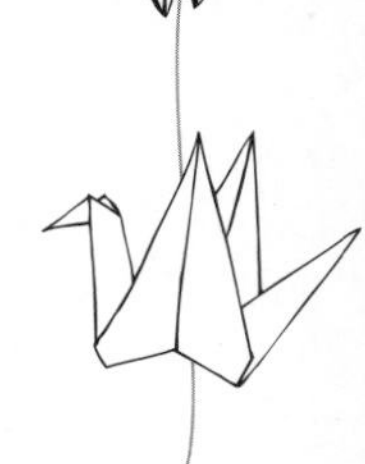

2. The grandmaster of origami was ____ .

   A. a Buddhist monk
   B. Sam Randlett
   C. Sasaki Sadako
   D. Yoshizawa Akira

3. Sadako turned the paper crane into a symbol of ____ .

   A. death
   B. peace
   C. survival
   D. freedom

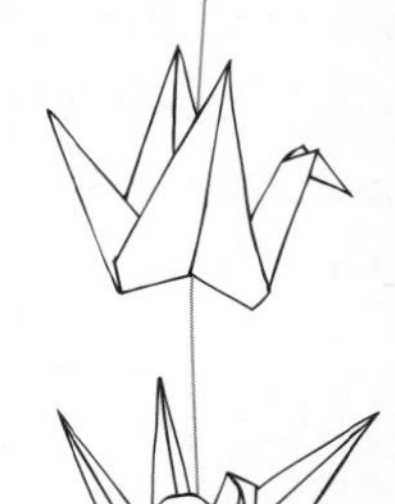

4. The ancient custom of special folding was ____ .

   A. to prevent unauthorized copying of important diplomas
   B. to mark special tea ceremonies
   C. to celebrate festivities
   D. to promote the art of origami

B. Read the clues to unscramble the words.

1. Papers of proof: **frecastietic** ____________
2. Custom: **natritido** ____________
3. It amuses: **menninarettet** ____________
4. State of being liked by many people: **aloupypirt** ____________
5. Not commonly found: **earr** ____________
6. Of the distant past: **cantine** ____________

Date : ____________________

Asking Polite Questions: Will, Would, and Could

We use "**will**", "**would**", and "**could**" to ask for assistance in a polite way.

Examples: "Would you please deliver this box to 30 Maple Avenue?" the shopowner asked Bob.
"Yes. Certainly," Bob replied.
"Could you open the door for me?" Bob asked Pam at the entrance.
"Yes. Of course," said Pam. "Will you buy some stationery on your way back?"
"Sure," said Bob.

A. Complete the following dialogues by using "will", "would", or "could" to ask polite questions. Choose the appropriate key phrase for each one.

help me open the windows
pick up the phone for me
turn the stereo down a bit
pick up a few cartons from the store

1. Victor: I'm trying to study, Bill.

   ____

   ____

   Bill: Oh yes. Sorry. I'll turn it down.

2. Mrs. Gladwin: There's no more milk in the fridge.

   ____

   ____

   Mr. Gladwin: Sure. No problem.

3. Jessica: The phone is ringing, but my hands are full.

   ____

   Gregory: Of course.

4. Mrs. Kemp: It's getting hot in the classroom.

   ____

   Vicki: Sure.

B. **Ask a polite question with "will", "would", or "could" for each scenario below.**

1. A group of children are playing in the yard and their ball went over the fence. They see someone walking by. One of the children asks:

____

____

2. Susan Abrams wants to talk to her mother. She calls her mother's office and the secretary picks up the phone. Susan asks the secretary:

____

3. It is dinner time. Mark wants some ketchup for his chicken fingers. The ketchup bottle is next to his sister Chelsea. Mark asks Chelsea:

____

4. The doorbell just rang. Except Marie, everyone is busy doing something. Mother asks Marie:

____

5. Carol wants to visit the shoe museum after school, and wants her sister Jenny to take the subway with her. She asks Jenny:

____

C. **Rewrite each of the following into polite questions.**

1. Can I get a hamburger with fries?

____

2. Can we go now?

____

3. Can you pass the salt?

____

____

4. I wonder if you can help me.

____

____

Did You Know?

"Could" is more polite than "can" because "could" suggests possibility, while "can" is definite – we use it to talk about ability and permission. By using "could" to ask for assistance, we give the other person "more room" to think about our request.

Date : ____________________

Mars the Red Planet

Much of our fascination with Mars has been well documented in various media such as movies, science fiction, and even art. The mystery of the Red Planet constantly fuels our imagination, especially now that there is more research on it with the help of robots. The flow of new data continues to hold our interest. Did life exist on Mars? Do we have clues to suggest it did?

Recent photos of the Red Planet have allowed us to make some of the most startling discoveries: traces of water vapour exist in the Martian atmosphere and water ice – ice with air bubbles – is visible at the Martian poles. Where there is water, there is life. Ice cannot sustain life but when melted, it can.

Studies done in simulations of the Martian atmosphere confirm that living organisms can survive under such conditions. Despite the planet's extreme cold, researchers believe that water may be present under the surface and that it may exist only during the day, when the temperature in the soil can range from -17 degrees to +27 degrees centigrade. These conditions are favourable for liquid water to exist.

But if water freezes at 0 degree centigrade, how is it possible for water on Mars to remain liquid when the overnight temperatures drop to about 100 degrees below freezing? Salt! Salt in the water can significantly lower the freezing point of a liquid by as much as 60 degrees centigrade. Indeed, analyses by robotic rovers have shown that Martian soil contains 10% to 20% salt. When Martian rocks are exposed to water, the two react to form salt and clay minerals.

Besides containing salt that would lower the freezing point, water also needs to be "on the move" to keep from freezing quickly. If water is constantly moving, the chances of it freezing would be delayed. Moving water with salt and minerals might be the right formula for water to exist on Mars.

Even though research and data give us information to make our hypotheses, scientists are still looking for confirmation. With Mars and the Earth in opposition in 2005 and 2006, NASA and the European Space Agency took advantage of this closeness to send space shuttles and rovers to Mars to gather more data. Until we hear more, stay tuned!

A. Try to circle the correct answers without looking back at the passage.

1. What is the main idea of the passage?

   A. Life currently exists on Mars and recent photos support this.

   B. Life may have existed on Mars and a number of findings support this.

   C. Life did not exist on Mars because there is no proof.

   D. Martians lived on Mars.

2. Traces of water vapour have been seen ____ .

   A. in the valleys

   B. on the surface

   C. near the Martian poles

   D. in the Martian atmosphere

3. One of the factors that might delay water from freezing is ____ .

   A. the heat from the sun

   B. the presence of salt and minerals

   C. the presence of living organisms

   D. the thickness of Martian water

4. The Martian day temperature ranges from ____ .

   A. 0 to 100 degrees centigrade

   B. -17 to +27 degrees centigrade

   C. 20 to 70 degrees centigrade

   D. -17 to +100 degrees centigrade

B. If you could travel to Mars, what would you take with you, and why?

____

____

____

Date : ____________________

Punctuation (1)

Periods, Question Marks, and Exclamation Marks

We use the **period (.)**, the **question mark (?)**, and the **exclamation mark (!)** for complete sentences.

Examples: Wasaga Beach is the world's largest freshwater beach. (declarative)
Please take this to the post office. (imperative)
Have you been to Collingwood? (interrogative)
Watch out for that car! (exclamatory)

A. Does each of the following sentences end in the most appropriate punctuation mark? If not, write the appropriate one in the box.

1. Summer is here and it is very hot today. ☐
2. What a hot day. ☐
3. The boys like to swim alongside the fish in the lake. ☐
4. Bobby asks Ted to jump into the water. ☐
5. Do you want to jump in! ☐
6. Whoohoo! Here I come? ☐
7. Ted swings towards the water while Jonathan and Ben look on! ☐
8. The birds can be heard in a distance. ☐
9. What a huge lake! ☐
10. This is a clean lake! ☐

Commas and Quotation Marks

We use the **comma** (,) to indicate one or more pauses in a sentence.

Examples: Giraffes, raccoons, and dolphins are all mammals.
Clara, could you give me your phone number?

We use **quotation marks** (“ ”) when words are part of a dialogue, or quoted from someone else.

Examples: “At the end of the way is freedom. Till then, patience,” said Buddha.
“Please help yourself to these cherries,” said Nina.
“Okay. Thanks!” replied Benjamin.

Note: If the sentence inside the quotation marks ends in a period, replace the period with a comma; if it ends in a question mark or an exclamation mark, keep the question mark or exclamation mark.

B. Punctuate the following passage with periods, question marks, exclamation marks, commas, and quotation marks.

The start of each sentence is capitalized for you.

Morrie and Alyssa love their treehouse Their father George had built it for them when they were five Because they love being outside their mother Leah can never find them in the house during the summer Wow What an amazing hiding place Morrie said when George first showed him the treehouse Alyssa is usually quiet and shy so she expressed her excitement with a wide smile instead Isn't this treehouse great George said to Leah one day Our kids now have so much fun inviting their friends over to the backyard They are so happy

Date : ____________________

Jack is doing a word search on the train. Read the clues below to see what words he has to find. Then circle them in the word search.

1. What word has the same spelling as the one meaning "to practise a skill"?
2. What is the word for a railway line?
3. What do you call the individual cars of a train?
4. What do you use to carry your clothes and other belongings on a vacation?
5. You find these in British Columbia.
6. If you look out of the window while riding the train, you might see beautiful ______ hills in a distance.
7. What do you call the main house on a farm?
8. What is the word for cows raised on farms?
9. What is the antonym of "urban"?
10. This word means "treeless, grassy plains".
11. What do you call a passage dug through a hill or mountain?
12. What is another word for "trip"?

e p c g n x d n r
l f a k a d f u c w p m
y t m a b t g a h p l d e p
r y c d u t y r u r a l k s
r f t b k h l t m p a d q w j r
o s r r f j e k h i i e p i c m
h t a x a i l n o n r i c o a i
c g c g j i n h u s i v t t r o
l f k u b o n w s j e j R g r a
o n s s d g u v e k s h o j i p
s t u n n e l r q o a b c l a k
h s e j t l g h n w p z k l g t
r o l l i n g p c e i s i d e l
g n f m s d c z a d y k e j s s
z l s u i t c a s e s g s w o w
w a b k p b k m e y n i l q
u m l t o d v
n h

Date : ____________________

Honeybees

Honey has made many a food and meal tasty and enjoyable to eat. Yet the busy bees that fly about us when we have our outdoor meals are most annoying!

There are two types of bees – the social bee and the solitary bee. Social bees, like the honeybee, live in communities or colonies and are divided into subgroups called castes. Solitary bees, like the carpenter bee, live alone or in very small groups.

As their name suggests, honeybees make honey. They live in a beehive made up of honeycombs, a structure made of wax produced by the bees. Each honeycomb has many six-sided holes called cubbyholes or cells. It is in these cells that the bees put their nectar, honey, or lay eggs.

As a community, honeybees are divided into three subgroups or castes: the queen bee, the worker bee, and the drone. Each caste has a very definite and rigid role or job. The queen bee only lays eggs into the waxy cells. The drones' only job is to mate with the queen bee, after which they die. It is the worker bees that are the real busy bees: they build the hive, collect the food, and care for the young. In each hive there are about 50 000 to 80 000 worker bees. These bees produce the honey we eat and the beeswax we use to make candles.

The farming of honey and beeswax by man is called apiculture or beekeeping. The farmer builds a small artificial hive called an apiary, which is a box hung with many trays of wax in wooden frames. The worker bees fill these honeycombs with honey, and when full, the farmer takes the trays out and collects the honey. When the apiary is over populated, the bees fly away in search of a new hive, usually an empty apiary that the farmer has built nearby.

The worker bees collect flower nectar with their long tongues and deposit it into a special "honey stomach". The nectar reacts with chemicals in the stomach to start the honey-making process. The worker bees then fly to their hives and deposit the nectar-chemical mixture into cells and later, honey is formed.

Next time when you spread honey on toast or use it in your tea, remember where it came from.

A. Write "T" for the true statements and "F" for the false ones.

1. The carpenter bee is a kind of solitary bee. ______
2. The drones' job is to protect the community. ______
3. The queen bee lays eggs and takes care of the bees in her community. ______
4. Most of the bees in a community are worker bees. ______
5. Cells are six-sided holes for storing eggs and honey. ______
6. People use beeswax for cooking. ______
7. The nectar reacts with chemicals in the bee's stomach to start the honey-making process. ______
8. Bees are farmed for their honey and beeswax. ______

B. Read the clues and complete the crossword puzzle with words from the passage.

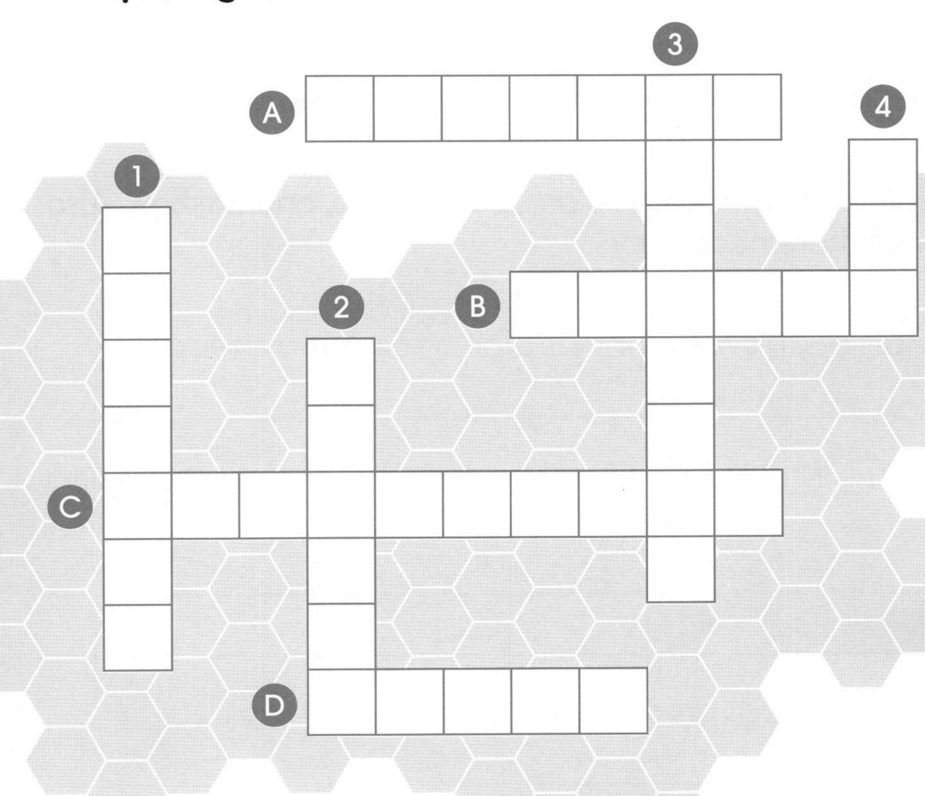

Across

A. a series of changes
B. a man-made beehive
C. beekeeping
D. fixed

Down

1. where food is digested
2. a sweet liquid in flowers
3. living alone
4. put

Date : ______________________

Punctuation (2)

Colons, Semicolons, and Dashes

There are other punctuation marks we use in addition to the comma to indicate pauses in a sentence. They are the following:

Colon (:) – used to join two separate sentences when the second explains the first; also used to introduce a list of items.

Examples: Rory is doing cartwheels: she has finally finished her book report.
The teacher ordered these supplies: paper, staplers, scissors, and glue.

Semicolon (;) – used to join two separate sentences when the second elaborates on the first; also used to replace conjunctions such as "and", "but", "since", and "so".

Examples: Our prices are wrong; we ordered from the old catalogue.
Three people built the model; only one took credit for it.

Dash (–) – used to insert explanatory material.

Example: Understanding one's limitations – time, ability, and money – makes it easier to make plans in life.

A. Rewrite the following sentences by adding colons, semicolons, and dashes. Also use periods and commas where necessary.

1. Peter likes a lot of animals on this farm horses pigs geese and sheep

____

2. Except me everyone in my family Mom Dad brother Jack and sister Anita likes the taste of olives.

____

____

3. The horse is happy it has just recovered from an illness

____

4. Peter was right the horse had eaten some moldy hay

____

Apostrophes

We use the **apostrophe** (') to show possession.

Examples: Lucy's bicycle is by the tree.
Lois's bicycle is nearby.
The shop around the corner sells girls' bicycles.
Lucy and Lois did a week's worth of cycling in one day!

We also use the apostrophe to form contractions.

Examples: Betty doesn't work on Tuesdays.
Who's the first in line?

B. Punctuate the passage using colons, semicolons, dashes, and apostrophes.

Ms. Duncans grade six class went to Kearney for a week-long trip in June. The kids learned a number of things how to canoe, how to make dreamcatchers, and how to work in teams. After breakfast each morning, they explored the wilderness with their camp leaders. One morning, they stopped by a marsh to learn about insects that live in water. No one liked learning about airborne insects, though, especially mosquitoes and black flies. Fortunately, everyone remembered to bring insect repellent. The camp leaders were glad that every kid had brought repellent in tubes aerosol cans are not good to the environment. After dinner each evening, a leader named Mike would grab his guitar and teach the kids a new song one of which was called "The Merry Moose" so the kids could sing their way back to the cabins afterwards.

Date : ______________________

Athletic Shoes – the Modern Day Sneakers

The athletic shoe market is a $13 billion industry. From the high-level competitive shoe to the everyday walking shoe, athletic footwear has become an important symbol in today's youth culture.

Plimsolls were the first rubber soled running shoes manufactured in the 1800s. The Goodyear Metallic Rubber Shoe Company discovered vulcanization – the bonding of rubber to cloth or other rubber components for sturdier adhesion. They manufactured rubber and canvas shoes under the brand name Keds between 1892 and 1913.

Keds were the first athletic shoes marketed in 1917. Eventually, an advertising agent named Henry Nelson McKinney coined the term "sneakers" because the rubber soles did not produce any noise when you walked in them.

Fashion plays a huge role in the design of today's sneakers. Many advertisers use field studies to target the youth market. Colour, style, fashion, and what is "hot" are important factors that need to be considered when designing an athletic shoe. However, the most important aspect of any true athletic shoe is its ability to enhance performance.

Before the 19th century, shoes were not designed to have a left and right side. Understanding of foot function and gait was later used in designing the early competitive running shoe. Starting in the late 1970s, with the input of sports medicine specialists and sports biomechanics experts, more and more shoes were customized for different sports. The need to accommodate various types and shapes of feet, the use of motion-control devices and new shock-absorbing materials were some of the factors used in athletic shoe manufacturing. In the 1990s, many renowned athletic shoe manufacturers tested new technology in their shoes such as Gel technology (Asics), TL composite (Air Jordan 12), and orthotic foot support (New Balance), to name a few.

Regardless of whether your running shoes have incorporated the latest technology or have the latest style and colour, they still have to fit and be comfortable.

A. **Complete the timeline of the development of athletic shoes based on the information in the passage.**

1800s

1892–1913

1917

1970s

1990s

B. **Circle the correct answers.**

1. The first rubber soled running shoes were called ____ .

   A. primrose   B. sneakers   C. plimsolls   D. athletic shoes

2. ____ is one of the factors considered important when designing athletic shoes for youth.

   A. What is hot
   B. The types of feet
   C. The shapes of feet
   D. Incorporating new technology

3. One group of professionals that gave shoe manufacturers crucial input was ____ .

   A. professors
   B. sports specialists
   C. athletes
   D. sports biomechanics experts

4. One way to improve athletic shoe design in the future is by ____ .

   A. having famous athletes endorse the product
   B. using research that looks at how athletes perform
   C. starting new trends
   D. making shoes with shock-absorbing materials

Date : ______________________

Voice: Active and Passive

We use the **active voice** when we want to talk about a person or thing **doing** something.

Example: Neil built a dog house yesterday.

We use the **passive voice** when we want to focus on the person or thing **affected by** something.

Example: A dog house was built yesterday.

A. Rewrite each of the following sentences in the passive voice. The first one is done for you.

When using the passive, we often don't mention the person or thing that performs the action.

1. Mother sewed a flower on Charmaine's bag.

   A flower was sewn on Charmaine's bag.

   ____

2. Mother tied Charmaine's hair with ribbons.

   ____

   ____

3. The flight attendant put Charmaine's bag in the overhead compartment.

   ____

4. More passengers filled the overhead compartments with bags.

   ____

5. The pilot prepared the plane for take-off.

   ____

B. Rewrite each of the following sentences in the active voice. The subject is given for you.

1. The seatbelts were unfastened.

   The passengers ______________________________ .

2. Passengers were served light snacks on the plane.

   The flight attendants ______________________________ .

3. The washrooms were not occupied yet.

   No one ______________________________ .

4. Charmaine was given some paper and crayons.

   A flight attendant ______________________________

   ______________________________ .

5. A cute airplane was drawn.

   Charmaine ______________________________

   ______________________________ .

Changing from the active to the passive and vice versa represents a shift in the point of view.

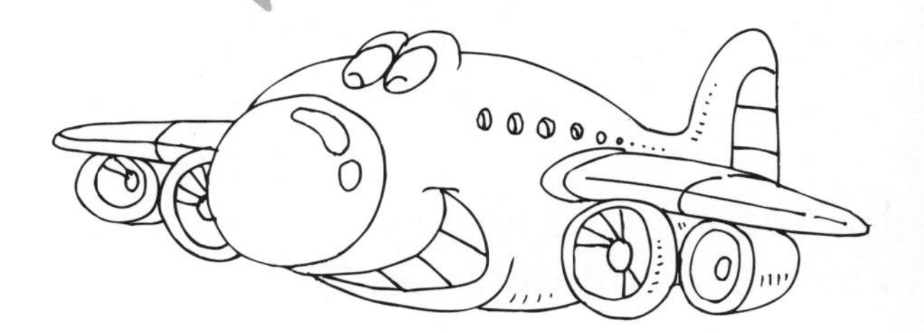

C. With verbs that can take two objects, we can form two different passive sentences. Write each of the following passive sentences in a different way. The first one is done for you.

1. Charmaine was given a meal of pasta with meatballs.

   A meal of pasta with meatballs was given to Charmaine.

2. Some extra napkins were handed to the passengers.

   ____

3. The passengers were shown a movie.

   ____

4. Earphones for the audio system were given to the passengers.

   ____

Date : ____________________

Avalanche

An avalanche is the falling away of a large mass of snow, ice, loosened rocks or earth, or any combination of these, down the side of a mountain. The mass of material can travel as fast as 160 kilometres per hour. Stormy winds, earth disturbances or tremors, intentional explosions, or skiers just skiing over the area can start an avalanche.

There are three kinds of avalanches. The first kind is the dry snow avalanche that is made up of light powdery snow and lots of air. It moves as fast as 160 km per hour, creating a huge cloud in its path. This is apparently the simplest kind of avalanche where loose snow falls off the steep slope of a mountain and gathers more snow as it rolls on.

The second kind is the wet snow avalanche. The heavier wet dense snow moves more slowly than dry snow and breaks off the mountainside slowly.

The third kind is a slab avalanche where a solid chunk of snow breaks loose as a slab and breaks into pieces as it slides and falls away. In the old days an avalanche was called loose snow, slab snow, or an ice avalanche.

Avalanches are dangerous to the outdoor enthusiast. Many lives have been lost in the winter mountain slopes because of them. Scientists study the geology, geography, weather, snow, and temperature of avalanche areas to recognize dangerous conditions. They correct these conditions by dropping explosives to trigger mini-avalanches so that big ones do not build up.

In the early 1970s at Roger's Pass in British Columbia, a Canadian armed forces artillery unit would fire shells into the mountainside to trigger preventative mini-avalanches in order to keep the Trans-Canada Highway open. Long-term prevention would be to plant trees and build fences to prevent excessive snow build-up.

Avalanches cannot be eliminated, but they can be controlled. Raising awareness among outdoor enthusiasts of what areas to avoid is another way to prevent avalanche-related fatalities.

A. Circle the correct answers.

1. What is one of the characteristics of the dry snow avalanche?

   A. dense B. slow-moving C. powdery

2. What was an avalanche called in the old days?

   A. tremor B. snow build-up C. loose snow

3. What is a possible cause of avalanches?

   A. strong winds B. heavy snow C. sun rays

4. One way to keep the Trans-Canada Highway open in the 1970s was to:

   A. fire shells at the snow-covered mountainside

   B. remove the snow from the mountainside

   C. build walls along the mountainside

B. Read the clues and complete the crossword puzzle with words from the passage.

Across

A. got rid of

B. on purpose

C. one who likes an activity very much

D. deaths

Down

1. cause
2. not dense
3. too much

A

1 2 3

B

C

D

Date : ____________________

Noun Phrases

A **noun phrase** functions like a noun in a sentence. It can be the subject, object, or the complement*. It can simply be one or more nouns, or a combination of nouns and other words like adjectives.

Example: Tiny Ashley (subject) is building a big snowman (object), which is her first snowman (complement) this winter.

* A complement is a noun phrase which follows "am", "is", or "are".

A. Underline the subject noun phrase in each of the following sentences.

1. Studious Matt surprised his friends by suggesting that they go shopping.
2. His buddies Gabe and Robin readily agreed and went along.
3. A fuzzy winter hat from the department store would be the perfect birthday gift for his mother, thought Matt.
4. Cute and tiny Gabe thought his mother might like one too.
5. Mischievous Robin, on the other hand, wanted to buy a scary toy spider for his little sister.

B. Underline the object noun phrase in each of the following sentences.

1. Rosie wants to buy a sweet treat.
2. The neighbourhood candy store sells giant lollipops.
3. Rosie tells the shopkeeper that lollipops are her favourite treats.
4. The shopkeeper tells Rosie that she also sells "extra fruity" lollipops.
5. Rosie promises to return next week and bring along her best friend Matt.

C. Underline the complement noun phrase in each of the following sentences.

1. Pete's Pet Shop around the corner is the oldest pet shop in town.
2. Apparently, the most popular pets are water animals.
3. What makes Pete's Pet Shop such a good place to buy pet food is the monthly "buy-one-get-one-free" special.
4. Of all the birds at the shop, the one that makes the most noise is a parrot named Sam.
5. Pete does not mind the noise, however, because Sam's favourite thing to say is "buy-one-get-one-free".

D. Decide if each underlined noun phrase is the subject (S), object (O), or complement (C).

1. Lindsay and her mom have just gone into a new grocery store. ______
2. The things they need to buy are bread, some deli, snacks, and detergent. ______

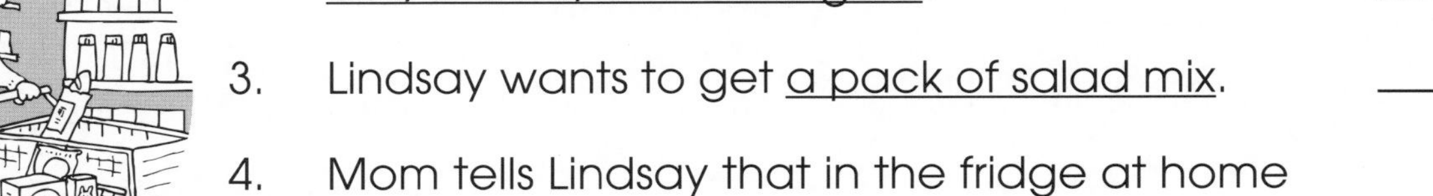

3. Lindsay wants to get a pack of salad mix. ______
4. Mom tells Lindsay that in the fridge at home are some chopped up cauliflower sticks. ______

5. The cheerful cashier hands Lindsay's mom some brand new dollar bills as change, which Lindsay wants to add to her collection. ______
6. Lindsay's mom thinks she will definitely come to this new store again. ______

Date : ____________________

SCUBA Diving

Can you dive underwater?

People have been diving shallow seabeds near coastlines since ancient times. Evidence suggests that ancient skin divers dove for shellfish off the coast of present day Peru as far back as some 4000 years ago. During the time of the early Greek civilizations, Greek and Turkish divers dove for sea sponge in the Aegean Sea while pearl divers in the Arabian Gulf hunted for pearl producing oysters.

In the beginning, divers had nothing but the natural capacity of their lungs to hold the air they needed. This gave them only two to three minutes to do their work underwater. So early ancient divers were always looking for ways to increase their breathing time.

2000 years ago, sponge divers in the Aegean Sea invented the water bladder, which was a leather air bag made of the skin of pigs, sheep, or goats. It was a waterproof bag in a single unripped piece with one opening, to be blown like a balloon and filled with air.

When the diver ran out of breath, he would get more air from the water bladder and continue to dive. This allowed him more time to explore. The water bladder was the first crude SCUBA device. SCUBA is the acronym for **S**elf-**C**ontained **U**nderwater **B**reathing **A**pparatus.

Captain Jacques-Yves Cousteau and Emile Gagnan invented the first aqualung in 1943. It is a metal cylindrical tank filled with compressed air, carried snugly on the diver's back. The diver breathes through a mouthpiece connected by a hose to the safety pressure valves on top of the tank. The valves control the air pressure so that the compressed air does not blow out the diver's lungs. In cold waters, the diver uses additional equipment such as a face mask, flippers, a weighted belt, and a wet suit.

Captain Cousteau went on to become a famous underwater explorer, capturing for the world the natural wonders of the sea. Maybe you too can do that one day.

A. Answer the following questions.

1. What was the water bladder made of?

____

2. Who were the first people to use the water bladder?

____

____

3. What is an aqualung and how does it work?

____

____

____

B. Find the six compound words in the passage. Write them in the spaces below and write a short sentence with each.

1. u___ ___ ___ ___ ___ ___ ___ ___ ___

____

2. w___ ___ ___ ___ ___ ___ ___ ___ ___

____

3. c___ ___ ___ ___ ___ ___ ___ ___ ___

____

4. s___ ___ ___ ___ ___ ___ ___ ___

____

5. m___ ___ ___ ___ ___ ___ ___ ___ ___

____

____

6. s___ ___ ___ ___ ___ ___

____

____

____

Did You Know?

The Cousteau Society, founded in 1974 to protect ocean life, has grown to include more than 300 000 members worldwide.

Date : ____________________

Adjective and Adverb Phrases

Adjective Phrases

An **adjective phrase** functions like an adjective in a sentence. It describes a noun.

Example: Megan has a very big smile on her face because she just got a cute and cuddly teddy bear for her birthday.

A. Underline the adjective phrase in each of the following sentences.

1. The fun house in Gabrielle's dream had a very pointy roof.
2. One section of the fun house was small and chubby.
3. Gabrielle liked the cute and spotted roof very much.
4. Inside the fun house was a big and funny looking clock.

B. Complete each of the following sentences with the appropriate adjective phrase.

sweet and crunchy
long and spiralled
long and gruelling
round and smooth
delightfully surprised

1. Gabrielle was ____________________ that the fun house had a ____________________ ____________________ staircase.
2. "But there's no way I can make this __________ ____________________ climb," thought Gabrielle.
3. Just then, Gabrielle saw an apple __________ ____________________ sitting on a note that read, "Eat me."
4. Just as she had guessed, Gabrielle felt charged with abundant energy after a ____________________ bite off the fruit.

Adverb Phrases

An **adverb phrase** functions like an adverb in a sentence. It describes a verb.

Example: Megan's brother thinks his sister is too easily pleased. He thinks the teddy bear is rather poorly made.

C. Complete each of the following sentences with the appropriate adverb phrase.

quite comfortably   unusually early
so quickly   very swiftly but carefully

1. Jason can build towers with cards ________________ ________________ that he amazes his friends.
2. Sometimes, he can finish building a tower ________________ in five minutes.
3. On occasion, Jason even gets up ________________ to engage in this new hobby of his.
4. The trick to building towers with cards, Jason says, is to put down each card ________________ .

D. Decide whether each underlined phrase is an adjective or adverb phrase by writing the correct question numbers in the boxes.

1. Every Saturday, a group of girls in Mrs. Stevens's class get together to do fun and creative activities.
2. The theme today is "Paper Crafts". With brightly coloured paper, the girls cut out different shapes.
3. Some decide very quickly that they will fold animals.
4. The girls want to ask Mrs. Stevens if they could make their get-together an after-school club. They are hopeful and excited.

Adjective Phrases

Adverb Phrases

Date : ____________________

Dazzling Colours in the Sky

What do Victoria Day and Canada Day have in common aside from being long weekends? Fireworks! Many of us are fascinated by the display of sparks, colours, and intricate designs in the night sky. We even make watching fireworks a regular family event.

The science of fireworks is called pyrotechnics. There are numerous pyrotechnic artists who travel all over the world to exhibit their specialty, whether as part of a special event such as the Olympics or for competition. These people are experts in the field. There are laws that regulate the use of fireworks because untrained users may get seriously hurt. Fireworks are, after all, explosives.

What is in a firework rocket? There is coarse gunpowder that is tightly packed as well as finer gunpowder more loosely packed. Small amounts of special chemicals are added to the gunpowder to create colours. For example, strontium compounds are used for producing red, sodium compounds for yellow, copper compounds for blue, and barium compounds for green. Charcoal is also added to produce that sparkling, flaming tail.

Skyrockets, as firework rockets are also called, operate along the same principle as military rockets. A fuse is needed to ignite the gunpowder. This could be paper that is rolled and soaked with saltpetre, a white and salty substance. When the coarse gunpowder is ignited after the fuse is lit, gases are formed and stream out of the tube, propelling the rocket into the air. At the peak of its flight, the coarse gunpowder ignites the finer gunpowder. This is when the rocket becomes fireworks!

"Roman candles", "lances", and "flowers" are some common types of fireworks. Roman candles consist of separate groups of coloured flames; lances produce a scene or picture; and flowers burst out petals in different colours.

The next time you and your family watch the fireworks, see if you can identify the different types by their names.

A. Circle the correct answers.

1. The science of fireworks is called ____ .

   A. gyrotechnics B. fireworks art
   C. fireworks technique D. pyrotechnics

2. Coarse gunpowder in the paper tube will ____ .

   A. explode the tube in mid-air B. create a flaming tail
   C. produce colour D. propel the rocket into the air

3. Finer gunpowder in the paper tube will ____ .

   A. produce colour B. create a flaming tail
   C. explode the tube in mid-air D. propel the rocket into the air

4. What compound produces blue in fireworks?

   A. sodium B. barium
   C. strontium D. copper

5. The different types of fireworks in the passage are ____ .

   A. Roman candles B. lances
   C. flowers D. all of the above

B. In your own words, describe what would happen if anybody could buy and use fireworks.

____

____

____

____

____

____

Did You Know?

The first fireworks were actually green bamboo thrown into fires to scare spirits away in ancient China.

Date :

You Deserve A Break!

Many Canadians come from countries whose names are on this multicultural fan. Unscramble and write the names on the lines.

1. ______________________

2. ______________________

3. ______________________

4. ______________________

5. ______________________

6. ______________________

7. ______________________

8. ______________________

9. ______________________

10. ______________________

Date : ____________________

Prepositional Phrases

A **prepositional phrase** begins with a preposition, such as "in", "on", "with", and "near". It functions as either an adjective or an adverb in a sentence – that is, it modifies either a noun or a verb.

Example: Sam has a mirror with sheets of dust, so he cleans it with the utmost zeal!

A. Underline the prepositional phrase that modifies a noun in each of the following sentences.

1. In our backyard live two birds with big wide beaks.

2. Today, they see a visitor above their cozy house.

3. The tiny visitor is a little shy, and is afraid to eat the seeds in the feeder.

4. To make the visitor feel welcome, the bird couple begin a song of the most delightful chirps.

5. The tiny visitor loosens up, and eats those seeds of great taste, which we put in the feeder only this morning.

6. The visitor flies away, but returns later with a baby by her side!

Were you able to identify all the prepositional phrases?

B. Underline the prepositional phrase that modifies a verb in each of the following sentences.

1. There are some birds that have built their home with a lot of twigs.
2. This morning, the mother brought her babies some worms after finishing her morning exercise.
3. Earlier, a scary crow had perched near the baby birds, but it flew away just as the mother returned.
4. The babies miss their father as he is on a trip with other birds, but they know he will return before winter.
5. The mother knows her babies will not be hungry until later in the afternoon, so she perches on a higher branch to keep watch while her babies nap.

C. Underline the prepositional phrase in each of the following sentences. Then determine what it modifies by writing "N" for noun or "V" for verb on the line.

1. My dad thinks red-eared turtles are beautiful because they have shells of green like jade. ______
2. My brother has a few budgies which he looks after with a lot of love. ______
3. Our pet parrot says such hilarious things that we all agree it has the style of a stand-up comedian. ______
4. My cousin has a cat that likes to purr in front of her face when she is asleep. ______
5. My mother likes watching butterflies, especially when they hover above a flower like they have just found the perfect spot. ______

Date : ______________________

Spider Webs

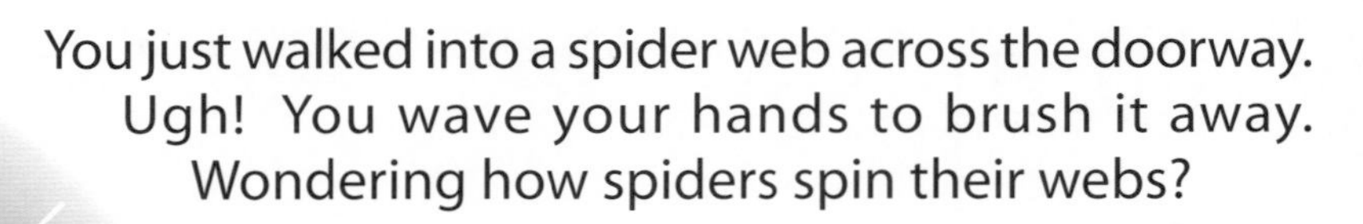

You just walked into a spider web across the doorway. Ugh! You wave your hands to brush it away. Wondering how spiders spin their webs?

Let's first learn about the outer anatomy of the spider. There are two main parts to a spider's body: the cephalothorax, which is the head fused to the thorax ("chest"), and the abdomen. Connected to each part of the body are attached parts called appendages, which are the long hairy legs. Each spider species has its own unique location for the appendages. The main parts of the body are joined by a very small waist called the pedicel.

There are over 30 000 species of spiders, which can be classified by their differences in either anatomy or behaviour. If we group them by behaviour, they fall into two classes: hunting spiders like the tarantula, which do not spin webs, and the web spinning spiders.

All spiders spin silk, but only web spinning spiders make webs to catch insects for food, such as the orb weaving common garden spider. The silk is made from special glands in the back portion of the abdomen, and comes out of the spider through openings called spinnerets, which act like hands to spin the silk into threads or strings. Each gland produces a different type of silk. Some silk is strong, but not sticky; others are sticky but delicate. It all depends on their use. Most spiders have five glands, and all have a minimum of three.

To make a web, a web spinning spider attaches strong silk called "draglines" or " bridge lines" in intervals to a firm and solid surface. It then drops vertically to make "foundation lines". The draglines and foundation lines make up the framework for the web. The spider is now ready to weave its trap from the centre out towards the edge.

Each species of web spinning spiders weaves a unique and identifiable web. The common golden garden spider builds a large web with zigzag bands, while the bowl and doily spider spins a web resembling a bowl suspended over a doily.

So before you walk through the doorway next time, see if there is a web. Take a detailed look. Happy observing!

A. Match the words on the left with their synonyms on the right to spin a web.

spin •	• fine
unique •	• base
abdomen •	• globe
foundation •	• distinctive
identifiable •	• recognizable
framework •	• structure
intervals •	• spaces
location •	• twirl
delicate •	• belly
orb •	• spot

B. Complete the sentences with words from the passage.

1. The two main parts of a spider's body are the ____________ and the ____________ .
2. The first silk lines in making a web are called ____________ .
3. Silk comes out of ____________ in the rear of a spider's abdomen.
4. Most spiders have five ____________ to produce ____________ .
5. ____________ are attached to each part of a spider's body.

Did You Know?

Charlotte, the main character in E.B. White's novel *Charlotte's Web*, is a barn spider who rebuilds her web every day.

Date : ____________________

Infinitive Phrases

An **infinitive phrase** contains a verb that follows "to".

Examples: Little Ben crawls toward his sister to hold her hand.
Candace reaches out to grab her brother's hand.

A. Underline the infinitive phrase in each of the following sentences.

1. Rachel and her cousins woke up early this Saturday morning to go to the amusement park.
2. They arrived at the park before most people to be among the first in line for their rides.
3. Both Rachel and her younger cousin Kim are tall enough to ride on the roller-coaster.
4. After the thrill of the roller-coaster, Rachel and Kim got ready to swing on the Swing of the Millennium.
5. Meanwhile, Rachel's other cousins Michelle and Liz were a bit hungry and ran off to get some food.
6. Since Kim loves horses, Rachel went with her to ride on the carousel.
7. Rachel thought the Spinning Octopus looked quite amazing, and walked over to look at the design.
8. Kim found a bench to sit down.
9. Michelle and Liz came back to share some French fries with Rachel and Kim.

B. **Choose the appropriate infinitive phrase to complete each of the following sentences.**

- to have enough time
- to see what it was like
- to accompany her
- to meet Rachel and Kim
- to wave at the boy

1. After lunch, Liz wanted ______________________________ to stand inside a giant teapot.
2. While in the teapot, Liz noticed a nearby giant pineapple, so she turned ______________________________ in it.
3. ______________________________ for other rides, Liz decided not to line up for the 3-D short film for kids.
4. Liz wanted to see the amusement park from somewhere high up, and urged Michelle ______________________________ on the Ferris wheel.
5. ______________________________, Liz and Michelle would line up for the Silly Coaster at four o'clock.

C. **Circle "T" if the sentence has an infinitive phrase and circle "F" if it does not.**

1.	Rachel and her cousins had a lot of fun on Saturday.	T	F
2.	That night, Rachel dreamt that she was flying in mid-air to catch cotton candy.	T	F
3.	In the middle of the night, Keith sleepwalked in his bedroom.	T	F
4.	Kim had a very good night's sleep and did not wake up in the middle of the night.	T	F
5.	Before she went to bed, Michelle wondered when might be the next time they go to the amusement park.	T	F

Date :

Tides

Tides are the regular rising and falling of the sea caused by gravitational attraction among the moon, the sun, and the Earth. All planetary objects exert gravitational pulls on one another.

Objects with a bigger mass have a stronger gravitational pull. However, the strength of the force decreases rapidly the farther away they are from each other. For example, the sun is big but far away from the Earth, so its pull might not be as strong. Compare this to the moon, which has a much smaller mass but is very close to the Earth, so at certain times it exerts a much stronger pull than the sun. It is the gravitational pulls of the sun and the moon that cause tides on Earth.

Tides in most parts of the world occur twice in one lunar day, which is 24 hours and 51 minutes. A rising tide is called a "flood tide" and a falling one, an "ebb tide". The highest tide of the month occurs just after a new or full moon, when the sun, the moon, and the Earth are aligned so that the gravitational pulls from the sun and the moon are strongest on Earth. This tidal bulge is called a "spring tide". High tides also occur when the moon is at its closest to the Earth along the orbit.

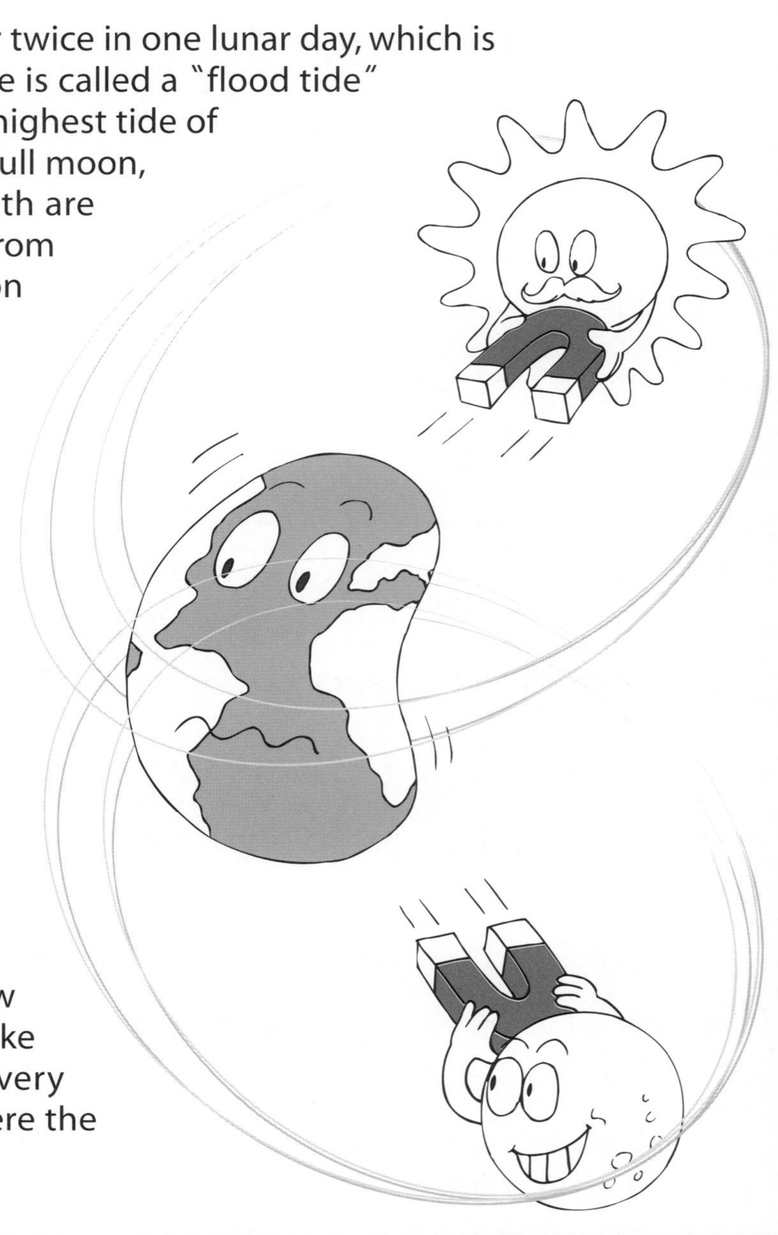

Sometimes the moon and the sun form a right angle with the Earth so that their pulls cancel each other out. This is when "neap tides" occur, when the difference between the higher and lower tides on Earth are at its minimum.

Depending on location and geography, the flood and ebb tides can be very gradual or very dramatic. For example, if you are in a wide bay, the tide changes might be only a few metres. But if you are in a bay shaped like a "U" or "V", the changes could be very dramatic, like in the Bay of Fundy where the tides could rise and fall by 15 metres.

A. Read the clues and complete the crossword puzzle with words from the passage.

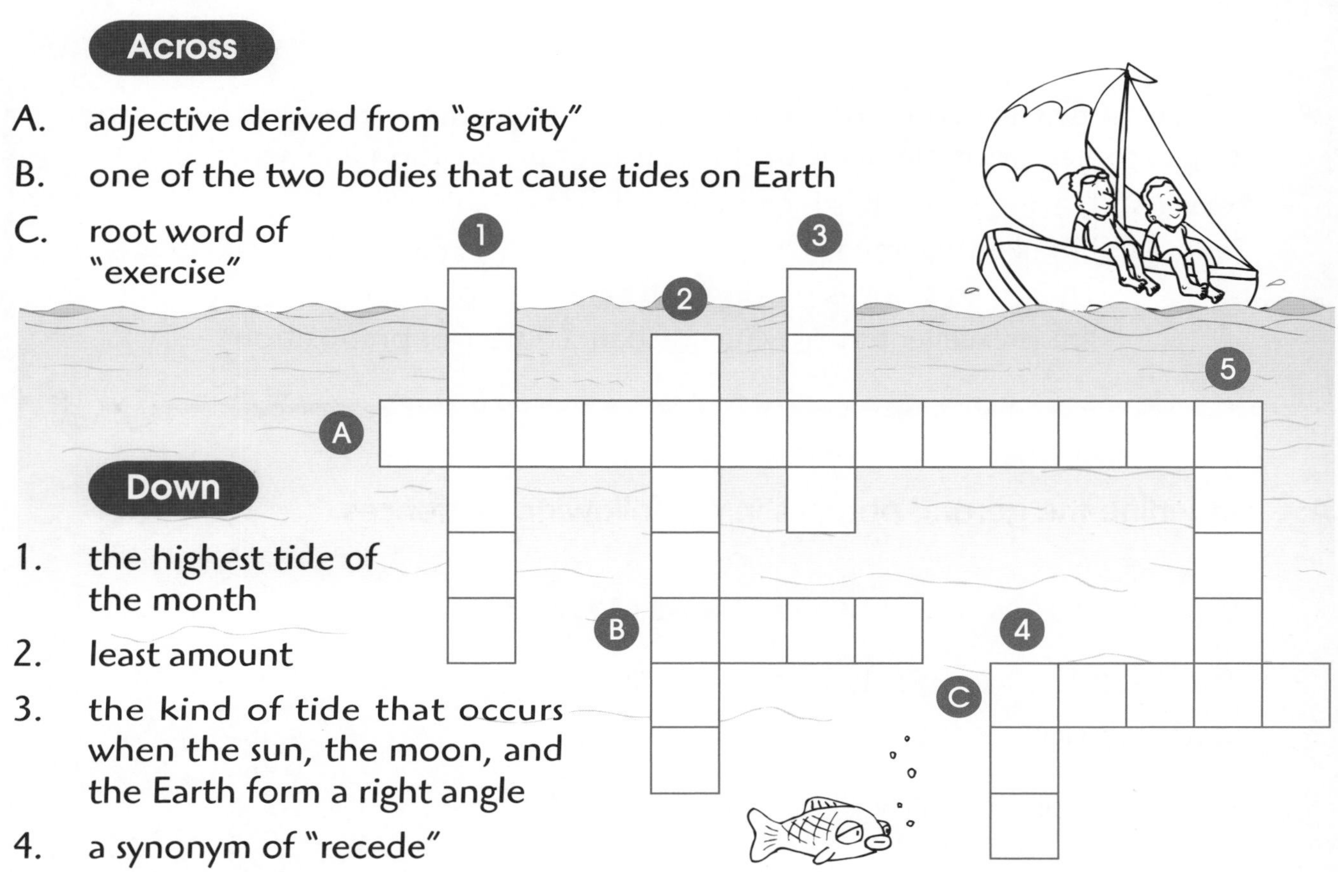

Across

A. adjective derived from "gravity"

B. one of the two bodies that cause tides on Earth

C. root word of "exercise"

Down

1. the highest tide of the month
2. least amount
3. the kind of tide that occurs when the sun, the moon, and the Earth form a right angle
4. a synonym of "recede"
5. day that lasts 24 hours 51 minutes

B. Use point form to answer the following questions.

1. How many cycles of tides does the Earth go through in approximately one day?

   ____

2. When does the highest tide occur?

   ____

3. What is the range in metres of tide changes?

   ____

4. What happens to their pulls when the sun and the moon form a straight line with the Earth?

   ____

Date : ______________________

Gerund Phrases

A **gerund phrase** contains a verb in the "-ing" form. It can function as the subject, object, complement, or the object of preposition in a sentence.

Examples: Playing softball is a game we all enjoy. (subject)
Jim likes playing softball with his buddies. (object)
The greatest joy is playing softball. (complement)
Jim is excellent at playing softball. (object of preposition)

A. Underline the gerund phrases in the following sentences.

1. "Baking cookies is an easy job," says Mrs. Fields.
2. "The best part about baking is eating the cookie dough," says Mr. Fields.
3. Daughter Leila loves making apple pies.
4. Mrs. Fields used to be good at making pastries as well, but she says they are too fattening, and so has not baked a single batch in years.
5. Mr. Fields loves sitting in the kitchen when the cookies are baking in the oven.
6. Living with the Fieldses is sometimes like living in a cookie factory.
7. Visitors love tasting Mrs. Fields's new recipes because they are always superb.
8. Making dinner may not be Leila's strong suit, but making dessert certainly is.
9. Being able to cook a decent meal is Leila's new year resolution.
10. Mrs. Fields loves shopping for all kinds of baking ingredients.
11. Visiting the Fieldses on Saturdays means inviting yourself in for sweet treats.
12. Mrs. Fields believes eating well and loving life are inseparable.

B. **Identify each underlined gerund phrase as subject (S), object (O), complement (C), or object of preposition (P).**

1. Marla is not very good at preparing meals. ______
2. Jack enjoys playing street hockey with his neighours. ______
3. Hanging around at her cousins' place is one of Rachel's favourite things to do. ______
4. Cindy likes sleeping over at her best friend's house on weekends. ______
5. Reading is like travelling to different places. ______
6. Amanda's favourite activity is spending long holidays in the family cottage. ______
7. Jack prefers playing hockey to playing basketball. ______
8. Reading storybooks is one of the best things to do in spare time. ______

C. **Choose the appropriate gerund phrase for each sentence.**

playing sports of all kinds | forgiving your siblings | looking after two babies | waiting for her turn | biting nails

1. Kevin is very athletic. He enjoys ______________________.
2. Mrs. Bourne just had a pair of twins, and has become very good at ______________________ at once.
3. ______________________ is one of Jane's bad habits, but she has made a resolution to get rid of it this year.
4. ______________________ for their mistakes is not hard to do.
5. Though the line-ups at the food court are long, Sadie does not mind ______________________ to order.

Date : ____________________

Telescopes

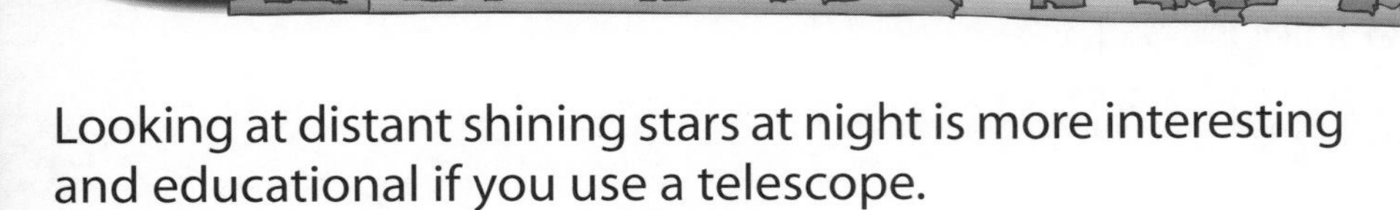

Looking at distant shining stars at night is more interesting and educational if you use a telescope.

A telescope is an optical instrument that makes distant objects like stars appear closer and larger when we view through it. It is usually a long tube or series of tubes with lenses inside that magnify distant objects.

Telescopes come in all shapes and sizes, from handheld ones like those in old pirate movies to huge and complex ones in planetariums. Despite their different sizes and shapes, they all work as either a refracting or a reflecting telescope. The refracting telescope focuses the image on the lens, while the reflecting telescope focuses the image on a mirror. There are also telescopes that are a combination of both.

The first refracting telescope was invented in 1608 in Holland by a lens grinder named Hans Lippershey. This news reached Galileo Galilei, a scientist and mathematician who later developed it into an astronomical instrument in 1609. He subsequently used it to discover sunspots and the satellites of Jupiter.

The first reflecting telescope was made by Isaac Newton in 1668. He used a concave mirror in the tube to collect the image, and viewed it through an eyepiece. There are two mirrors in most reflecting telescopes. The primary mirror collects the main image to be reflected in the secondary mirror, which then aims the image through an eyepiece for viewing. Different locations of the secondary mirror result in different reflecting telescopes like the Gregorian, Newtonian, and coude telescopes.

The subject of telescopes must also include the mention of binoculars, which are two small telescopes fixed side by side, with one eyepiece for each eye. Also called "opera glasses", binoculars have a number of lenses and often a prism in their small tubes. The prism makes images appear right side up to the viewer.

The portability of binoculars makes them very practical on field trips and long expeditions. But when doing scientific field work, sometimes you have no choice but to carry a cumbersome telescope. It all depends on which optical instrument, a telescope or pair of binoculars, can get the job done.

A. **Write "T" for the true statements and "F" for the false ones.**

1. Opera glasses are binoculars. ______
2. Refracting telescopes focus the image on a mirror. ______
3. Binoculars are two telescopes side by side. ______
4. Isaac Newton invented the first reflecting telescope in 1668. ______
5. Some telescopes are both refracting and reflecting. ______
6. The first refracting telescope was invented in England. ______

B. **Give one-word answers to the following questions.**

1. What do you call the pieces of transparent material used in glasses and cameras? ______
2. What is the word meaning "to make something appear larger than it really is"? ______
3. Where do you go to see movements of planets and stars under a curved roof? ______
4. What other word can you use to describe something extremely huge? ______
5. Jupiter is one of the nine planets in the solar system. Can you name another one? ______
6. What is the name of the scientist who became famous for wondering why things fall down and not "fall up"? ______
7. What is the adjective that describes things to do with "the eye"?

______

8. Find a compound word in the passage.

______

Did You Know?

Galileo Galilei was the first to prove with a telescope that the Earth orbits around the sun and not the other way round.

Date : ______________

Independent and Dependent Clauses

An **independent clause** can function as a complete sentence.

Example: A monster appeared in the movie and the children screamed.
(independent) (independent)

A **dependent clause** cannot function as a complete sentence. It needs an independent clause to make its meaning complete.

Example: Though the monster disappeared, the children still screamed.
(dependent) (independent)

A. Write "I" in the circle if the underlined clause is independent; write "D" if it is dependent.

1. When it is nice outside, Gabriel likes to climb trees.
2. Zadie likes riding her bicycle.
3. When spring arrives, Marie will plant lots of flowers.
4. When are you arriving?
5. Before you leave, remember to pack a sweater in the suitcase.
6. How much are these nectarines?
7. You can mail the card.
8. If we go there early in the morning, we could avoid the crowds.
9. The children all went out to play because it was a sunny day.
10. The girls did better than the boys in this year's spelling bee.

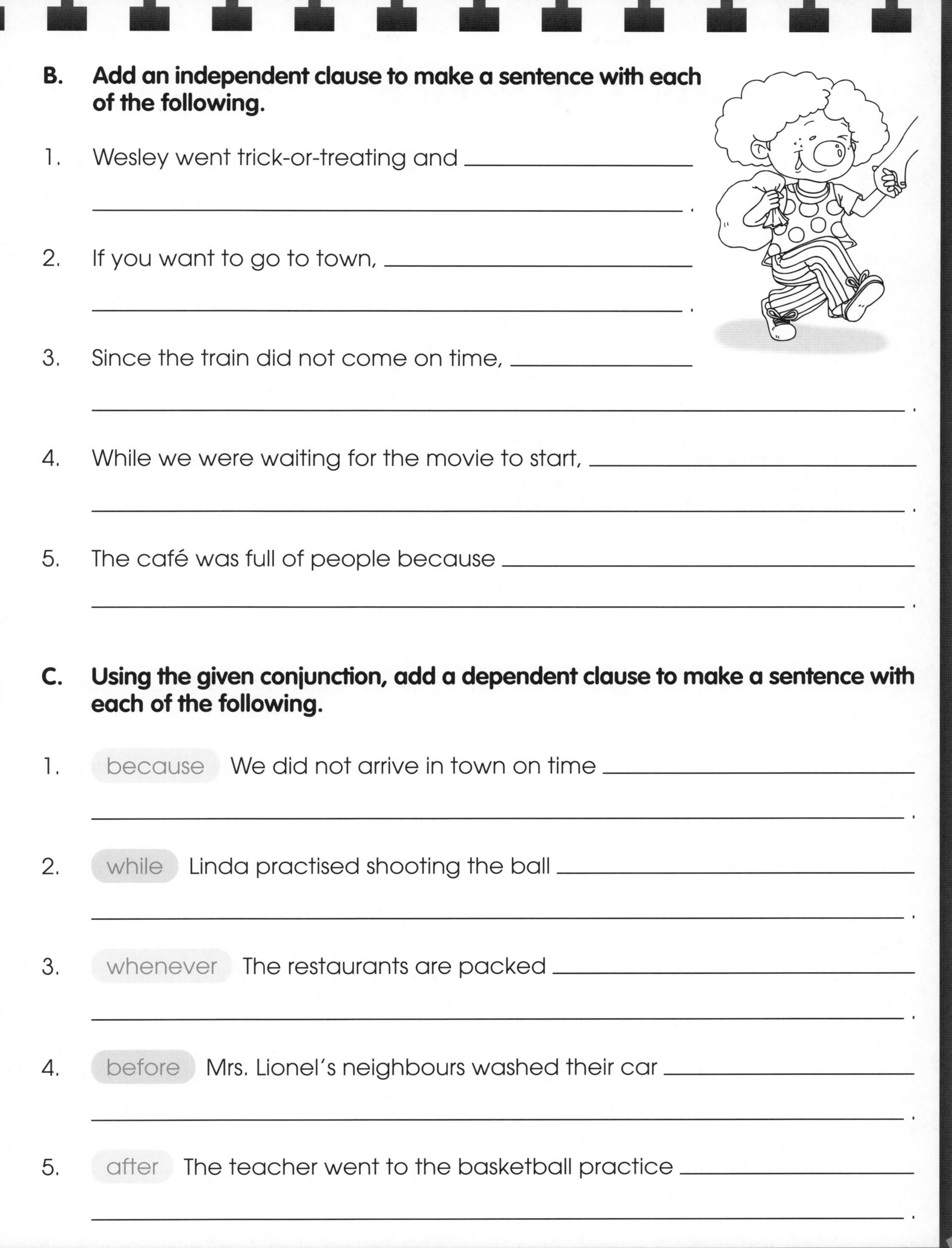

B. Add an independent clause to make a sentence with each of the following.

1. Wesley went trick-or-treating and ______________________ .

2. If you want to go to town, ______________________ .

3. Since the train did not come on time, ______________________ .

4. While we were waiting for the movie to start, ______________________ .

5. The café was full of people because ______________________ .

C. Using the given conjunction, add a dependent clause to make a sentence with each of the following.

1. because We did not arrive in town on time ______________________ .

2. while Linda practised shooting the ball ______________________ .

3. whenever The restaurants are packed ______________________ .

4. before Mrs. Lionel's neighbours washed their car ______________________ .

5. after The teacher went to the basketball practice ______________________ .

Date : ____________________

Motor Car Racing

Motor sport is a very popular spectator event in many parts of the world. The variety of races can be very confusing. To make it easier, we can keep in mind four major factors: how to win, where to drive, types of cars, and how long the races take.

There are two ways to win. You could race against the clock, whereby the driver with the fastest time wins, or you could race against other drivers, whereby the winner is the first to pass the finish line.

Race courses include open road courses and closed circuit tracks. During the early days of car racing in the late 1890s, races were held on public roads. But this became too dangerous for both spectators and drivers, so the races were moved to closed-off roads.

Closed circuit courses can be grouped into four types. The first type is the straightaway, like a drag strip, which is just a straight road. The second is the road racing course that has curves and turns with hills and dips like the Mosport Park in Bowmanville, Ontario. Third, we have the oval track like in Indianapolis, U.S.A. The fourth is a combination of an oval track and a road course.

The third factor to know about is the types of cars driven. This is such a huge subject that scores of books have been written on it. Let us first talk about Formula One cars. These are built according to an exact formula set by the Federation Internationale de l'Automobile (F.I.A.), the governing body for motor sports. Then you have sports cars. These are either production sports cars or specially built sport racing cars. There are also stock cars, which look like passenger cars, but have been altered for racing. Lastly, there are the dragsters, designed for very short races.

The fourth factor is how long the races last. For example, drag racing takes about five seconds to complete. The endurance races in Daytona, Florida and Le Mans, France take 24 hours. The Indianapolis 500 and the Mille Miglia ("1000 miles") take as much time as is needed to finish 500 or 1000 miles.

This information will hopefully guide you the next time the engines start on television. Vroom! Vroom!

A. Circle the correct answers.

1. What ways are there to win a car race?

A. against fast horses
B. against the world record
C. against other drivers
D. against the driver's personal record
E. against time
F. C and E

2. Car racing began in ____ .

A. the late 18th century
B. the early 19th century
C. the late 19th century
D. the early 20th century
E. the late 20th century
F. the early 18th century

3. Which of the following is NOT true?

A. Spectators watched from the roadside in the early days of car racing.
B. Motor sport is a popular event in many countries.
C. The F.I.A. sets the standards for building Formula One cars.
D. The F.I.A. sets the standards for all race cars.
E. There is a road racing course in Bowmanville, Ontario.
F. Dragsters are designed for very short races.

B. Quite a few official car races are in foreign languages, such as "Mille Miglia" (Italian) and "Grand Prix" (French). Even the governing body for motor sports is in French, "Federation Internationale de l'Automobile". Why do you think that is? Write a short response.

____

____

____

____

____

____

Date : ____________________

Adjectival and Adverbial Clauses

An **adjectival clause** gives information about a noun in a sentence.
Example: The children, who are back in the classroom now, are making paintings.
"Who are back in the classroom now" gives information about "the children".

An **adverbial clause** tells where or when the action of a verb takes place.
Example: The football players did not arrive until the stadium was packed.
"Until the stadium was packed" tells when the football players arrived.

A. Write "adj" or "adv" for each underlined clause.

1. The children played at the park before they went home. ______
2. The food, which has gone bad in the fridge, has been thrown away. ______
3. Benny put the book back where he found it. ______
4. Mr. Lo went into the staff room after he had dismissed his students. ______
5. The children in Mr. Adam's class do well whenever there is a pop quiz. ______
6. The little geese follow Mr. Hillside wherever he goes. ______
7. Tom is the one who always knows what to do. ______
8. After we had finished our homework, we played catch in the field. ______
9. My cousin, who comes from Vancouver, is enjoying her stay. ______
10. The train, which is being stalled, will not arrive for a while. ______
11. Before we had our snacks, we all went swimming. ______
12. My uncle will not arrive until nine o'clock tonight. ______

B. Rewrite each of the following sentences by adding an adjectival clause.

1. This yo-yo is my sister's.

2. This boy is my son.

3. That book is my cousin's favourite.

4. The team played very well.

5. The newspapers are a mess.

C. Rewrite each of the following sentences by adding an adverbial clause.

1. The rabbits are having a race.

2. Ben and June said hello.

3. Jennifer is slowing down.

4. Bus 53 will not leave.

5. The birds returned.

6. Carla and Rose will visit.

Date : ______________________

You Deserve A Break!

Sunny the Flower doesn't want to do his crossword puzzle because he wants to relax. Read the clues and help Sunny finish his crossword.

Across

A. the first colour in the rainbow

B. what you get by mixing red and white

C. a past tense that is also a flower

D. another word for "red"

E. a glossy brown nut

F. When you are shy, you might _____ .

G. the biggest flower on this page

Down

1. a red Christmas plant
2. "red" in French
3. a fruit associated with teachers
4. "Mr. Sandman, give me a dream. Make her complexion like _____ and cream."
5. a deep brown
6. a brownish red
7. a girl's name meaning "bright red"
8. what you get by mixing red and blue

A
B
C
D
E
F
G
1
2
3
4
5
6
7
8

Date : ____________________

Jet Aircraft

Wow! You are at an air show! Look at the speed and listen to the sounds of the planes. Do you know them by engine type? Are they jets, propellers, or gliders? Some of the more exciting types of aircraft are jets. Developed towards the end of World War II, the jet has since dominated the field of aviation design.

The jet is a form of gas-turbine engine that moves the aircraft by powerful exhaust forced out from the rear nozzles of the engine. Highly pressurized fuel is ignited in the combustion chamber and hot gases are forcefully blown through the rear exhaust vents to produce forward thrust.

In 1930, Sir Frank Whittle patented the first jet engine. He designed and built the first British jet aircraft, a Gloster E28/39, and flew it in May of 1941.

The first passenger jet was the British Comet. The famous and popular Boeing 707 was introduced in 1954. Today we have the Airbus, a large body passenger jet, the Boeing 747, as well as lots of other jet aircraft.

Try to spot out a few things when looking at an aircraft in the sky. Is it a passenger or military plane? Is it a jet or a propeller? How many engines does it have and where are they located?

For example, a Boeing 707 would likely be a passenger jet. It is powered by four engine pods, two under each wing. Other jet aircraft have their engines in different locations.

Fighter jets are entirely different. Most fighter jets have their engine in the fuselage, or the main body of the plane; very few of them have it under the wings. Early jet fighters like the U.S. F-86 Saber, the MiG 17 and 19 all have their engine running through the fuselage.

One of the fun things about being at an air show is identifying aircraft in all their variations.

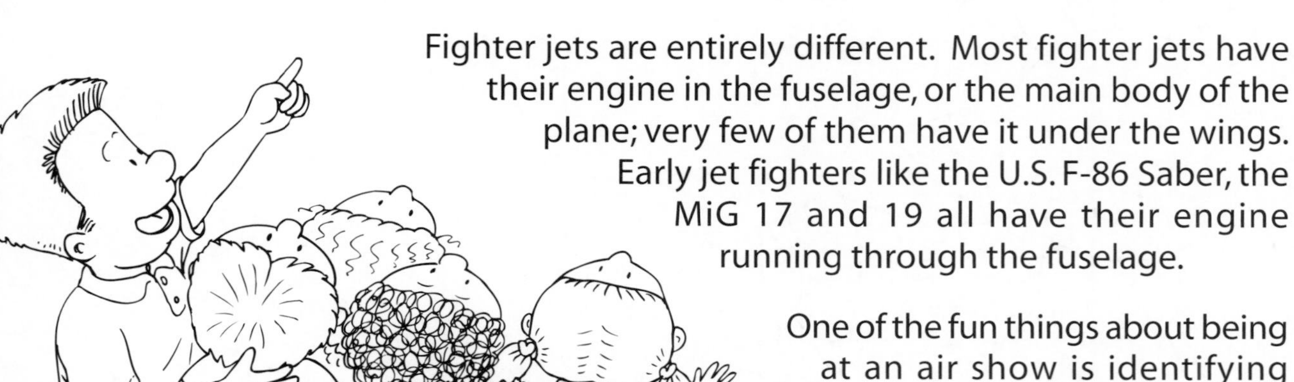

A. **Match each word in the left column with its synonym in the right column.**

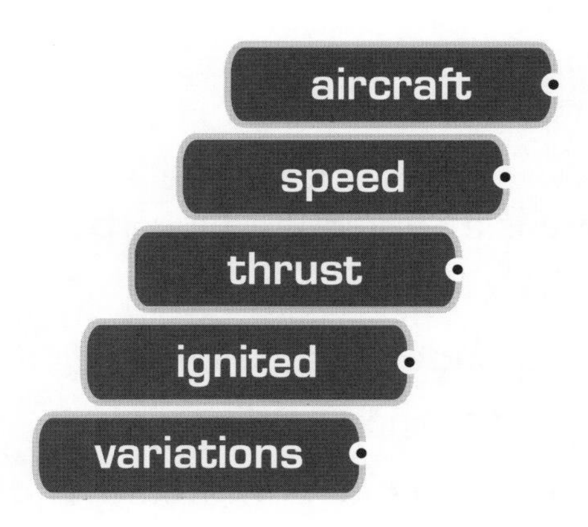

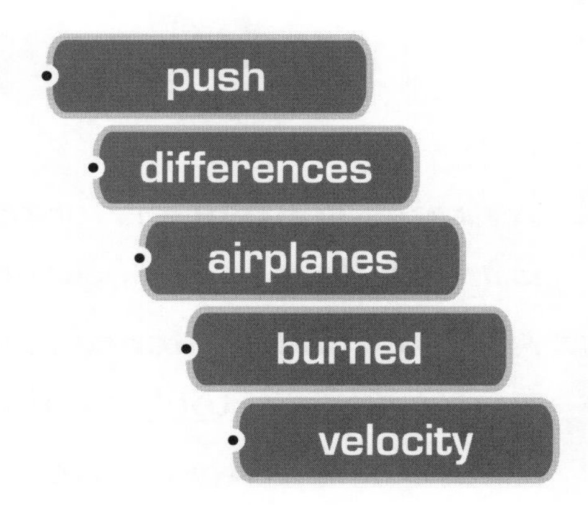

B. **Write "T" for the true statements and "F" for the false ones.**

1. Sir Edmund Hilary patented the first jet engine. ______
2. The first British jet was flown in May of 1941. ______
3. The first passenger jet was the British Comet. ______
4. The Boeing 707 was introduced in 1954. ______
5. The fuselage is the rear of the airplane. ______

C. **Based on what you have learned from the passage, how would you design your own jet? Make a sketch of it in the space below.**

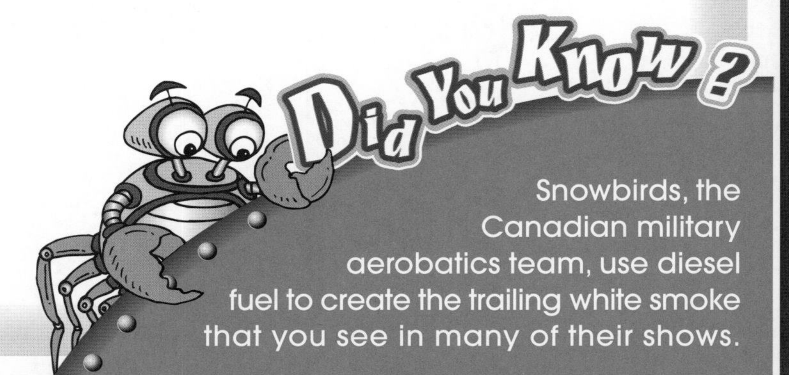

Date : ____________________

Sentences: Simple, Compound, and Complex

A **simple sentence** is formed whenever there is a subject and a verb.

Example: Randy took out the garbage.

A **compound sentence** has two or more independent clauses.

Example: Randy took out the garbage but he forgot the recycling bin.

A **complex sentence** has an independent clause and one or more dependent clauses.

Example: Randy took out the garbage because it is collection day tomorrow.
(independent) (dependent)

A. Classify the following sentences by writing the question numbers in the correct boxes.

1. Robert likes to go swimming in the morning.
2. Mr. Chips next door has just left for vacation.
3. Carrie has a very chatty parrot.
4. Florence was named after her mother.
5. Mike would rather eat olives than pickles.
6. Gabby has been collecting stamps since she was six.
7. Lois will arrive today and she will leave the following Sunday.
8. Jenna likes playing in the band but she does not like morning rehearsals.

B. Count the number of independent clauses in each of the following sentences. Write the number on the line.

1. Fabio likes tuna but he does not like it in mayonnaise. ______
2. Rory likes tuna and he likes salmon, but he does not like them hot. ______
3. Molly did not want to wear a dress at first, but she changed her mind later. ______
4. Sara and Julie both like strawberry ice cream, but only Julie likes buying it from the ice cream truck. ______
5. Craig has just gone out and he will return in a few minutes, but he will have to head back out soon for a softball practice. ______

C. Using the given conjunction, add a dependent clause to each of the following to make a complex sentence.

1. after Wanda adopted a dog ______________________________ .
2. before Wendy finished her new book ______________________________ .
3. because Cherie wants a new pair of sneakers ______________________________ .
4. since Lily and Jo have known each other ______________________________ .
5. so Mrs. Stow did not want to cook today, ______________________________ .
6. because Mel and Joey did not see the movie yesterday ______________________________ .

Date :

Liz's Pets

"I don't understand why my parents won't let me have a flying squirrel," said Liz. "Maybe it's just that they don't want it flying around the house and soiling your furniture," replied Ben. "Why don't you consider getting a cat or a dog instead?"

The next day at school, Liz was all excited to share her news with Ben. Her eyes were beaming. "I think I found the perfect pet! I'm going to convince my parents to get me a hamster," said Liz happily. "A hamster?" said Ben surprisingly. "I never thought you'd want a hamster. It's too normal for you," he said with a smile.

"Well, I've done my research and here are the facts," said Liz. "I read that there are several kinds of hamsters. They are a type of rodent that originally lived mostly in Europe and Asia. There are about 15 types and the two best known are the golden hamster and the common hamster. Golden hamsters are about 18 centimetres long and have a short tail. They have light reddish-brown fur on their backs and white fur on their bellies, while common hamsters, also called black-bellied hamsters, have black fur on their underside. They are slightly bigger. They measure about 28 centimetres and weigh up to 900 grams. They are nocturnal and live alone. They dig separate compartments for nesting, food storage, and body wastes. They sound clean. I think my parents will like that. They eat fruits, seeds, green vegetables, and small animals. Also, if I wanted my hamsters to have babies, the female golden hamster would have a litter of six or seven. I can give you one if you like, Ben," said Liz. "The books I read also say that hamsters should be kept in a metal cage or plastic enclosure. I should get wood shavings or dried grass to line the floor to absorb their urine and faeces. Aside from providing them with fruits and vegetables, I can also feed them small grains or oats. Of course, I need to put fresh water in the cage for them. They live to about three or four years old. Ben, what do you think?" asked Liz. "I think your parents will be happy you chose a hamster and not a flying squirrel," said Ben.

Liz managed to convince her parents to get her two hamsters, and named them Hammy and Fritzie. Her parents were much relieved that the new pets will not be flying all around the house!

A. **Use point form to complete the following chart about hamsters.**

Hamsters

Places of Origin	
Size	Golden: Common:
Appearance	Golden: Common:
Diet	
Behaviour	
Lifespan	

B. **Answer the following questions.**

1. Why do you think Liz wanted to keep a flying squirrel at first?

____

2. Why do you think a hamster is a more suitable pet than a flying squirrel?

____

3. What would you like to keep as a pet? Why?

____

Did You Know?

All hamsters are solitary, burrowing, and nocturnal animals. Their sleeping habits are different from those of guinea pigs, which sleep during the night.

Date : ____________

Run-on Sentences

A **run-on sentence** occurs when independent clauses run together without proper punctuation and/or conjunctions.

Examples: The holiday felt short it lasted only four days. (✘)
The holiday felt short. It lasted only four days. (✔)
Helen left the city she couldn't stand the congestion. (✘)
Helen left the city because she couldn't stand the congestion. (✔)

A. Rewrite each of the following into separate sentences with proper punctuation.

1. The dog wagged its tail it was happy.

 ____

 ____

2. The car was shiny it was new.

 ____

3. The softball game was delayed Ben went home late.

 ____

4. The weather was nice the children played at the park.

 ____

5. Mark read a book it was about a travelling musician.

 ____

6. The train arrived early Kelly missed it.

 ____

7. There was a breeze the children flew a kite.

 ____

8. It was Play Day the children were exhausted by four o'clock.

 ____

B. Rewrite the following into sentences with the given conjunctions.

There may be more than one way to rewrite some of these. Choose what first comes to mind. Remember to put a comma before the conjunction where necessary.

1. Kathy went to a farm she brought home a lot of fruits.

____

2. Barry took a short cut he ended up getting lost.

____

3. We stopped for lunch we were starving.

____

4. William got to the station the train arrived.

____

5. The closet was full there was no room to put new clothes.

____

C. Rewrite the following into sentences with proper punctuation and the given conjunctions.

1. The dog wagged its tail it was happy Glen came home. (because)

____

2. The game was delayed Ben went home late he went straight to bed. (so)

____

3. The train was early Kelly missed it she caught the next one soon after. (but)

____

Date : ____________________

Bridges

Bridges make our journeys across lakes, rivers, canyons, dangerous roads, and railway tracks safer and shorter. They are among the largest structures built and range from a few metres to several kilometres in length. A bridge must be strong enough to support not only its own weight but also that of the people and vehicles on it. It also needs to resist strong winds, earthquakes, and changes in temperature.

Different bridges serve different purposes. How do engineers decide what type of bridge to build? They need to determine its length and width, the maximum load the bridge will carry, as well as the building materials.

Bridges fall into seven main types:

1. Girder bridges are road bridges, with ends of beams ("girders") resting on piers.
2. Truss bridges are commonly built over canyons and rivers, and are supported by frameworks called trusses arranged in triangles.
3. Arch bridges are among the oldest, with one or more arches across the entire span. The weight of the load is transferred along the curve of the arches to the bottom.
4. Cantilever bridges are built over waterways and consist of two beams ("cantilevers") extending from opposite sides of the waterway. Interestingly, the cantilever bridge has kept its name even though truss frameworks are often incorporated.
5. Suspension bridges are built to cover long distances. Two towers support cables where a roadway hangs. Strong winds will make these bridges sway, so a thick structure called a stiffening girder is used to support the roadway.
6. Cable-stay bridges are similar to suspension bridges but are used if the foundation can only support one tower.
7. Drawbridges were built in those medieval castles surrounded by a moat. Many of today's drawbridges open in the middle to let large ships pass underneath.

The next time you see a bridge, take a look around. Was it a good idea to build that type of bridge there?

A. **Read the clues and complete the crossword puzzle with words from the passage.**

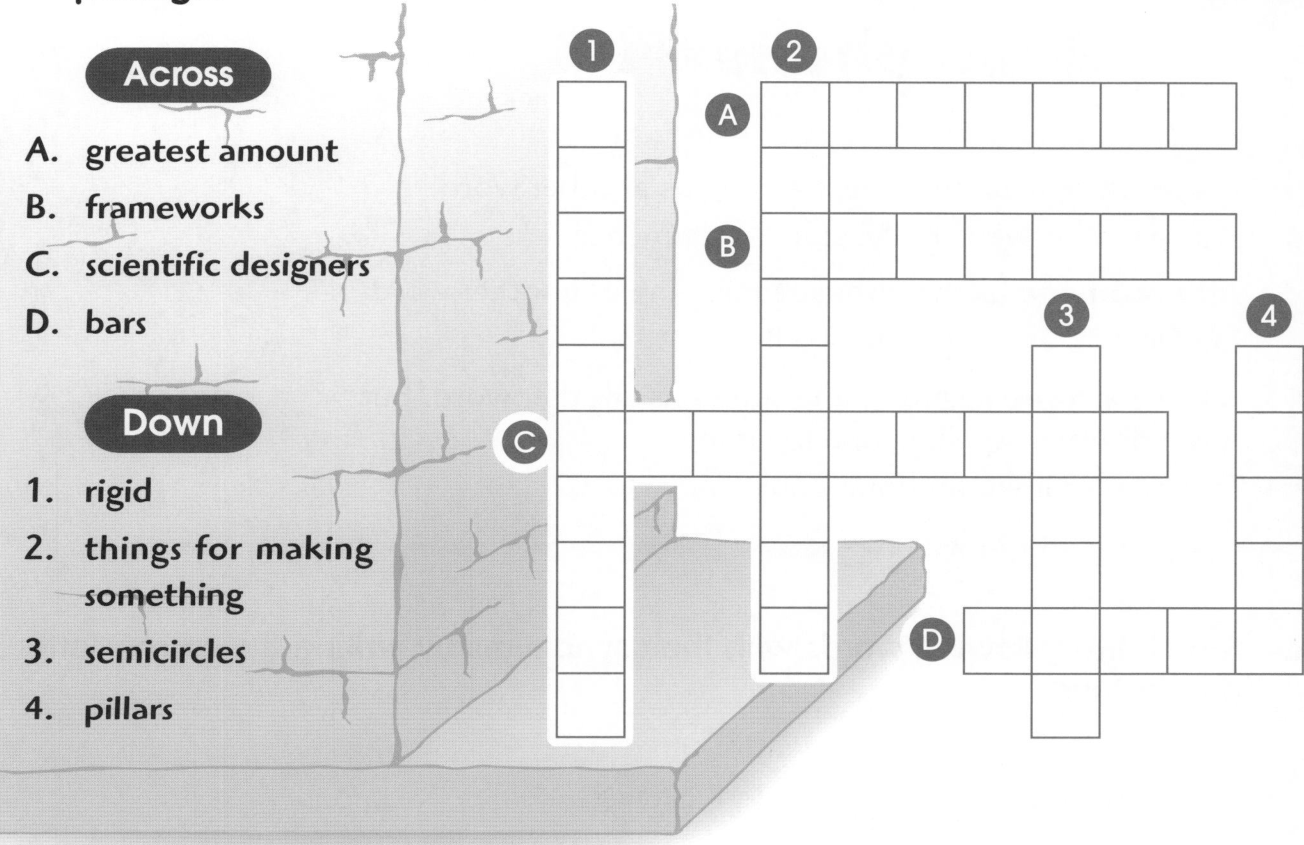

B. **Answer the following questions.**

1. Name some of the natural occurrences that bridges need to resist.

____

2. How are bridges useful?

____

3. Why do you think arch bridges have such a long history? Where else do you see arches being used?

____

____

____

____

Did You Know?

The Confederation Bridge, a girder structure, is the link between Prince Edward Island and mainland New Brunswick. At 12.9 km long and 11 m wide, it rests on 62 piers and is the longest bridge in Canada.

Date : ____________________

Synonyms, Antonyms, and Homophones

A **synonym** has the same meaning as another word.
Examples: answer – reply; start – commence

An **antonym** has the opposite meaning of another word.
Examples: come – go; buy – sell

A **homophone** has the same sound as another word, but has a different spelling and meaning.
Examples: fair – fare; hour – our

A. Match the following words with their synonyms by writing the correct letters on the lines.

A.	*recall*	1.	brave	______
B.	*strong*	2.	cheerful	______
C.	*happy*	3.	modern	______
D.	*new*	4.	remember	______
E.	*daring*	5.	powerful	______

B. Match the following words with their antonyms by writing the correct letters on the lines.

A.	*pessimistic*	1.	real	______
B.	*temporary*	2.	transparent	______
C.	*opaque*	3.	optimistic	______
D.	*everywhere*	4.	nowhere	______
E.	*imaginary*	5.	permanent	______

C. **Match words on the left with their homophones on the right. Then find synonyms for the homophones by writing the correct letters on the lines.**

1. through •	• allowed ____		A. **purchase**
2. deer •	• coarse ____		B. **expensive**
3. heel •	• threw ____		C. **simple**
4. write •	• dear ____		D. **recover**
5. plane •	• heal ____		E. **rough**
6. aloud •	• plain ____		F. **correct**
7. course •	• right ____		G. **tossed**
8. bye •	• buy ____		H. **permitted**

D. **Write a synonym (S), an antonym (A), or a homophone (H) for each of the following words. Then write a sentence with your answer.**

1. teach S ____ ________________________

2. weight H ____ ________________________

3. never A ____ ________________________

4. forecast S ____ ________________________

5. nose H ____ ________________________

6. cease S ____ ________________________

Date : ______________________

Day

67

Deadly Plants

Some of the most colourful and exotic living things on Earth are among the deadliest. There are numerous species of plants in the forest, jungle, meadow, or even the garden that we may come across without knowing how poisonous they are.

A poisonous plant is injurious to animals or human beings. They range from being mildly irritating to the skin to being deadly. There are about 700 species of poisonous plants in Canada and the U.S. One of the deadliest seeds is from the rosary pea plant. They are so deadly that simply eating one seed is enough to kill! The seeds are only used in necklaces, bracelets, and rosaries for their attractive red and black colour.

Some plants belong to poisonous families but are non-poisonous themselves. Examples are the tomato, potato, and eggplant, all of which belong to the nightshade family, *Solanaceae*. Although nightshades are highly poisonous, these vegetables are not. But keep in mind that potato and rhubarb leaves are poisonous. Also, apricots, cherries, and peaches are delicious fruits, but their pits are poisonous.

Another group of poisonous plants belongs to the mushroom family. Distinguishing between poisonous and non-poisonous mushrooms is very difficult. It is crucial that we should never eat or chew any part of a plant without knowing for certain that it is harmless. If someone is suspected of having eaten a poisonous plant, there are poison control centres that people can contact to get advice or treatment.

Poisonous plants do have their uses though. Flowers like the foxglove, azalea, hyacinth, and mistletoe are poisonous, but they also make our gardens beautiful. Some plants are also used to make insecticides. Another invaluable use is in the making of medicines. Poisons extracted from plants such as digitalis and quinine can be taken in controlled doses. Be they poisonous or not, all kinds of plants have beneficial uses.

A. Answer the following questions in your own words.

1. Are all plants from the same family poisonous? If not, give an example.

2. What uses can we make of certain poisonous plants? Name a few of these plants and their uses.

3. How do we use seeds from the rosary pea plant?

4. What is the most important thing you learned from this passage?

B. Unscramble the words in parentheses to complete each sentence.

1. The definition of a poisonous plant is "one that is (sourjuini) ______________ to an animal or a human being".
2. The Christmas plant (temetolis) ______________ is poisonous, but it can also be used to beautify our homes and gardens.
3. The seed from the (orrysa) ______________ pea plant is so deadly that eating a single seed can kill a human being.
4. The pits of cherries, peaches, and (corapits) ______________ are poisonous.
5. Potatoes, tomatoes, and eggplants belong to the (dinethagsh) ______________ family, *Solanaceae*.

Did You Know?

"Mistletoe" comes from two Old English words: *mistel* for "dung" and *tan* for "twig". This makes the mistletoe "dung on a twig". The plant got its name because people noticed it would appear on a branch or twig where birds had left their droppings.

Date : ____________________

Building Vocabulary with Root Words

A **root word** is the basic form of a word without prefixes, suffixes, or changes that make it a derived form.

Examples: "<u>Decide</u>" is the root word of "decision" and "decisive".
"<u>Happy</u>" is the root word of "happily" and "happiness".

A. Use each root word to make two new words. Then circle the synonym of the root word. The first question is done for you.

1. collect	n: collection		adj: collective	
synonym	take	invite	receive	(gather)
2. understand	n: ____________		adj: ____________	
synonym	think	comprehend	ponder	wonder
3. invent	n: ____________		adj: ____________	
synonym	make	start	plan	create
4. adapt	n: ____________		adj: ____________	
synonym	move	accept	adjust	approve
5. character	n: ____________		adj: ____________	
synonym	role	actor	story	play

B. **Use each root word to make two new words. Then circle the antonym of the root word.**

1. begin	n: ____________ adj: ____________
antonym	end wrap close done
2. hard	n: ____________ adj: ____________
antonym	loose difficult easy relaxed
3. respond	n: ____________ adj: ____________
antonym	quiet tell loud ask
4. defend	n: ____________ adj: ____________
antonym	charge offend protect move

C. **Complete each of the following sentences with some of the new words in (A) and (B).**

1. The movie that my friends and I saw was an ____________ of the book we read.

2. The story's fast pace is very ____________ of this writer's style.

3. The food critic told the cook that his dish was very ____________ .

4. The consonant digraph "ch" makes up the ____________ letters of "charm".

5. The bigger the class, the bigger the ____________ for the teacher.

Date : ______________________

Deadly Animals

Certain species of snakes, bees, scorpions, and spiders use a poisonous substance to kill or paralyze their prey. Venom, as this poison is called, is produced in the venom gland and injected into the victim in various ways.

What is in the venom that is so potent to paralyze even a large animal? The combination of toxic substances depends on the type of animal, reptile, or insect.

Some venoms contain poison that blocks the transmission of nerve impulses to muscle cells, causing numbing and paralysis. Others slow or stop the heart. Some disintegrate the walls of blood capillaries, causing swelling and massive bleeding.

Wasps, bees, hornets, and scorpions poison their prey with stingers. The Africanized honeybee and its closely related European honeybee behave in a similar fashion. As crop pollinators and honey producers, neither is likely to sting when gathering nectar and pollen from flowers, but will do so if provoked. Stingers are effective weapons because they deliver venom that causes pain once injected into the skin. Melittin is the major chemical responsible for the pain of a honeybee sting. It stimulates the nerve endings of pain receptors in the skin and causes a sharp pain lasting a few minutes, followed by a dull ache. The tissue may still be sensitive for a few days.

With the exception of king cobras and black mambas, very few snakes are actually aggressive toward human beings unprovoked. But once they bite, their fangs inject venom into their prey. Snake venom is a modified form of saliva that has evolved into aiding chemical digestion. During envenomation – the bite that injects venom or poison – the venom passes from the venom gland through a duct into the snake's fangs, and finally into its prey. Snake venom is a combination of numerous substances causing varying effects, from local tissue damage to damage to the heart.

Like a snake, a spider bites its victim to inject venom. By contrast, fish and some sea creatures use their bony spines to inject venom to paralyze their prey.

As toxic as venom may be, surprisingly, there are beneficial uses for it. In fact, venom can be used to treat illnesses. The venom from the Malayan pit viper is used to treat certain types of heart attacks. Cobra venom is used to treat severe pain, and bee venom is used to relieve arthritis. Other effects are also currently being studied.

A. Circle the correct answers.

1. Which of the following is true?

   A. Venom injected into the prey does not always kill.

   B. Venom is found in most animals, reptiles, and insects.

   C. Venom is a poison that many animals use to paralyze or kill their prey.

2. How is venom injected?

   A. from bites only

   B. from bites and stingers

   C. from bites, stingers, and bony spines

3. Some reptiles may attack when unprovoked, such as ____ .

   A. cobras and pythons

   B. king cobras and black mambas

   C. anacondas and rattlesnakes

4. Some illnesses that venom can be used to treat are ____ .

   A. heart attacks and severe pain

   B. arthritis

   C. A and B

B. Find the derivatives in the passage for the following words.

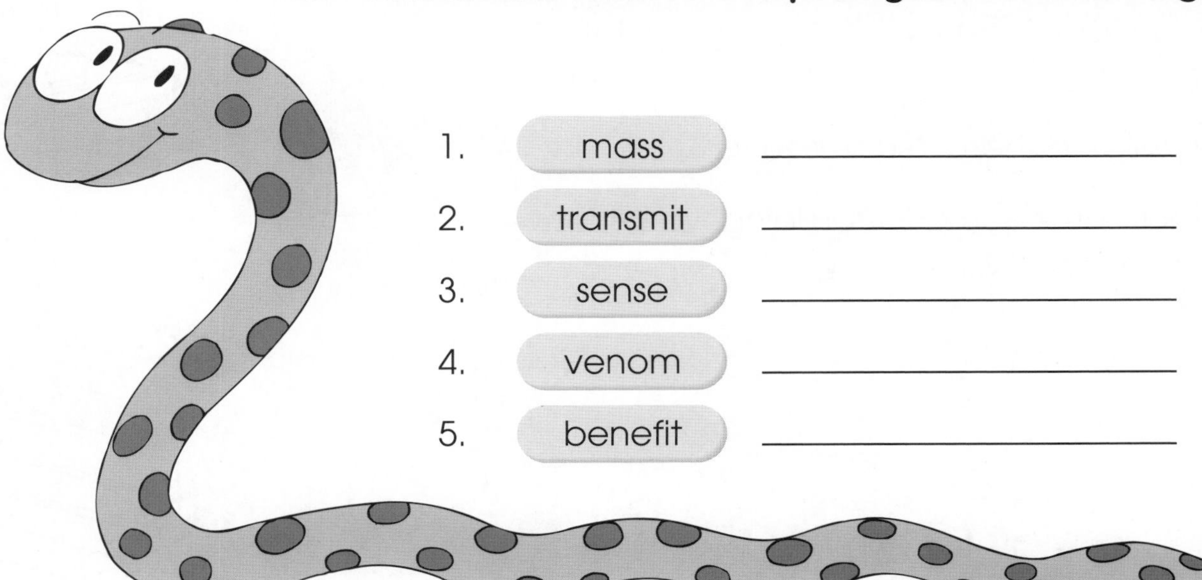

1. mass ______________________
2. transmit ______________________
3. sense ______________________
4. venom ______________________
5. benefit ______________________

Date : ____________________

What might you find in a city? Read the clues below and write your answers in the sky.

1. a very tall building in the city
2. the opposite of "ancient"
3. the style or manner of buildings
4. There is a ____ called St. Lawrence in Montreal.
5. a very tall free-standing structure
6. a place where people visit to see historically important things like paintings or dinosaur bones
7. an area by the coast where boats and ships are safe
8. The city is alive with glittering ____ at night.
9. the view of the city against the sky
10. the image of something in the water or mirror
11. You will find these in a harbour.
12. If your home is in a tall building, you might have a room with a ____ .

1.
2.
3.
4.
5.
6.
7.
8.
9.
10.
11.
12.

Date : ______________________

Tips for Better Writing

Wordiness vs. Choppy Sentences

Wordiness occurs when we use unnecessary words to make simple statements.

Example: Sara walks to school with a friend on many occasions. (✗)
Sara often walks to school with a friend. (✔)

Sometimes, sentences may not convey an idea effectively when they are too short.

Example: Sara is a student. She goes to a public school. The school is in town. (✗)
Sara is a student at a public school in town. (✔)

A. Rewrite each of the following accordingly.

1. Terry travelled across the country by means of riding the bicycle.

____

____

2. Montreal is a bilingual city. It is a city in Quebec.

____

3. Due to the fact that there was a storm, school was cancelled.

____

4. The storm subsided. It was calm again. School resumed.

____

5. Laurie is at the skating rink. She has a pair of new skates.

____

6. Prior to the start of the show, no one arrived at the theatre.

____

7. Joshua switched to another school. The school is in the countryside.

____

Homophone Errors

It is important not to confuse words that sound the same.

Example: Laura finished the hole cake by herself. (✗)
Laura finished the whole cake by herself. (✔)

B. Circle the wrong word in each of the following and rewrite the sentence with the correct one.

1. I here that you have just moved to a new house.

2. The guests will arrive on the our.

3. Mrs. Hunter helped her daughter untie a not.

4. The different groups will meat at the station early in the morning.

5. When Hilary has nothing to do, she stairs out of the window.

6. Robin told me that she had red the book.

7. Greta wants to learn how to sow dresses.

8. Chris takes the same root to school every day.

9. The weather is nice because the son has come out.

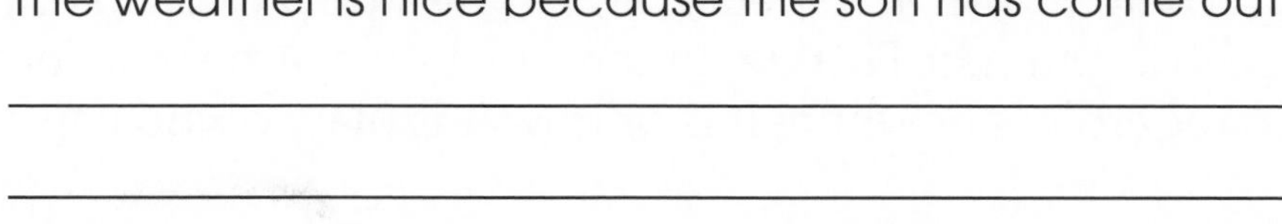

Date :

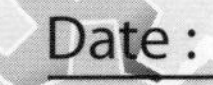

Day 72

Frisbee

The use of flying discs in games has existed since 400 B.C. Discus throwing by the Greeks was an event in the Olympic games. Although the origin of the hurling disc as toy is still debatable, the "Frisbee" as we know it today actually started out as a plate for baking pies.

Around the 1930s, employees at the Frisbie Baking Company in Bridgeport, Connecticut, U.S. used to toss their metal pie plates back and forth, so much so that customers ended up doing the same and about 5000 pie plates were reportedly lost. When the company opened up a bakery close to Yale University, the students would toss the metal pie plates around campus for fun. Passers-by would be warned with "Frisbie!" whenever a plate was approaching.

It was Walter Frederick Morrison and Warren Franscioni who changed the toy from metal to plastic; they perfected and patented the flying disc. At the time, there were reports of UFO sightings and the public was obsessed with flying saucers. Capitalizing on this, Morrison called the toy "Flying Saucer". Later, when sales slowed, the name was changed to "Pluto Platter". In 1957, a toy company called Wham-O bought the rights to the toy and wanted to market it with a different name. After having heard the popular use of the word "Frisbie-ing", the company owner decided to call the toy "Frisbee".

Who would have predicted that a simple flying disc could provide so many people with unlimited hours of fun? The airfoil design makes use of the air current as it moves, while the spinning gyro motion provides stability during flight. Frisbees can be thrown at great speeds and can travel up to 55 metres when thrown with a backhand flip. It could imitate a boomerang when thrown at a specific angle with the proper spin. There are even games with rules such as Ultimate Frisbee – a combination of American football, soccer, and basketball. But regardless of where it is or how it is played, you can never mistake a Frisbee!

A. **Put the following events in order by writing 1, 2, 3, 4, and 5 on the lines.**

_____ Wham-O bought the rights to the hurling disc toy.

_____ The hurling disc toy was renamed "Pluto Platter" when sales slowed.

_____ When the Frisbie Baking Company opened up a bakery close to Yale University, the students would toss the pie plates around campus for fun.

_____ Morrison and Franscioni changed the hurling disc toy from metal to plastic.

_____ Employees at the Frisbie Baking Company treated their pie plates as toys.

B. **Write the root word of each word. Determine whether the root word is a noun (N), a verb (V), or an adjective (A). Then use it to create a sentence.**

1. debatable

debate	V

2. passers-by

3. stability

4. combination

5. university

Date : ____________________

Similes and Metaphors

Similes

A **simile** is a comparison of two things that have characteristics in common. We use "as" or "like" to link the two things.

Examples: The dinner roll was as hard as a rock.
That little girl was feisty like a ferret.

A. Rewrite each of the following sentences with a simile.

1. The children hurried home.

2. The petals were blown away.

3. The engine roared.

4. The baby is cute.

5. The plane took off.

6. The entire room was blue.

7. The newspapers were thick.

8. Memories fade.

Metaphors

A **metaphor** is a comparison of two things with common characteristics, without the use of "as" or "like". In the comparison, we describe something as though it were something else.

Examples: My little brother is a jewel.
My new pet is the centre of the universe.

B. Underline the metaphor in each of the following sentences.

1. The bird in my backyard is a rock star.
2. My children are the world to me.
3. My best friend is a rose among thorns.
4. The demonstrators were roaring waves.
5. The Earth is becoming a hothouse because of global warming.

C. Use a simile or metaphor to complete each of the following sentences.

1. My cousin charged into the house like ______________________ .
2. The dog runs as fast as ______________________ .
3. My dad is as tall as ______________________ .
4. My sister nibbled on her food like ______________________ .
5. Lizzy is very chatty. She is the ______________________ in our class.
6. Angelo is a fast runner. He is the ______________________ on our team.
7. Neil never sits still. He is the ______________________ in the house.
8. Darren is the first to finish the race. He is a ______________________ .
9. Rene loves being in water. She is a ______________________ .

Date : ____________________

Slinky

More than 60 years ago, a device called the Slinky was sold as a toy and has since been entertaining children and adults all over the world. From its accidental discovery on board a United States Navy ship during WWII to its becoming a toy in households everywhere, the Slinky has a fascinating story.

A naval engineer named Richard James discovered the Slinky by chance in 1943. He was developing an anti-vibrational device for instruments on the ship. His torsion-spring did not work out as an anti-vibrational device, but it did fall off some workbench and start to flip-flop in an interesting way.

Upon returning home, James told his wife about the torsion-spring. They improved it by using long steel ribbon and tightly twisting it into a coil-spiral spring and – Voila! The Slinky was born. It was first sold at the Gimbels Department Store in Philadelphia in 1945, and 300 million Slinkys have been sold worldwide since then.

What is so fascinating about the Slinky is that it is such a simple toy. It does not need any electrical power, brakes, gears, or motor, but only itself and a height from which to fall down. Yet it displays very important principles of physical science: an object will remain at rest, or continue in motion, until an external force acts upon it. This is the basic physical principle of inertia.

The Slinky also demonstrates states of potential energy and kinetic energy. When the toy is on top of the stairs, it has inertia and stored potential energy. When your hand tips the coil down, you are the external force acting upon it. When the Slinky falls down the stairs, it is showing kinetic energy in action.

This simple toy also demonstrates many other physical principles, but let us save these for another day!

A. The synonyms of these words are all from the passage. Circle them in the word search. They may be in any direction.

tool power making plain interesting

laws movement unintentional outside

d	a	m	e	x	p	l	a	s	i	t	m	o	n	e	e	t	a	r
b	e	v	e	r	l	e	b	u	h	c	o	r	w	n	u	s	s	p
e	n	v	i	s	i	l	a	l	o	e	t	o	a	e	b	i	o	r
a	i	f	i	o	o	i	o	c	m	r	i	b	n	r	e	m	m	i
c	g	z	u	c	t	z	n	y	c	v	o	e	d	g	a	p	n	n
h	h	e	x	t	e	r	n	a	l	i	n	r	e	y	c	l	e	c
b	t	p	l	a	n	a	j	s	e	a	d	t	r	p	d	e	u	i
f	a	s	c	i	n	a	t	i	n	g	o	e	e	e	s	r	m	p
a	v	e	a	e	r	b	o	s	r	n	n	g	n	r	o	w	o	l
l	i	o	d	e	v	e	l	o	p	i	n	g	r	t	r	y	n	e
l	a	n	a	o	m	t	v	e	s	t	q	u	w	e	a	t	c	s
v	n	i	c	x	r	h	i	s	i	e	u	y	e	s	z	l	i	t

B. Match the definitions with the correct words by writing the correct letters on the lines.

1. what the Slinky has when it is about to fall ______
2. the age of the Slinky ______
3. what the Slinky has when it is not moving ______
4. what the Slinky has when it is falling down the stairs ______
5. what James used to improve his torsion-spring ______

A. inertia
B. 60 years
C. kinetic energy
D. brakes
E. physical principles
F. potential energy
G. long steel ribbon

Date : ____________________

Topic Sentences

The **topic sentence** introduces the main idea of a paragraph. A good topic sentence should:
- introduce the topic in a focused manner, without wordiness;
- give enough information on the topic;
- create interest for the reader.

A. Circle the letter of the most appropriate topic sentence for each topic.

1. The Lion in the Circus

   A. Because the man on stage was a substitute, the lion in the circus did not perform the tricks as planned.

   B. Due to the fact that the man on stage was a substitute, the lion in the circus did not perform the tricks that had been planned in advance.

   C. The lion did not want to move.

2. The Tallest Man's Visit

   A. The world's tallest man came to visit.

   B. The world's tallest man visited Calgary on Sunday and befriended a boy named Nathan.

   C. The world's tallest man came to visit Calgary on Sunday and met a boy named Nathan and became his friend.

3. Two Orphans Now in School

   A. Clare and Joseph, who have never gone to school, are now attending a special school.

   B. Clare and Joseph, orphans in Toronto who have never gone to school, are now attending The City School for Needy Children.

   C. Two of the city's orphans are now going to school.

B. Write an interesting and informative topic sentence for each paragraph below. Then add a title for each.

1. Title: ______________________

   Topic sentence: ______________________

   ____

   By using pictures and real-life examples to explain various math concepts, Mr. Adam has helped his students develop a deeper interest in the topics taught. Even those who would have normally done poorly on tests are now doing almost as well as the rest of the class. This is good news for other math teachers, who are planning to apply Mr. Adam's method in their classrooms as well.

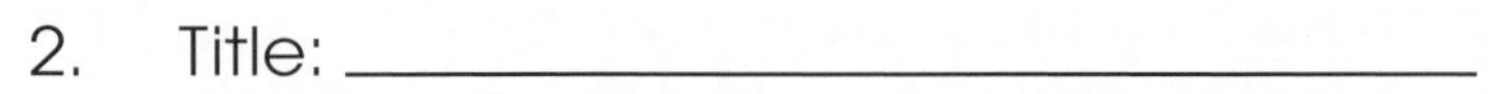

2. Title: ______________________

   Topic sentence: ______________________

   ____

   There are now over thirty factories in the city, and some of them are quite close to residential communities. According to Dr. Shapiro, a specialist in respiratory illnesses, the number of patients who see him for problems has doubled over the past ten years.

3. Title: ______________________

   Topic sentence: ______________________

   ____

   Ten different bands came together to perform the crowd's favourite songs. The concert raised over $50 000 for third world countries, making this year's efforts the best ever. The mayor as well as everyone in the city are very proud of this accomplishment, and all hope they can beat the record in next year's concert.

Date :

The Bow and Arrow

In the *Lord of the Rings* trilogy, hundreds of arrows flying towards their targets make some of the most exciting film scenes. Impressed?

The bow and arrow are among the oldest and most widely used tools in human history. Featured widely in the human imagination, they have been used for hunting, as a weapon of war, and as an instrument for sport.

We do not know how the bow and arrow came to be, but evidence of their use dates back to prehistoric times. The primitive bow can shoot an arrow about 18 metres away. Before that, men had to use their bare hands, stones, clubs, or spears to hunt for food and defend themselves. Even with spears, primitive men had to get quite close to their targets to be effective. The bow and arrow allowed hunters to hunt at a farther distance, thereby reducing their chances of being attacked by animals.

The bow and arrow were an excellent weapon of war. Between prehistoric times and the mid-1500s, the bow and arrow went through many stages of improvements. But with the invention and widespread use of firearms in the mid-1500s, the bow and arrow moved from being the primary tool for hunting and warfare to being used mainly in the sport of archery.

Sport archery covers many events such as archery, field archery, flight archery, and clout archery. Some events can be done both indoors and outdoors, while others can only be done outdoors. The most common event is target archery, where the archer is required to shoot at a target marked with different scoring rings. The red bull's eye in the centre is worth ten points. In flight archery, the archer who shoots the farthest distance wins. Federation Internationale de Tir a l'Arc, founded in 1931, is the governing body for sport archery.

With their long history, the bow and arrow certainly make for riveting storytelling. No wonder they are so often featured in movies!

A. The antonyms of these words are all from the passage. Circle them in the word search. They may be in any direction.

advanced
covered
increasing
modern
offend
rarely
regressions
unimportant

t	c	v	u	m	a	t	c	p	i	n	m	q	n
p	n	r	e	d	u	c	i	n	g	u	o	p	l
r	b	h	i	f	p	d	s	r	s	c	i	r	o
i	r	b	a	r	e	l	e	a	v	c	g	e	k
c	p	k	e	n	r	k	r	f	u	i	u	h	w
z	r	o	l	e	s	m	i	d	e	s	k	i	m
d	i	m	p	r	o	v	e	m	e	n	t	s	p
u	m	l	u	c	k	n	c	a	i	h	d	t	n
c	a	p	r	i	m	i	t	i	v	e	i	o	l
i	r	e	y	i	g	l	s	o	t	i	b	r	e
n	y	o	m	w	i	d	e	l	y	d	c	i	h
g	s	c	q	j	d	u	n	u	o	v	l	c	s

B. Draw an arrow to match each clue with the correct answer.

1. involves shooting the arrow the farthest distance
2. became the primary weapon in warfare in the 1500s
3. scored as ten points
4. able to shoot an arrow 18 metres away
5. involves shooting at a target with different scoring rings

- primitive bow
- target archery
- flight archery
- firearms
- bull's eye

Did You Know?

Apollo and Ulysses, as well as other characters in Greek mythology, are often portrayed with a bow and arrow.

Date : ____________________

Writing Paragraphs (1)

A **paragraph** consists of one or more sentences on an idea or topic. A good paragraph often has the following:

topic sentence – the main idea

supporting details – information such as facts and examples

conclusion sentence – a summary of the main idea or a solution to a problem

One of the easiest types of paragraphs to write is the **narrative paragraph**. It describes an event or tells a story.

A. Underline the topic sentence, supporting details, or the conclusion sentence as indicated for each narrative paragraph.

1. **Topic sentence**

Today, each child in class had to write a riddle and pass it to the person sitting behind them. Marie got Jonathan's riddle and took a very long time to figure it out; the answer was "Marie". Apparently, Jonathan had written a riddle about her, something she would never have expected!

2. **Supporting details**

Natalie fell and hurt herself when she went for a bike ride yesterday. The strap on her left sandal got caught in the pedal and she lost balance. Natalie hurt her knee but luckily, she did not injure her kneecap. She told herself that she would wear her sneakers when riding the bike next time.

3. **Conclusion sentence**

Jason is excited about his new rocket model. At first, he did not know where to put each piece, but he eventually figured it out after many trials and errors. The bottom section of the model was the hardest to build, and Jason did not finish it until he had tried ten different ways! Now that the model is complete, Jason proudly displays it in his room.

B. Write a narrative paragraph on each given topic.

1. **Title:** At School Today

Topic sentence: ____________________

Supporting details: ____________________

Conclusion sentence: ____________________

2. **Title:** At Home Today

Topic sentence: ____________________

Supporting details: ____________________

Conclusion sentence: ____________________

Date : ____________________

Pirates

"Ship ahoy!" yells the lookout on a merchant ship. The captain looks through his telescope to see if it is a pirate ship. After all, he is sailing the Spanish Main.

During the height of piracy between the 1500s and 1700s, the Spanish Main – the Caribbean Sea and the northern part of the South American mainland – was a hotbed of pirate activity. Pirates would attack the crew and passengers of merchant ships and steal their goods and treasures.

The lookout, the sailor keeping watch for a ship over the horizon, was the first warning signal. He would be housed in his "crow's nest", an enclosed platform high atop the ship's masthead, and would call the captain once he spotted a ship over the horizon.

When the captain heard the call, he would look through his telescope and check to see what ship it was. If it was a friendly ship, he would continue on his way, while still keeping an eye out. If not, he must try to outrun the pirates because he would not have enough men to fight them.

Friendly ships were your own warships, allied privateers, and neutral merchant ships. Unfriendly ships were enemy warships, enemy privateers, hostile merchant ships, and the buccaneers. How would the captain know what ship he was looking at?

You recognized your enemies by the type of flag they were flying or the absence of one, coupled with a fast-speed approach. In the 1700s, the Jolly Roger – the famous white skull and crossbones on a black flag – was a common pirate flag.

Pirates of the Spanish Main in the 1500s to the 1700s were called buccaneers. The name "buccaneer" comes from the French word "boucanier", meaning someone who uses a Brazilian wooden grill called "boucan" for roasting and curing meat. A privateer was a sea raider licensed by a country at war to raid enemy ships on its behalf. Technically, privateers were not pirates because they did not rob for their own interests.

The captain's best defence was a good lookout and his own quick decisive action. He must outrun pirates and avoid being boarded by bad guys with their grapnels and boarding planks!

A. Find words from the passage that match the following.

1. __________ line where the Earth meets the sky
2. __________ precious gems
3. __________ top of a ship
4. __________ unfriendly
5. __________ trader

B. Write "T" for the true statements and "F" for the false ones.

1. The crow's nest was the lookout point of a ship. ____
2. "Buccaneer" is a kind of wooden grill. ____
3. The absence of a flag on a ship meant it was a friendly ship. ____
4. The Jolly Roger was the flag of all pirate ships. ____
5. The Spanish Main was full of pirate activity. ____

C. Answer the following questions.

1. What did pirates use to board the ships they wanted to attack?

2. Why was a privateer not a pirate?

3. Describe the Jolly Roger.

4. If you were the captain of a merchant ship in 1602, which areas would you avoid, and why?

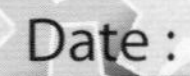

Date : ____________________

Day 79

Writing Paragraphs (2)

Descriptive Paragraphs

A **descriptive paragraph** describes something or someone. For example, you can describe your best friend, including details such as what she is like and where she lives.

A. Write a descriptive paragraph on one of the suggested topics.

Title: ____________________

Topic sentence: ____________________

____

____

Supporting details: ____________________

____

____

____

____

Conclusion sentence: ____________________

____

____

Persuasive Paragraphs

A **persuasive paragraph** tries to convince the reader of something. It may start with a phrase such as "I think that...", followed by a support section that includes sentences such as "One reason is..." or "For example..." The conclusion sentence may be "This is why I think that..."

B. Write a persuasive paragraph on one of the suggested topics.

Why It Is Good to Read Every Day

Why I Like Playing Music

Why a Dog Is a Kid's Best Friend

Why It Is Good to Exercise Every Day

Title: ______________________________

Topic sentence: ______________________________

____

____

Supporting details: ______________________________

____

____

____

____

Conclusion sentence: ______________________________

____

____

Date : ____________________

You Deserve A Break!

Buried in these holes are riddles about different shapes. Solve them and write your answers in the spaces provided.

1. It all began with a pen.

2. "Fair and honest" is "fair and ____________ ".

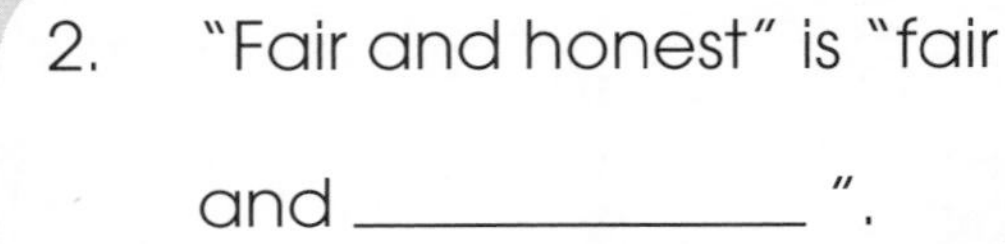

3. It's a female because it has a girl's name.

4. It's got a tangle but it surely isn't tangled.

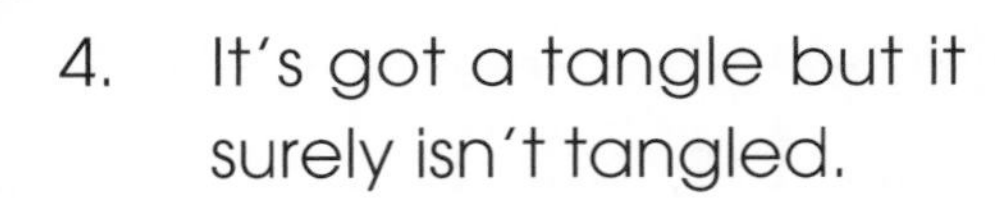

5. It's a male but only refers to itself as "he".

6. It certainly sounds like it's the wrong bus.

____

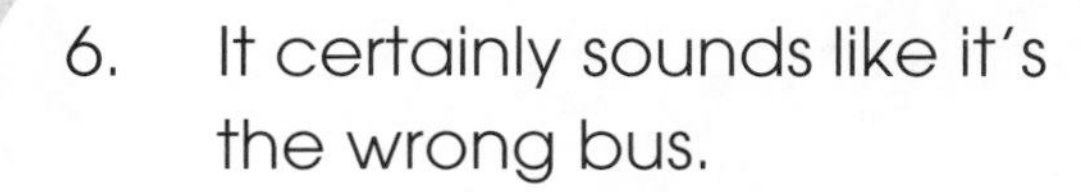

7. This shape is always telling you to catch something.

____

8. It goes round and round.

____

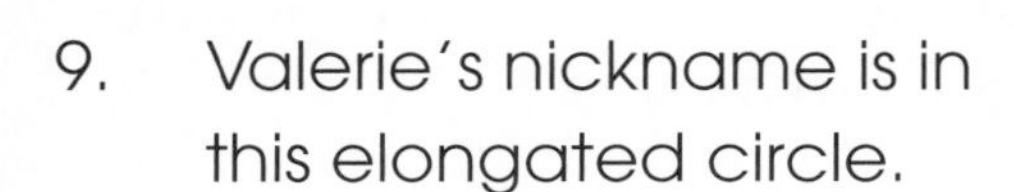

9. Valerie's nickname is in this elongated circle.

____

10. You'll find the tenth month here but only in short form.

____

Date : ____________________

The Turtle

The only reptile with a shell is the turtle. Its shell is like a suit of armour for protection. Because some can live to about a hundred years old, the turtle symbolizes longevity.

Turtles are found in most habitats, except in cold regions where they cannot regulate their body temperature to adjust to the cold. Their habitats range from deserts and forests to rivers and the sea. There are about 250 turtle species and many are indigenous to North America. They vary in size from about 10 centimetres to about 2.4 metres in length.

Land turtles have short heavy legs while water turtles have long legs with webbed feet. Sea turtles have legs that look like paddles with flippers, which are good for swimming. The hip and shoulder bones are inside the ribcage so that the legs can be withdrawn. But did you know that the sea turtle cannot retract its head into its shell?

Turtles have well-developed senses of sight and touch, and can hear low-pitched sounds as well as a human being. Though they have no teeth, they possess strong beaks with hard edges to break up their food. Combined with strong jaws, they are able to eat both animals and plants. Map turtles and soft-shelled turtles eat mainly animals.

In harsh winters, turtles and tortoises hibernate by burrowing themselves in soil or under rotting vegetation. Some species that live in hot and dry climates go into a state of limited activity called estivation.

Baby turtles hatch from eggs that are fertilized within the female's body. Except for sea and freshwater turtles, the eggs are laid on land between late spring and late autumn. The eggs, varying from one to 200 depending on the species, are then covered in soil. The mother leaves the eggs in the soil and does not return. Once they are hatched, the babies have to find food and protect themselves. This is the most vulnerable stage for young turtles as predators wait to eat them.

Because of pollution, destruction of their habitats, and human beings hunting them for food and ornaments, the turtle population is endangered. Think about what you can do to protect these creatures.

A. **Choose from the given words to complete the following sentences.**

1. ____________________ means long life.
2. To sleep for a long period of time in winter is to ____________________ .
3. A state of limited activity is called ____________________ .
4. Turtles cannot ____________________ their body temperature in extremely cold weather.

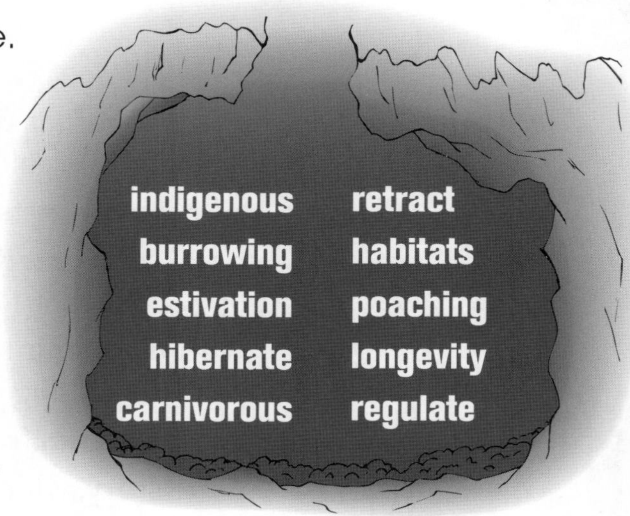

5. Many species of turtles are ____________________ to North America.

B. **Can you find passage words that are antonyms of the following? Write them in the spaces provided and write a sentence with each one.**

1. prey ____________________

2. lack ____________________

3. mild ____________________

4. creation ____________________

Date : ____________________

Understanding a Story

A **story** is often about a conflict or situation that needs to be solved. To understand a story, we could break it down into the following parts:

setting – the time and place of the story

main characters – characters directly involved in the conflict

minor characters – characters with limited involvement in the conflict, but who usually interact with the main characters to move the story along

plot – the development of events from beginning to end

conflict – the heart of the story, which may involve a character against another, against themselves, or against nature

suspense – a technique by which the story holds back information from the reader to gradually build up the ending

Read the following story. Then answer the questions on the next page.

Mom and Dad have gone out to attend a business dinner, and so Jonathan and Ben have the house all to themselves. The two boys never find it hard to entertain themselves. Jonathan is watching *Star Wars* on TV and Ben is reading *Goosebumps* in the basement.

At about a quarter to ten, Ben notices some beams of light moving across the ceiling in the basement. They come from the small window at the corner. He has never seen this before.

He goes up to the TV room, and Jonathan tells him he has also seen the same beams of light. Just then, they hear footsteps at the front door. It cannot be Mom and Dad because they will not be home until midnight. Is a burglar trying to break into their house?

As they are wondering what to do, the sound of the footsteps have gone away. Should they peek from the bedroom window to see what the lights and footsteps are all about?

But the footsteps have come back! They sound closer and closer to the front door! "Grab the baseball bat!" Ben says to Jonathan. "But these bad guys might have a gun!" Jonathan replies. Very scared now, the two boys run into the basement to hide in a closet.

"Hi boys!" Mom calls. "Why is the house so dark?" Dad asks. It has taken a while for the parents to find their boys, who hid themselves too well downstairs. "We saw flashes of light and heard strange footsteps," says Ben. "It must have been us," says Mom. "We pulled into the driveway and came to the door, but forgot the keys, so we went back to the car to get them."

"What about those beams of light?" asks Jonathan. "They must be from the car as we were pulling up to the driveway."

1. What is the setting of the story?

   Time: ____________________

   Place: ____________________

2. Who are the characters in the story?

   Main: ____________________

   Minor: ____________________

3. Describe the plot.

   ____

   ____

   ____

4. Describe the conflict.

   ____

   ____

   ____

5. Do you think the suspense is effective? Why or why not?

   ____

   ____

Date :

A Knight's Armour

Whack! Smash! Swoosh! These are the strikes and blows that a knight of medieval Europe had to face. They came from weapons like the "mace", the "morning star", or the sword. To protect himself and become an expert swordsman, a knight had to wear metal body armour.

At first, knights used chain mail armour, which consisted of flexible interlocking metal links. But as the weapons became heavier, the chain mail armour could not protect them against the new weapons.

Around the 1300s, the knights started to use plate armour, made of thin metal plates molded to different parts of the body. The armour would even be beautifully decorated and artistically finished. Sacrificing movement for protection, this new armour became so heavy that a fully suited knight would sometimes need help from squires and servants to mount on a horse.

What is the anatomy of armour?

A helmet was made for the head and neck. It consisted of a bowl, a ventail (a movable piece of metal in the front), a beaver (another movable piece of metal to protect the chin and mouth), jugular (armour to protect the jugular vein in the neck), and gorget (armour for the throat).

The shoulders and arms would have a neck guard, a pouldron, rerebrace, elbow cop, vambrace (to protect the forearm), and gauntlet (heavy leather glove covered with metal plates).

Armour for the torso and hips would be a breastplate with lance-rest, taces, fald, cuirrass (metal plate for the back with a breastplate), and a tasse (metal skirt to protect the trunk and thigh).

The legs and feet would be protected by a cuisse (metal plate for the thigh), knee cop, greave (shin guard), and solleret (foot guard).

Think about the body protection for playing hockey or baseball, for skateboarding or roller-skating. Is it not a modern version of the medieval plate armour?

A. Match the words with their definitions by writing the letters on the lines.

1. cuirass ______
2. tasse ______
3. beaver ______
4. cuisse ______
5. solleret ______
6. gorget ______
7. gauntlet ______
8. jugular ______

A. plate for the back
B. metal skirt
C. mouth and chin piece
D. thigh guard
E. armour for the throat
F. foot guard
G. armour for the neck
H. glove

B. Unscramble the letters in parentheses to complete each sentence.

1. Whenever Catherine goes roller-skating, she would wear shin guards, which would have been called (vareges) ______________ in medieval armour.

2. When riding the bicycle, it is always safe to wear a (meelth) ______________ .

3. Though the puck comes flying with every scoring attempt, Dave does not worry about getting hurt because his protective gear is just like a knight's (muraro) ______________ .

C. Answer the following questions.

1. Which type of armour was more common before the 1300s?

____

2. Which type of armour was popular after the 1300s?

____

3. What were the pros of using plate armour? What were the cons?

____

____

Date : ______________________

Creating a Story

Creating a story may seem like a difficult task: we might get "writer's block" when faced with a blank sheet of paper. However, it is much easier to create a story if we first write down notes for the different parts of our story.

A. Create your own story by first developing its different parts.

Setting

Time: ______________________

Place: ______________________

Characters

Main: ______________________

Minor: ______________________

Plot

____

____

____

Conflict

____

____

____

Suspense

____

____

____

B. **Use what you have developed in (A) to write your story.**

Title: ______________________________

Date : ____________________

The Kiwi – a Fruit or a Bird?

Whenever someone mentions "kiwi", most of us would think of the fruit. Few of us would actually think of the bird, unless we have been to New Zealand.

As the national bird of New Zealand, the kiwi belongs to a now extinct order of birds called the moas. There are five kinds of kiwis and three are closely related: the Brown Kiwi, the Little Spotted Kiwi, and the Great Spotted Kiwi. The kiwi lives in forests, shrubs, and grasslands. Surprisingly, many New Zealanders have never seen their national bird because it is semi-nocturnal.

The kiwi is a flightless bird the size of a chicken, with two-inch wings and no tail. Covered in coarse and bristly feathers, this bird has a long slender bill with nostrils at the lower end, giving it an excellent sense of smell. Besides feeding on berries, leaves, and seeds, it also uses its flexible bill to dig up worms, insects, and grubs. Despite its awkward looks, the kiwi can outrun a human being, and can use its three-toe feet to kick and slash its enemies.

The female gives birth to one or two clutches of eggs either in natural holes or burrows. The size of the kiwi egg is approximately a quarter of its mother's weight. The male then takes over the job of incubating the eggs. Incubation can last about eleven weeks. The male loses weight during nest care because he does not leave except on occasion.

Upon hatching, the young kiwi already has adult plumage. The parents do not feed the babies because they still feed on the reserves of yolk in their own belly. The young leave the burrow after about six to ten days to search for food with their parents.

The kiwi's lifespan is about 20 years. It had no predators until the Maoris – aboriginal people of the New Zealand islands – arrived. As is the case with many other animal species, human beings became their predominant threat. Other factors that reduced the kiwi population include the destruction of habitats, pollution, and the introduction of predators not indigenous to New Zealand, such as opossums.

This bird is so valued in its native homeland that today, New Zealanders are known as "Kiwis". The bird emblem is found in the coats of arms, badges, and crests of many organizations in the country.

A. Find the missing sentence and write the correct letter on the line.

1. The female gives birth to one or two clutches of eggs. ______ The mother does not feed the young because the babies still feed on their reserves of yolk.

   A. The kiwi's lifespan is about 20 years.

   B. The male then takes over the job of incubating the eggs and nest care.

   C. The young leave the burrow after about six to ten days to search for food with the parents.

2. ______ Human beings then became their predominant threat. Factors such as pollution and habitat destruction also reduced the kiwi's population.

   A. The kiwi's lifespan is about 20 years.

   B. It uses its long bill to dig for worms, insects, and grubs.

   C. The kiwi had no natural predators until the Maoris arrived.

B. Circle the correct answers.

1. How is the kiwi different from most birds?

   A. It cannot fly.

   B. It cannot swim.

   C. It does not have feathers.

2. Most New Zealanders have never seen the kiwi because ______ .

   A. it runs off quickly

   B. it hides in the forests

   C. it is semi-nocturnal

3. Kiwis cannot fly because ______ .

   A. they have three toes

   B. they have a long bill

   C. they have short wings

C. Can you think of any similarities between kiwi the fruit and kiwi the bird? In what ways are they similar?

____

____

Date : ____________________

Writing a Poem

Rhyming Couplets

Some poems consist of lines with ending words that rhyme – that is, they consist of **rhyming couplets**.

Example: Humpty Dumpty sat on a wall,
Humpty Dumpty had a great fall.

A. Write in the missing words to complete the poem below.

An Old Children's Rhyme for Remembering the Parts of Speech

Every name is called a NOUN,
As *field* and *fountain*, *street* and ____________________ ;
In place of noun the PRONOUN stands,
As *he* and *she* can clap their ____________________ ;
The ADJECTIVE describes a thing,
As *magic wand* or *bridal* ____________________ ;
The VERB means action, something done –
To *read* and *write*, to *jump* and ____________________ ;
How things are done the ADVERBS tell,
As *quickly*, *slowly*, *badly*, ____________________ ;
The PREPOSITION shows relation,
As *in* the street or *at* the ____________________ ;
CONJUNCTIONS join, in many ways,
Sentences, words, *or* phrase *and* ____________________ ;
The INTERJECTION cries out, "*Hark*!
I need an exclamation ____________________ !"

Synonym Poems

A **synonym poem** contains the following:
- a title, which is the main idea
- a rhyming couplet
- a first line that contains three or more synonymous words

Example: Dance
Classic, modern, ballet, and tap
So many rehearsals, no time to nap

B. Create a synonym poem for each of the titles below. You may find a thesaurus useful for this exercise.

Summer

Christmas

Camping

Games

Date : ____________________

Vantage Vista

Nothing is more satisfying than a panoramic view. It is an eye-opening experience when you are viewing the landscape from a height.

Where do we find places higher than our surroundings?

We can see great views from locations that are natural or man-made. Natural viewing locations could be mountains, cliffs, rolling hills and ridges, tall trees, and escarpments. For example, the highest point in Ontario is Ishpatina Ridge. At 693 metres high, most adventurers would canoe, portage, hike, and climb up to the summit. Canoeing is peaceful, but portaging between lakes is hard work. Once the adventurers reach the base of the mountain, they would strike camp and hike up the mountain. If it is a steep mountain face to the vantage point, the adventurer would have to climb. It is an adventure just getting there. But the reward is a breathtaking view.

We find man-made viewing positions in tall buildings, the CN Tower, viewing platforms, and on aircraft such as hot-air balloons and airships. When viewing from an aircraft, the vantage point might be too high to see the detail of a landscape. We might only see checker-board shapes.

How high should we go so that we do not lose too much detail?

Some interesting man-made structures for viewing the scenic landscape are the old fire towers of northern Ontario. A few of them are still standing. Some have been repaired and made safer for visitors to climb, like the one in Temagami atop Caribou Mountain. When you reach the top of the tower in the cupola and look 360 degrees, the view is spectacular, a reward for the scary climb.

So adventurers, in order to get great views, be high enough to see far, but close enough to make out detail and contrast.

A. Answer the following questions.

1. What is the name of the highest point in Ontario?

2. How does one get to the highest point in Ontario?

3. How high is the highest point in Ontario?

4. What man-made structure is on top of Caribou Mountain?

5. Name some natural viewing locations.

B. The clues below refer to certain words in the passage. Find and use them to write sentences.

1. unbroken

2. steep slopes at edges of plateaus

3. raised level surfaces

4. highest point

Did You Know?

In 1982, Calgary native Laurie Skreslet became the first Canadian to reach the summit of Mount Everest. In 2003, he published a children's book about his life and his conquest of the world's tallest mountain.

Date : ____________________

Formal and Informal Writing

Formal Writing

A good example of formal writing is the **business letter**. It has a specific purpose and usually contains three paragraphs.

Paragraph 1 – states the purpose of your letter

Paragraph 2 – gives details of the subject of your letter

Paragraph 3 – suggests a course of action, offers a solution, or asks for follow-up

A. You have recently purchased a video game. Write a formal letter to the company to tell them how you like or dislike their product.

Formal salutation → Dear ____________________ :

First paragraph → ____________________

Second paragraph → ____________________

Third paragraph → ____________________

Formal closing → Yours truly,

____

Informal Writing

Informal writing does not have to follow precise rules of grammar. The sentence structure can be casual, and contractions are often used. We tend to write informally in postcards, notes, greeting cards, and e-mails.

Example: We all went skating at Orkus Skatepark. (formal)
Went skating at Orkus Skatepark. (informal)

B. Rewrite the following letter into an informal e-mail.

Dear Tina,

My family and I arrived in Montreal on Saturday. I am having a great time here! On Sunday, we all went skating at Orkus Skatepark, the largest indoor skatepark in Canada.

Although I have been here for only a few days, I am already talking to my cousins in French. They speak English too, but I am going to practise my French with them so that I can surprise Madame LeBlanc in the new year.

We will spend two days in Ottawa before coming back to Toronto. I hope all is well with you. I will write again soon.

Sincerely,

Chantal

. . . .

____

____

____

____

____

____

____

____

Date : ____________________

Some Common Errors

Confusing Words

Some words are easily confused because they have similar spellings or meanings.

Examples: I always seek Grandpa for advise. (✘)
I always seek Grandpa for advice. (✔)
There are five candy bars between all of us. (✘)
There are five candy bars among all of us. (✔)

A. Underline the correct word(s) for each of the following sentences.

1. Mr. Slean gives his dog a (bathe / bath) once a month.
2. An (oral / aural) exam is a test in listening.
3. Maggie enjoys (outdoor / outdoors) sports.
4. It looks like the bus (maybe / may be) late.
5. What is the (effect / affect) of putting salt on ice?
6. Leila took a deep (breathe / breath) before taking her first dive.
7. Cory always (looses / loses) things in the classroom.
8. The children were (already / all ready) for the principal's visit.
9. No one likes mustard (except / accept) Jason.
10. A speaking exam is an (oral / aural) exam.
11. I have a big closet in my room for my (clothes / cloths).
12. Canada is a country of many (immigrants / emigrants).
13. (Astronomy / Astrology) is the science of stars and planets.
14. The bride and groom stood at the church (alter / altar).

Misspelled Words

We often misspell certain words because there are too many exceptions to the rule in English spelling.

Examples: abundent (✘)
abundant (✔)
begining (✘)
beginning (✔)

B. Which of the following words are misspelled? Circle them and write the correct spelling on the lines.

1. acceptible ____________
2. edible ____________
3. acheive ____________
4. environment ____________
5. parallell ____________
6. wierd ____________
7. tobogan ____________
8. lettice ____________

C. Underline the correctly spelled word to complete each of the following sentences.

1. The changes in fashion trends are (becoming / becomming) a bore.
2. We need a new (vacum / vacuum) in the house.
3. The main (entrance / entrence) to the building is on the north side.
4. Sally wonders if it is (necessary / neccessary) to buy more food.
5. On the (twelfth / twelvth) day of Christmas, my friend sang to me.
6. There is a lot of (potatos / potatoes) in the kitchen.
7. How many lines of (symetry / symmetry) are there in a circle?
8. Billy ate a huge piece of (chocolate / chocalate) in his dream.

Date : ______________________

You Deserve A Break!

Amy, Brenda, Dylan, and Steve are playing a trivia game. Use the clue board on the right to answer the questions on the lines.

1. What is the name of the bird that can fly backward?
2. Which group of living things makes noise with their wings?
3. What is the fastest animal on six legs?
4. What word contains the same letters as "silent"?
5. Which are the only two animals that can see behind themselves?
6. What animal has 3000 teeth arranged in several rows?
7. What is the longest word in English with all its letters in alphabetical order?
8. What is the world's largest mammal?
9. What animal can use its tongue to clean its ears?
10. Which insect's name rhymes with "flutterby"?

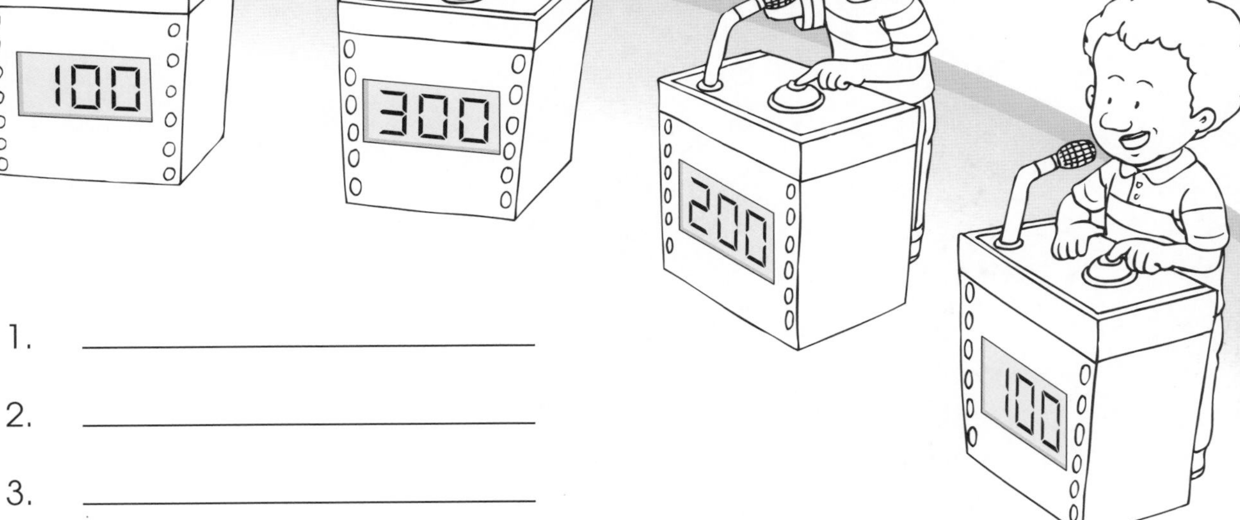

1. ______________________________

2. ______________________________

3. ______________________________

4. ______________________________

5. ______________________________

6. ______________________________

7. ______________________________

8. ______________________________

9. ______________________________

10. ______________________________

Assessment of MATHEMATICS

Grade

5

Check ✔ the letter which represents the correct answer in each problem.

① Sixty thousand sixty-three is ______ .

Ⓐ 6063 Ⓑ 60 063 Ⓒ 60 603 Ⓓ 6603

② What is the product of 0.036 x 100?

Ⓐ 360 Ⓑ 36 Ⓒ 3.6 Ⓓ 0.36

③ The remainder of $5\overline{)9463}$ is ______ .

Ⓐ 1 Ⓑ 2 Ⓒ 3 Ⓓ 4

④ Which of the following is not equal to 6 x 9 x 5?

Ⓐ 6 x 5 x 9 Ⓑ 9 x 6 x 5 Ⓒ 30 x 9 Ⓓ 45 x 5

⑤ What is the tenths digit in the product of 6.48 x 5?

Ⓐ 4 Ⓑ 3 Ⓒ 2 Ⓓ 0

⑥ Which of the following fractions is not equivalent to 1.5?

Ⓐ $1\frac{5}{100}$ Ⓑ $1\frac{50}{100}$ Ⓒ $1\frac{5}{10}$ Ⓓ $1\frac{1}{2}$

⑦ Which of the following 2-D shapes can make a tiling pattern?

Ⓐ Ⓑ Ⓒ Ⓓ

⑧ A triangle with 3 equal sides is a/an ______ triangle.

Ⓐ isosceles Ⓑ equilateral Ⓒ scalene Ⓓ right

⑨ A ______ has 8 vertices and 6 faces. 2 of its faces are rectangular in shape.

Ⓐ cube Ⓑ pyramid Ⓒ tetrahedron Ⓓ rectangular prism

⑩ ♥ in the multiplication sentence 12 x ♥ = 72 is ______ .

Ⓐ 6 Ⓑ 4 Ⓒ 3 Ⓓ 2

Do the calculation.

⑪ $\begin{array}{r} 37 \\ \times\ 49 \\ \hline \end{array}$	⑫ $9\overline{)8145}$	⑬ $\begin{array}{r} 6273 \\ 1028 \\ +\ 3761 \\ \hline \end{array}$	⑭ $6\overline{)5.1}$

⑮ 5.73 x 4 = ________	⑯ 7963 – 1206 = ________
⑰ 13.04 ÷ 8 = ________	⑱ 2.59 x 6 = ________
⑲ 0.67 + 7.49 = ________	⑳ 8.26 – 5.97 = ________

Complete the equivalent fractions or write the fractions in lowest terms.

㉑ $\frac{3}{8} = \frac{\quad}{24}$ ㉒ $\frac{2}{5} = \frac{12}{\quad}$ ㉓ $\frac{4}{7} = \frac{20}{\quad}$ ㉔ $\frac{6}{11} = \frac{\quad}{55}$

㉕ $\frac{6}{9} =$ ______ ㉖ $\frac{16}{56} =$ ______ ㉗ $\frac{15}{25} =$ ______ ㉘ $\frac{28}{48} =$ ______

Mr. Scott's class is allocated a small plot in the school yard for planting. Look at the plan and solve the problems.

Tomato	Tulip	Rose
Tomato	Pansy	Hydrangea

2 m

3 m

㉙ What is the area of the field? ________ m^2

㉚ What is the perimeter of the field? ________ m

㉛ If the field is divided into 6 equal portions, what fraction (in lowest terms) of the field is for tomatoes? ________

㉜ The children want to put lawn edging around the outside of the whole field and individual portions. How many metres of lawn edging are needed? ________ m

㉝ The children bought 6 pots of tomatoes for $2.64 each. How much did they pay in all? $ ________

㉞ They bought 8 pots of pansies for $9.12. How much did each pot of pansies cost? $ ________

Fill in the missing numbers.

35. The highest mountain in North America is 6.19 km high, 2650 m lower than Mount Everest, the highest mountain in the world. The height of Mount Everest is ________ km.

36. The average mass of a rhino is 3.56 t, about 2.83 t less than that of an elephant. The average mass of an elephant is ________ kg.

37. The tallest penguin in the world is about 1.2 m tall, about ________ cm shorter than a grown-up ostrich, which is 2.7 m tall.

38. The volume of a stone, which displaces 426 mL water when completely immersed, is ________ cm^3.

Draw the shapes and do the measurements.

39. Construct a triangle using the given point and straight line. ×	40. Use the given line to construct an angle of 135° with both arms of the angle equal to 3 cm. Then make a triangle. 3 cm
The measures of the 3 angles are ________________.	The length of the 3rd side of the triangle is ______ mm.

Name the 3-D figures. Then draw all the faces that make up each figure.

	3-D figure	Name	Faces
41			
42			

Mr. Scott's class is responsible for preparing drinks in the Games Day. Help the children solve the problems.

43. 5 servings of orange juice are made by mixing 1 cup of concentrated orange juice with 4 cups of water. Complete the chart.

Concentrated orange juice (no. of cups)	1	2	4	5	10
Water (no. of cups)	4				
No. of servings	5				

44. Describe the rule that relates the numbers in the 1st and 2nd rows in each column to that in the 3rd row.

____

45. How many cups of concentrated orange juice and cups of water are needed for making 200 servings?

________ cups of concentrated orange juice and ________ cups of water

Complete the following questions to find out the ribbon designed by the children for the winners.

46. Translate shape A 2 units right. Label the translation image B. Label the image of point Q by R.

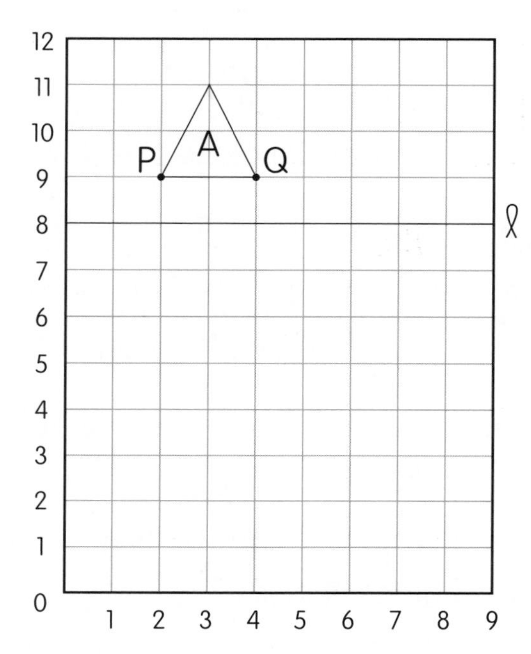

47. Reflect A and B over ℓ. Label the images C and D. Label the images of P and R by S and T.

48. Coordinates of S : (_____ , _____)

Coordinates of T : (_____ , _____)

49. Rotate A $\frac{1}{4}$ turn counterclockwise about (3,8). Label the image E.

50. Rotate B $\frac{1}{4}$ turn clockwise about (5,8). Label the image F.

51. Locate the following points on the grid.

L (2,0)   M (4,2)   N (6,0)

52. Join the points T → N → M → L → S.

Look at the records of 6 finalists in the 100-m race. Find the answers.

Records in seconds	21	20	23	21	21	23

53. What is the mean of the records? _______ seconds

54. What is the mode of the records? _______ seconds

The tally chart below shows the number of ribbons presented to the winners. Complete the bar graph to show the data and answer the questions. Remember to write fractions in lowest terms.

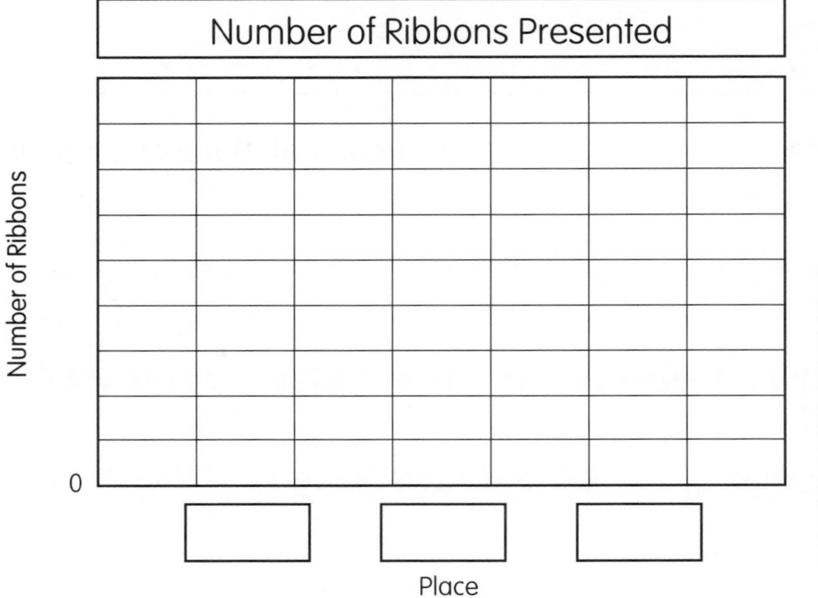

	No. of Ribbons
1st place	卌 卌 卌 卌 卌
2nd place	卌 卌 卌 卌 卌 卌
3rd place	卌 卌 卌 卌 卌 卌 卌 卌 卌

56. How many more children are awarded the 3rd place ribbon than the 1st place one? _____ more

57. How many children are awarded in all? _____ children

58. 10 girls get a 1st place ribbon. What is the probability of picking a girl from the 1st place winners? __________

59. 35 girls get the 2nd or 3rd place. What fraction of the winners are boys? __________

60. What is the probability of picking a boy from the 2nd or 3rd place winners? __________

61. The number of ribbons presented for different places are not the same. Give a reason.

____

Assessment of LANGUAGE

Grade

5

A. **Draw a line separating the complete subject from the complete predicate in each of the following sentences.**

1. The evening sun continued to warm the swimmers.
2. The children drew pictures of their families.
3. He collected spiders and other insects.
4. The colourful birds sang sweetly in the tropical trees.
5. They wondered what time it was.
6. My teacher did not allow us to refer to the book.

B. **Circle the transitive verbs and underline the intransitive verbs in the following sentences.**

1. The cute dog ran fast in the park yesterday.
2. Mom tells us a story every night before we go to bed.
3. Pansy has left her bag in the gym.
4. The fairy waved her wand and disappeared into thin air.
5. Baby Ginny giggles whenever we play this song.
6. Did you stay until the party ended?

C. **Complete the following sentences with adjectives and adverbs of your own.**

1. The ____________ kitten toyed ____________ with the spool of thread.
2. The ____________ child ____________ learned how to use the software.
3. The ____________ skater moved ____________ around the rink.
4. The ____________ fans cheered ____________ for the closing pitcher.
5. The ____________ musicians played the tune ____________ .
6. We ____________ reached the top of the ____________ building.

D. Complete the following sentences with suitable articles or conjunctions.

1. (An, A) ________ huge wave splashed against the shore.
2. They finished their work (and, but) ________ went out to play.
3. They tried the spicy food (but, and, or) ________ didn't like it.
4. Hand me (the, a, an) ________ book on my desk, please.
5. She tried to find the house with (an, a, the) ________ yellow door.
6. There is (a, the) ________ tool we've been looking for all day.
7. We will either go for a bike ride (but, if, or) ________ we will go for a swim.
8. (A, the) ________ Mr. Watson would like to have (a, the) ________ word with you.

E. Underline the subordinating conjunction in each sentence below that joins the dependent clause and the independent clause.

1. Whenever a stranger comes to the door, her dog barks.
2. He will be late for school unless he gets a ride.
3. If he tries very hard, he will succeed.
4. The artist painted the scenery because he thought it was beautiful.
5. She won the race even though she stumbled at the start.
6. However hard he tried, he could not open the lid.

F. Identify each sentence as compound or complex.

(A) After he finished school, he went to work at the hardware store.

(B) The school group went on a class trip and visited the zoo.

(C) All students had to write a test unless they were in grade six.

(D) They took turns trying but no one was able to solve the problem.

(E) When you pass by the shop, please buy a newspaper for me.

Compound Sentence

Complex Sentence

G. Combine each group of short sentences into one longer sentence. Use conjunctions or create compound sentences.

1. They played soccer. They played in the park. They played on Monday nights

   ____

2. He bought inline skates. He tried inline skating yesterday.

   ____

3. The cars were lined up. Traffic was heavy. The traffic was on the highway.

   ____

4. The swimming pool was crowded. They went to the pool. They couldn't get into the pool.

   ____

   ____

H. Complete each of the following sentences with appropriate pronouns.

1. The students were told that __________ had to stay after school.
2. We were asked to talk about __________ vacation.
3. He was repairing __________ bicycle.
4. When John and Richard left, no one saw __________ leave.
5. All the students ate __________ lunch in the cafeteria.
6. Susan, Tricia, and Paula took __________ books to the library.

I. Complete the sentences below with suitable relative pronouns.

1. The girl __________ we met at the theatre is my cousin.
2. This is the book __________ everyone is reading this summer.
3. The friends __________ came to the party brought gifts.
4. The coat __________ is still hanging in the closet belongs to Martha.
5. This is the place __________ my dad works.
6. The cake __________ you ate just then was made by Janet.

J. Underline the direct object in each sentence below.

1. The goalie stopped the puck on the goal line.
2. Their grandfather told them stories of the old days.
3. The birds built a nest in the tree.
4. After the snowstorm, they shovelled piles of snow.

K. Circle the objects in the prepositional phrases in the sentences below.

1. They waited under the tree to avoid the hot sun.
2. In the hallway stood the students who were late for school.
3. The wind on the water was refreshing for the boaters.
4. The car in the ditch was being pulled out by a tow truck.
5. The leader of the group gave directions to the museum.

L. Underline the indirect objects in the sentences below.

1. He gave him some very good advice.
2. She asked her teacher some questions about the project.
3. He bought his mother a big birthday cake.
4. She fed them hot dogs and hamburgers for lunch.
5. They asked us the directions but we said we didn't know the right way to go.

M. State whether each underlined verbal is a gerund, a participle, or an infinitive.

1. Riding a horse is fun but not easy. ____________
2. His computer was excellent for playing games. ____________
3. You shouldn't touch the boiling water. ____________
4. He will find a way to solve the problem. ____________
5. He used a riding lawn mower because the lawn was so large. ____________
6. He asked to ride his bicycle to the store instead of walking. ____________

N. Change the following sentence fragments to complete sentences.

1. Walking home from school

____

____

2. During the afternoon

____

____

3. Whenever we get the chance

____

____

4. If the bus is gone

____

____

5. Since I woke up this morning

____

____

6. With the teacher's permission

____

____

1 Numbers to 100 000 (1)

1A. 53 840 ; Fifty-three thousand eight hundred forty
B. 25 207 ; Twenty-five thousand two hundred seven
2. 20 400 3. 30 010 4. 16 720
5. 43 205 6. 82 016 7. 90 562
8. 20 000 ; 70 9. 7000 + 600 + 80 + 9
10. 60 000 + 8000 + 200 + 30 + 7
11. 50 000 + 9000 + 100 + 60 + 4
12. 2 ten thousands 13. 8 thousands
14. 7 hundreds 15. 5 ten thousands
16. 3 ones 17. 8 tens
18. 4 ten thousands 19. 5 hundreds
20. 46 000 ; 47 000 ; 48 000 ; 51 000 ; 52 000 ; 56 000 ; 57 000 ; 59 000 ; 60 000 ; 63 000 ; 64 000 ; 67 000 ; 68 000
21. 15 035 ; 16 036 ; 17 037 ; 19 039 ; 22 042 ; 23 043 ; 25 045 ; 27 047

2 Numbers to 100 000 (2)

1. 35 631 2. 65 479 3. 20 816
4. 60 000 5. 89 427 6. 71 654
7. 65 479, 76 549, 94 657 8. 31 004, 32 011, 32 068
9-12. (Suggested answers)
9. 27 000 10. 83 000
11. 43 750 12. 75 000
13. 73 999 14. 25 000 15. 2
16. 44 096 17. 76 833
18-19. (Suggested answers)
18. 20 045 ; 20 054 ; 20 504 ; 20 540 ; 24 500 ; 25 400
19. 20 358 ; 20 385 ; 20 835 ; 20 853 ; 28 350 ; 28 530
20. 19 000 21. 27 000 22. 34 000
23. 88 000 24. 39 000 25. 30 000
26. 95 000 27. 86 000 28. 70 000
29. 30 000 30. 90 000

3 Counting by 11's and 12's

1. Circle every 11 bees. ; 11 ; 22 ; 33 ; 44 ; 55 ; 66 ; 77 ; 88 ; 99
2. Circle every 12 bees. ; 12 ; 24 ; 36 ; 48 ; 60 ; 72 ; 84 ; 96 ; 108
3.
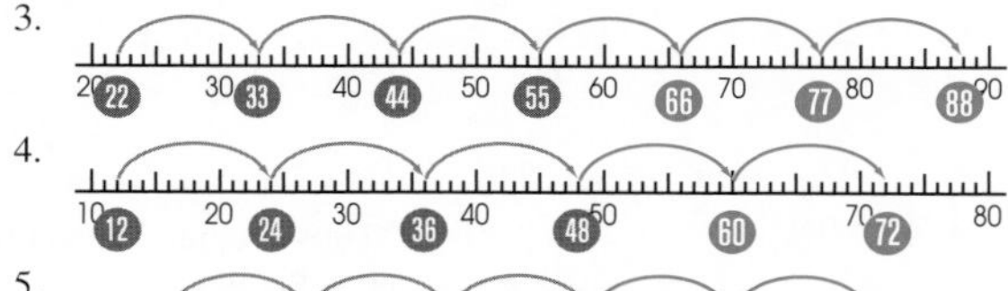

4.
5.

6.
7. 8.
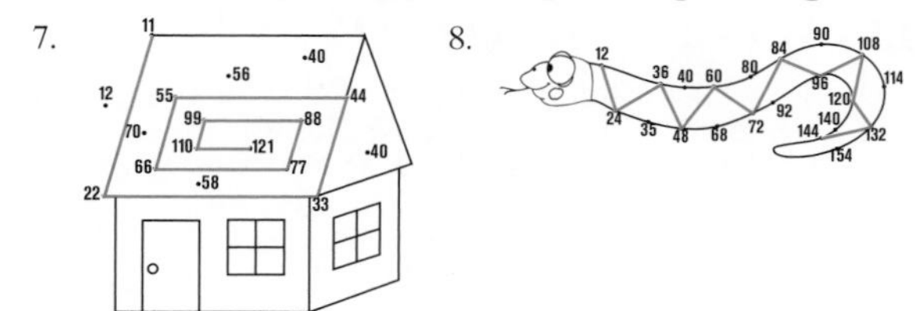

4 Addition & Subtraction of 4-Digit Numbers (1)

1. 4937 2. 4391 3. 4208
4. 2135 5. 8196 6. 1135
7. 7392 8. 1712 9. 3663
10. 3840 11. 2905 12. 6868
13. 2547 − 1642 = 905
14. 8635 − 2594 = 6041
15. 1564 + 2345 = 3909
16. 3069 + 1652 = 4721
17. 1008 − 945 = 63
18. 2441 + 5477 = 7918

19a. 2450 + 2450 ; 4900 ; 4900
b. 2450 – 1090 ; 1360 ; 1360
20a. 988 + 1480 ; 2468 ; 2468
b. 1480 – 379 ; 1101 ; 1101
21a. 4360 – 2665 ; 1695 ; 1695
b. 4360 + 4360 ; 8720 ; 8720
22a. 2800 – 353 ; 2447 ; 2447
b. 2800 – 280 ; 2520 ; 2520

5 Addition & Subtraction of 4-Digit Numbers (2)

1. 5361 ; 5361 − 1837 = 3524
2. 6805 ; 6805 − 3988 = 2817
3. 3879 ; 3879 – 1793 = 2086
4. 4210 ; 4210 – 986 = 3224
5. 5163 ; 5163 – 3869 = 1294
6. 5643 ; 5643 – 827 = 4816
7. 4511 ; 4511 – 2563 = 1948
8. 6645 ; 6645 – 2579 = 4066
9. 2200 ; 3022 10. 3266 ; 2095
11. 8400 12. 5690 13. 2695
14. 3531 15. 3942 16. 1996
17. 1624 mL 18. 3948 cm 19. 7367 apples

6 Multiplication of 2-Digit Numbers

1. 18 x 46 : 108 ; 720 ; 828
2. 47 x 25 : 235 ; 940 ; 1175
3. 23 x 17 : 161 ; 230 ; 391
4. 54 x 32 : 108 ; 1620 ; 1728
5. 345 6. 1044
7. 1216 8. 2244
9. 945 10. 324
11. 50 ; 30 ; 1500 12. 30 x 70 = 2100
13. 40 x 60 = 2400 14. 40 x 20 = 800
15. 36 x 25 : 180 ; 720 ; 900 ; 900
16. 12 x 14 : 48 ; 120 ; 168 ; 168
17. 46 x 38 : 368 ; 1380 ; 1748 ; 1748
18. 97 x 12 : 194 ; 970 ; 1164 ; 1164
19. 16 x 33 : 48 ; 480 ; 528 ; 528
20. 18 x 45 : 90 ; 720 ; 810 ; 810

7 Distributive Property of Multiplication

1. 3 ; 60 ; 3 ; 480 ; 24 ; 504
2. 2 ; 100 ; 2 ; 700 ; 14 ; 686
3. 80 ; 1 ; 80 ; 1 ; 320 ; 4 ; 324
4. 80 ; 3 ; 80 ; 3 ; 720 ; 27 ; 693
5. 90 ; 1 ; 90 ; 1 ; 540 ; 6 ; 534
6. 9 x (40 + 8) = 9 x 40 + 9 x 8 = 360 + 72 = 432
7. (90 + 2) x 7 = 90 x 7 + 2 x 7 = 630 + 14 = 644
8. (70 – 3) x 5 = 70 x 5 – 3 x 5 = 350 – 15 = 335
9. (50 + 3) x 8 = 50 x 8 + 3 x 8 = 400 + 24 = 424
10. (80 – 4) x 2 = 80 x 2 – 4 x 2 = 160 – 8 = 152
11. 3 x (100 – 1) = 3 x 100 – 3 x 1 = 300 – 3 = 297
12-15. (Individual answers for checking the circles)
12A. 99 x 12 : 198 ; 990 ; 1188
B. = 12 x (100 – 1)
= 1200 – 12
= 1188
13A. 71 x 21 : 71 ; 1420 ; 1491
B. = 21 x (70 + 1)
= 1470 + 21
= 1491

14A.
```
  58 ;
x 16
 348
 580
 928
```
B. = (60 – 2) x 16
= 960 – 32
= 928

15A.
```
  98 ;
x 32
 196
2940
3136
```
B. = (100 – 2) x 32
= 3200 – 64
= 3136

8 Dividing 4-Digit Numbers (1)

1.
```
  1637R1
2)3275
  2
  12
  12
    7
    6
    15
    14
     1
```
2.
```
   677R1
9)6094
  54
   69
   63
    64
    63
     1
```
3.
```
  1458R3
5)7293
  5
  22
  20
   29
   25
    43
    40
     3
```
4.
```
   774R3
7)5421
  49
   52
   49
    31
    28
     3
```
5.
```
   777R2
6)4664
  42
   46
   42
    44
    42
     2
```
6. 1002 7. 476R5 8. 1944R3
9. 868 10. 822 11. 2045R1
12. 1181R6 13. 1253R5
14. ✔ ; 358 x 8 = 2864 ; 2864 + 2 = 2866
15. ✘ ; 1068R2 ; 1068 x 4 = 4272 ; 4272 + 6 = 4278
16. ✔ ; 545 x 7 = 3815 ; 3815 + 1 = 3816
17. ✔ ; 4329 x 2 = 8658 ; 8658 + 1 = 8659
18. ✘ ; 1675R2 ; 1676 x 3 = 5028 ; 5028 + 1 = 5029
19. ✘ ; 651R2 ; 650 x 6 = 3900 ; 3900 + 3 = 3903
20. 1456 ;
a. 1456 ÷ 7 ; 208 ; 208 b. 1456 ÷ 8 ; 182 ; 182
21. 4760 g ; 4760 ÷ 5 ; 952 ; 952

9 Dividing 4-Digit Numbers (2)

1.
```
     61R11
42)2573
   252
    53
    42
    11
```
2.
```
     123
28)3444
   28
    64
    56
     84
     84
```
3.
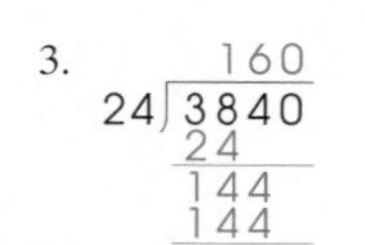
```
     160
24)3840
   24
   144
   144
```
4.
```
      76R14
60)4574
   420
    374
    360
     14
```
5. 50R63 6. 112 7. 167
8. 77R17 9. 93 10. 103R29
11.
```
     68R43
53)3647
   318
    467
    424
     43
```
12.
```
     75R20
48)3620
   336
    260
    240
     20
```
13. 77R8 ; 7200 ÷ 90 = 80
14. 143R30 ; 6900 ÷ 50 = 138
15. 135R21 ; 5000 ÷ 40 = 125
16. 3429 ÷ 25 ; 137R4 ; 137 ; 4
17. 4446 ÷ 38 ; 117 ; 117
18a. 1000 ÷ 56 ; 17R48 ; 17 ; 48
b. 3000 ÷ 75 ; 40 ; 40

10 Solving Problems Involving Division

1. 3565 ÷ 31 ; 115 ; 115 2. 1024 ÷ 4 ; 256 ; 256
3. 2000 ÷ 8 ; 250 ; 250 4. 6000 ÷ 75 ; 80 ; 80
5. 1000 ÷ 39 ; 25R25 ; 25 ; 25
6. 1288 ÷ 12 ; 107R4 ; 107 ; 4
7. 5000 ÷ 98 ; 51R2 ; 52
8. 1008 ÷ 8 ; 126 ; 126
9. 1250 ÷ 48 ; 26R2 ; 26 ; 2

11 Multiplication and Division

1. 83 2. 1024 3. 3608
4. 7 5. 25 6. 3976
7. 48 ; 25 ; 1200 ; 1200 ; 25 ; 48
8. 74 ; 24 ; 1776 ; 1776 ; 24 ; 74
9. 82 ; 35 ; 2870 ; 2870 ; 35 ; 82
10. 9 ; 155 ; 1395 ; 1395 ; 155 ; 9
11a. 8 b. 2456
12a. 45 b. 810
13. 671R2 14. 2278 15. 254R4
16. 676 17. 135R13 18. 2520
19. 1178 20. 278R10 21. 74R11
22. 1652 23. 227R2 24. 495
25. 1248 26. 2538 27. 167R3
28. 82R37 29. 291R7 30. 2116
31. 1633 32. 403R4

12 Word Problems

1. 15 x 92 ; 1380 ; 1380 2. 1038 ÷ 3 ; 346 ; 346
3. 2034 ÷ 9 ; 226 ; 226 4. 45 x 12 ; 540 ; 540
5. 18 x 45 ; 810 ; 810 6.
```
     145 ; 145
16)2320
   16
    72
    64
     80
     80
```
7. 75 men ;
```
  69
x 12
 138
 690
 828
```
; The owner needs to buy 828 roses.

8. 576 muffins ;
```
    126
8)1008
  8
  20
  16
   48
   48
```
; She needs 126 boxes.

9. 3500 mL ;
```
     21R5
95)2000
   190
    100
     95
      5
```
; 22 cups are needed to hold all the apple juice.

13 Two-step Problems (1)

1. 15 x 26 ; 390 ; 390 + 79 ; 469 ; 469
2. 225 x 3 ; 675 ; 675 – 308 ; 367 ; 367
3. 1120 ÷ 5 ; 224 ; 224 + 39 ; 263 ; 263
4. 16 x 3 ; 48 ; 48 + 25 ; 73 ; 73
5. 75 ÷ 3 ; 25 ; 25 – 9 ; 16 ; 16
6. 435 – 286 ; 149 ; 149 x 9 ; 1341 ; 1341
7. 2814 ÷ 2 ; 1407 ; 1407 x 3 ; 4221 ; 4221

14 Two-step Problems (2)

1. x ; 1455 ; 1455 ; – ; 1129 ; 1129
2. ÷ ; 32 ; 32 ; x ; 512 ; 512
3. x ; 2 ; 236 ; 236 ; + ; 354 ; 354
4. + ; 458 ; 1285 ; 1285 ; ÷ ; 257 ; 257
5. No. of eggs at first ; 34 x 12 = 408 ;
No. of eggs left ; 408 – 59 = 349 ; 349
6. Capacity of half-filled tank ; 1195 – 345 = 850 ;
Capacity of full tank ; 850 x 2 = 1700 ; 1700
7. Monthly savings ; 2680 – 2480 = 200 ;
Time needed ; 1800 ÷ 200 = 9 ; 9
8. No. of cookies in all ; 456 + 126 = 582 ;
No. of cookies in each bag ; 582 ÷ 6 = 97 ; 97 ; 6

15 Standard Units for Lengths

1. km 2. mm 3. m
4. dm 5. km 6. cm
7. 4000 8. 4 9. 3
10. 5 11. 50 12. 2
13. 0.4 14. 8 15. <
16. > 17. < 18. <
19. < 20. >
21.

A: 4 cm, 3 cm, 5 cm
B: 5 cm, 5 cm, 4 cm
C: 3 cm, 3 cm, 3 cm
D: 6 cm, 5 cm, 2.5 cm

a. A, B b. B, D
22A. 18.8 cm ; 6 cm B. 12.6 cm ; 4 cm C. 22 cm ; 7 cm

16 Time (1)

1A. 8 ; 09
B. Sept 26, 2005 ; 2005 09 26
C. Jan 5, 2007 ; 2007 01 05
D. Jan 16, 2007 ; 2007 01 16
E. Apr 17, 2008 ; 2008 04 17
F. Apr 20, 2008 ; 2008 04 20
G. May 8, 2010 ; 2010 05 08
2. 11 3. 12
4. 23 5. 9
6A. 6:45:14 B. 7:38:55 C. 1:03:18
D. 11:25:42 E. 6:14:29 F. 3:19:48
G. 12:55:22 H. 5:08:52
7. 8. 9. 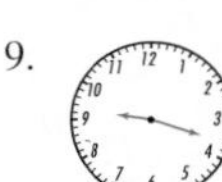
10. 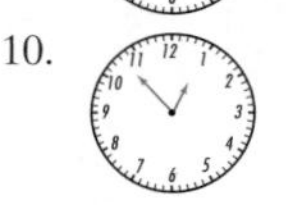 11.  12. 

17 Review

1-3. (Suggested answers for the numbers in between)
1. 97653 ; 63975 ; 35679 2. 98610 ; 68109 ; 10689
3. 65432 ; 45632 ; 23456 4. 7022
5. 1668 6. 1477 7. 2742

8.
```
  39
x 46
 234
1560
1794
```
9.
```
  54
x 73
 162
3780
3942
```
10.
```
  408R2
9)3674
  36
    74
    72
     2
```
11.
```
  1701R3
4)6807
  4
  28
  28
     7
     4
     3
```
12. 4555 13. 1689 14. 2262
15. 3760 16. 2304 17. 424R13
18. 952 19. 444R6
20. 55 ; 66 ; 77 ; 99 21. 36 ; 48 ; 84 ; 96
22. 76 + 68 ; 144 ; 144 x 8 ; 1152 ; 1152
23. 1275 ÷ 15 ; 85 ; 85
24. 1250 + 982 ; 2232 ; 2232 ÷ 2 ; 1116 ; 1116
25. 1:37:46 26. 5:26:13 27. 12:48:05
28. 29. 30.

18 You Deserve A Break!

1a. 1 ; 792 b. 100 ; 4 ; 936 c. 2 ; 348
2.
```
   127          126
8)1016   ;   9)1134   ; Check B
  8             9
  21            23
  16            18
   56            54
   56            54
```
3. Total no. of treats: 85 x 12 = 1020 ;
No. of days: 1020 ÷ 15 = 68 ;
Mario's treats will last 68 days.
4a. 16 b. 1564
c. 44 d. 1575
5a. 94 000 ; 38 000 ; 89 000 ; 60 000 ; 52 000
b. 90 000 ; 20 000 ; 30 000 ; 80 000 ; 60 000
6. May 3, 2006 ; 2006 05 03 ; May 12, 2006 ; 2006 05 12 ; 8:27:56

19 Time (2)

1A.
```
  9:18:19  (17 79)
- 9:15:47
  0:02:32
```
2 min 32 s ;

B.
```
  8:32:15  (31 75)
- 7:31:46
  1:00:29
```
1 h 29 s ;

C.
```
  12:09:34  (11 69)
- 11:27:31
   0:42:03
```
42 min 3 s ;

D.
```
  3:36:05  (35 65)
- 2:26:26
  1:09:39
```
1 h 9 min 39 s

2. 48 min 31 s 3. 10 min 25 s 4. 2 h 58 min 22 s
5. 1 h 10 min 38 s 6. 4 h 16 min 7. 8 h 17 min
8. 2 h 42 min 9. 1 h 8 min 10. 3 h 2 min
11. 3 h 7 min 12. 4 h 13 min 13. 3 h 38 min
14. Lisa 15. Sue 16. 10:19 a.m.
17. 11:28 a.m. 18. 6:02 p.m. 19. 5:07 p.m.
20. 4:23 p.m. 21. 11:17 p.m. 22. 7:52 a.m.
23. 10:18 a.m.

20 Speed

1. 45 ÷ 9 ; 5 2. 24 ÷ 8 ; 3 3. 255 ÷ 3 ; 85
4. 140 ÷ 4 ; 35 5. 1980 ÷ 9 ; 220 6. 3
7. 2 8. 4
9a. 68 b. 80 c. 189
10. 68 ÷ 2 = 34 ; 34
11. 189 ÷ 3 = 63 ; His average speed is 63 km/h.
12. Distance: 80 x 2 x 5 = 800 ; Speed: 800 ÷ 10 = 80 ; His average speed is 80 km/h.

21 Perimeters of Polygons

1.

A: 45 mm, 45 mm, 45 mm, 45 mm
B: 22 mm, 30 mm, 30 mm, 22 mm
C: 26 mm, 52 mm, 52 mm, 26 mm
D: 60 mm, 63 mm, 47 mm
E: 25 mm, 31 mm, 35 mm, 52 mm
F: 17 mm, 17 mm, 17 mm, 17 mm, 17 mm, 17 mm

	Perimeter
A	180 mm
B	104 mm
C	156 mm
D	170 mm
E	143 mm
F	102 mm

2. 8 km
3. 48 m ; 288 m 4. 125 cm ; 1000 cm
5. Perimeter: 3 + 4 + 5 = 12 ; 12 cm

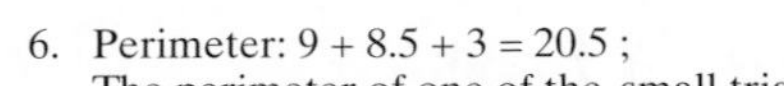

6. Perimeter: 9 + 8.5 + 3 = 20.5 ;
   The perimeter of one of the small triangles is 20.5 cm.
7. Perimeter: 4 + 4 + 4 + 4 = 16 ;
   The perimeter of the square is 16 cm.

22 Perimeters of Irregular Polygons

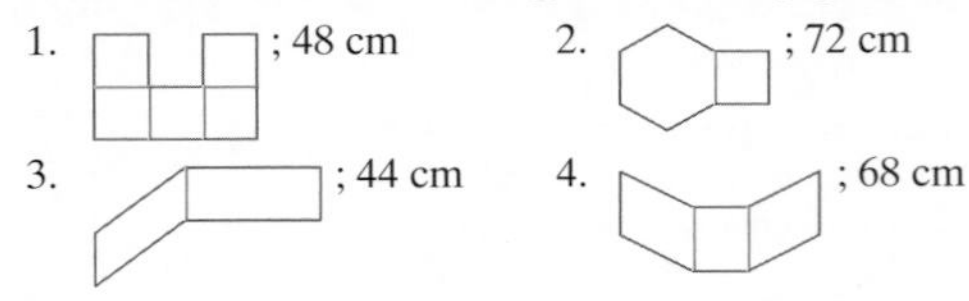

1. ; 48 cm 2. ; 72 cm
3. ; 44 cm 4. ; 68 cm
5. 76 cm 6. 70 cm 7. 70 cm
8. 58 cm 9. 46 – 7 – 12 – 12 = 15 ; 15 cm
10. 5 + 7 + 5 + 7 + 5 + 7 + 5 + 7 = 48 ;
    The perimeter of the flower is 48 cm.
11. 13 + 13 + 13 + 12 + 5 = 56 ;
    The perimeter of the irregular shape is 56 cm.

23 Perimeters of Rectangles and Squares

1A. 4 x 26 = 104 (cm) B. 2 x 18 + 2 x 14 = 64 (cm)
C. 2 x 42 + 2 x 28 = 140 (m) D. 2 x 64 + 2 x 30 = 188 (cm)
E. 4 x 19 = 76 (m) F. 2 x 72 + 2 x 25 = 194 (mm)
G. 2 x 45 + 2 x 12 = 114 (cm)
2A. 20 cm B. 56 m C. 16 km
D. 7 cm E. 18 m F. 34 cm
3A. 26 cm B. 66 m C. 90 m
D. 25 cm E. 9 m F. 32 mm
4. 2 x 45 + 2 x 35 ; 160 ; 160 cm
5. 32 ÷ 4 ; 8 ; 8 cm
6. 84 ÷ 2 – 16 ; 26 ; 26 cm
7. 2 x 12 + 2 x 16 ; 56 ; 56 cm

24 Areas of Polygons

1.

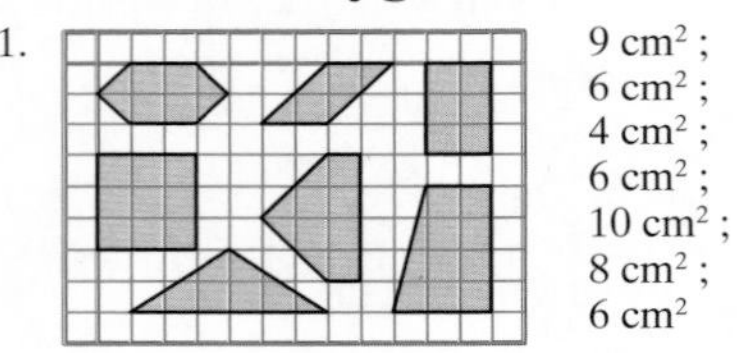

9 cm^2 ;
6 cm^2 ;
4 cm^2 ;
6 cm^2 ;
10 cm^2 ;
8 cm^2 ;
6 cm^2

2. Trapezoid 3. Parallelogram
4. Triangle, Rectangle, Hexagon
5. 24 cm^2
6. Triangle: 32 cm^2 ; Parallelogram: 24 cm^2 ;
   Hexagon: 12 cm^2 ; Trapezoid: 42 cm^2

7-9. (Suggested answers)

7. 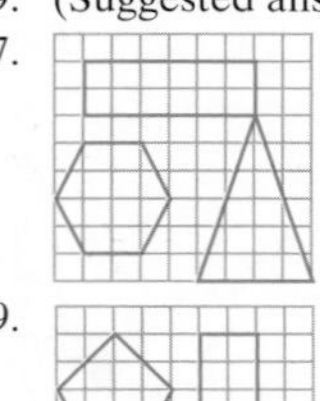

8. 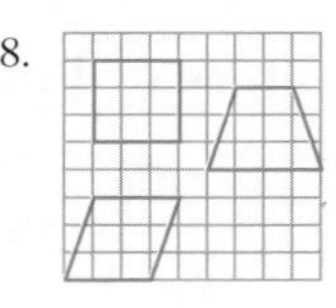

9.

25 Areas of Irregular Polygons

1A. 12 cm^2 B. 9 cm^2
C. 10 cm^2 D. 10 cm^2
2. A ; B
3. A ;
4. 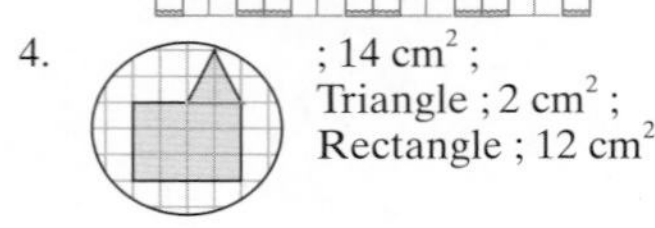
   ; 14 cm^2 ;
   Triangle ; 2 cm^2 ;
   Rectangle ; 12 cm^2

5. ; 8 cm^2 ;
   Square ; 4 cm^2 ;
   Parallelogram ; 4 cm^2
6. ; 12 cm^2 ;
   Trapezoid ; 6 cm^2 ;
   Hexagon ; 6 cm^2
7. Area: 10 cm^2 ; 11 cm^2 ; 13 cm^2 ; 16 cm^2
   Perimeter: 16 cm ; 16 cm ; 16 cm ; 16 cm
8. No 9. No

26 Areas of Rectangles and Squares

1. 9 x 9 ; 81 (cm^2) 2. 16 x 10 ; 160 (cm^2)
3. 48 x 36 ; 1728 (cm^2) 4. 12 x 12 ; 144 (m^2)
5. 16 x 16 ; 256 (mm^2) 6. 4 x 2 ; 8 (m^2)
7. 22 x 28 ; 616 (cm^2)
8A. 126 cm^2 B. 195 cm^2 C. 1098 cm^2
D. 477 cm^2 E. 96 m^2 F. 92 cm^2
9a. 29 ; 22 b. 638

27 Volume (1)

1A. 35 cm^3 B. 41 cm^3 C. 19 cm^3
D. 26 cm^3 E. 16 cm^3
2. B 3. C and E 4. 19
5. 585 cm^3 ; 640 cm^3 ; 500 cm^3 ; Check B
6. 560 cm^3 ; 400 cm^3 ; 630 cm^3 ; Check C
7. 540 cm^3 ; 400 cm^3 ; 500 cm^3 ; Check A
8. 24 cm^3 ; 48 cm^3 ; 1000 cm^3

28 Volume (2)

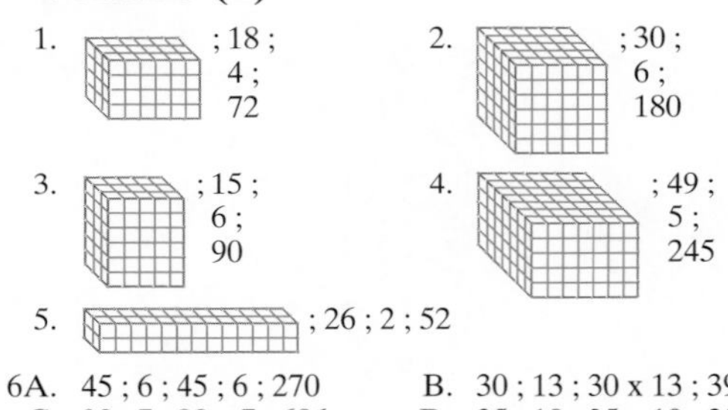

1. ; 18 ; 4 ; 72 2. ; 30 ; 6 ; 180
3. ; 15 ; 6 ; 90 4. ; 49 ; 5 ; 245
5. ; 26 ; 2 ; 52
6A. 45 ; 6 ; 45 ; 6 ; 270 B. 30 ; 13 ; 30 x 13 ; 390
C. 98 ; 7 ; 98 x 7 ; 686 D. 35 ; 10 ; 35 x 10 ; 350
E. 108 ; 4 ; 108 x 4 ; 432
7. 2970 cm^3 8. 99

29 Relating Volume and Capacity (1)

1. 15 000 2. 50 3. 56 000
4. 72 5. 84 6. A
7. B 8. A 9. A
10.

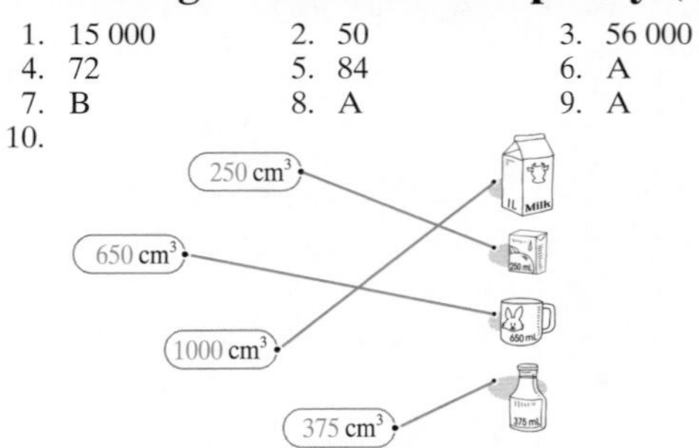

11. 4000 cm^3 12. 12 boxes 13. 150 mL

30 Relating Volume and Capacity (2)

1. 400 cm^3 ; 500 cm^3 ; 2400 cm^3 ; 600 cm^3 ; 4500 cm^3 ; 300 cm^3
2a. 120 cm^3 3a. 150 cm^3
b. b.

4. 400 cm^3 ; 200 cm^3 5. 1000 cm^3 ; 400 cm^3
6. 1050 cm^3 ; 200 cm^3

31 Mass (1)

1. kg 2. g 3. mg
4. t 5. t 6. kg
7. 3000 8. 6 9. 0.032
10. 2.5 11. 0.009 12. 0.886
13. 4000 14. 0.46 15. 2500
16. 1040 17. 0.068 ; 68
18. 0.48 ; 480 000 19. 0.0024 ; 2400
20. 0.0649 ; 64 900 21. 0.065 ; 65 000
22. 0.00109 ; 1090 23. D ; B ; A ; C
24. A ; C ; B ; D 25. A ; D ; C ; B ; E

32 Mass (2)

1. 600 ; 154 ; About 4 baseballs
2. 6200 ; 150 050 ; About 24 elephants
3. 0.42 ; 400 ; 950 4. 2.018 ; 0.645 ; 3
5A. 1200 ; 1.2 B. 8500 ; 8.5 C. 3000 ; 3
6. C 7. A 8. B

33 Improper Fractions and Mixed Numbers

1. $\frac{11}{6}$; $1\frac{5}{6}$ 2. $\frac{5}{2}$; $2\frac{1}{2}$ 3. $\frac{10}{3}$; $3\frac{1}{3}$
4. $\frac{11}{4}$; $2\frac{3}{4}$
5. $10 \div 3 = 3 \text{ R } 1$ (3)10, 9, 1 ; $3\frac{1}{3}$
6. $12 \div 7 = 1 \text{ R } 5$ (7)12, 7, 5 ; $1\frac{5}{7}$
7. $17 \div 5 = 3 \text{ R } 2$ (5)17, 15, 2 ; $3\frac{2}{5}$
8. $25 \div 9 = 2 \text{ R } 7$ (9)25, 18, 7 ; $2\frac{7}{9}$
9. 3 ; $\frac{12+2}{3}$; = $\frac{14}{3}$
10. $\frac{2 \times 5 + 4}{5} = \frac{10 + 4}{5} = \frac{14}{5}$
11. $\frac{1 \times 7 + 3}{7} = \frac{7 + 3}{7} = \frac{10}{7}$
12. $\frac{3 \times 6 + 5}{6} = \frac{18 + 5}{6} = \frac{23}{6}$
13. $\frac{2 \times 4 + 3}{4} = \frac{8 + 3}{4} = \frac{11}{4}$
14a. $\frac{6}{5}$; $1\frac{1}{5}$ b. $\frac{6}{4}$; $1\frac{2}{4}$ ($1\frac{1}{2}$)
15a. $\frac{5}{2}$; $2\frac{1}{2}$ b. $\frac{5}{3}$; $1\frac{2}{3}$

34 Equivalent Fractions

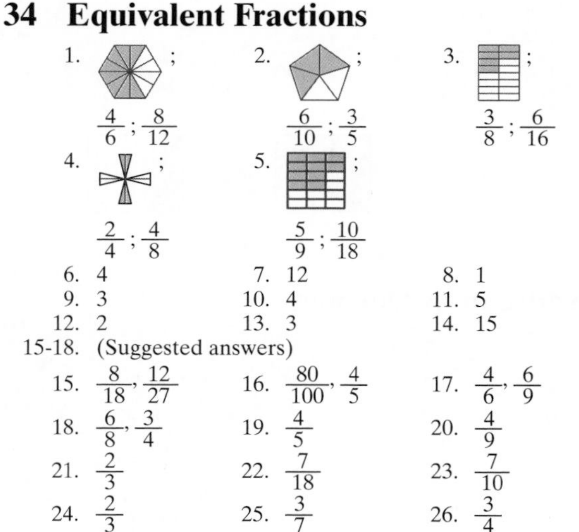

1. $\frac{4}{6}$; $\frac{8}{12}$ 2. $\frac{6}{10}$; $\frac{3}{5}$ 3. $\frac{3}{8}$; $\frac{6}{16}$
4. $\frac{2}{4}$; $\frac{4}{8}$ 5. $\frac{5}{9}$; $\frac{10}{18}$
6. 4 7. 12 8. 1
9. 3 10. 4 11. 5
12. 2 13. 3 14. 15
15-18. (Suggested answers)
15. $\frac{8}{18}$, $\frac{12}{27}$ 16. $\frac{80}{100}$, $\frac{4}{5}$ 17. $\frac{4}{6}$, $\frac{6}{9}$
18. $\frac{6}{8}$, $\frac{3}{4}$ 19. $\frac{4}{5}$ 20. $\frac{4}{9}$
21. $\frac{2}{3}$ 22. $\frac{7}{18}$ 23. $\frac{7}{10}$
24. $\frac{2}{3}$ 25. $\frac{3}{7}$ 26. $\frac{3}{4}$
27. $\frac{19}{22}$ 28. $\frac{6}{8}$, $\frac{5}{14}$ 29. $\frac{9}{20}$, $\frac{2}{3}$
30. $\frac{3}{4}$, $\frac{14}{20}$ 31. $\frac{13}{40}$, $\frac{4}{5}$

35 Review

1. 20 cm ; 21 cm^2 2. 20 m ; 14 m^2
3. 18 x 4 = 72 (mm) ; 18 x 18 = 324 (mm^2)
4. 2 x 4 + 2 x 10 = 8 + 20 = 28 (cm) ; 4 x 10 = 40 (cm^2)
5. 28 ÷ 2 – 9 = 14 – 9 = 5 (m) ; 9 x 5 = 45 (m^2)
6. 20 ÷ 4 = 5 (cm) ; 5 x 5 = 25 (cm^2)
7. 5:51:42 – 5:27:16 = 0:24:26 ; 24 min 26 s
8. 3:27:35 – 2:19:54 = 1:07:41 ; 1 h 7 min 41 s
9. 9:34:00 + 0:46:00 = 10:20:00 ; 10:20 a.m.
10. 250 mL ; C 11. 50 mL ; A
12. 800 mL ; D 13. 30 mL ; B
14-15. (Suggested answers)
14. $\frac{1}{3}$, $\frac{2}{6}$ 15. $\frac{1}{5}$, $\frac{4}{20}$ 16. $\frac{16}{5}$
17. $2\frac{1}{4}$ 18. $\frac{20}{3}$ 19. $2\frac{1}{7}$
20. $\frac{96}{3}$ = 32 (km/h) 21. $\frac{78}{2}$ = 39 (km/h)
22. $\frac{368}{4}$ = 92 (km/h)

36 You Deserve A Break!

1A. 68 B. 80 C. 72
Ted: B Marco: A Billy: C
2. 64 m/s ; 65.8 m/s ; 60.7 m/s
3. Marco
4. (Suggested drawings)
4a. $1\frac{2}{7}$; b. $1\frac{5}{9}$;
c. $\frac{5}{4}$; d. $\frac{8}{3}$;
5. A 6. 36 cm^2 ; 481 cm^2
7. A

37 Comparing and Ordering Fractions

1. $\frac{5}{9}$ 2. $\frac{7}{8}$ 3. $\frac{3}{2}$
4. $\frac{1}{3}$ 5. $\frac{4}{6}$ 6. $\frac{2}{9}$
7. $\frac{12}{7}$ 8. $\frac{22}{5}$ 9. $\frac{4}{6}$
10. $\frac{6}{8}$ 11. $\frac{14}{4}$ 12. $5\frac{1}{2}$
13. $1\frac{1}{3}$ 14. $3\frac{1}{2}$ 15. $\frac{11}{4}$
16. $1\frac{4}{5}$ 17. > 18. <
19. > 20. < 21. <
22. < 23. > 24. >
25. < 26. < 27. $\frac{5}{12}$, $\frac{1}{2}$, $\frac{2}{3}$
28. $\frac{7}{18}$, $\frac{5}{9}$, $\frac{2}{3}$ 29. $\frac{11}{14}$, $\frac{6}{7}$, $\frac{9}{7}$ 30. $\frac{11}{20}$, $\frac{7}{10}$, $\frac{4}{5}$
31. $\frac{3}{5}$, $\frac{9}{10}$ 32. $\frac{5}{6}$, $\frac{2}{3}$

38 More about Fractions

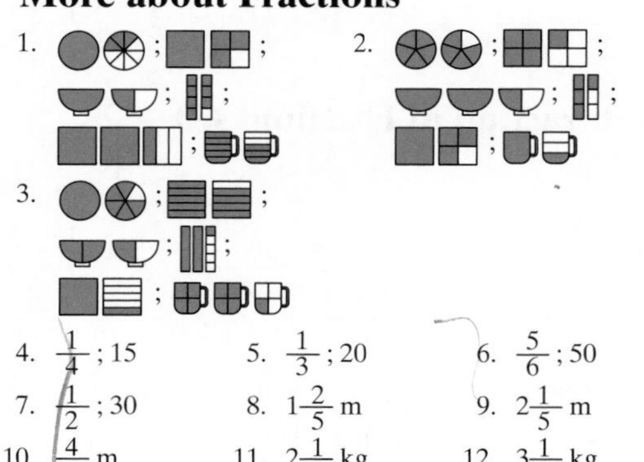

4. $\frac{1}{4}$; 15 5. $\frac{1}{3}$; 20 6. $\frac{5}{6}$; 50
7. $\frac{1}{2}$; 30 8. $1\frac{2}{5}$ m 9. $2\frac{1}{5}$ m
10. $\frac{4}{5}$ m 11. $2\frac{1}{2}$ kg 12. $3\frac{1}{5}$ kg

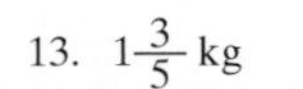

13. $1\frac{3}{5}$ kg　14. $\frac{27}{50}$ kg

39 Addition of Fractions (1)

1.  ; $\frac{1}{4}$; $\frac{2}{4}$; $\frac{3}{4}$
2.  ; $\frac{1}{5}$; $\frac{3}{5}$; $\frac{4}{5}$
3. $\frac{2+4}{9} = \frac{6}{9} = \frac{2}{3}$
4. $\frac{1+1}{4} = \frac{2}{4} = \frac{1}{2}$
5. $\frac{3+1}{10} = \frac{4}{10} = \frac{2}{5}$
6. $\frac{2+3}{7} = \frac{5}{7}$
7. $\frac{1+2}{6} = \frac{3}{6} = \frac{1}{2}$
8. $\frac{3+4}{8} = \frac{7}{8}$
9. $\frac{4}{5}$　10. $\frac{9}{10}$　11. $\frac{3}{4}$
12. $\frac{2}{3}$　13. $\frac{5}{6}$　14. $\frac{2}{3}$
15. $\frac{5}{7}$　16. $\frac{4}{5}$　17. $\frac{2}{3}$
18. $\frac{1}{4} + \frac{1}{4}$; $\frac{1}{2}$; $\frac{1}{2}$ L
19. $\frac{3}{10} + \frac{1}{10}$; $\frac{2}{5}$; $\frac{2}{5}$ kg
20. $\frac{3}{9} + \frac{2}{9}$; $\frac{5}{9}$; $\frac{5}{9}$ m^2
21. $\frac{4}{10} + \frac{4}{10}$; $\frac{4}{5}$; $\frac{4}{5}$ m
22. $\frac{1}{12} + \frac{3}{12}$; $\frac{1}{3}$; $\frac{1}{3}$ h

40 Addition of Fractions (2)

1. 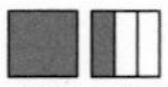 ; $\frac{5}{9}$; $\frac{7}{9}$; $1\frac{1}{3}$
2. 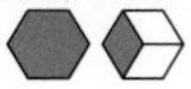 ; $\frac{4}{6}$; $\frac{4}{6}$; $1\frac{1}{3}$
3. $\frac{7}{10} + \frac{6}{10} = \frac{13}{10} = 1\frac{3}{10}$ (m)
4. $\frac{3}{5} + \frac{3}{5} = \frac{6}{5} = 1\frac{1}{5}$ (kg)
5. $\frac{2}{3} + \frac{1}{3} = \frac{3}{3} = 1$ (L)
6. $\$\frac{8}{10} + \$\frac{4}{10} = \$\frac{12}{10} = \$1\frac{1}{5}$
7. 1　8. $1\frac{1}{8}$　9. $1\frac{1}{5}$
10. $1\frac{1}{3}$　11. $1\frac{2}{5}$　12. $1\frac{2}{7}$
13. $\frac{11}{12}$　14. $1\frac{3}{10}$　15. $1\frac{2}{9}$
16. $1\frac{1}{5}$　17. $1\frac{5}{8}$　18. $1\frac{1}{4}$
19. A, D　20. C, D　21. A, B

41 Subtraction of Fractions (1)

1. $\frac{2}{9}$; $\frac{6}{9}$; $\frac{2}{3}$
2. $\frac{7}{8}$; $\frac{3}{8}$; $\frac{4}{8}$; $\frac{1}{2}$
3. $\frac{3}{5}$　4. $\frac{1}{2}$　5. $\frac{1}{6}$
6. $\frac{1}{4}$　7. $\frac{3}{7}$　8. $\frac{1}{3}$
9. $\frac{1}{2}$　10. $\frac{1}{2}$　11. $\frac{1}{3}$
12. $\frac{6}{11}$　13. $\frac{1}{2}$　14. $\frac{3}{5}$
15. $\frac{1}{10}$　16. $\frac{5}{9}$　17. $\frac{7}{9}$
18. $\frac{8}{12}$　19. $\frac{9}{12}$　20. $\frac{2}{10}$
21. $\frac{9}{10} - \frac{1}{10}$; $\frac{4}{5}$; $\frac{4}{5}$ m
22. $\frac{6}{7} - \frac{5}{7}$; $\frac{1}{7}$; $\frac{1}{7}$ kg
23. $\frac{11}{12} - \frac{1}{12}$; $\frac{5}{6}$; $\frac{5}{6}$ h
24. $\frac{7}{8} - \frac{4}{8}$; $\frac{3}{8}$; $\frac{3}{8}$ L

42 Subtraction of Fractions (2)

1. $\frac{10}{10}$; $\frac{3}{10}$; $\frac{7}{10}$
2. 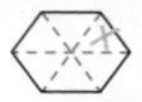 ; $\frac{6}{6}$; $\frac{1}{6}$; $\frac{5}{6}$
3. 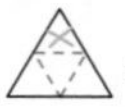 ; $\frac{4}{4}$; $\frac{1}{4}$; $\frac{3}{4}$
4. 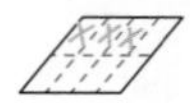 ; $\frac{8}{8} - \frac{3}{8} = \frac{5}{8}$
5. 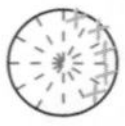 ; $\frac{12}{12} - \frac{5}{12} = \frac{7}{12}$
6.  ; $\frac{10}{10} - \frac{8}{10} = \frac{2}{10} = \frac{1}{5}$
7. 1st piece: $\frac{5}{6}$ m ; $\frac{7}{10}$ m ; 2nd piece: $\frac{1}{2}$ m ; $\frac{1}{4}$ m ; $\frac{3}{4}$ m
8. Sue: $\frac{1}{2}$ kg ; $\frac{7}{10}$ kg ; Ted: $\frac{1}{5}$ kg ; $\frac{2}{3}$ kg ; $\frac{1}{2}$ kg

9. $1 - \frac{2}{3}$; $\frac{1}{3}$; $\frac{1}{3}$ m
10. $1 - \frac{8}{9}$; $\frac{1}{9}$; $\frac{1}{9}$ m
11. $1 - \frac{2}{5}$; $\frac{3}{5}$; $\frac{3}{5}$ h
12. $1 - \frac{4}{8}$; $\frac{1}{2}$; $\frac{1}{2}$ bottle

43 Decimals (1)

1. 3.16 ; 3 and 16 hundredths
2. 2.78 ; 2 and 78 hundredths
3. 4.05 ; 4 and 5 hundredths
4. Colour 35 squares. ; 0.5 or 5 tenths ; 0.08 or 8 hundredths
5. Colour 22 squares. ; 0.4 or 4 tenths ; 0.02 or 2 hundredths
6. Colour 11 squares. ; 0.1 or 1 tenth ; 0.09 or 9 hundredths
7. 70 ; 0.70 ; 0.70
8. 6 ; 60 ; 0.6 ; 0.60 ; 0.6 ; 0.60
9. 1 ; 10 ; 0.1 ; 0.10 ; 0.1 ; 0.10　10. 4.23
11. 0.19　12. 1.39　13. 4.78
14. 3.16　15. 4.81　16. 4.04 ; 4.06
17. 9.35 ; 9.31　18. 1.79 ; 2.09

44 Decimals (2)

1. 8.24 ; 8.40 ; 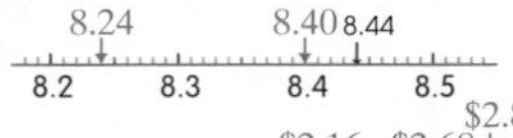

2. 2.68 ; 2.16 ; 2.86 ; 2.66 ; 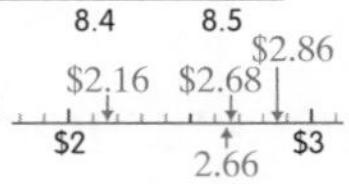

3. 8.19 ; 8.99 ; 9.09 ; 8.09 ; 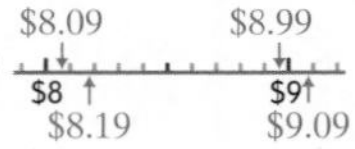

4-9. (Suggested answers)
4. 6.30　5. 3.95　6. 9.00
7. 2.75　8. 7.90　9. 4.99
10. 4　11. 7　12. 5
13. 9　14. 10　15. 8
16. 6　17. 2　18. 8
19. 2　20. C　21. B
22. 3.5　23. 4.7　24. 5.7

45 Relating Fractions and Decimals

1. 0.46 ; 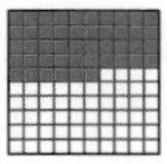
2. $\frac{88}{100}$; 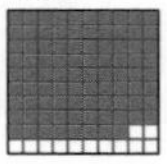
3. $\frac{9}{100}$; 0.09
4. 0.42 ; 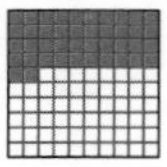
5. $\frac{30}{100}$; 0.30
6. $\frac{9}{100}$
7. 0.04 ; $\frac{5}{10}$; $\frac{4}{100}$
8. 0.2 ; $\frac{2}{10}$; $\frac{9}{100}$
9. 4 ; 3
10. 62 ; 6 ; 2 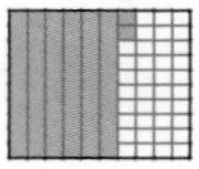
11. 18 ; 1 ; 8 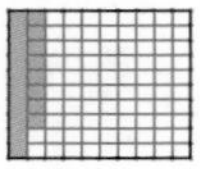
12. A　13. B

46 Addition of Decimals

1. 107.61 ; $\begin{array}{r} 32.76 \\ +\ 74.85 \\ \hline 107.61 \end{array}$
2. 109.57 ; $\begin{array}{r} 95.69 \\ +\ 13.88 \\ \hline 109.57 \end{array}$
3. 164.78 ; $\begin{array}{r} 149.40 \\ +\ 15.38 \\ \hline 164.78 \end{array}$
4. 149.57 ; $\begin{array}{r} 145.97 \\ +\ \ 3.60 \\ \hline 149.57 \end{array}$
5. 10.61　6. 108.51　7. 107.27
8. 12.57　9. 16.25　10. 33.16
11. 154.46　12. 109.36　13. 20.93
14. 17.81　15. 11.01　16. 12.18
17. 4.04　18. 2.76　19. 3.68
20. 5.08　21. 4.23 kg　22. $3.74
23. 1.5 L　24. 6.94 km　25. 2.94 kg

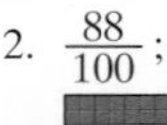

47 Subtraction of Decimals

1. 27.81 2. 27.82 3. 63.27
4. 70.34 5. 82.34 6. 48.02
7. 59.12 8. 28.86 9. 64.84
10. 82.6 ; 18.3 ; 64.3 11. 104.7 ; 40.9 ; 63.8
12. 97.0 ; 72.3 ; 24.7
13. $260.37 14. $49.86 15. $62.49
16. $31.05 17. $81.66 18. $72.35
19. 87.55 – 20.99 ; 66.56 ; $66.56
20. 10 – 3.68 ; 6.32 ; 6.32 m
21. 1.85 – 1.69 ; 0.16 ; 0.16 kg
22. 90 – 79.18 ; 10.82 ; $10.82

48 Addition and Subtraction of Decimals

1. 81.62 2. 517.11 3. 18.78
4. 50.88 5. 113.52 6. 1031.13
7. 60.16 8. 709.68 9. 115.84
10. 235.37 11. 233.89 12. 159.6
13. 266.2 ; 90 ; 177 ; 267 14. 765.93 ; 821 ; 55 ; 766
15. 435.04 ; 352 + 83 = 435 16. 29.86 ; 106 – 76 = 30
17. 49.03 ; 83 – 34 = 49 18. 187.94 ; 60 + 128 = 188
19. 106.71 ; 94.08 20. 23.54 ; 109.22 21. 77.2
22. 106.87 23. 35.21 24. 118.88
25. 8.06 26. 52.11 27. 42.81 kg
28. 145.33 kg 29. 144.01 kg 30. 52.32 kg

49 Multiplication of Decimals

1. 65.4 2. 19 3. 501
4. 31.6 5. 47 6. 809
7. 1230 8. 29.4 9. 61.1
10. 970 11. 13.56 12. 34.2
13. 50.8 14. 31.8 15. 26.4
16. 59.5 17. 19.45 18. 374
19. 114.3 20. 198.24 21. 117.6
22. 77.08
23. Total Weight: 2.8 kg ; 7 kg ; 12.6 kg
Total Cost: $11.98 ; $29.95 ; $53.91
24. Total Length: 137.4 m ; 183.2 m ; 366.4 m
Total Cost: $28.26 ; $37.68 ; $75.36
25. 10.22 L 26. 231.45 g 27. 117.9 g
28. $37.95 29. 287.36 g 30. 16.1 cm

50 Division of Decimals

1. 0.96 2. 0.185 3. 0.94
4. 0.0245 5. 2.41 6. 1.27
7. 0.068 8. 0.25 9. 0.063
10. 0.003 11. 0.086 12. 0.177
13. 3.42
6)20.52
18
25
24
12
12
14. 9.8
7)68.6
63
56
56
15. 1.78
16. 5.32 17. 0.78 18. 3.67
19. 11.6 20. 6.34 21. 3.5
22. 1.27 23. 0.86 24. 0.59
25. 9.92
4)39.68
36
36
36
8
8
| 10
4)40
4
26. 10.9
5)54.5
5
45
45
| 11
5)55
5
5
5
27. 12.03
8)96.24
8
16
16
24
24
| 12
8)96
8
16
16
28. 12.07
7)84.49
7
14
14
49
49
| 12
7)84
7
14
14

29. 9.12 ÷ 8 ; 1.14 ; $1.14 30. 1.17 ÷ 3 ; 0.39 ; $0.39
31. 2.52 ÷ 6 ; 0.42 ; $0.42 32. 15.66 ÷ 9 ; 1.74 ; $1.74
33. 1.26 ÷ 9 ; 0.14 ; 0.14 kg

51 Multiplication and Division of Decimals

1. 27.58 2. 137.7 3. 40.48
4. 134.7
5. 2.7
6)16.2
12
42
42
6. 2.3
7)16.1
14
21
21
7. 0.47
5)2.35
20
35
35
8. 1.16
8)9.28
8
12
8
48
48
9. 25.2
10. 1.29 11. 2.31 12. 1.43
13. [4].5 9
x [3]
1 3.7 7
14. 3.[5]
5)[1]7.[5]
[1][5]
2[5]
2 5
15. 1[7].8
x [6]
1[0]6.8
16a. 6.4 x 6 ; 38.4 ; 38.4 kg b. 6.4 ÷ 8 ; 0.8 ; 0.8 kg
17a. 12.99 ÷ 3 ; 4.33 ; $4.33 b. 0.84 x 4 ; 3.36 ; 3.36 m
18a. 2.4 x 5 ; 12 ; 12 L b. 2.4 ÷ 4 ; 0.6 ; 0.6 L
19. 2.1 ÷ 7 ; 0.3 ; 0.3 m

52 Money (1)

1. (Individual answers for estimates)
A. $430.56 B. $106.36 C. $500.61
D. $120.11 E. $110.60
2. Three hundred eighty-five dollars and forty-nine cents ;
$100 $100 $100 25¢ 10¢ 10¢
$50 $20 $10 $5 1¢ 1¢ 1¢ 1¢
3. Two hundred seventy-six dollars and eight cents ;
$100 $100
$50 $20 $5 $1 5¢ 1¢ 1¢ 1¢
4. Four hundred three dollars and sixty-two cents ;
$100 $100 $100 $100 $2 $1 25¢ 25¢ 10¢ 1¢ 1¢
5. Eight hundred nineteen dollars and thirty-four cents ;
$100 $100 $100 $100 $2 $2 25¢ 5¢ 1¢ 1¢ 1¢ 1¢
$100 $100 $100 $100
$10 $5
6. $929.50 ; $899.49 ; $867.12 ; $768.55 ; $729.50
7. $200

53 Review

1. $\frac{4+5}{9} = \frac{9}{9} = 1$ 2. $\frac{1+1}{8} = \frac{2}{8} = \frac{1}{4}$
3. $\frac{6-1}{7} = \frac{5}{7}$ 4. $\frac{12-7}{12} = \frac{5}{12}$
5. $\frac{11-5}{15} = \frac{6}{15} = \frac{2}{5}$ 6. $\frac{9+7}{10} = \frac{16}{10} = 1\frac{6}{10} = 1\frac{3}{5}$
7. $\frac{1}{3}, \frac{7}{18}, \frac{4}{6}$ 8. $\frac{3}{5}, \frac{2}{3}, \frac{11}{15}$ 9. $\frac{1}{4}, \frac{2}{6}, \frac{5}{12}$
10. < 11. > 12. >
13. < 14. > 15. <
16. 11.32 17. 16.46 18. 70.35
19. 18.04 20. 167.67 21. 2.84
22. 37.8 23. 206.24 24. 255.15
25. 42.6 26. $100 $20 $5 10¢ 10¢
27. $100 $50 $20 $5 $1 25¢ 5¢ 1¢ 1¢ 1¢
28. $1 - \frac{1}{8}$; $\frac{7}{8}$; $\frac{7}{8}$ kg 29. $\frac{8}{9} + \frac{8}{9}$; $1\frac{7}{9}$; $1\frac{7}{9}$ kg
30a. $10.74 b. 0.48 L
31a. $9.26 b. 0.62 kg

54 You Deserve A Break!

1-12. Red ; Green ; Yellow ; Green ; Green ; Green ; Red ; Red ; Yellow ; Red ; Yellow ; Yellow ; Yellow ; Yellow

55 Money (2)

1A. \$ 58.29 + \$ 40.55 = \$ 98.84   B. \$ 58.29 + \$ 39.88 = \$ 98.17   C. \$ 39.88 + \$ 40.55 = \$ 80.43

2. \$1.16   3. \$0.43
4. Cat: \$32.75 ; Bear: \$45.49 ; Giraffe: \$40.91 ; Gorilla: \$55.35
5. \$ 50.00 − \$ 45.49 = \$ 4.51 ; \$4.51   6. \$ 32.75 + \$ 55.35 = \$ 88.10 ; \$88.10
7. \$ 45.49 + \$ 45.49 = \$ 90.98 ; \$90.98   8. \$ 40.91 − \$ 8.88 = \$ 32.03 ; \$32.03

56 2-D Shapes

1. Rectangle ; 4 ; 4   2. Hexagon ; 6 ; 6
3. Pentagon ; 5 ; 5   4. Octagon ; 8 ; 8
5. Parallelogram ; 4 ; 4   6. B, D, E
7. ; 2   8. ; 4   9. ; 2
10. ; 6   11. ; 2

12-14. (Suggested answers)

12.
13.

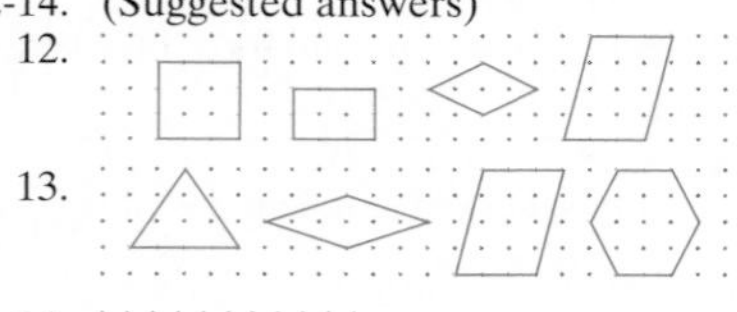

14.

57 Lines of Symmetry

1. 2.
3. 4.
5. 6. 7.

8a. A, C   b. J, M ; O   c. F, G, N
d. I, K   e. B, D, E, H, L
9. EDDIE ; BOB ; TOMMY
10.

58 Tile Patterns

1.

2. B, C, D, E, F, H, I
3. rectangle, square ;   4. pentagon, rhombus ;
5. (Suggested answers)

59 Sorting Angles

1A. ∠PQR or ∠RQP ; an obtuse angle
B. ∠ABC or ∠CBA ; an right angle
C. ∠ONM or ∠MNO ; an acute angle
D. ∠RST or ∠TSR ; an obtuse angle
2. Acute Angle: ∠PQR, ∠STU, (∠VWX), ∠OPQ
Right Angle: ∠ABC, ∠CDE, ∠XYZ
Obtuse Angle: ∠HIJ, (∠KLM)

3-4. (Suggested drawings)
3. ∠PQR ; ∠LMN ; ∠ABC ; 4. ∠BCD ; ∠PQR ; ∠OLM ;

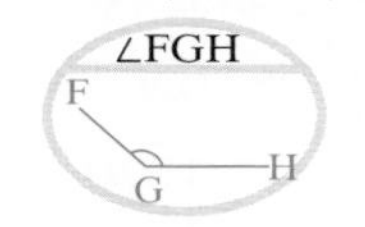

60 Reading and Measuring Angles

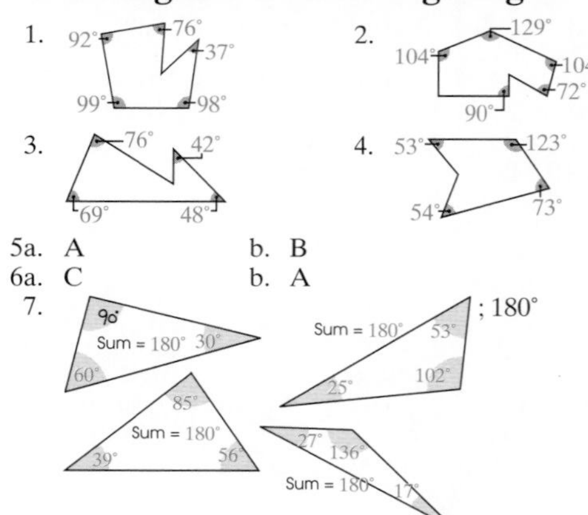

61 Constructing Angles

1.

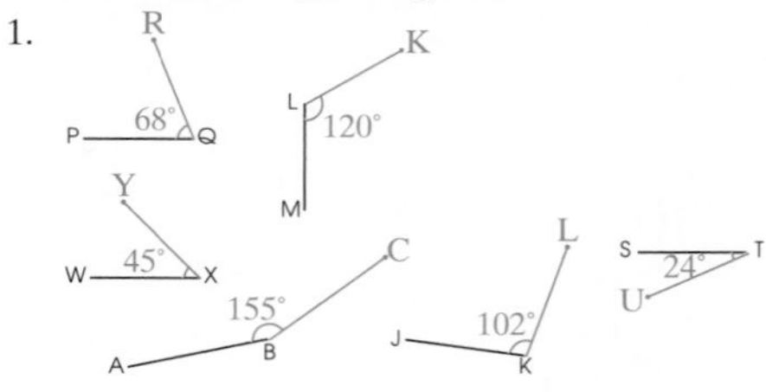

2.  or 

2:00 10:00

3. 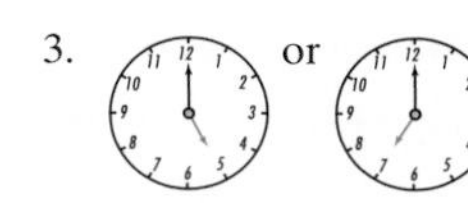

5:00 or 7:00

4. 32° ; 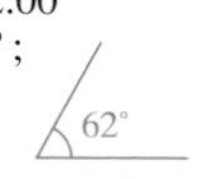

5. 132° ;
87°

6. 124° ;
124°

7. 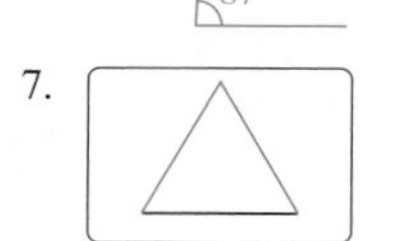

62 Classifying Triangles

1. 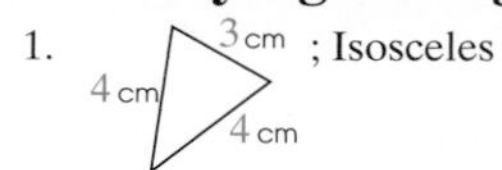

; Isosceles

2. 3 cm, 3 cm, 3 cm ; Equilateral

3. 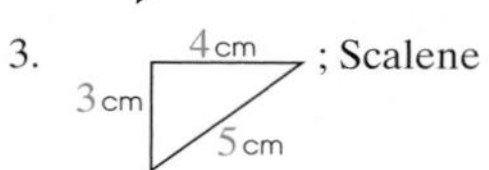

; Scalene

4. 5 cm, 2 cm, 5 cm ; Isosceles

5. 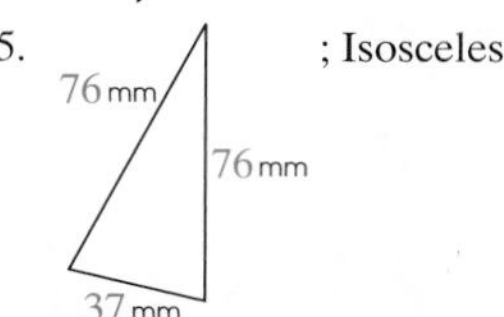

; Isosceles

6. (Suggested drawings)

7. Acute Triangle: B, F ; Obtuse Triangle: D, E, H ;
   Right Triangle: A, C, G

8A. Acute isosceles triangle B. Right isosceles triangle
C. Right scalene triangle D. Obtuse scalene triangle
E. Right isosceles triangle

9. ✘ 10. ✔ 11. ✔

63 Constructing Triangles

1-4. (Suggested answers)

1. 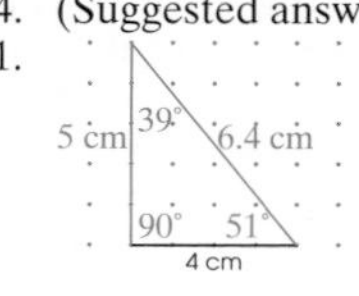

2.
5 cm
45°
7.1 cm
90°
45°
5 cm

3. 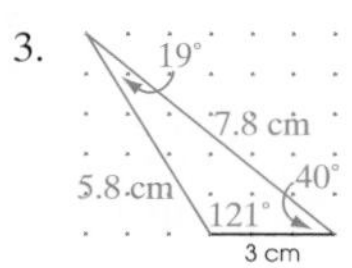

4.
3.6 cm
112°
3.6 cm
34°
34°
6 cm

5. ; 90° ; 4.2 cm ; 4.2 cm ; isosceles

6. 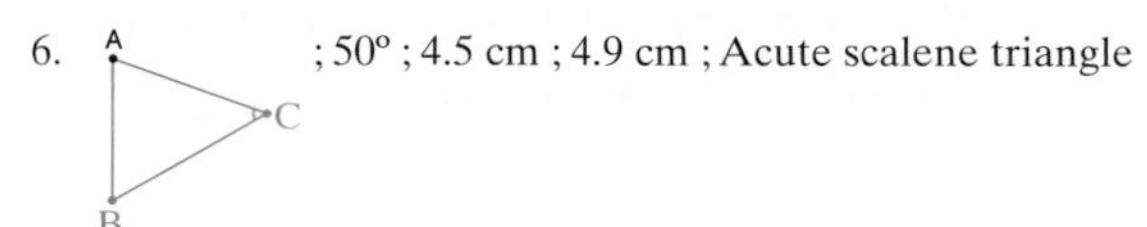

; 50° ; 4.5 cm ; 4.9 cm ; Acute scalene triangle

7. (Suggested answer)

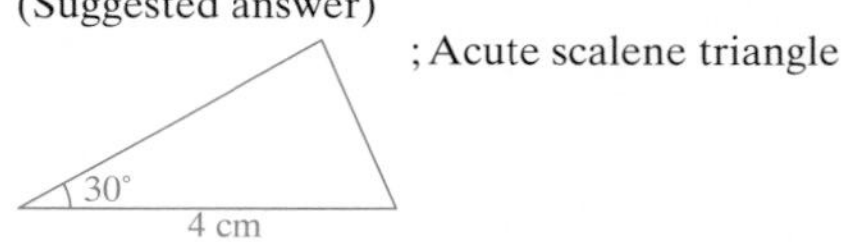

; Acute scalene triangle

64 Sorting 3-D Figures

1. 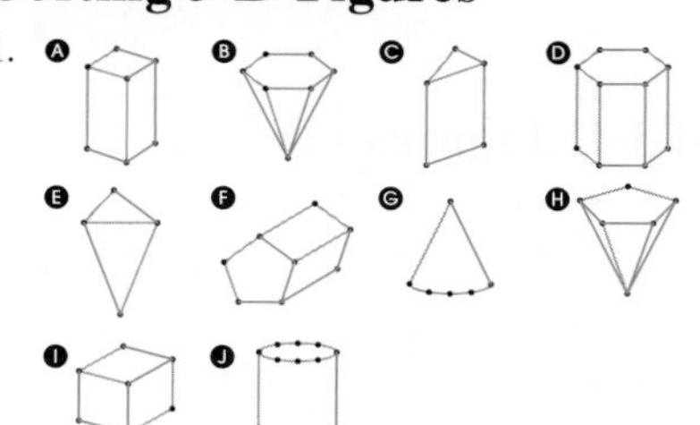

2. B, C, E, H ;
   A, D, F, G, I, J
3. A, C, D, F ;
   B, E, G, H, I, J
4. G, J ;
   A, B, C, D, E, F, H, I
5. A, C, D, F, I, J ;
   B, E, G, H

6a. rectangular pyramid ; rectangular prism
b. rectangular prism ; hexagonal prism
c. pentagonal prism ; rectangular prism
d. Each has a rectangular prism.

7a. triangular prism ; rectangular prism
b. rectangular prism ; rectangular pyramid
c. pentagonal pyramid ; triangular prism
d. Each has 9 faces.

8-9. (Suggested answers)

8. 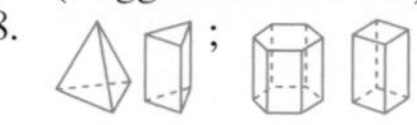

9. 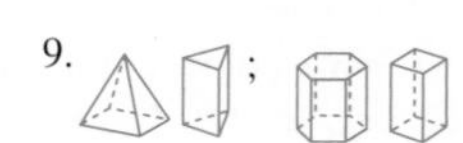

65 Nets of 3-D Figures (1)

1. D ; H ; A ; F ; G ; B
2. 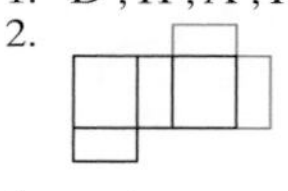
3. 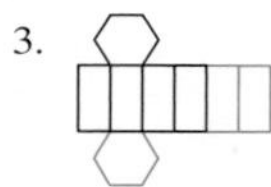
4. 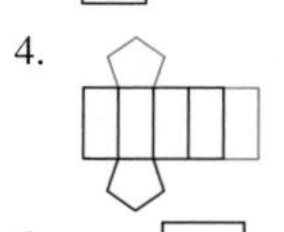
5. 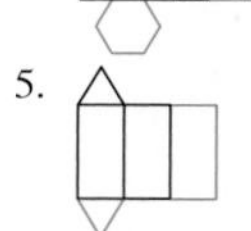
6. 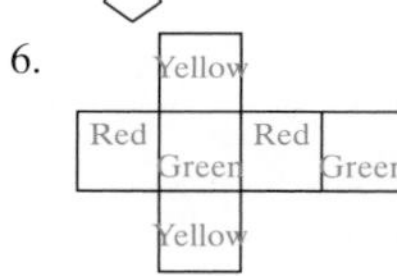

7. A, B, D, E

66 Nets of 3-D Figures (2)

1. A
2. B
3. B
4. C
5.
6. 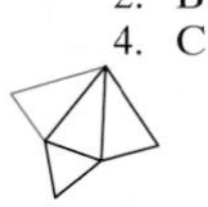
7. 
8. A, D, F
9. (Suggested drawings)

67 Views of 3-D Figures (1)

1. A
2. B
3. A
4. C
5. Front View Side View Top View
6. Front View Side View Top View
7. Front View Side View Top View
8. Front View Side View Top View

9. 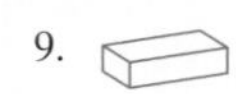 10. 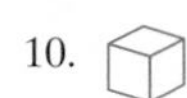 11.

68 Views of 3-D Figures (2)

1. E ; A ; B ; D ; C
2. 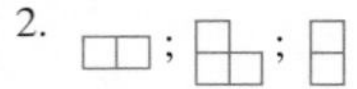
3.
4.
5.

6a. 12 b. 8 c. 6

69 Transformations (1)

1. 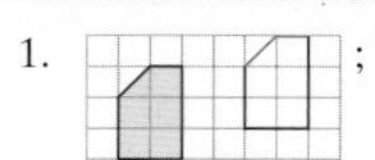 ;
4 units right, 1 unit up
2. ;
4 units left, 2 units down
3. 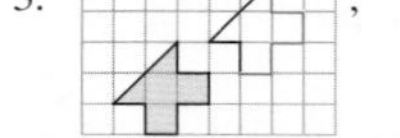 ;
3 units right, 2 units up
4. 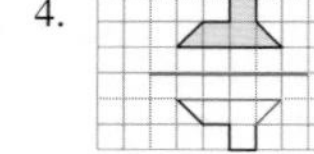
5.
6.
7.
8.
9.
10.
11.
12. ;

70 Transformations (2)

1. Translation, Reflection or Rotation ;
2. Translation, Rotation ;

3-6. (Suggested answers)
3.
4.
5.
6.
7. (Suggested answers)
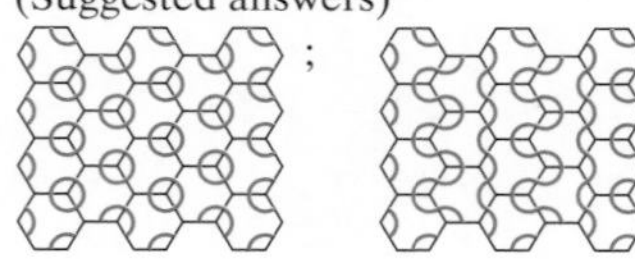

71 Review

1-2. (Suggested answers)
1. 2.
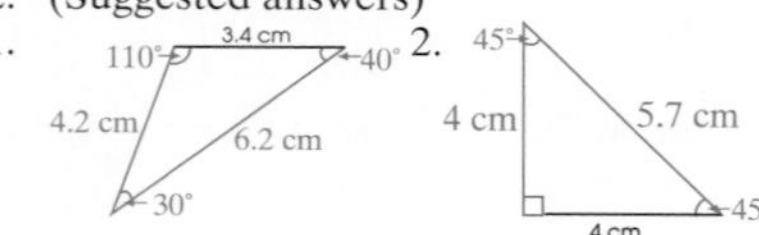

3. Hexagonal prism ;
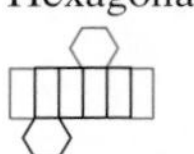
4. Cube ;
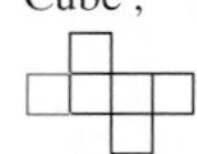
5. Triangular pyramid ;
6. Pentagonal pyramid ;
7. 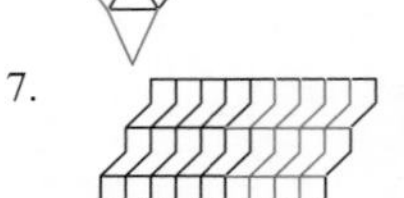 ; 

8-9. (Suggested answers)
8. 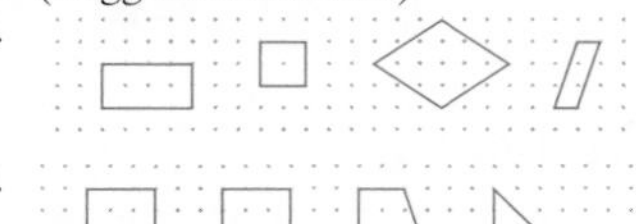
9.
10. Translation: move 5 units right and 1 unit up
11. Reflection ;
12. Rotation ;
13. Triangular pyramid
14. $18.75

72 You Deserve A Break!

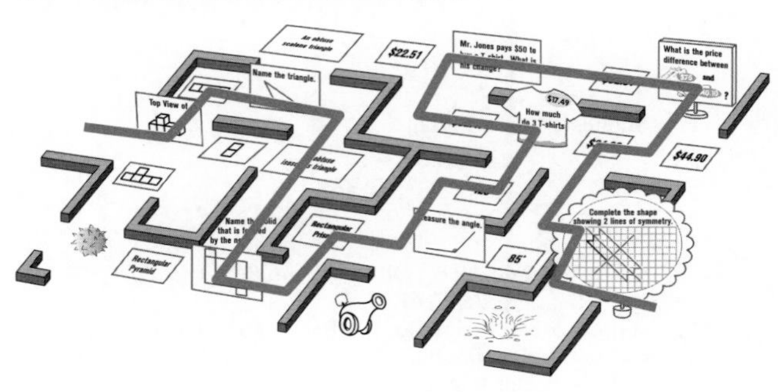

73 Coordinate Systems (1)

1. Amy (6,5) ; Ann (6,1) ; Ivy (3,1) ; Sam (6,3) ; Sue (3,5) ; Ted (0,5) ; Tina (0,1) ; Tom (0,3) ; Vera (5,6) ; Sid (7,4)
2. (1,1), (1,6), (2,3), (3,0), (3,3), (4,2), (5,1), (5,4) ; Ivy
3. 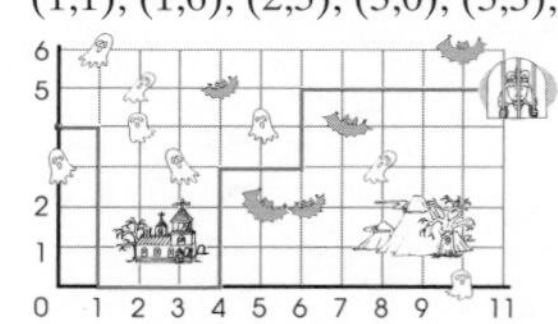
4. (1,0) ; (4,0) ; (4,3) ; (6,3) ; (6,5)
5. 200 m

6a. (4,5), (5,2), (6,2), (7,4), (10,6)
b. (4,5)

7a. (0,3), (1,6), (2,4), (2,5), (3,3), (5,4), (8,3), (10,0)
b. (3,3)

74 Coordinate Systems (2)

1. 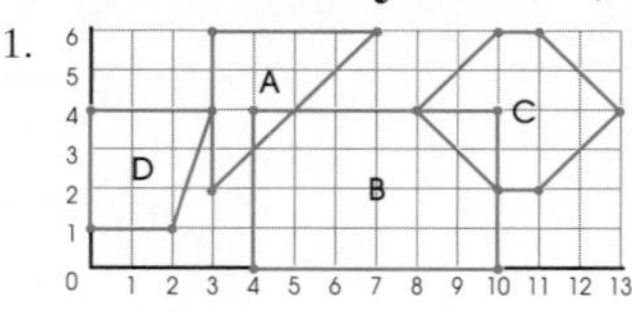

A. Triangle
B. Rectangle
C. Hexagon
D. Trapezoid

2 & 5a. 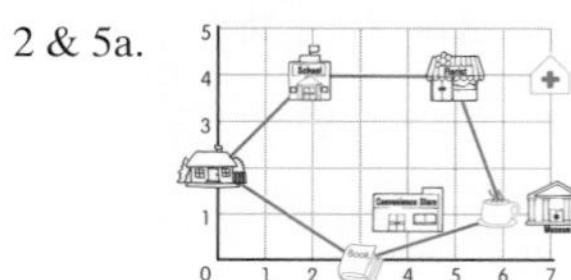

3. museum
4. Judy's house

5b. school, florist, coffee shop, library
c. coffee shop

75 Number Patterns and Pattern Rules

1. 75 ; 25 ; 15 ; 5
2. 114 ; 454 ; 906 ; 905
3. 11 ; 25 ; 53 ; 109
4. 450 ; 460 ; 120 ; 65
5. + 10 ; ÷ 5 ; 20 ; 4 ; 14
6. – 3 ; x 3 ; 96 ; 288 ; 285
7. x 4 ; – 1 ; 364 ; 363 ; 1452
8. ÷ 2 ; – 4 ; 32 ; 28 ; 14
9. 20 ; + 6 ; 26 ; + 7 ; 33 ; + 8 ; 41 ; 21 ; 23 ; 26 ; 30 ; 35 ; 41
10. – 10 ; 60 ; – 12 ; 48 ; – 14 ; 34 ; – 16 ; 18 ; 314 ; 310 ; 304 ; 296 ; 286 ; 274
11. 23 ; x 2, + 1 ; 47 ; x 2, + 1 ; 95 ; x 2, + 1 ; 191 ; 19 ; 39 ; 79 ; 159 ; 319 ; 639

12-13. (Suggested answers for the two pairs of numbers)

12. Divide the 1st number by 2 ; then add 1 ; 1st number: 8, 12 ; 2nd number: 5, 7
13. Subtract 2 from the 1st number ; then multiply by 3 ; 1st number: 3, 4 ; 2nd number: 3, 6

76 Creating Patterns

1-3. (Suggested patterns)

1.
2.
3.

4-5. (Suggested answers)

4. 13 ; 26 ; 29 ; 58 ; 61 ; + 2, x 3: 6 ; 18 ; 20 ; 60 ; 62 ; x 3, + 2: 3 ; 5 ; 15 ; 17 ; 51 ; x 2, + 3: 12 ; 15 ; 30 ; 33 ; 66
5. 4 ; 16 ; 15 ; 60 ; 59 ; – 4, x 1: 86 ; 86 ; 82 ; 82 ; 78 ; x 1, – 4: 70 ; 66 ; 66 ; 62 ; 62 ; x 4, – 1: 160 ; 159 ; 636 ; 635 ; 2540
6. ; 4 x 4 = 16
7. ; 1 + 2 + 3 + 4 + 5 + 4 + 3 + 2 + 1 = 25

77 Problems Involving Patterns

1a. 100 ; 120
b. 140¢
c. 560¢
d. Next Tuesday

2a. 300 ; 275
b. 250¢
c. Day 9
d. 5 quarters

3. Tommy: 120, 140 ; Wayne: 90, 100 ; Sean: 60, 55 ; Peter: 320, 640

4a. 20 ; 20
b. He got 40 points in the 1st game. Then he got 10 points more each time.
c. He got 85 points in the 1st game. Then he got 5 points less each time.
d. He got 10 points in the 1st game. Then he doubled his points each time.

5. Tommy: 160 ; Wayne: 110 ; Sean: 50 ; Peter: 1280
6. No
7. Yes

78 Simple Equations

1-7. (Individual guessing)

1. 12
2. 70
3. 12
4. 135
5. 75
6. 8
7. 7
8. 32
9. 38
10. 216
11. 20
12. 75
13. 10
14. 65 ; 35
15. $k \times 6 = 36$; 6
16. $24 \div y = 4$; 6
17. $52 - a = 50$; 2
18. $p \div 5 = 3$; 15
19. B ; 27
20. C ; 3

79 Pictographs

1. 180 ; 140 ; 190 ; 150
2. 68
3. 120
4. 370
5. (Suggested answer)

6. $799
7. 325 sandwiches
8. Sandwich

9-10. (Suggested answer)

9. There is a special deal on fried chicken today.
10. Sandwich, because it has the biggest number of customers.

80 Reading Bar Graphs

1. 50 ; 25 ; 75 ; 55
2. 75
3. 80
4. 200
5. 660
6. Winterfresh: 200 ; 350 ; 175 ; 150 ; Whitening: 275 ; 225 ; 300 ; 350
7. 575
8. A&B Convenience Store
9. Uncle Joe's Mart
10. 19
11. 250

81 Making Bar Graphs

1. Children's Savings (Savings ($): Derek, Marco, Jessica, Jane)
2. $22.5
3. 3 rolls
4. $7.50
5. Number of Containers Collected (No. of Containers; Types of Containers: Bottle, Can, Box, Carton)
6. Can
7. Carton
8. 30 fewer
9. 320 containers
10. 5 containers
11. 5 recycle boxes

82 Reading Circle Graphs

1. The Children's Favourite Sports
2. 5 kinds ; hockey, soccer, tennis, basketball, and baseball.
3. Hockey
4. Soccer
5. Baseball
6. $\frac{1}{3}$
7. 20 children
8. 20 children
9. Waffle
10. Cereal

11a. $\frac{1}{5}$
b. $\frac{3}{10}$
c. $\frac{1}{10}$
d. $\frac{2}{5}$

12a. 4 children
b. 6 children
c. 2 children
d. 8 children

13. A

83 Making Circle Graphs

1. (Pear, Apple, Orange)

2a. $\frac{1}{4}$
b. $\frac{1}{3}$
c. $\frac{5}{12}$

3. Pear

4a. 10 pears
b. 5 pears

5. (White Chocolate, Peanut Butter, Oatmeal Raisin, Chocolate Chip)

6. oatmeal raisin 7. 2 8. 4
9. 2 ; 5 ; 8 ; 1 10.

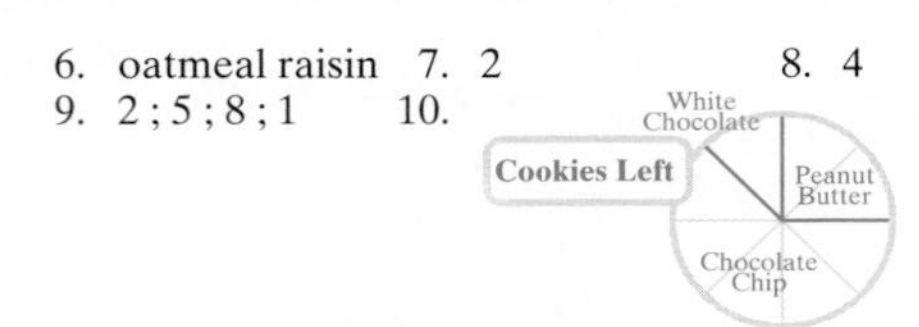

84 Reading Line Graphs

1. 600 2. 300 3. 6000
4. 100 5. 1250 6. $2.50
7. $12.50 8. $2.50
9. September and November 10. $65
11. $60 12. $10 13. $17.99
14. $29.12

85 Making Line Graphs

1. Joseph's Spending 2. $4

3. 8 cards 4. $37 5. 20 cards
6. Number of Tickets Sold

7. 380 tickets 8. August, because it is summer time.
9. The sales will be higher in December because of the Christmas holidays.

86 Mean and Mode

1. 5 kg ; 5.8 kg 2. 47 m ; 36 m 3. 2 L ; 2.4 L
4. 14°C ; 16°C 5. 17.6 cm^2 ; 16.4 cm^2
6. 47 g ; 43.2 g 7. 60 marbles ; 64 marbles
8. 180 g ; 179 g 9. $65.85 ; $86.45

87 Probability (1)

1a. $\frac{1}{2}$ b. $\frac{3}{10}$ c. $\frac{1}{5}$
2a. $\frac{2}{3}$ b. $\frac{1}{3}$ c. $\frac{1}{6}$

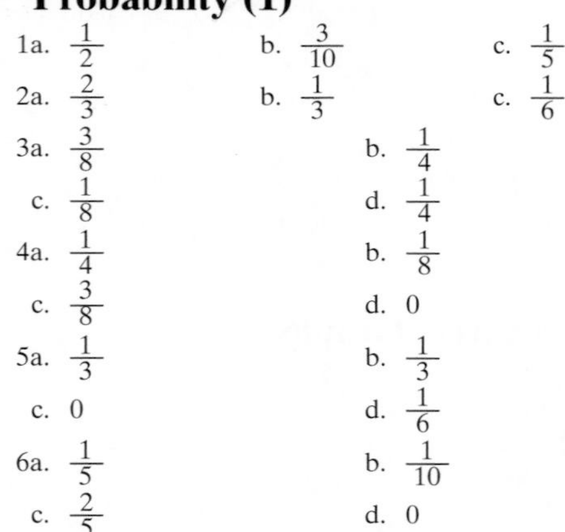

3a. $\frac{3}{8}$ b. $\frac{1}{4}$
c. $\frac{1}{8}$ d. $\frac{1}{4}$
4a. $\frac{1}{4}$ b. $\frac{1}{8}$
c. $\frac{3}{8}$ d. 0
5a. $\frac{1}{3}$ b. $\frac{1}{3}$
c. 0 d. $\frac{1}{6}$
6a. $\frac{1}{5}$ b. $\frac{1}{10}$
c. $\frac{2}{5}$ d. 0
7. Mr. Hall's spinner, because it is most likely to land on the ice cream cone section among the 3 spinners.
8. Mrs. Wood's spinner, because the probability of getting candies by spinning Mrs. Wood's spinner is 0.

88 Probability (2)

1. Bread: B ;
Filling: ES, TB ;
Combination: W and CB ; W and ES ; B and TB ; B and CB ; B and ES
2. 6 possible combinations
3a. $\frac{1}{6}$ b. $\frac{1}{3}$
c. $\frac{1}{2}$ d. 0
4. Yo-yo: Puppet, Yo-yo, Sorry, Top — Yo-yo & Puppet, Yo-yo & Yo-yo, Yo-yo & Sorry, Yo-yo & Top
Sorry: Puppet, Yo-yo, Sorry, Top — Sorry & Puppet, Sorry & Yo-yo, Sorry & Sorry, Sorry & Top
Top: Puppet, Yo-yo, Sorry, Top — Top & Puppet, Top & Yo-yo, Top & Sorry, Top & Top
5. 16 possible combinations
6a. $\frac{9}{16}$ b. $\frac{3}{8}$ c. $\frac{3}{8}$
d. $\frac{1}{16}$ e. $\frac{1}{16}$ f. $\frac{2}{16}$ or $\frac{1}{8}$
7. 30 children

89 Review

1. 36 cm ; 30 cm 2. 18.9 kg ; 23 kg
3. 21°C ; 20°C 4. 14.3 mL ; 16.7 mL
5. Flowers in Aunt Lisa's Flower Shop

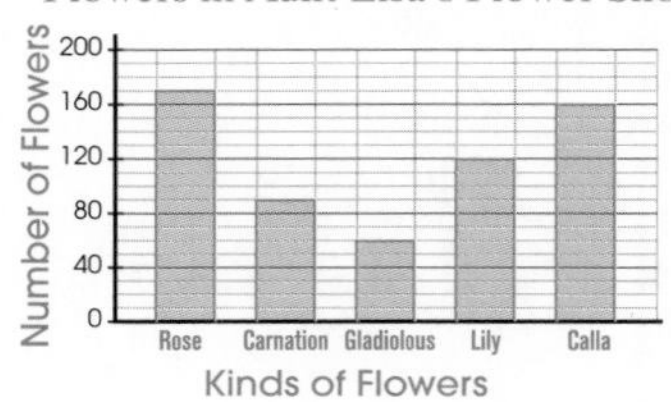

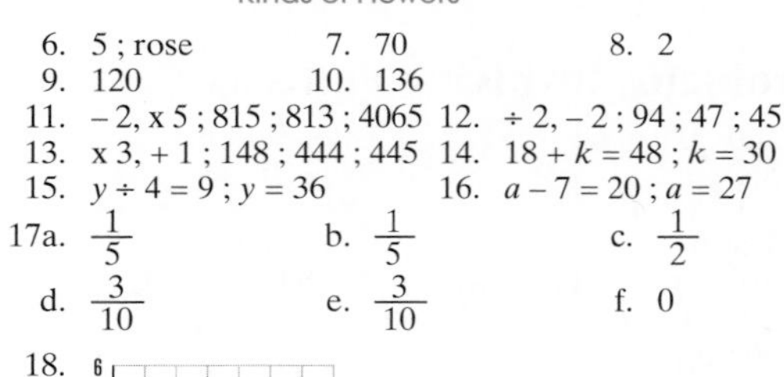

6. 5 ; rose 7. 70 8. 2
9. 120 10. 136
11. – 2, x 5 ; 815 ; 813 ; 4065 12. ÷ 2, – 2 ; 94 ; 47 ; 45
13. x 3, + 1 ; 148 ; 444 ; 445 14. $18 + k = 48$; $k = 30$
15. $y \div 4 = 9$; $y = 36$ 16. $a - 7 = 20$; $a = 27$
17a. $\frac{1}{5}$ b. $\frac{1}{5}$ c. $\frac{1}{2}$
d. $\frac{3}{10}$ e. $\frac{3}{10}$ f. 0
18.

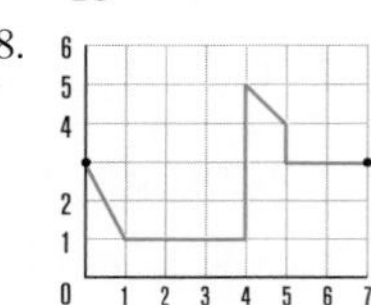

90 You Deserve A Break!

1. 250 2. 725
3. 250 4. 137.50
5a. (0,2) b. (1,3) c. (3,2)
d. (7,0) e. (9,2)
6. (8,1) ; (1,1) ; (1,3)
7. No. of Children Playing in Silver Centre

8. (Suggested answer)
5000, because the number of children playing in Silver Centre has been increasing and there should be more children playing during summer holidays.

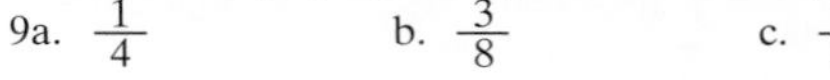

9a. $\frac{1}{4}$ b. $\frac{3}{8}$ c. $\frac{1}{8}$

1 Canoe Travel in Early Canada

A. 1. F 2. T 3. T
4. F 5. F 6. T

B. 1. They learned to travel this (way) from the native (tribes).
2. These connecting foot (trails) between (lakes) and (rivers) are called "(portages)".
3. At the (end) of each (portage) they would repack the (canoes) and start paddling along another (river) or (lake) again.

C. portage

2 Nouns

A. 2. solo ; CC
3. Toronto Symphony Orchestra ; CP
4. pocket ; CC
5. tranquilizer ; UC
6. handkerchief ; CC
7. water ; UC
8. hall ; CC
9. something ; UC
10. phlegm ; UC
11. dream ; CC
12. time ; CC

B. 1. E 2. F 3. B
4. D 5. C 6. A

C. 1. ability 2. humility
3. promotion 4. remembrance
5. attendance 6. television
7. togetherness 8. tolerance
9. competence 10. kindness
11. goodness 12. solidity

3 The Mysterious Bermuda Triangle

A. 1. C 2. C 3. B

B. 1. viewing 2. unreal
3. chaotic / stormy 4. unearthly
5. discrepancy 6. remedy
7. stormy / chaotic 8. discontinued

4 Direct and Indirect Objects

A. 1. D 2. D 3. I
4. D 5. I

B. 1. D 2. I 3. D ; I
4. D ; I 5. D 6. D ; I
7. N 8. D 9. D
10. N

C. Direct Objects:
snack ; bottom of the staircase ; mouse ; creeps ; feeling ; something ; wisp of air ; house ; wind ; cat ; cape ; cabinet
Indirect Objects:
her ; her ; home ; it

5 Bats

A. 1. C 2. C 3. A

B. 1. B 2. D 3. C 4. A

C. 1. (Suggested answer)
There are no insect-eating bats in the polar regions because the weather there is too cold for insects, and so there is no food for bats.
2. Bats aren't as bad as people might think because they pollinate plants and keep insect populations in balance.

6 Pronouns: Subject, Object, and Reflexive

A. S: 4 ; 5 ; 6
O: 3 ; 7
R: 1 ; 2 ; 8

B. 1. myself 2. himself
3. herself 4. themselves
5. ourselves

C. 1. It 2. me 3. I
4. you 5. They

7 Boomerangs – Shapes that Fly

A. Returning:
Shape: flat and curved
Movement: changes direction in mid-flight and returns to thrower
Use: games; ceremony; hunting (occasionally)
Non-Returning:
Shape: straighter and heavier at one end
Movement: travels in a straighter line
Use: hunting; fighting

B. D ; C ; A ; B

C. 1. tool 2. regular
3. unique / unusual 4. curved
5. spins 6. instructions

8 Demonstrative Pronouns

A. 1. these 2. this 3. That
4. That 5. ones 6. ones
7. this 8. that 9. Those

B. 1. That; This 2. that; those
3. 4.
5. Those; These 6. These; Those
7. one; ones

9 Glass – from Sand to Almost Anything

A. 1. It is heated until it melts into a syrup-like or water-like consistency, and then blown or poured into a mould to set.
2. A long blowpipe is dipped into the melted glass and air is blown through the pipe to make different shapes.
3. Fiberglass is not "pure" glass.
4. (Individual answer)
5. (Individual answer)

B. 1. G 2. J 3. A 4. H
5. F 6. C 7. B 8. I
9. E 10. D

10 You Deserve A Break!

Nouns: brakes ; lights ; passengers ; wheel
Verbs: drive ; park ; pass ; stop
Adjectives: careful ; safe ; slow ; stuck
(Colour the cars with these words.)
brakes ; safe

11 Interrogative Pronouns

A. 1. Who 2. Whose 3. What
4. Who 5. What 6. Whose
7. which 8. What 9. what
10. which 11. what 12. whom

B. 1. F 2. C 3. D
4. G 5. H

C. (Suggested answers)
1. Whom are you looking for?
2. Which one do you like better, the pastel drawing or the painting?
3. With whom did you speak after school?
4. What is the best snack?

12 To See Mars – a Chance in a Lifetime

A. 1. F 2. T 3. T
4. T 5. F 6. T

B. 1. opposition 2. 60 000
3. southeastern 4. elliptical
5. illusion

13 Relative Pronouns

A. 1. that 2. where
3. which 4. whose
5. when 6. whom
7. that 8. who

B. 1. which 2. which
3. that 4. that
5. that 6. which

C. 1. that 2. that
3. whom
4. This is the person I work with.

14 Mars Rovers and Landers

A. A. INDESTRUCTIBLE B. PHENOMENAL
C. COMPONENTS
1. INNOVATIONS 2. DATA
3. SOPHISTICATED 4. COMMAND
5. RESEARCH

B. 1. F 2. T 3. T 4. T
5. F 6. F 7. T 8. T

15 Transitive and Intransitive Verbs

A. 1. I 2. I 3. T
4. T 5. I

B. 1. bought ; T 2. jumps / giggles ; I
3. giggles / jumps ; I 4. contain ; T
5. recognize ; T 6. makes ; T

C. 1. savour 2. melt
3. persuade 4. ponders
5. patrol

D. (Individual writing)

16 Hybrid Cars

A. Hybrid cars are better for the environment.

B. (Suggested answers)
1. an increase in climatic temperatures
2. the production of carbon dioxide from car emissions
3. the reduction of greenhouse gases
4. Some ways are riding a bike instead of driving, conserving energy by turning off lights when not using them, and planting more trees.
5. Submarines are hybrids because they use electric power in combination with diesel or nuclear power.

17 Subject-Verb Agreement

A. 1. was 2. are
3. would 4. will
5. is 6. finds

B. 1. rabbit
2. Sara
3. The tourists
4. Sara's parents
5. Mr. Selby

C. 1. news 2. Mathematics
3. Physics 4. Classics
5. team 6. group
7. staff 8. family

18 Cool Sweat in Hot Times

A. 1. T 2. F
3. T 4. F
5. T 6. T

B. 1. ultra-violet rays 2. evaporation
3. wetness 4. clog

C. (Suggested answers)
1. Our body sweats through the skin to keep us cool.
2. High humidity slows down evaporation; low humidity speeds it up.

19 Present Tense: Simple and Progressive

A. 1. is showing 2. are running
3. is blowing 4. is chewing
5. is going 6. are preparing
7. is simmering 8. is shining
9. is burning

B. 1. sings 2. am arriving
3. looks 4. likes
5. is planning 6. is thinking
7. reads 8. gives

C. (Suggested writing)
1. a. The farmers milk their cows every day.
   b. The farmers are milking their cows now.
2. a. The children lie in the meadow every afternoon.
   b. The children are lying in the meadow.
3. a. Daphne and Sophia fall asleep in front of the television every night.
   b. Daphne and Sophia are falling asleep in front of the television.

20 You Deserve A Break!

A. abilities ; berries ; cherries ; copies ; doilies ; ferries ; fireflies ; galleries ; hobbies ; identities ; lilies ; pennies ; skies
Matt's special words: berry ; cherry ; ferry

B. ability ; 4 gallery ; 3
identity ; 4 telescope ; 3

21 Weather or Climate?

A. A. ATMOSPHERE B. ALTITUDE
1. TEMPERATURE 2. FEATURES
3. HUMIDITY 4. EQUATOR

B. 1. D 2. D 3. B 4. B

22 Past Tense: Simple and Progressive

A. 1. called 2. was removing
3. were clapping 4. saw ; waved
5. went 6. congratulated
7. was leading

B. 1. was flying 2. talked
3. was walking 4. was rehearsing
5. played 6. was taking
7. had 8. spotted ; decided

C. 1. drunk ; drank 2. drawed ; drew
3. 4. bended ; bent

23 Aurora Borealis

A. 1. B 2. A 3. E
4. D 5. C

B. 3 ; 4 ; 5 ; 1 ; 2

C. 1. australis 2. borealis
3. Aurora 4. Arctic
5. mythology

24 Future Tense: Simple and Progressive

A. 1. will watch 2. will ring
3. will be visiting 4. will be
5. will be riding

B. 1. will be attending 2. will turn
3. will play 4. will be swimming

C. 1. will be seeing 2. will go
3. will snap 4. will be looking

D. 1. would go
2. would be going
3. would have gone
4. would have been going

Answers

25 Boxing

A. 1. thongs 2. cestuses 3. strength
4. Greece 5. gambling

B. A. MAYHEM B. CONFIDENCE
C. PUGILISM D. PANKRATION
E. FEINTING F. STRAIGHT
1. GLADIATORS 2. MODIFICATIONS

26 Comparative and Superlative Adjectives

A. 1. safer ; safest 2. happier
3. most forgetful 4. greater ; greatest
5. biggest 6. friendlier ; friendliest
7. sadder ; saddest 8. nicer ; nicest
9. more important 10. thinner ; thinnest
11. more influential ; most influential
12. easier ; easiest
13. tinier ; tiniest
14. more marvellous ; most marvellous

B. (Individual writing)

C. 1. tidiest 2. most splendid
3. 4.

D. (Suggested answers)
1. good: better ; best 2. bad: worse ; worst

27 Campfire

A. 1. F 2. T 3. F 4. T

B. 4 ; 5 ; 3 ; 2 ; 1

C. campfire ; campsites ; firewood ; marshmallows ; nowadays ; woodsman

28 Creating Adjectives from Verbs

A. 1. charming ; charmed
2. annoying ; annoyed
3. frightening ; frightened
4. interesting ; interested
5. embarrassing ; embarrassed
6. boring ; bored
7. welcoming ; welcomed
8. moving ; moved

B. 1. frightened 2. bored
3. annoying 4. charming
5. moving

C. (Suggested answers)
1. most interesting 2. more convincing
3. more bored 4. most depressing
5. more confusing

D. (Suggested answers)
1. pleased 2. prepared
3. disappointed 4. thrilled
5. satisfied

29 Erica's Journal

A. 1. C 2. D 3. C

B. (Individual answers)

30 You Deserve A Break!

1. tuba 2. saxophone 3. trombone
4. French horn 5. clarinet 6. trumpet
7. baritone 8. flute

31 Comparative and Superlative Adverbs

A. 1. clearly ; more clearly ; most clearly
2. serious ; more seriously ; most seriously
3. careful ; carefully ; most carefully
4. beautiful ; beautifully ; more beautifully
5. strong ; strongly ; most strongly
6. common ; more commonly ; most commonly
7. quietly ; more quietly ; most quietly
8. gentle ; more gently ; most gently
9. rational ; rationally ; most rationally
10. important ; importantly ; more importantly
11. easy ; easily ; most easily
12. happy ; more happily ; most happily
13. simply ; more simply ; most simply

B. 1. later
2. earlier
3. more frequently
4. sooner

C. 1. lovingly 2. daringly
3. benevolently 4. inventively
5. truthfully
(Individual writing of sentences)

32 Secret Writing

A. 1. F 2. T 3. T 4. F
5. T 6. T 7. T 8. T

B. 1. 03182516201507180113
2. cryptogram
3. (Individual answer) 4. (Individual answer)

33 Conjunctions

A. 1. and ; before 2. until

3. after 4. unless
5. or 6. if
7. Although 8. because
9. since 10. and

B. 1. because / since 2. but / while
3. unless / although 4. Although ; still
5. when / while

C. 1. not only ; but also
2. Either ; or
3. both ; and / neither ; nor / not only ; but also
4. whether ; or
5. neither ; nor

34 Moon Phases

A. 1. T 2. T 3. F
4. T 5. T

B. A. COZY B. OUTSHINES
C. CIVILIZATIONS D. CALENDARS
1. CYCLE 2. OBSERVATION
3. PHASES

35 Modal Verbs: Can and Could

A. 1. A 2. A 3. P 4. A
5. P 6. A 7. P 8. A

B. Ability: 2 ; 5 ; 6 Permission: 3 ; 4
Possibility: 1 ; 7 ; 8

36 Origami

A. 1. B 2. D 3. B 4. A

B. 1. certificates 2. tradition
3. entertainment 4. popularity
5. rare 6. ancient

37 Asking Polite Questions: Will, Would, and Could

A. (Suggested writing)
1. Could you turn the stereo down a bit, please?
2. Will you pick up a few cartons from the store?
3. Could you pick up the phone for me, please?
4. Would you help me open the windows?

B. (Suggested writing)
1. Could you pick up the ball for us, please?
2. Could I speak to Mrs. Abrams, please?
3. Will you pass the ketchup, please?
4. Could you open the door, Marie?
5. Jenny, would you take the subway with me?

C. (Suggested writing)
1. Could I get a hamburger with fries, please?
2. Could we go now?
3. Could you pass the salt, please?
4. I was wondering if you could help me.

38 Mars the Red Planet

A. 1. B 2. D 3. B 4. B

B. (Individual answer)

39 Punctuation (1)

A. 1. 2. ! 3. 4.
5. ? 6. ! 7. . 8.
9. 10. .

B. Morrie and Alyssa love their treehouse. Their father George had built it for them when they were five. Because they love being outside, their mother Leah can never find them in the house during the summer. "Wow! What an amazing hiding place!" Morrie said when George first showed him the treehouse. Alyssa is usually quiet and shy, so she expressed her excitement with a wide smile instead. "Isn't this treehouse great?" George said to Leah one day. "Our kids now have so much fun inviting their friends over to the backyard. They are so happy."

40 You Deserve A Break!

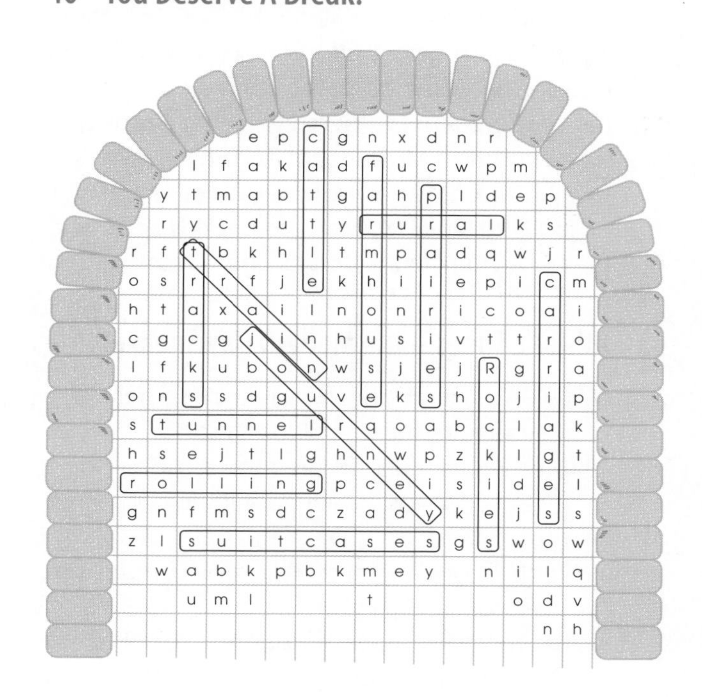

41 Honeybees

A. 1. T 2. F 3. F 4. T
5. T 6. F 7. T 8. T

B. A. PROCESS B. APIARY
C. APICULTURE D. RIGID
1. STOMACH 2. NECTAR
3. SOLITARY 4. LAY

42 Punctuation (2)

A. 1. Peter likes a lot of animals on this farm: horses, pigs, geese, and sheep.
2. Except me, everyone in my family – Mom, Dad, brother Jack, and sister Anita – likes the taste of olives.
3. The horse is happy: it has just recovered from an illness.
4. Peter was right; the horse had eaten some moldy hay.

B. Ms. Duncan's grade six class went to Kearney for a week-long trip in June. The kids learned a number of things: how to canoe, how to make dreamcatchers, and how to work in teams. After breakfast each morning, they explored the wilderness with their camp leaders. One morning, they stopped by a marsh to learn about insects that live in water. No one liked learning about airborne insects, though, especially mosquitoes and black flies. Fortunately, everyone remembered to bring insect repellent. The camp leaders were glad that every kid had brought repellent in tubes; aerosol cans are not good to the environment. After dinner each evening, a leader named Mike would grab his guitar and teach the kids a new song – one of which was called "The Merry Moose" – so the kids could sing their way back to the cabins afterwards.

43 Athletic Shoes – the Modern Day Sneakers

A. 1800s: the first rubber soled running shoes were manufactured, called Plimsolls
1892-1913: manufacturers made rubber and canvas shoes under the brand name Keds
1917: the marketing of athletic shoes began with Keds
1970s: more shoes were designed for different sports, with input from sports medicine and sports biomechanics experts
1990s: new technology was being tested by many manufacturers, like putting orthotic foot support in shoes

B. 1. C 2. A 3. D 4. B

44 Voice: Active and Passive

A. 2. Charmaine's hair was tied with ribbons.
3. Charmaine's bag was put in the overhead compartment.
4. The overhead compartments were filled with bags.
5. The plane was prepared for take-off.

B. (Suggested writing)
1. unfastened their seatbelts
2. served the passengers light snacks on the plane
3. occupied the washrooms yet
4. gave Charmaine some paper and crayons
5. drew a cute airplane

C. 2. The passengers were handed some extra napkins.
3. A movie was shown to the passengers.
4. The passengers were given earphones for the audio system.

45 Avalanche

A. 1. C 2. C 3. A 4. A

B. A. ELIMINATED B. INTENTIONAL
C. ENTHUSIAST D. FATALITIES
1. TRIGGER 2. LOOSE
3. EXCESSIVE

46 Noun Phrases

A. 1. Studious Matt
2. His buddies Gabe and Robin
3. A fuzzy winter hat from the department store
4. Cute and tiny Gabe
5. Mischievous Robin

B. 1. a sweet treat
2. giant lollipops
3. the shopkeeper
4. "extra fruity" lollipops
5. her best friend Matt

C. 1. the oldest pet shop in town
2. water animals
3. the monthly "buy-one-get-one-free" special

4. a parrot named Sam
5. "buy-one-get-one-free"

D. 1. S 2. C 3. O
4. C 5. O 6. S

47 SCUBA Diving

A. 1. It was made of the skin of pigs, sheep, or goats.
2. The first people to use the water bladder were sponge divers in the Aegean Sea.
3. An aqualung is a metal cylindrical tank filled with compressed air. The diver carries it on his back and breathes through a mouthpiece connected to safety pressure valves.

B. 1. underwater 2. waterproof
3. coastlines 4. shellfish
5. mouthpiece 6. seabeds
(Individual writing of sentences)

48 Adjective and Adverb Phrases

A. 1. very pointy
2. small and chubby
3. cute and spotted
4. big and funny looking

B. 1. delightfully surprised ; long and spiralled
2. long and gruelling
3. round and smooth
4. sweet and crunchy

C. 1. so quickly
2. quite comfortably
3. unusually early
4. very swiftly but carefully

D. Adjective Phrases: 1 ; 2 ; 4
Adverb Phrases: 3

49 Dazzling Colours in the Sky

A. 1. D 2. D 3. C
4. D 5. D

B. (Individual answer)

50 You Deserve A Break!

1. Chile 2. Philippines
3. Greece 4. Somalia
5. Portugal 6. Iran
7. Nigeria 8. China
9. India 10. Japan

51 Prepositional Phrases

A. 1. with big wide beaks
2. above their cozy house
3. in the feeder
4. of the most delightful chirps
5. of great taste
6. by her side

B. 1. with a lot of twigs
2. after finishing her morning exercise
3. near the baby birds
4. before winter
5. on a higher branch

C. 1. of green like jade ; N
2. with a lot of love ; V
3. of a stand-up comedian ; N
4. in front of her face ; V
5. above a flower ; V

52 Spider Webs

A. spin – twirl ; unique – distinctive ; abdomen – belly ; foundation – base ; identifiable – recognizable ; framework – structure ; intervals – spaces ; location – spot ; delicate – fine ; orb – globe

B. 1. cephalothorax ; abdomen
2. draglines / bridge lines
3. spinnerets
4. glands ; silk
5. Appendages

53 Infinitive Phrases

A. 1. to go to the amusement park
2. to be among the first in line for their rides
3. to ride on the roller-coaster
4. to swing on the Swing of the Millennium
5. to get some food
6. to ride on the carousel
7. to look at the design
8. to sit down
9. to share some French fries with Rachel and Kim

B. 1. to see what it was like
2. to wave at the boy
3. To have enough time
4. to accompany her
5. To meet Rachel and Kim

C. 1. F 2. T 3. F
4. F 5. F

Answers

54 Tides

A. A. GRAVITATIONAL
B. MOON
C. EXERT
1. SPRING
2. MINIMUM
3. NEAP
4. EBB
5. LUNAR

B. 1. two cycles
2. just after a new or full moon
3. a few metres to 15 metres
4. they are strongest

55 Gerund Phrases

A. 1. Baking cookies
2. eating the cookie dough
3. making apple pies
4. making pastries
5. sitting in the kitchen
6. Living with the Fieldses ; living in a cookie factory
7. tasting Mrs. Fields's new recipes
8. Making dinner ; making dessert
9. Being able to cook a decent meal
10. shopping for all kinds of baking ingredients
11. Visiting the Fieldses on Saturdays ; inviting yourself in for sweet treats
12. eating well ; loving life

B. 1. P 2. O 3. S
4. O 5. O 6. C
7. P 8. S

C. 1. playing sports of all kinds
2. looking after two babies
3. Biting nails
4. Forgiving your siblings
5. waiting for her turn

56 Telescopes

A. 1. T 2. F 3. T
4. T 5. T 6. F

B. 1. lenses
2. magnify
3. planetarium
4. astronomical
5. (Individual answer)
6. Isaac Newton
7. optical
8. eyepiece

57 Independent and Dependent Clauses

A. 1. D 2. I 3. D
4. I 5. I 6. I
7. I 8. D 9. D
10. I

B. (Individual writing)

C. (Individual writing)

58 Motor Car Racing

A. 1. F 2. C 3. D

B. (Individual answer)

59 Adjectival and Adverbial Clauses

A. 1. adv 2. adj 3. adv
4. adv 5. adv 6. adv
7. adj 8. adv 9. adj
10. adj 11. adv 12. adv

B. (Individual writing)

C. (Individual writing)

60 You Deserve A Break!

A. RED B. PINK
C. ROSE D. CRIMSON
E. CHESTNUT F. BLUSH
G. SUNFLOWER
1. POINSETTIA 2. ROUGE
3. APPLE 4. PEACHES
5. MAHOGANY 6. MAROON
7. SCARLET 8. PURPLE

61 Jet Aircraft

A. aircraft – airplanes ; speed – velocity ; thrust – push ; ignited – burned ; variations – differences

B. 1. F 2. T 3. T
4. T 5. F

C. (Individual drawing)

62 Sentences: Simple, Compound, and Complex

A. Simple: 1 ; 2 ; 3 ; 4 ; 5
Compound: 7 ; 8
Complex: 6

B. 1. 2 2. 3 3. 2
4. 2 5. 3

C. (Individual writing)

63 Liz's Pets

A. Places of Origin:
Europe and Asia
Size:
Golden: 18 cm long ; Common: 28 cm long and up to 900 g
Appearance:
Golden: short tail, light reddish-brown back and white belly ; Common: black belly
Diet:
fruits, seeds, green vegetables, small animals
Behaviour: nocturnal and solitary
Lifespan:
three or four years

B. (Individual answers)

64 Run-on Sentences

A. (Suggested answers)
1. The dog wagged its tail. It was happy.
2. The car was shiny – it was new.
3. The softball game was delayed. Ben went home late.
4. The weather was nice; the children played at the park.
5. Mark read a book: it was about a travelling musician.
6. The train arrived early. Kelly missed it.
7. There was a breeze; the children flew a kite.
8. It was Play Day – the children were exhausted by four o'clock.

B. (Suggested writing)
1. Kathy went to a farm and she brought home a lot of fruits.
2. Barry took a short cut, but he ended up getting lost.
3. We stopped for lunch because we were starving.
4. William got to the station before the train arrived.
5. The closet was full, so there was no room to put new clothes.

C. (Suggested writing)
1. The dog wagged its tail. It was happy because Glen came home.
2. The game was delayed. Ben went home late, so he went straight to bed.
3. The train was early. Kelly missed it, but she caught the next one soon after.

65 Bridges

A. A. MAXIMUM   B. TRUSSES
C. ENGINEERS   D. BEAMS
1. STIFFENING   2. MATERIALS
3. ARCHES   4. PIERS

B.
1. Strong winds, earthquakes, and changes in temperature are some natural occurences that bridges need to resist.
2. Bridges make it safer and faster to travel across lakes, rivers, canyons, dangerous roads, and railway tracks.
3. (Individual answer)

66 Synonyms, Antonyms, and Homophones

A. 1. E   2. C
3. D   4. A
5. B

B. 1. E   2. C
3. A   4. D
5. B

C.
1. threw ; G
2. dear ; B
3. heal ; D
4. right ; F
5. plain ; C
6. allowed ; H
7. coarse ; E
8. buy ; A

D. 1. educate   2. wait
3. always   4. predict
5. knows   6. stop
(Individual writing of sentences)

67 Deadly Plants

A.
1. No. An example is the tomato, which belongs to the poisonous nightshade family.
2. (Suggested answer)
We can make our gardens beautiful with foxgloves, azaleas, hyacinths, and mistletoes, and make medicines with digitalis and quinine.
3. We use seeds from the rosary pea plant to make necklaces, bracelets, and rosaries.
4. We should never eat or chew any part of a plant without knowing for certain it is harmless.

B. 1. injurious   2. mistletoe
3. rosary   4. apricots
5. nightshade

Answers

68 Building Vocabulary with Root Words

A. (Suggested answers)
2. understanding ; understandable ; comprehend
3. invention ; inventive ; create
4. adaptation ; adaptable ; adjust
5. characterization ; characteristic ; role

B. (Suggested answers)
1. beginner ; beginning ; end
2. hardiness ; hardy ; easy
3. responsibility ; responsible ; ask
4. defence ; defensive ; offend

C.
1. adaptation
2. characteristic
3. inventive
4. beginning
5. responsibility

69 Deadly Animals

A.
1. A
2. C
3. B
4. C

B.
1. massive
2. transmission
3. sensitive
4. envenomation
5. beneficial

70 You Deserve A Break!

1. skyscraper
2. modern
3. architecture
4. river
5. tower
6. museum
7. harbour
8. lights
9. skyline
10. reflection
11. boats / ships
12. view

71 Tips for Better Writing

A. (Suggested writing)
1. Terry travelled across the country by riding the bicycle.
2. Montreal is a bilingual city in Quebec.
3. School was cancelled because there was a storm.
4. The storm subsided and it was calm again, so school resumed.
5. Laurie is at the skating rink with a pair of new skates.
6. No one arrived at the theatre before the show started.
7. Joshua switched to another school in the countryside.

B.
1. here; I hear that you have just moved to a new house.
2. our; The guests will arrive on the hour.
3. not; Mrs. Hunter helped her daughter untie a knot.
4. meat; The different groups will meet at the station early in the morning.
5. stairs; When Hilary has nothing to do, she stares out of the window.
6. red; Robin told me that she had read the book.
7. sow; Greta wants to learn how to sew dresses.
8. root; Chris takes the same route to school every day.
9. son; The weather is nice because the sun has come out.

72 Frisbee

A. 5 ; 4 ; 2 ; 3 ; 1

B.
2. pass ; V
3. stable ; A
4. combine ; V
5. universe ; N

(Individual writing of sentences)

73 Similes and Metaphors

A. (Individual writing)

B.
1. a rock star
2. the world
3. a rose among thorns
4. roaring waves
5. a hothouse

C. (Individual writing)

74 Slinky

A.

d	a	m	e	x	p	l	a	s	i	t	m	o	n	e	e	t	a	r
b	e	v	e	r	l	e	b	u	h	c	o	r	w	n	u	s	s	p
e	n	v	i	s	i	l	a	l	o	e	t	o	a	e	b	i	o	r
a	i	f	i	o	o	i	o	c	m	r	i	b	n	r	e	m	m	i
c	g	z	u	c	t	z	n	y	c	v	o	e	d	g	a	p	n	n
h	h	e	x	t	e	r	n	a	l	i	n	r	e	y	c	l	e	c
b	t	p	l	a	n	a	j	s	e	a	d	t	r	p	d	e	u	i
f	a	s	c	i	n	a	t	i	n	g	o	e	e	e	s	r	m	p
a	v	e	a	e	r	b	o	s	r	n	n	g	n	r	o	w	o	l
l	i	o	d	e	v	e	l	o	p	i	n	g	r	t	r	y	n	e
l	a	n	a	o	m	t	v	e	s	t	q	u	w	e	a	t	c	s
v	n	i	c	x	r	h	i	s	i	e	u	y	e	s	z	l	i	t

B.
1. F
2. B
3. A
4. C
5. G

75 Topic Sentences

A. 1. A 2. B 3. B

B. (Suggested writing)

1. A New Method of Teaching Math ; Ever since Mr. Adam applied his new method of teaching math in the classroom, the results have been very encouraging.
2. The City's Air Quality ; As the air quality of the city gets worse by the year, more and more people are getting sick.
3. The City's Charity Concert ; The city's annual fundraising concert took place yesterday at the Blue Mount Stadium.

76 The Bow and Arrow

A.

t	c	v	u	m	a	t	c	p	i	n	m	q	n
p	n	r	e	d	u	c	i	n	g	u	o	p	l
r	b	h	i	f	p	d	s	r	s	c	i	r	o
i	r	b	a	r	e	l	e	a	v	c	g	e	k
c	p	k	e	n	r	k	r	f	u	i	u	h	w
z	r	o	l	e	s	m	i	d	e	s	k	i	m
d	i	m	p	r	o	v	e	m	e	n	t	s	p
u	m	l	u	c	k	n	c	a	i	h	d	t	n
c	a	p	r	i	m	i	t	i	v	e	i	o	l
i	r	e	y	i	g	l	s	o	t	i	b	r	e
n	y	o	m	w	i	d	e	l	y	d	c	i	h
g	s	c	q	j	d	u	n	u	o	v	l	c	s

B. 1. flight archery 2. firearms
3. bull's eye 4. primitive bow
5. target archery

77 Writing Paragraphs (1)

A.

1. Today, each child in class had to write a riddle and pass it to the person sitting behind them.
2. The strap on her left sandal got caught in the pedal and she lost balance. Natalie hurt her knee but luckily, she did not injure her kneecap.
3. Now that the model is complete, Jason proudly displays it in his room.

B. (Individual writing)

78 Pirates

A. 1. horizon 2. treasures 3. masthead
4. hostile 5. merchant

B. 1. T 2. F 3. F
4. F 5. T

C.

1. Pirates used grapnels and boarding planks to board the ships they wanted to attack.
2. A privateer was not a pirate because he did not rob for his own interests.
3. The Jolly Roger is a black flag with a white skull and crossbones.
4. (Suggested answer)
   I would avoid the Caribbean Sea and the northern part of the South American mainland because they were full of pirate activity.

79 Writing Paragraphs (2)

A. (Individual writing)

B. (Individual writing)

80 You Deserve A Break!

1. pentagon 2. square
3. polygon 4. rectangle
5. hexagon 6. rhombus
7. trapezoid 8. circle
9. oval 10. octagon

81 The Turtle

A. 1. Longevity 2. hibernate
3. estivation 4. regulate
5. indigenous

B. 1. predator 2. possess
3. harsh 4. destruction
(Individual writing of sentences)

82 Understanding a Story

(Suggested writing)

1. in the evening ; at home
2. Jonathan and Ben ; Mom and Dad
3. Jonathan and Ben see strange lights and hear footsteps while home alone, but they find out later that what scared them at first were actually Mom and Dad coming home.
4. The two brothers are scared and wonder if they should grab a baseball bat to fight the "bad guys".
5. (Individual answer)

83 A Knight's Armour

A. 1. A 2. B 3. C
4. D 5. F 6. E
7. H 8. G

B. 1. greaves 2. helmet 3. armour

C. 1. The chain mail armour was more common before the 1300s.
2. The plate armour was popular after the 1300s.
3. The pros of using plate armour were better protection and better looks ; the cons were lack of flexibility and the need for assistance to mount on a horse.

84 Creating a Story

A. (Individual writing)

B. (Individual writing)

85 The Kiwi – a Fruit or a Bird?

A. 1. B 2. C

B. 1. A 2. C
3. C

C. (Individual answer)

86 Writing a Poem

A. town ; hands ; ring ; run ; well ; station ; phrase ; mark

B. (Individual writing)

87 Vantage Vista

A. 1. The highest point in Ontario is Ishpatina Ridge.
2. One gets there by canoeing, portaging, hiking, and climbing.
3. It is 693 metres high.
4. An old fire tower is on top of Caribou Mountain.
5. (Individual answer)

B. 1. panoramic 2. escarpments
3. platforms 4. summit
(Individual writing of sentences)

88 Formal and Informal Writing

A. (Individual writing)

B. (Suggested writing)
Hi Tina,
Just arrived in Montreal on Saturday. Having a great time here! Went skating at Orkus Skatepark on Sunday.
It's only been a few days, but I'm already talking to my cousins in French. They speak English too but I'm going to practise my French with them. Have got to surprise Madame LeBlanc in the new year.
We'll spend two days in Ottawa before coming home. Hope all is well with you. Will write again soon.
Chantal

89 Some Common Errors

A. 1. bath 2. aural
3. outdoor 4. may be
5. effect 6. breath
7. loses 8. all ready
9. except 10. oral
11. clothes 12. immigrants
13. Astronomy 14. altar

B. 1. (acceptible); acceptable
2.
3. (acheive); achieve
4.
5. (parallell); parallel
6. (wierd); weird
7. (tobogan); toboggan
8. (lettice); lettuce

C. 1. becoming 2. vacuum
3. entrance 4. necessary
5. twelfth 6. potatoes
7. symmetry 8. chocolate

90 You Deserve A Break!

1. hummingbird 2. insects
3. cockroach 4. listen
5. parrot and rabbit 6. shark
7. almost 8. whale
9. giraffe 10. butterfly

Assessment of Mathematics

1. B
2. C
3. C
4. D
5. A
6. A
7. D
8. B
9. D
10. A
11.
$$\begin{array}{r} 37 \\ \times\ 49 \\ \hline 333 \\ 1480 \\ \hline 1813 \end{array}$$
12.
$$\begin{array}{r} 905 \\ 9\overline{)8145} \\ \underline{81} \\ 45 \\ \underline{45} \end{array}$$
13. 11 062
14.
$$\begin{array}{r} 0.85 \\ 6\overline{)5.1} \\ \underline{48} \\ 30 \\ \underline{30} \end{array}$$
15. 22.92
16. 6757
17. 1.63
18. 15.54
19. 8.16
20. 2.29
21. 9
22. 30
23. 35
24. 30
25. $\frac{2}{3}$
26. $\frac{2}{7}$
27. $\frac{3}{5}$
28. $\frac{7}{12}$
29. 6
30. 10
31. $\frac{1}{3}$
32. 16
33. 15.84
34. 1.14
35. 8.84
36. 6390
37. 150
38. 426
39. 

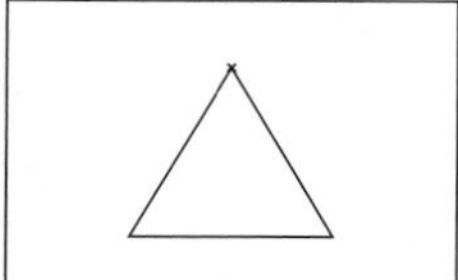

60°, 60°, 60°

40.

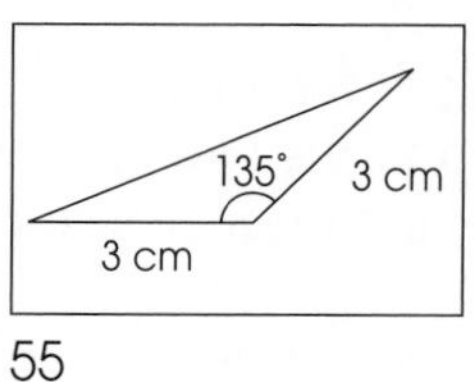

55

41. Rectangular prism

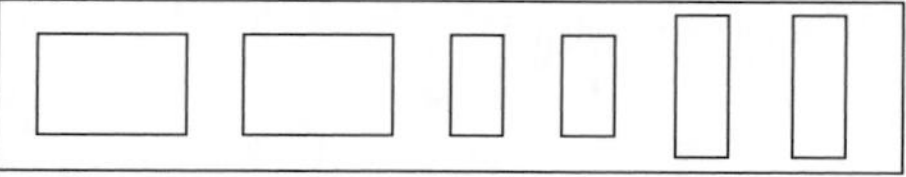

42. Square Pyramid

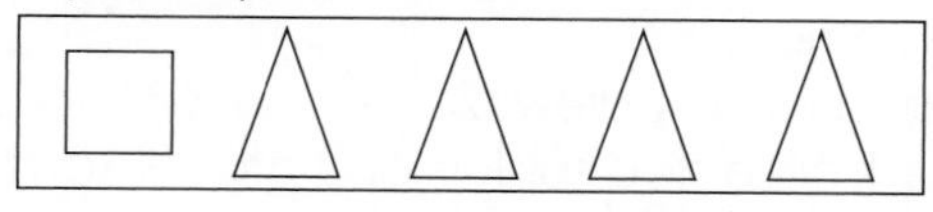

43. 8 ; 16 ; 20 ; 40 ; 10 ; 20 ; 25 ; 50
44. No. in the 1st row + No. in the 2nd row = No. in the 3rd row
45. 40 ; 160

46 - 52.

48. S (2, 7) ; T (6, 7)

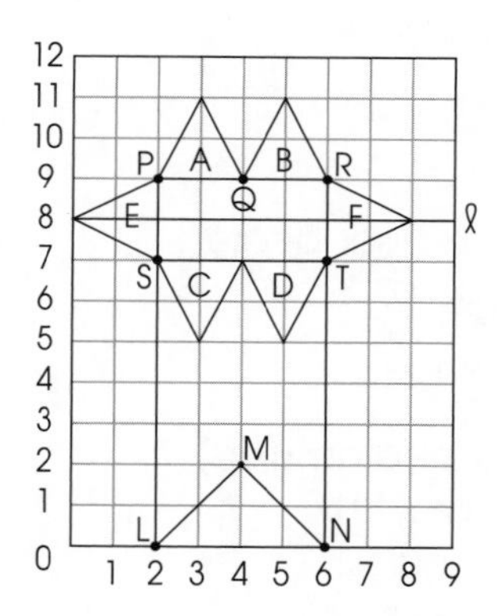

53. 21.5
54. 21
55.

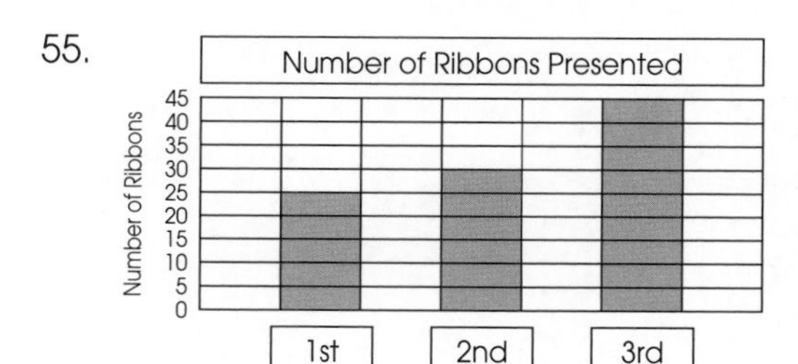

56. 20
57. 100
58. $\frac{2}{5}$
59. $\frac{11}{20}$
60. $\frac{8}{15}$
61. (Suggested answer)
There may be more than 1 child getting the 2nd or 3rd place in the same event.

Assessment of Language

A. 1. The evening sun | continued to warm the swimmers.
2. The children | drew pictures of their families.
3. He | collected spiders and other insects.
4. The colourful birds | sang sweetly in the tropical trees.
5. They | wondered what time it was.
6. My teacher | did not allow us to refer to the book.

B. 1. ran
2. tells; go
3. left
4. waved; disappeared
5. giggles ; play
6. stay ; ended

C. (Suggested answers)
1. cute ; playfully
2. bright ; quickly
3. skilled ; swiftly
4. excited ; wildly
5. talented ; professionally
6. finally ; tall

D. 1. A
2. and
3. but
4. the
5. the
6. the
7. or
8. A ; a

E. 1. Whenever
2. unless
3. If
4. because
5. even though
6. However

F. 1. Compound: B, D ; Complex: A, C, E

G. (Suggested answers)
1. On Monday nights, they played soccer in the park.
2. He bought inline skates and yesterday tried skating.
3. The cars were lined up in the heavy, highway traffic.
4. When they went to the pool, it was so crowded they couldn't get in.

H. 1. they
2. our
3. his
4. them
5. their
6. their

I. 1. whom
2. that
3. who
4. which
5. where
6. which

J. 1. puck
2. stories
3. nest
4. piles

K. 1. tree
2. hallway ; school
3. water ; boaters
4. ditch ; truck
5. group ; museum

L. 1. him
2. teacher
3. mother
4. them
5. us

M. 1. gerund
2. participle
3. participle
4. infinitive
5. participle
6. infinitive

N. (Suggested answers)
1. He walked home from school.
2. During the afternoon, we went swimming.
3. Whenever we get the chance, we organize a game of tennis.
4. If the bus is gone, we will walk home.
5. I woke up this morning.
6. With the teacher's permission, we played in the gymnasium.